Council of the County of Aberdeen.

EDUCATION COMMITTEE.

.... School.

1. This book is the property of the Aberdeenshire Education Committee.
2. The pupil to whom it is issued will be held responsible for its safe keeping and good condition, and may be required to replace it if it is lost, damaged or soiled. Any such loss or damage should be reported immediately to the school.
3. The fact that the pupil or another member of his/her household is suffering from infectious or contagious disease should be reported immediately to the teacher.
4. A pupil leaving school during the session must return all books belonging to the school before he leaves.

Date of Issue	Name of Pupil	Class
	Gwendoline Morrison	

ARITHMETIC——*POST PRIMARY*

THREE YEARS' COURSE SUITABLE FOR

MODERN : CENTRAL : TECHNICAL

ADVANCED DIVISION : SECONDARY

CONTINUATION AND EVENING SCHOOLS

REVISED EDITION.

ARITHMETIC

—— *A THREE YEARS' COURSE* ——

CONTINUING

"CLASS" ARITHMETIC SERIES

BY

ALEXANDER SYMON, M.A., B.Sc.,

—— AUTHOR OF THE NEW GEOMETRY, ——

AND

GEORGE D. W. MILLIKIN, M.A.

o   o   o   ●

———— *SUITABLE FOR* ————

MODERN . CENTRAL . TECHNICAL

ADVANCED DIVISION . SECONDARY

: : AND EVENING SCHOOLS : :

ROBERT GIBSON & SONS (GLASGOW), LTD.

Publishers, ...   GLASGOW.

1941.

Printed in Great Britain at the Press of the Publishers.

PREFACE.

THE original aim of this work was to meet what had been represented to us as a much-felt need for a book on Arithmetic, suitably designed for the Courses of Study in Supplementary and Continuation Classes.

As the work proceeded, however, the treatment of the subjects became more extensive and the scope of the book itself more comprehensive than was originally intended, and in its final form it more than fully covers all that is required for Higher Grade Schools.

In the treatment of the text our guiding principle has been " one step at a time," each step being illustrated by *worked examples* followed by an exercise of well-graded examples to be worked out by the pupils. In the working of the illustrative examples we have aimed at *simplicity, lucidity,* and *conciseness,* and, for the better attainment of that aim, obvious details of the working have been left to be performed by the pupil.

While the unitary method has received a fairly extensive treatment, we follow it up with " the ratio method," as we have termed it, which we have allowed to supersede the old " simple proportion " and " compound proportion " modes of treatment.

We have attached considerable importance to the idea and meaning of *Ratio,* and have endeavoured to show the power and effectiveness of the " *ratio* " as an instrument in the solution of most arithmetical questions, applying it to Rates, Taxes, Bankruptcy, Insurance, Foreign Exchange, Profit and Loss, Interest, Present Worth and Discount, Stocks and Shares, which are all seen to come under the *Ratio Method.*

Each chapter closes with a collection of numerous examples, which have been carefully constructed so as to avoid needless labour and waste of time on the part of the pupil when the inculcation of methods and principles is the main end in view, and in constructing the examples on " carpeting of floors " and " papering of walls," etc., we have kept in view the actual trade practice that obtains.

Recurring Decimals, Present Worth and Discount, Stocks and Shares, are dealt with, though briefly, for the sake of their educational value, and at the end of the book we have inserted a large collection of Intermediate Leaving Certificate Examination Questions for revision and testing purposes.

Finally, in issuing this little volume, we would express the hope that it will prove a useful aid to teachers and students of arithmetic.

In issuing a further edition of this work we desire to record our indebtedness to Mr. JAMES KNIGHT, J.P., F.E.I.S., F.R.S.E., M.A., D.Sc., Glasgow, Mr. EDWARD KERR, M.A., and Mr. JOHN W. BUTTERS, M.A., B.Sc., F.R.S.E., for certain emendations and improvements.

At the request of Headmasters of Continuation Schools we have also added a new section on Areas and Volumes other than Rectangular, which we trust will enhance the usefulness of the book.

REVISED EDITION.

The original text has been retained intact, the worked examples revised and supplementary questions of a more advanced type added to a number of the Exercises, thereby increasing the scope and usefulness of the book.

CONTENTS.

TABLES.

BRITISH AND DECIMAL SYSTEMS.

BRITISH.		DECIMAL.	

Money.

BRITISH		DECIMAL
4 farthings (f.) = 1 penny (d.)		(*U.S.A.*) 100 cents
		$\quad$= 1 dollar
12 pence $\quad$ = 1 shilling (s.)		(*France*) 100 centimes
		$\quad$= 1 franc
20 shillings $\quad$ = 1 pound (£)		(*Germany*) 100 pfennige
		$\quad$= 1 mark

Also

Proposed British System.

2 shillings $\quad$ = 1 florin.		10 mils $\quad$ = 1 cent
5 shillings $\quad$ = 1 crown		10 cents $\quad$ = 1 florin
21 shillings $\quad$ = 1 guinea		10 florins = 1 pound

Length.

Length (Metric).

BRITISH		DECIMAL
12 inches (in.) = 1 foot (ft.)		10 millimetres (mm.)
3 feet $\quad$ = 1 yard (yd.)		$\quad$= 1 centimetre (cm.)
5½ yards $\quad$ = 1 pole (pl.)		10 centimetres
40 poles $\quad$ = 1 furlong (fur.)		$\quad$= 1 decimetre (dm.)
8 furlongs $\quad$ = 1 mile (ml.)		10 decimetres
Also		$\quad$= 1 metre (m.)
22 yards $\quad$ = 1 chain (ch.)		10 metres = 1 dekametre (Dm.)
10 chains $\quad$ = 1 furlong		10 dekametres
and		$\quad$= 1 hectometre (Hm.)
100 links $\quad$ = 1 chain		10 hectometres
1,760 yards $\quad$ = 1 mile		$\quad$= 1 kilometre (Km.)
6 ft. $\quad$ = 1 fathom		
and 6,080 ft. $\quad$ = 1 nautical mile		1 metre $\quad$ = 39·37 ins. nearly
1 inch = 2·54 cm.		1 kilometre = $\quad$ ·6214 mls., or
1 yard = $\quad$·914 metres.		$\frac{5}{8}$ nearly

9

BRITISH.

Area (sq. = Square).

144 sq. inches	= 1 sq. foot
9 sq. feet	= 1 sq. yard
30¼ sq. yards	= 1 sq. pole
40 sq. poles	= 1 rood (ro.)
4 roods	= 1 acre (ac.)
640 acres	= 1 sq. mile

Also

484 sq. yds.	= 1 sq. chain
10 sq. ch.	= 1 acre
4,840 sq. yds.	= 1 acre

DECIMAL.

Area (sq. = Square).

100 sq. millimetres	= 1 sq. centimetre
100 sq. centimetres	= 1 sq. decimetre
100 sq. decimetres	= 1 sq. metre
100 sq. metres	= 1 sq. dekametre
100 sq. dekametres	= 1 sq. hectometre
100 sq. hectometres	= 1 sq. kilometre

Also (for Land Measurement).

100 centi-ares (ca.)	= 1 are (a.)
100 ares	= 1 hectare (Ha.)

1 are = 1 square dekametre.

A hectare is about 2½ acres.

Volume (c. = Cubic).

1,728 c. inches	= 1 c. foot
27 c. feet	= 1 c. yard
1 cubic metre	= 1·3 c. yds. nearly.

Volume (c. = Cubic).

1,000 c. millimetres	= 1 c. centimetre
1,000 c. centimetres	= 1 c. decimetre
1,000 c. decimetres	= 1 c. metre
1 stere	= 1 cubic metre

BRITISH.

Capacity.

Liquid Measure.

4 gills = 1 pint (pt.)
2 pints = 1 quart (qt.)
4 quarts = 1 gallon (gal.)

Dry Measure.

2 gallons = 1 peck (pk.)
4 pecks = 1 bushel (bush.)
8 bushels = 1 quarter (qr.)

1 gallon = 4·546 litres.

Weight (Avoirdupois).

16 drams (dr.) = 1 ounce (oz.)
16 ounces = 1 pound (lb.)
14 pounds = 1 stone (st.)
8 stones = 1 hundred-
weight (cwt.)
20 hundredweights
= 1 ton

Also

28 pounds = 1 quarter (qr.)
4 quarters = 1 cwt.
112 pounds = 1 cwt.
7,000 grains = 1 lb.
437½ grains = 1 oz.

Grains used by Apothecaries.

1 grain = ·0648 gm.
1 lb. = ·4563 Kg.

DECIMAL.

Capacity (Liquids and Grains).

10 millilitres (ml.)
= 1 centilitre (cl.)
10 centilitres
= 1 decilitre (dl.)
10 decilitres = 1 litre (l.)
10 litres = 1 dekalitre (Dl.)
10 dekalitres
= 1 hectolitre (Hl.)
10 hectolitres
= 1 kilolitre (Kl.)

1 litre = 1 c.dm. = 1,000 c.c.
1 litre = ·22 gallon nearly.

Weight.

10 milligrams (mg.)
= 1 centigram (cg.)
10 centigrams
= 1 decigram (dg.)
10 decigrams
= 1 gram (g.)
10 grams = 1 dekagram (Dg.)
10 dekagrams
= 1 hectogram (Hg.)
10 hectograms
= 1 kilogram (Kg.)

Also

100 kilograms = 1 quintal (Q.)
1,000 kilograms = 1 tonne (T.)

1 gram = 15·4 grains
nearly.

1 kilogram = 2·2 lbs. nearly.

TABLES OF WEIGHTS NOW OUT OF USE.

Troy Weight.	Apothecaries' Weight.
24 grains = 1 pennyweight (dwt.)	20 grains = 1 scruple (sc.)
20 dwts. = 1 ounce (oz.)	3 scruples = 1 dram (dr.)
12 ounces = 1 pound (lb.)	8 drams = 1 ounce (oz.)

Note.—The ounce is the same in both tables, and is equal to 480 grains, but differs from the ounce *Avoirdupois*, which is equal to $437\frac{1}{2}$ grains.

TIME.

	Also
60 seconds = 1 minute	
60 minutes = 1 hour	365 days = 1 year
24 hours = 1 day	366 days = 1 leap year
7 days = 1 week	12 months = 1 year

The number of days in the months are given in the following :—

    " *Thirty* days hath September, April, June, and November,
      All the rest have *thirty-one*, except February alone,
      Which has *twenty-eight*, and in a leap year *twenty-nine*."

The leap years are those divisible by 4, like 1920, but if the year ends in " 00," like 1900, it is not a leap year unless it is divisible by 400. Thus 1600 was a leap year, but 1900 was not.

ANGLES AND PAPER MEASURE.

Angles.	Paper.
60 seconds = 1 minute	24 sheets = 1 quire
60 minutes = 1 degree	20 quires = 1 ream
90 degrees = 1 right angle	10 reams = 1 bale

ADDITIONAL QUESTIONS SUITABLE FOR
THE THIRD YEAR ARE CONTAINED IN
THE BOOK OF TESTS ISSUED ANNUALLY
REPRINTING THE PAPERS SET AT THE
L.C. EXAMINATIONS————INTERMEDIATE
STAGE, - - ⚬ • • • • •

ARITHMETIC.

CHAPTER I.

Revisal Exercises on Compound Quantities.

(a) MONEY.

EXERCISE 1.

Add the following :—

(1)		
£	s.	D.
17	14	6
18	13	9
16	17	8
9	5	6
7	8	6

(2)		
£	s.	D.
9	12	8
6	13	4
17	8	6
9	5	4
8	3	6

(3)		
£	s.	D.
9	13	4
5	18	6
7	15	4
19	6	7
8	5	6

(4)		
£	s.	D.
5	8	8
9	4	3
6	7	2
13	15	6
7	16	8

(5)		
£	s.	D.
16	12	8
94	16	7
18	15	8
24	13	6
19	16	11

(6)		
£	s.	D.
25	16	7
36	18	10
35	17	11
56	19	8
48	15	10

(7)		
£	s.	D.
42	15	6
29	18	11
76	17	10
94	18	10
26	16	8

(8)		
£	s.	D.
78	19	11
26	15	8
96	14	11
75	16	10
92	17	8

(9)		
£	s.	D.
78	19	$5\frac{1}{2}$
43	16	$7\frac{1}{4}$
83	15	$10\frac{3}{4}$
76	19	$8\frac{1}{2}$
89	16	$10\frac{3}{4}$

(10)		
£	s.	D.
85	16	$7\frac{1}{4}$
96	17	$5\frac{3}{4}$
42	19	$10\frac{3}{4}$
98	16	$7\frac{1}{2}$
65	15	$8\frac{1}{2}$

(11)		
£	s.	D.
93	16	$5\frac{1}{2}$
78	17	$10\frac{1}{4}$
64	9	$9\frac{3}{4}$
59	8	$8\frac{1}{2}$
38	15	$7\frac{3}{4}$

(12)		
£	s.	D.
69	18	$5\frac{1}{2}$
48	17	$8\frac{1}{4}$
56	16	$9\frac{3}{4}$
79	18	$10\frac{3}{4}$
84	17	$9\frac{1}{2}$

(13)		
£	s.	D.
588	13	$4\frac{1}{4}$
462	15	$9\frac{3}{4}$
87	16	$10\frac{1}{2}$
95	18	$11\frac{1}{4}$
678	15	$9\frac{3}{4}$
85	16	$10\frac{1}{2}$

EXERCISE 1—*Continued.*

(14)				(15)				(16)				(17)		
£	S.	D.		£	S.	D.		£	S.	D.		£	S.	D.
765	14	$3\frac{3}{4}$		967	17	$9\frac{3}{4}$		7	15	$8\frac{1}{2}$		95	11	$10\frac{1}{2}$
859	15	$7\frac{1}{4}$		879	16	$8\frac{1}{2}$		56	13	9		7	19	$6\frac{3}{4}$
259	16	$9\frac{1}{2}$		765	13	$7\frac{1}{4}$		859	15	$8\frac{3}{4}$		458	15	$8\frac{1}{4}$
76	15	$4\frac{3}{4}$		89	16	$5\frac{3}{4}$		65	17	9		96	16	$9\frac{3}{4}$
95	16	$7\frac{1}{2}$		7	15	$7\frac{1}{2}$		786	16	$5\frac{3}{4}$		78	7	$5\frac{1}{4}$
385	17	$8\frac{1}{4}$		856	16	$9\frac{3}{4}$		98	18	$11\frac{1}{2}$		95	9	$11\frac{3}{4}$

(18)				(19)				(20)				(21)		
£	S.	D.		£	S.	D.		£	S.	D.		£	S.	D.
187	16	$9\frac{1}{2}$		97	19	$8\frac{3}{4}$		956	16	$9\frac{1}{2}$		87	15	$9\frac{1}{2}$
97	18	$5\frac{3}{4}$		187	16	$5\frac{1}{4}$		68	18	$10\frac{3}{4}$		765	16	8
87	15	$6\frac{1}{2}$		6,252	17	$9\frac{3}{4}$		978	16	$9\frac{1}{2}$		2,526	15	$9\frac{3}{4}$
289	16	$9\frac{1}{2}$		789	18	$10\frac{1}{2}$		56	7	10		87	16	9
76	18	$10\frac{3}{4}$		98	19	$5\frac{3}{4}$		2,526	6	$8\frac{3}{4}$		76	15	4
65	15	$9\frac{1}{2}$		672	18	$9\frac{1}{2}$		786	16	$9\frac{1}{4}$		878	16	$9\frac{3}{4}$
				84	9	$5\frac{1}{4}$		97	10	$8\frac{1}{2}$		97	18	$10\frac{3}{4}$
				168	7	$8\frac{3}{4}$		87	19	$6\frac{3}{4}$		89	17	$9\frac{1}{2}$

EXERCISE 2.

(1) Subtract 15s. 9d. from 19s. 11d.
(2)   ,,   17s. 8d. from 19s. 5d.
(3)   ,,   £1 2s. 9d. from £1 5s. 6d.
(4)   ,,   £5 6s. 8d. from £7 18s. 5d.
(5)   ,,   £11 16s. 5d. from £12 19s. 4d.
(6)   ,,   £26 15s. 8d. from £29 15s. 11d.
(7)   ,,   £45 11s. 9d. from £50 19s. 8d.
(8)   ,,   £650 0s. 5d. from £672 10s. 11d.
(9)   ,,   £3 9s. $2\frac{1}{2}$d. from £4 19s. $11\frac{3}{4}$d.
(10)   ,,   £4 10s. $5\frac{1}{4}$d. from £5 11s. $9\frac{1}{4}$d.
(11)   ,,   £15 16s. $10\frac{3}{4}$d. from £17 18s. $9\frac{1}{2}$d.
(12)   ,,   £12 17s. $8\frac{1}{2}$d. from £16 11s. $5\frac{1}{4}$d.
(13)   ,,   £98 16s. $5\frac{1}{4}$d. from £118 17s. $9\frac{3}{4}$d.

EXERCISE 2—*Continued*.

(14) Subtract £187 11s. 9¾d. from £987 15s. 8¼d.

(15) ,, £956 18s. 1½d. from £1,015 15s. 0¾d.

(16) ,, £786 15s. 2¾d. from £856 19s. 11¾d.

(17) ,, £685 19s. 3½d. from £1,000 11s. 10½d.

(18) ,, £876 15s. 9½d. from £952 19s. 1¾d.

(19) ,, £56 13s. 6d. from £60.

(20) ,, £78 15s. 9¾d. from £100.

(21) ,, £985 16s. 2½d. from £1,000.

(22) ,, £850 16s. 8¼d. from £10,000.

(23) ,, £765 10s. 8d. from £1,000 19s. 5½d.

(24) ,, £625 13s. 4¾d. from £700.

EXERCISE 3.

(1) Reduce £615 19s. 3d. to pence ; £718 19s. 10½d. to halfpence.

(2) Reduce £510 11s. 8½d. to halfpence ; and £1,719 10s. 5¼d. to farthings.

(3) Reduce (*a*) £1,716 15s. ; (*b*) £162 10s. ; (*c*) £161 5s. ; to crowns.

(4) Reduce £181 10s. ; £25 12s. 6d. ; £187 15s. ; £691 7s. 6d. ; £87 17s. 6d. ; £69 2s. 6d. ; £76 5s., to half-crowns.

(5) Reduce £97 4s. ; £187 10s. ; £96 2s. ; £87 6s. ; £198 12s. ; £79 18s. ; £56 14s. ; £75 8s. ; £576 16s. to florins.

(6) How many threepences are in (*a*) £65 15s. 6d. ; (*b*) £178 18s. 9d. ; (*c*) £65 10s. 3d. ; (*d*) £42 13s.

(7) Add together £65 12s. ; £34 17s. 6d. ; £98 18s. ; £68 15s. 6d. ; and £78 12s. 6d., and then reduce the answer to sixpences.

(8) Reduce to pounds, shillings, pence (*a*) 9,567 farthings ; (*b*) 8,562 halfpence ; (*c*) 8,567 pence.

(9) Find the number of pounds, shillings, pence in 765 half-crowns ; 876 florins ; 156 guineas ; 753 crowns.

(10) Find the sum in pounds, shillings, pence of 750 farthings ; 986 halfpence ; 786 pence ; and 653 threepences.

(11) How many halfpence are there altogether in 24 guineas, 7 crowns, 18 half-crowns, 70 florins, and 17 shillings ?

(12) How many parcels costing 11½d. each can I purchase with £23 19s. 2d. ?

(13) Find the sum in pounds, shillings, pence of 65 guineas, 85 crowns, 65 half-crowns, 73 florins, 39 shillings, and 77 sixpences.

(14) From the sum of £85 19s. 11½d. and £65 19s. 10¾d. take the difference between £125 11s. 10d. and £35 15s. 8½d.

(15) Add together 76 crowns, 36 half-crowns, 82 shillings, 76 sixpences, 34 threepences, 95 pence, and 101 halfpence, and reduce the answer to halfpence.

(16) Subtract the sum of £69 15s. 8½d. and £15 16s. 7¼d. from 450 crowns.

(17) How many oranges costing 1½d. each can be procured with £5 11s. 4½d. ?

(18) From the difference between £232 11s. 10½d. and £114 16s. 5¾d. take the difference between £135 16s. 8d. and £58 11s. 9¾d.

(19) How many lbs. of sugar, each lb. costing 5½d., can be purchased with £67 16s. 2½d ?

(20) Add together £67 18s. 9½d., £72 6s. 5¾d., £22 11s. 8½d., £30 6s. 9¾d., and subtract the sum from £300.

(21) Find the total value of 63,142,000 pennies, 20,267,200 half-pence, and 1,415,600 farthings.

EXERCISE 4.

(1) Divide the sum of £16 19s. 9¾d., £72 15s. 8¾d., and £123 16s. 8½d. by 9.

(2) A sum of money was divided among 635 persons. Each received £1 15s. 6d. Find the sum.

(3) A sum of £653 10s. 3¾d. was divided among 525 persons. What did each receive ?

(4) Out of a sum of money 34 men received 16s. 8¾d., and there was 3s. 5½d. over ; how much was the original sum ?

(5) A man buys 12 horses at £67 12s. 6d. each, 32 cows at £42 13s. 6d. each, and 58 sheep at £2 3s. 8d. each ; how much in all does he pay ?

(6) If 200 sheep can be bought for £385 8s. 4d., what is the cost of each sheep ?

(7) How many times can £12 6s. 9½d. be subtracted from £150, and what is the value of the remainder ?

(8) Three war certificates, each of the value of 15s. 6d., were bought by each of the inhabitants of a town whose population was 68,234. What was the amount subscribed ?

(9) A total of £21,014 2s. 6d. was subscribed in buying war saving certificates at 15s. 6d. by the population of a town. If the population is 5,423, how many certificates on an average were bought by each inhabitant ?

(10) If £6,715 10s. 11¼d. be divided equally among 675 persons, what does each receive ?

(11) The profits of a business amounting to £961 2s. 0½d. are equally among divided the partners. If each receives £28 5s. 4¼d., what is the number of partners ?

(12) A man bought 74 pieces of cloth for £440 6s. at 5s. 8d. per yard, how many yards were there in each piece ?

(13) Find the whole cost of 50 articles at 13s. 7½d. each, 72 articles at 16s. 8¾d. each, and 95 articles at 16s. 8¾d. each.

(14) How may parcels valued at £2 7s. 3½d. each can be made up from £900, and how much more would be required to make up one parcel more ?

(15) How many times can £6 16s. 8½d. be subtracted from £650, and what is the value of the remainder ?

(16) A man bought 358 cattle at £13 11s. 8½d. each. How much did he pay for the lot ?

(17) In one year Britain imported 106,222,723 cwts. of wheat, which cost £45,160,274. Find to the nearest penny the average cost per cwt.

(18) In the Post Office Savings Bank a sum of £178,965,038 has been deposited by 8,567,168 persons. Find to the nearest shilling the deposit per person.

(19) In one year we imported 3,956,125 cwts. of butter, to the value of £10,615,312. Find to the nearest penny the price per cwt.

(20) Goods to the value of £782,965,034 were imported into the United Kingdom in one year. Find to the nearest shilling how much that is per head. The population is 44,850,000.

(b) WEIGHTS AND MEASURES.

EXERCISE 5.

Add the following :—

(1)

Cwts.	Qrs.	Lbs.	Ozs.
16	2	3	5
7	3	15	11
6	2	14	12
7	1	9	10
14	3	16	11

(2)

Tons	Cwts.	Qrs.	Lbs.	Ozs.	Drs.
17	13	2	15	11	12
6	14	2	11	4	6
13	17	1	21	15	14
2	6	3	15	4	8
9	7	3	6	10	11

(3)

Tons	Cwts.	Qrs.	Lbs.	Ozs.	Drs.
16	7	2	10	11	12
13	4	3	20	11	13
14	15	0	15	9	0
7	16	2	16	8	7
9	18	1	26	0	6

(4)

Miles	Fur.	Poles	Yds.
10	7	16	3
15	6	24	4
16	5	13	4
4	2	7	2
8	3	19	3

(5)

Miles	Yds.	Ft.	Ins.
21	142	2	6
8	9	1	7
21	115	2	9
23	624	1	10
4	1,011	2	8

(6)

Miles	Fur.	Poles	Yds.	Ft.	Ins.
6	7	31	5	2	11
7	5	23	4	1	10
13	4	17	1	1	6
25	8	25	2	2	5
6	6	10	3	2	9

(7)

Miles	Fur.	Chs.	Yds.	Ft.
6	7	8	8	2
13	6	7	7	1
17	6	9	8	1
22	4	5	9	1
13	3	2	6	2

(8)

Days	Hours	Min.	Sec.
6	22	35	25
13	11	45	32
15	16	15	16
24	17	19	42
11	9	11	53

(9)

Days	Hours	Min.	Sec.
16	18	24	36
32	17	53	43
27	15	45	37
11	14	23	41
19	21	25	13

(10)

Ozs.	Dwts.	Grains
11	11	19
9	9	11
8	15	8
6	16	21
7	18	9

(11)

Lbs.	Ozs.	Dwts.	Grs.
6	9	15	19
7	10	16	21
8	5	4	12
3	11	17	9
12	8	16	22

EXERCISE 5—*Continued.*

(12)			
Acres	Roods	Sq.poles	Sq.yds.
5	3	30	20
6	2	25	15
15	1	22	16
14	3	15	25
3	1	37	21

(13)			
Acres	Roods	Sq.poles	Sq.yds.
2	0	38	25
1	3	24	12
15	1	16	13
6	2	25	27
3	0	14	16

(14)		
Sq.yds.	Sq. ft.	Sq. ins
10	8	25
12	6	113
3	5	116
4	7	28
15	3	94

(15)			
Qrs.	Bushels	Pecks	Gallons
6	3	3	1
4	7	2	1
3	5	3	0
4	7	2	1
2	6	1	1

(16)		
Gallons	Quarts	Pints
6	3	1
2	2	1
4	2	0
3	1	1
2	3	1

(17) Subtract 13 tons 2 cwts. 3 qrs. 12 lbs. from 16 tons 10 cwts. 1 qr. 10 lbs.

(18) ,, 5 tons 10 cwts. 3 qrs. 13 lbs. 5 ozs. from 10 tons 11 cwts. 1 qr. 25 lbs. 2 ozs.

(19) ,, 3 miles 5 fur. 6 poles 5 yds. from 7 miles 3 fur. 15 poles 2 yds.

(20) ,, 2 miles 2 fur. 17 poles 5 yds. 2 ft. 3 ins. from 3 miles 1 fur. 10 poles 2 yds. 1 ft. 6 ins.

(21) ,, 6 days 15 hours 28 minutes 15 seconds from 13 days 21 hours 10 minutes 25 seconds.

(22) ,, 16 ac. 3 ro. 15 sq. poles 10 sq. yds. from 25 ac. 2 ro. 11 sq. poles 9 sq. yds.

(23) ,, 10 lbs. 3 ozs. 5 dwts. 22 grains from 24 lbs. 2 ozs. 4 dwts. 18 grains.

(24) ,, 25 bush. 3 pecks 1 gallon from 56 bush. 1 peck.

(25) ,, 2 years 35 days 2 hrs. 45 mins. from 5 years 21 days 6 hrs. 15 mins.

EXERCISE 6.

(1) Reduce 5 tons 13 cwts 2 qrs. 11 lbs. 5 ozs. to ounces.

(2) One truck carried 11 tons 3 cwts. 2 qrs. 14 lbs. of coal. Find the weight carried by a train of 26 trucks.

(3) How many drams are there in 7 tons 3 cwts. 14 lbs. ?

(4) How many stones are there in 23 tons 7 cwts. ?

(5) $210\frac{1}{2}$ tons of coal are mined from a colliery each day. How many trucks, each holding 10 tons 10 cwts. 2 qrs., would be required to distribute this amount ?

(6) Reduce 765,324 drams to tons, cwts, etc.

(7) How many bags of coal, each weighing 1 cwt. 2 qrs. 3 lbs., can be obtained from a truck of coal weighing 9 tons 3 cwts. 2 qrs. 11 lbs., and what weight remains over ?

(8) Find the price of 3 cwts. 2 qrs. 11 lbs. of tea at $11\frac{1}{2}$d. per lb.

(9) How many half-stones of potatoes can be got from a pit containing 5 tons 13 cwts. 2 qrs. ?

(10) How many drams are there in 27 tons 19 cwts. 2 qrs. ?

(11) How long will 30 tons of coal last for 5 fires, each fire consuming 24 lbs. per day ?

(12) How many fields, each containing 41 ac. 2 ro. 15 poles are there in 13 square miles ?

(13) How many pieces of ribbon 2 ft. 9 ins. in length can be cut from a roll of ribbon 55 yards long ?

(14) Reduce 61,234,567 drams to tons.

(15) What is the weight of 39 barrels, each weighing 3 cwts. 3 qrs. 16 lbs. ?

(16) A loaded truck weighs 17 tons 6 cwts. 100 lbs., and the truck itself weighs 2 tons 10 cwts. ; it contains 320 equal packages. What is the weight of each package ?

(17) What is the weight of 2 millions of $\frac{1}{2}$-oz. nails ?

(18) If a boy has 350 pieces of string, each 3 ft. 4 ins. in length, how much is this short of $\frac{1}{2}$ mile ?

(19) If a man's step is 2 ft 9 ins. in length, and he takes 1,350 steps on a journey, what is the length of the journey ?

(20) How many seconds are there in 10 ordinary years ?

(21) Reduce 1,000,000 inches to miles, fur. . . .

(22) Find the number of minutes between 6.30 p.m. on 1st February and 11 p.m. on 5th May.

(23) The circumference of a racing track is 275 yards ; how many times must a cyclist go round to complete 10 miles ?

(24) The circumference of a wheel is $9\frac{1}{2}$ feet in length ; find the distance travelled after it has made 2,168 revolutions.

(25) There are 25 fields on a farm, each measuring 22 acres 3 roods 12 sq. poles. What is the size of the farm ?

(26) How many allotments, each 4 sq. poles 15 sq. yards, can be made from a field containing 34 acres ?

(27) Reduce 7 miles 3 fur. 14 poles 2 yards 2 feet 6 inches to inches.

(28) The distance round a field is 3 fur. 6 poles 2 yards 2 feet. How far does a person walk who goes round the field 35 times ?

(29) Into how many lots can 114 tons 10 cwts. 2 qrs. 14 lbs. be divided so that each lot contains 16 cwts. 1 qr. 12 lbs. 8 ozs. ?

(30) If a sovereign weighs 156 grains, how many sovereigns can be made from 13 lbs. (av.) of gold ?

(31) How many grains are there in 2 lbs. 6 ozs. 10 dwts. ?

(32) How many vessels, each holding 3 quarts 1 pint, can be filled from a vat containing 1,300 gallons ?

(33) How many fields, each containing 13 ac. 2 ro. 15 sq. poles 11 sq. yds., are there in 149 acres 2 ro. 9 sq. poles ?

(34) Find in seconds the difference between February and March of this year.

PROBLEMS—Additional Examples.

(35) 7 lbs. of beef and 4 lbs. of mutton cost 16s. 9d., and 11 lbs. of beef and 8 lbs. of mutton cost £1 8s. 9d. What is the cost of 1 lb. of mutton ?

(36) 21 telegraph posts erected at equal intervals stretch for a quarter of a mile. What is the distance between two of the posts ?

(37) A ton of sugar cost £23 6s. 8d. If it was sold at a profit of £7, what price per lb. was charged for it ?

(38) An engine travelling at 45 miles per hour took $5\frac{1}{2}$ seconds to cross a bridge. Find the length of the bridge in yards.

(39) A merchant bought 56 gallons of oil at 7s. per gallon, and sold it at 1s. 1d. per pint. What profit did he make ?

(40) A ton of potatoes was bought at $10\frac{1}{2}$d. per stone. One quarter of them were sold as smalls at 9d. per stone, and the remainder were sold at 1s. 3d. per stone. What profit was made on the whole transaction ?

(41) £96 6s. 5d. was divided among 95 people. 42 of them each received 3s. 10d. more than each of the others. How much did each of the 42 receive ?

(42) Sugar was bought at £1 5s. 8d. per cwt. and sold at $3\frac{1}{2}$d. per lb. How many cwts. had to be sold in order to make a profit of £12 5s. ?

(43) A field 66 yards wide was divided into drills each 2 ft. 3 ins. wide. How many drills were there ? If the field was 150 yards long, how many miles did the man walk while he was drilling the field ?

(44) A tank contained 930 gallons. It was found that in 18 minutes the outflow pipe could run off 69 gallons 3 qts. How long would it take to empty the tank ?

(45) A sack of potatoes cost 9s. 9d. If potatoes cost £6 10s. per ton, how many stones did the sack contain ?

(46) A man paid a bill of £19 5s. for petrol for his car. If his car can do 30 miles to the gallon of petrol, and petrol cost 1s. $4\frac{1}{2}$d. per gallon, how many miles had his car run ?

(47) A field contained 5 acres 1,540 sq. yards. It was divided into plots each containing 1 rood 220 sq. yards. How many plots were there ?

(48) A man works 8 hours a day on week days and 5 on Saturdays. He is paid at the rate of 1s. 10d. per hour and $\frac{1}{4}$ more for overtime. If a week's wages amount to £4 16s. 3d., how many hours overtime has he worked ?

CHAPTER II.

FACTORS AND MULTIPLES.

(a) PRIME AND COMPOSITE NUMBERS.

NUMBERS are either **prime** or **composite.** When a number cannot be divided **exactly** by any number except itself and unity it is called a **Prime Number.** Other numbers are called **Composite Numbers.**

Thus 7, 11, 29 are prime numbers, while 6, 15, 28 are composite numbers.

It is important to know the smaller prime numbers.

The following are the first 25 prime numbers :—

    2, 3, 5, 7, 11, 13, 17, 19, 23, 29, 31, 37, 41, 43, 47, 53, 59, 61, 67, 71, 73, 79, 83, 89, 97.

To find out whether a number is prime, try whether the smaller prime numbers 2, 3, 5, etc., divide it exactly.

Thus, if we wish to find out whether 193 is prime or not, divide it by 2, 3, 5, 7, 11, 13, 17, . . . We find that none of these divides into it exactly. We need not try to divide it by a higher number than 17, because the quotient obtained on dividing by 17 is less than 17 itself. If a number divides into another exactly, the quotient obtained must also divide into it exactly. For example, since 7 divides into 21, giving quotient 3, so 3 must divides into 21, giving quotient 7. Thus, if a number higher than 17 could divide into 193 exactly, then the quotient obtained, **which would be less than 17,** would also divide into 193 exactly ; but we have already tried the numbers less than 17 and found that none of them divides into 193 exactly. So we stop trying other numbers, and conclude that 193 is a prime number.

The rule, then, for finding whether a number is prime is to—

Divide it by the prime numbers 2, 3, 5, . . . If any number divides into it exactly it is not prime. If no number divides into it exactly it is prime, and *we stop trying as soon as the quotient becomes less than the number we are trying.*

It is useful to note that a number is exactly divisible by—

2 if it ends in 2, 4, 6, 8, 0 (even numbers),
3 if the sum of the figures is divisible by 3,
5 if the last figure is 5 or 0,
11 if the difference between the sum of the alternate digits (beginning with the units digit) and the sum of the remaining digits is 11 or 0.

EXERCISE 7.

Find which of the following are prime and which composite :—

(1) 57.	**(2)** 67.	**(3)** 73.	**(4)** 87.	**(5)** 97.
(6) 111.	**(7)** 113.	**(8)** 131.	**(9)** 141.	**(10)** 147.
(11) 149.	**(12)** 157.	**(13)** 161.	**(14)** 163.	**(15)** 165.
(16) 181.	**(17)** 187.	**(18)** 191.	**(19)** 197.	**(20)** 213.
(21) 301.	**(22)** 353.	**(23)** 381.	**(24)** 431.	**(25)** 437.

Write down the prime numbers between

    (26) 100 and 120.   **(27)** 180 and 200.

(b) FACTORS, PRIME FACTORS.

A **factor** of a number is another number which divides it exactly. Thus 7 is a factor of 35. So also is 5, and 12 is a factor of 36.

A prime number has no factors, but all composite numbers have factors, and every composite number may be expressed as the product of prime numbers or factors.

For example, $90 = 9 \times 10 = 3 \times 3 \times 2 \times 5 = 2 \times 3^2 \times 5$.

When 90 is expressed as $2 . 3^2 . 5$ it is said to be **broken up into its prime factors.**

To break up a number into its **prime factors,** we simply divide it by any **prime number** that will divide it exactly, and then divide the quotient in the same way, and so on till the last quotient is one.

Example 1.—Break up 90 into its prime factors.

```
2 | 90
3 | 45
3 | 15
5 | 5
    1
```

Divide 90 by 2,
then   45 by 3,
then   15 by 3.

$\therefore \quad 90 = 2 \times 3^2 \times 5$.

Example 2.—Break up 53,550 into prime factors.

```
 2 | 53,550
 3 | 26,775
 3 |  8,925
 5 |  2,975
 5 |    595
 7 |    119
17 |     17
   |      1
```

$\therefore\ 53,550 = 2 \times 3 \times 3 \times 5 \times 5 \times 7 \times 17$
$= 2 \cdot 3^2 \cdot 5^2 \cdot 7 \cdot 17.$

EXERCISE 8.

Break up into prime factors—

(1) 70. (2) 105. (3) 154. (4) 455.
(5) 220. (6) 315. (7) 252. (8) 525.
(9) 1,575. (10) 1,512. (11) 2,835. (12) 2,420.
(13) 3,465. (14) 7,735. (15) 7,245. (16) 2,431.
(17) 5,775. (18) 16,380. (19) 13,310. (20) 16,632.

(c) HIGHEST COMMON FACTOR.

If a number is a factor of two or more numbers it is called a **common factor** of these numbers.

Thus 7 is a common factor of 35 and 77.

Numbers which have no common factor are said to be **prime to one another,** though they may not themselves be prime numbers, as 8 and 15.

Two numbers may have several common factors.

Thus 5, 7, 35 are all common factors of the numbers 70 and 105. Of these 35 is the highest.

Thus the **Highest Common Factor** of two or more numbers is the largest number that divides each of them exactly.

To find the Highest Common Factor (H.C.F.) of two or more numbers, break them up into their prime factors. The H.C.F. can then be obtained by multiplying the common prime factors together.

Example 1.—Find the H.C.F. of 120 and 105.

$$120 = 2 \times 2 \times 2 \times 3 \times 5 = 2^3 \times 3 \times 5.$$
$$105 = 3 \times 5 \times 7.$$

Here we see that the only factors common to the two numbers are 3 and 5.

$$\therefore \quad \text{the H.C.F.} = 3 \times 5 = 15.$$

Example 2.—Find the H.C.F. of 840 and 1,980.

If we break up the numbers into prime factors we find :—

$$840 = 2 \times 2 \times 2 \times 3 \times 5 \times \; 7 = 2^3 \times 3 \; \times 5 \times \; 7,$$
$$\text{and } 1,980 = 2 \times 2 \times 3 \times 3 \times 5 \times 11 = 2^2 \times 3^2 \times 5 \times 11.$$

The common factors are 2^2, 3, and 5.

$$\therefore \quad \text{H.C.F.} = 2^2 \times 3 \times 5 = 60.$$

Example 3.—Find H.C.F. of 2,520, 2,475, and 3,510.

Breaking the numbers up into prime factors, we find :—

$$2,520 = 2^3 \times 3^2 \times \; 5 \times \; 7,$$
$$2,475 = 3^2 \times 5^2 \times 11$$
$$3,510 = 2 \; \times 3^3 \times \; 5 \times 13,$$
$$\therefore \quad \text{H.C.F.} = 3^2 \times 5 = 45.$$

EXERCISE 9.

Break up into prime factors and hence find the H.C.F. of—

(1) 30, 42.	**(2)** 45, 60.	**(3)** 240, 264.
(4) 450, 480.	**(5)** 322, 414.	**(6)** 560, 600.
(7) 42, 63, 147.	**(8)** 300, 460, 720.	**(9)** 150, 210, 525.
(10) 693, 819.	**(11)** 1,638, 3,465.	**(12)** 1,365, 1,287.
(13) 770, 1,260.	**(14)** 420, 792.	**(15)** 3,960, 4,620.
(16) 1,680, 1,848.	**(17)** 363, 429, 1,155.	
(18) 1,365, 1,785, 2,310.	**(19)** 924, 5,005, 2,695.	

Additional Examples.—

(20) 702, 1,092, 1,521.	**(21)** 1,188, 1,540, 2,772.
(22) 1,632, 2,091, 2,499.	**(23)** 855, 1,254, 1,539.
(24) 1,958, 2,541, 2,057.	**(25)** 1,752, 2,088, 2,424.
(26) 964, 700, 1,915.	**(27)** 3,402, 4,455, 6,561.

(d) MULTIPLES, LOWEST COMMON MULTIPLE.

A multiple of a number is another number which it divides exactly.

Thus 6, 8, 14 are all multiples of 2, because 2 divides into each of them exactly.

Note.—A number is a factor of any multiple of itself.

If a number is exactly divisible by two or more numbers, it is a **common multiple** of these numbers.

For example, 12 is a common multiple of 2, 3, 4, 6, because they all divide into it exactly.

The smallest number which is exactly divisible by two or more numbers is called the **Lowest Common Multiple** of these numbers.

Thus the lowest common multiple (L.C.M.) of 2, 3, 10 is 30, because 30 is the smallest number which each of them will divide into exactly.

The L.C.M. of two or more numbers may be found by breaking up the numbers into their prime factors.

Example 1.—Find the L.C.M. of 4, 6 and 15.

$4 = 2^2$
$6 = 2 \times 3$
$15 = 3 \times 5$

Evidently a number which is to contain 4 as a factor must contain 2^2, and to contain 6 it must contain 3, and if it contains 15 it must also contain 5.

Thus the lowest number that will contain each of the three given numbers as factors is $2^2 \times 3 \times 5$.

$$\therefore \text{ the L.C.M.} = 2^2 \times 3 \times 5 = 60.$$

Thus our rule is :—

Multiply all the different prime factors together, taking the highest power of each.

Example 2.—Find the L.C.M. of 8, 12, 45, 28.

$8 = 2^3$
$12 = 2^2 \times 3$
$45 = 3^2 \times 5$
$28 = 2^2 \times 7.$ $\therefore$ $\text{L.C.M.} = 2^3 \times 3^2 \times 5 \times 7 = 2,520.$

A convenient method is as follows :—

Write down the numbers in a row. Divide by the lowest prime number by which any of the given numbers is divisible, writing the quotients below along with the other numbers. Continue this process until all the quotients are 1.

2	8,	12,	45,	28
2	4,	6,	45,	14
2	2,	3,	45,	7
3	1,	3,	45,	7
3	1,	1,	15,	7
5	1,	1,	5,	7
7	1,	1,	1,	7
	1,	1,	1,	1

$$\text{L.C.M.} = 2^3 \times 3^2 \times 5 \times 7 = 2,520.$$

Then the L.C.M. is the product of all the divisors.

If in any row one of the numbers is a factor of another it may be ignored and cut out because it is contained in the larger number.

Example 3.—Find L.C.M. of 12, 15, 24, 30, 42, 36, 45.

2	12,	15,	24,	30,	42,	36,	45
2			12,	15,	21,	18,	45
2			6,		21,	9,	45
3			3,		21,		45
3					7,		15
5					7,		5
7					7,		1
					1,		1

$$\therefore \;\; \text{L.C.M.} = 2 \times 2 \times 2 \times 3 \times 3 \times 5 \times 7 = 2,520.$$

Note.—**Divide by prime numbers only in using this method.**

EXERCISE 10.

Find the L.C.M. of—

(1) 4, 6, 8.

(2) 9, 12, 16.

(3) 12, 14, 16, 28.

(4) 15, 20, 28, 30.

(5) 16, 18, 24, 36.

(6) 18, 21, 35, 42.

(7) 7, 9, 12, 81.

(8) 5, 11, 42, 66, 75.

(9) 13, 36, 39, 50, 117.

(10) 18, 27, 32, 128.

(11) 38, 56, 72, 84.

(12) 8, 12, 15, 18, 21.

(13) 12, 15, 18, 24, 27, 36.

(14) 15, 20, 25, 30, 35, 50.

(15) 8, 25, 35, 40, 45, 60.

(16) 21, 33, 28, 55, 56.

(17) 72, 96, 180, 256.

(18) 14, 42, 45, 56, 72.

(19) 15, 33, 55, 70, 121.

(20) 24, 63, 56, 39, 91.

(21) 44, 49, 63, 99, 154.

(22) 28, 27, 42, 36, 126.

(e) H.C.F. BY LONG DIVISION METHOD.

A **common factor** of two numbers is also a factor of the **sum** and of the **difference** of the numbers.

Thus, for example, 7 is a common factor of 77 and 63, 77 being 11 *times* 7 or 11 **sevens**, and 63 being 9 *times* 7 or 9 **sevens.**

Now, $77 + 63 = 11$ **sevens** $+ 9$ **sevens** $= 20$ **sevens** or 20×7, and $77 - 63 = 11$ **sevens** $- 9$ **sevens** $= 2$ **sevens** or 2×7.

Thus 7 is a factor of the *sum* or the *difference* of the two numbers, 77 and 63. In the same way it is a factor of the sum or difference of any multiples of these numbers.

This gives rise to another method for finding the H.C.F. of two numbers, which is as follows :—

Divide the larger number by the smaller, then the smaller by the remainder, and so on till there is no remainder.

The last divisor is the H.C.F. of the numbers.

Example 1.—Find the H.C.F. of 63 and 77.

```
4 | 63 | 77 | 1
  | 56 | 63 |
  ----|----
    7 | 14 | 2
      | 14 |
```

Divide as shown. Then 7, the last divisor, is the H.C.F. of 63 and 77.

By the principle shown above, the H.C.F. of 63 and 77 is contained in their difference 14, and is, therefore, a common factor of 14 and 63. So the H.C.F. of 14 and 63 is a factor of 77 (14 + 63). Thus the H.C.F. of 14, 63 is the same as that of 63, 77. And in the same way 7, 14 have the same H.C.F., which must, therefore, be 7.

If the last divisor is 1, then the numbers have no common factors at all, and are then prime to one another.

To find the H.C.F. of **three or more numbers** by this method, find the H.C.F. of the first two numbers, and then the H.C.F. of this answer and the third number, and so on.

Example 2.—Find the H.C.F. of 345, 805, 667.

```
3 | 345 | 805 | 2
  | 345 | 690 |
  |-----|-----|
  |     | 115 |

1 | 115 | 667 | 5
  |  92 | 575 |
  |-----|-----|
  |  23 |  92 | 4
  |     |  92 |
```

Find H.C.F. of 345 and 805. This is 115.

Then find H.C.F. of 115 and 667. The result is 23.

∴ 23 is the H.C.F. of the three numbers.

EXERCISE 11.

Find the H.C.F., by division method, of :—

(**1**) 391, 437.　　(**2**) 325, 403.　　(**3**) 468, 540.
(**4**) 555, 629.　　(**5**) 1,197, 1,767.　　(**6**) 2,799, 3,110.
(**7**) 1,863, 3,483.　　(**8**) 1,547, 4,277.　　(**9**) 297, 2,997.
(**10**) 1,919, 3,737.　　(**11**) 403, 6,200.　　(**12**) 5,875, 6,157.
(**13**) 7,371, 9,555.　　(**14**) 2,328, 3,395.　　(**15**) 2,405, 6,305.
(**16**) 1,421, 4,109.　　(**17**) 3,311, 5,753.　　(**18**) 2,369, 7,725.
(**19**) 7,371, 9,555, 27,391.　　(**20**) 17,261, 13,202, 15,498.
(**21**) 1,694, 2,310, 3,094.　　(**22**) 11,295, 15,813, 16,566.

Show that the following pairs of numbers are prime to each other :—

(**23**) 791, 970.　　(**24**) 942, 1,043.　　(**25**) 3,883, 4,310.

The L.C.M. of two large numbers may be found by first finding the H.C.F. by the division method.

Example.—Find the L.C.M. of 407 and 703.

$$
\begin{array}{r|r|r|l}
1 & 407 & 703 & 1 \\
  & 296 & 407 & \\
\hline
1 & 111 & 296 & 2 \\
  & 74 & 222 & \\
\hline
  & 37 & 74 & 2 \\
  &   & 74 & \\
\hline
\end{array}
$$

First find the H.C.F.
H.C.F. $= 37$.
Then divide each number by 37 ; we get
$$407 = 37 \times 11$$
and $\quad 703 = 37 \times 19.$
$\therefore$ L.C.M. $= 37 \times 11 \times 19$
$$= 7,733.$$

EXERCISE 12.

Find the H.C.F. and hence the L.C.M. of—

(1) 279, 315.   **(2)** 429, 585.   **(3)** 319, 493.
(4) 221, 247.   **(5)** 2,646, 3,465.   **(6)** 2,835, 4,085.
(7) 1,189, 1,271.   **(8)** 4,305, 4,515.   **(9)** 6,541, 8,651.
(10) 9,116, 9,964.   **(11)** 9,447, 10,653.   **(12)** 13,039, 13,481.

Break up into prime factors and hence find the H.C.F. and the L.C.M. of—

(13) 462, 546, 588.   **(14)** 72, 120, 168.
(15) 1,680, 1,890, 2,310.   **(16)** 128, 144, 192.
(17) 595, 935, 1,309.   **(18)** 910, 1,155, 3,185.

The following section may be omitted at the first reading.

(*f*) APPLICATION OF H.C.F. AND L.C.M.

The solution of various types of problems involves the finding of the H.C.F. or L.C.M. of numbers. We give an example or two.

Example 1.—What is the least number which when divided by 6, 15, or 25 leaves a remainder 4 in each case?

The number required must evidently be 4 more than the smallest number which 6, 15, and 25 will all divide into exactly. Hence we find the L.C.M. of these numbers and add 4 to it.

Now, the L.C.M. of 6, 15, 25 is 150. $\therefore$ the number required $= 150 + 4 = 154.$

Example 2.—The circumferences of two wheels are 213 ins. and 219 ins. in length. What is the size of the largest cogs that can be cut in each so that they can work together ?

Here we have to find the largest number which divides into both 213 and 219 exactly—that is, the H.C.F. of these numbers.

The H.C.F. of 213 and 219 is 3. ∴ Size of cog required = 3 ins.

EXERCISE 13.

(1) What is the least number which, when divided by 6, 8, or 12, leaves a remainder 3 in each case ?

(2) What is the least number which, when divided by 15, 16, or 18, leaves a remainder 1 in each case ?

(3) Find the greatest number which will divide 1,669 and 1,993 and leave remainders 19 and 13 respectively.

(4) Find the greatest number which will divide 1,516 and 1,734 and leave remainders 25 and 30 respectively.

(5) What is the smallest number that must be added to 84 so that the result may be a multiple of 15 and of 18 ?

(6) An account can be paid by an exact number of florins or of half-crowns. Find the smallest amount it can be.

(7) Find the least sum of money that can be paid either in florins, half-crowns, crowns, or half-guineas.

(8) What is the least sum of money that contains 7s. 6d, 12s. 6d., and 18s. each an exact whole number of times ?

(9) If a dollar is worth 4s. 2d., what is the smallest number of dollars that can be given for an exact number of half-crowns ?

(10) If a franc is worth 9d. and a dollar 4s. 1½d., find in dollars the least sum of money that can be paid exactly by a whole number of francs or of dollars.

(11) Two cylinders measure 250 ins. and 300 ins. respectively in circumference. Find the shortest length of cord that can be twined round each of them an exact whole number of times.

(12) The front wheel of a carriage is 10 ft. in circumference and the back wheel 12 ft. How far does the carriage travel before the same point on each wheel is again in contact with the ground ?

(13) The circumferences of two wheels measure 471 mm. and 879 mm. respectively. Find the size of the largest cogs that can be cut in each so that they may work together.

(14) What is the smallest possible size of a regiment which can be arranged in companies of 40, 56, 72, or 84 ?

(15) Two bells toll at intervals of 16 secs. and 18 secs. respectively. If they commence to toll at the same moment, how long will it be before they both toll at the same moment again ?

(16) Three bells toll at intervals of 20, 24, and 30 secs. respectively. If they all commence at the same moment, after what time will they all three toll again together ?

(17) Three men start to cycle round a circular path. They can complete the circuit in 4 mins., 5 mins., and 6 mins. respectively. Find when all three will pass the starting point together again.

(18) Two cyclists starting together go round a circular track at 15 miles and 20 miles per hour respectively. If the length of the track is one mile, when will they first pass the starting point together ?

(19) Two cogged wheels work into each other. Their circumferences are 30 ins. and 48 ins. respectively in length. Find what distance a point in the circumference of either wheel must travel before both wheels make an exact whole number of complete revolutions, and find the number of revolutions of each wheel in that time.

Additional Examples.

(20) A rectangular lawn, 30 yards by 13 yards 1 ft. 10 ins. is to be laid with square pieces of turf of equal size. Find the length of the largest turf that can be used.

(21) A gardener wished to plant a number of flowers. He found that he could plant them in groups of 24, 28, 36, or 42. What was the smallest number of plants he could have ?

(22) The wall of a bathroom 8 ft. 9 ins. long is to be tiled to a height of 4 ft. 7 ins. with square tiles of equal size. Find the size of the largest tile that can be used.

CHAPTER III.

VULGAR FRACTIONS.

(a) MEANING OF FRACTIONS AND MIXED NUMBERS.

A **fraction** is a part of a whole. In estimating the fraction we suppose the whole divided into a number of equal parts. The fraction will consist of one or more of these parts.

The number of equal parts into which the whole is divided is called the **denominator** (*namer*) of the fraction, and the number of these parts taken is called the **numerator** (*numberer*).

The fraction is written with the numerator above the denominator and separated from it by a line.

Thus, if the whole (or unit) is divided into 4 equal parts, a fraction consisting of 3 of these parts would be written :—

$$\frac{3}{4}, \text{ and named `` \textbf{three-fourths.}''}$$

The numerator and denominator are spoken of as the **terms** of the fraction.

The student knows, from examining his foot rule, that $\frac{6}{8}$ of an inch is the same as $\frac{3}{4}$ of an inch. Thus, $\frac{6}{8} = \frac{3}{4}$ or $\frac{3}{4} = \frac{6}{8}$. We have, therefore, the following important fact :—

The value of a fraction is not altered if its numerator and denominator are both multiplied or both divided by the same number.

This enables us to reduce a fraction to its lowest terms.

Example 1.—Reduce $\frac{25}{30}$ to its lowest terms.

Divide both numerator and denominator by 5. $\therefore \frac{25}{30} = \frac{5}{6}$.

It may be difficult to find by trial a factor of both numerator and denominator. In such a case find their H.C.F. Divide each by it ; the fraction is then reduced to its lowest terms.

Vulgar Fractions.

Example 2.—Reduce $\dfrac{1177}{1391}$ to its lowest terms.

The H.C.F. of 1177 and 1391 will be found to be 107. Divide each by 107 ; we find $1177 \div 107 = 11$ and $1391 \div 107 = 13$.

$$\therefore \quad \frac{1177}{1391} = \frac{107 \times 11}{107 \times 13} = \frac{11}{13}.$$

EXERCISE 14.

Reduce to their lowest terms :—

(1) $\dfrac{6}{10}$.   (2) $\dfrac{15}{45}$.   (3) $\dfrac{56}{84}$.   (4) $\dfrac{144}{1728}$ (5) $\dfrac{132}{143}$.

(6) $\dfrac{130}{143}$.   (7) $\dfrac{187}{221}$.   (8) $\dfrac{285}{399}$.   (9) $\dfrac{299}{391}$.   (10) $\dfrac{1015}{1595}$.

(11) $\dfrac{2387}{2728}$.   (12) $\dfrac{711}{3792}$.   (13) $\dfrac{1155}{1485}$.   (14) $\dfrac{1243}{1469}$.   (15) $\dfrac{1785}{1995}$.

(16) $\dfrac{5564}{5694}$.   (17) $\dfrac{18585}{23895}$.   (18) $\dfrac{5994}{6534}$.   (19) $\dfrac{21412}{31613}$.   (20) $\dfrac{35334}{47263}$.

Fractions of Unity—that is, fractions with the numerator less than the denominator—are called **proper fractions.**

If the inches on a foot rule are each divided into eight equal parts, and we take 8 or more of these (say 11), we have fractions where the numerator is equal to or greater than the denominator, as $\dfrac{8}{8}$ or $\dfrac{11}{8}$. Such fractions are called **improper fractions.**

Now 11 **eighths** $=$ 8 **eighths** $+$ 3 **eighths** $=$ **one unit** $+$ 3 **eighths**

That is, $\dfrac{11}{8} = 1 + \frac{3}{8}$, which may be written $1\frac{3}{8}$.

A number like $1\frac{3}{8}$, consisting of a whole number and a proper fraction, is called a **mixed number.** We thus see that an improper fraction may be converted into a mixed number.

Example 1.—Convert $\frac{9}{4}$ into a mixed number.

Divide 9 by 4, giving 2 units and 1 fourth. $\therefore \frac{9}{4} = 2\frac{1}{4}$.

Also, a **mixed number** may be converted into an improper fraction.

Example 2.—Convert $3\frac{1}{5}$ into an improper fraction.

Multiply 3 by 5, giving 15 fifths, add 1 fifth. $\therefore 3\frac{1}{5} = \frac{16}{5}$.

EXERCISE 15.

Convert into mixed numbers—

(1) $\frac{7}{4}$.   **(2)** $\frac{17}{8}$.   **(3)** $\frac{25}{6}$.   **(4)** $\frac{100}{13}$.   **(5)** $\frac{863}{37}$.   **(6)** $\frac{1013}{41}$.

Convert into improper fractions—

(7) $3\frac{1}{4}$.   **(8)** $5\frac{3}{7}$.   **(9)** $17\frac{13}{14}$.   **(10)** $21\frac{5}{17}$.   **(11)** $23\frac{5}{11}$.   **(12)** $17\frac{9}{16}$.
(13) $8\frac{11}{15}$.   **(14)** $12\frac{17}{20}$.   **(15)** $32\frac{3}{28}$.   **(16)** $9\frac{19}{35}$.   **(17)** $18\frac{25}{27}$.   **(18)** $30\frac{7}{48}$.

(*b*) COMPARISON OF FRACTIONS.

To compare fractions we must reduce them to the same denominator.

Thus to compare $\frac{3}{4}$ and $\frac{5}{8}$ we multiply both terms of the fraction $\frac{3}{4}$ by 2, getting $\frac{6}{8}$. Thus $\frac{3}{4} = \frac{6}{8}$, and is, therefore, greater than $\frac{5}{8}$.

In comparing a number of fractions, the most convenient denominator to use is the **L.C.M.** of all the denominators. This is the Lowest Common Denominator (L.C.D.).

Example 1.—Convert $\frac{5}{7}, \frac{3}{8}, \frac{5}{12}, \frac{9}{14}$ into fractions with the same denominator, and arrange them in order of magnitude.

2	7, 8, 12, 14
2	4, 6, 7
2	2, 3, 7
3	1, 3, 7
7	1, 1, 7
	1, 1, 1

∴ L.C.M. $= 2^3 \times 3 \times 7 = 168$.

We first find L.C.M. of denominators $= 168$.

$$\frac{5}{7} = \frac{5 \times 24}{7 \times 24} = \frac{120}{168}$$

7 divided into 168 gives 24.
∴ Multiply both terms of $\frac{5}{7}$ by 24.

$$\frac{3}{8} = \frac{3 \times 21}{8 \times 21} = \frac{63}{168}$$

8 divided into 168 gives 21.
∴ Multiply both terms of $\frac{3}{8}$ by 21.

$$\frac{5}{12} = \frac{5 \times 14}{12 \times 14} = \frac{70}{168}$$

12 divided into 168 gives 14.
∴ Multiply both terms of $\frac{5}{12}$ by 14.

$$\frac{9}{14} = \frac{9 \times 12}{14 \times 12} = \frac{108}{168}$$

14 divided into 168 gives 12.
∴ Multiply both terms of $\frac{9}{14}$ by 12.

Comparing the numerators of the new fractions, we see that the order of magnitude is $\frac{120}{168}, \frac{108}{168}, \frac{70}{168}, \frac{63}{168}$, or $\frac{5}{7}, \frac{9}{14}, \frac{5}{12}, \frac{3}{8}$.

We can also convert a whole number into a fraction with any denominator we choose in the same way. We may consider 1 to be the denominator of a whole number.

Example 2.—Convert 6 into a fraction with 5 for denominator.

$$6 = \frac{6}{1} = \frac{6 \times 5}{1 \times 5} = \frac{30}{5}.$$

EXERCISE 16.

Reduce to the Lowest Common Denominator—

(1) $\dfrac{2}{3}, \dfrac{1}{6}, \dfrac{3}{8}$.

(2) $\dfrac{3}{7}, \dfrac{4}{5}, \dfrac{8}{21}$.

(3) $\dfrac{5}{1}, \dfrac{8}{3}, \dfrac{9}{7}$.

(4) $\dfrac{3}{8}, \dfrac{5}{12}, \dfrac{7}{15}$.

(5) $\dfrac{5}{9}, \dfrac{7}{18}, \dfrac{7}{24}$.

(6) $\dfrac{3}{11}, \dfrac{4}{7}, \dfrac{2}{5}$.

Arrange in order of magnitude, putting greatest first—

(7) $\dfrac{7}{18}, \dfrac{11}{30}, \dfrac{5}{12}$.

(8) $\dfrac{3}{5}, \dfrac{6}{11}, \dfrac{7}{15}, \dfrac{17}{33}$.

(9) $\dfrac{5}{9}, \dfrac{9}{16}, \dfrac{13}{24}$.

(10) $\dfrac{5}{12}, \dfrac{7}{16}, \dfrac{9}{26}$.

(11) $\dfrac{11}{36}, \dfrac{9}{28}, \dfrac{7}{24}$.

(12) $\dfrac{11}{23}, \dfrac{7}{16}, \dfrac{34}{69}$.

(13) Express 8, 12, 31 as fractions with denominator 5.

(14) Express 12, 13, 17 as fractions with denominator 11.

(15) Express 3, 7, 19 as fractions with denominator 13.

(c) ADDITION OF FRACTIONS.

To add fractions with the **same denominators,** we have merely to add the numerators.

Example 1.—$\dfrac{3}{7} + \dfrac{5}{7} + \dfrac{2}{7} = \dfrac{3+5+2}{7} = \dfrac{10}{7} = 1\dfrac{3}{7}.$

To add fractions with **different denominators,** we must first reduce them to a **common denominator** (the L.C.M. of their denominators), and then add the numerators.

Example 2.—$\dfrac{5}{6} + \dfrac{4}{15} + \dfrac{7}{10} = \dfrac{25}{30} + \dfrac{8}{30} + \dfrac{21}{30}$

$$= \dfrac{25+8+21}{30}$$

$$= \dfrac{54}{30} = 1\dfrac{24}{30} = 1\dfrac{4}{5}.$$

EXERCISE 17.

Simplify—

(1) $\dfrac{1}{8} + \dfrac{4}{8} + \dfrac{7}{8}.$ **(2)** $\dfrac{4}{9} + \dfrac{5}{9} + \dfrac{7}{9}.$ **(3)** $\dfrac{1}{2} + \dfrac{1}{3}.$

(4) $\dfrac{1}{3} + \dfrac{1}{4}.$ **(5)** $\dfrac{2}{3} + \dfrac{3}{4}.$ **(6)** $\dfrac{3}{4} + \dfrac{1}{6} + \dfrac{1}{2}.$

(7) $\dfrac{2}{3} + \dfrac{5}{6} + \dfrac{4}{9}.$ **(8)** $\dfrac{1}{6} + \dfrac{2}{9} + \dfrac{5}{12}.$ **(9)** $\dfrac{7}{12} + \dfrac{5}{9} + \dfrac{3}{16}.$

(10) $\dfrac{3}{5} + \dfrac{11}{15} + \dfrac{13}{20}.$ **(11)** $\dfrac{2}{3} + \dfrac{5}{8} + \dfrac{11}{12} + \dfrac{13}{16}.$

(12) $\dfrac{1}{2} + \dfrac{1}{3} + \dfrac{1}{5} + \dfrac{3}{8}.$ **(13)** $\dfrac{3}{11} + \dfrac{2}{3} + \dfrac{6}{21} + \dfrac{5}{7}.$

(14) $\dfrac{11}{15} + \dfrac{3}{5} + \dfrac{13}{16} + \dfrac{13}{20}.$ **(15)** $\dfrac{4}{7} + \dfrac{5}{14} + \dfrac{8}{21}.$

(16) $\dfrac{2}{3} + \dfrac{5}{9} + \dfrac{7}{18}.$ **(17)** $\dfrac{4}{5} + \dfrac{2}{3} + \dfrac{7}{15}.$

Additional Examples.—

(18) $\dfrac{15}{16} + \dfrac{9}{11} + \dfrac{17}{22}.$ **(19)** $\dfrac{7}{9} + \dfrac{17}{20} + \dfrac{25}{36} + \dfrac{115}{144}.$

(20) $\dfrac{11}{15} + \dfrac{7}{16} + \dfrac{31}{35} + \dfrac{59}{84}.$ **(21)** $\dfrac{13}{14} + \dfrac{7}{12} + \dfrac{43}{66} + \dfrac{19}{21}.$

(22) $\dfrac{17}{18} + \dfrac{7}{10} + \dfrac{37}{45} + \dfrac{63}{80}.$ **(23)** $\dfrac{11}{15} + \dfrac{17}{20} + \dfrac{13}{24} + \dfrac{19}{33}.$

In adding **mixed numbers,** add the integers by themselves and the fractions by themselves.

$$\textit{Example.—}\, 2\tfrac{1}{3} + 4\tfrac{5}{6} + 3\tfrac{7}{8} = 2 + 4 + 3 + \tfrac{1}{3} + \tfrac{5}{6} + \tfrac{7}{8}$$

$$= 9 + \frac{8 + 20 + 21}{24} = 9 + \frac{49}{24}$$

$$= 9 + 2\tfrac{1}{24} = 11\tfrac{1}{24}.$$

EXERCISE 18.

Simplify—

(1) $2\frac{1}{4} + 1\frac{1}{5} + \frac{2}{3}$.   (2) $2\frac{1}{17} + 4 + 1\frac{3}{34}$.   (3) $3\frac{4}{11} + 1\frac{1}{5} + \frac{7}{55}$.

(4) $\frac{13}{7} + 2\frac{1}{14} + \frac{5}{21}$.   (5) $\frac{7}{23} + 4\frac{3}{46} + 5\frac{1}{4}$.   (6) $\frac{5}{13} + 3\frac{2}{17} + \frac{4}{11}$.

(7) $5\frac{1}{2} + 3\frac{1}{4} + 7\frac{1}{6}$.   (8) $3\frac{2}{3} + 7\frac{4}{9} + 4\frac{5}{6}$.   (9) $4\frac{1}{2} + 8\frac{3}{11} + 3\frac{5}{22}$.

(10) $7\frac{1}{5} + 4\frac{1}{3} + 6\frac{3}{4}$.   (11) $5\frac{1}{2} + 2\frac{3}{4} + 3\frac{5}{8}$.

(12) $3\frac{1}{5} + \frac{2}{3} + 3\frac{11}{15} + 2\frac{13}{20}$.   (13) $4\frac{1}{8} + 2\frac{11}{12} + 3\frac{7}{15} + 8\frac{7}{10}$.

(14) $7\frac{1}{14} + 3\frac{13}{42} + 2\frac{13}{56} + 1\frac{11}{24}$.   (15) $6\frac{1}{3} + 8\frac{1}{9} + \frac{3}{7}$.

(16) $3\frac{5}{18} + 2\frac{13}{45} + 1\frac{13}{25} + 4\frac{11}{30}$.

Additional Examples.—

(17) $7\frac{3}{4} + 4\frac{4}{5} + 2\frac{7}{9} + 10\frac{11}{15}$.

(18) $21\frac{7}{11} + 13\frac{8}{9} + 17\frac{9}{16} + 3\frac{5}{24}$.

(19) $102\frac{7}{8} + 19\frac{5}{12} + 31\frac{15}{32} + 4\frac{9}{20}$.

(20) $38\frac{8}{21} + 18\frac{13}{18} + 24\frac{23}{28} + 7\frac{5}{16}$.

(21) $13\frac{8}{11} + 9\frac{7}{8} + 11\frac{13}{18} + 5\frac{8}{21}$.

(22) $3\frac{6}{7} + 18\frac{11}{15} + 14\frac{5}{12} + 7\frac{9}{16}$.

(23) $7\frac{9}{10} + 6\frac{19}{42} + 3\frac{11}{14} + 15\frac{23}{36} + 5\frac{3}{8}$.

(c) SUBTRACTION OF FRACTIONS.

To subtract one fraction from another we must first reduce them to the same denominator as in addition, and in the case of mixed numbers the integral and fractional parts should be treated separately.

Example 1. $\dfrac{5}{7} - \dfrac{2}{11} = \dfrac{55-14}{77} = \dfrac{41}{77}.$

Example 2. $5\dfrac{7}{9} - 3\dfrac{5}{12} = (5-3) + \left(\dfrac{7}{9} - \dfrac{5}{12}\right)$ Here we take 3 from 5 and $\dfrac{5}{12}$ from $\dfrac{7}{9}$ and add the result.

$$= 2\dfrac{28-15}{36} = 2\dfrac{13}{30}.$$

EXERCISE 19.

Simplify—

(1) $\dfrac{7}{9} - \dfrac{2}{9}.$

(2) $\dfrac{3}{4} - \dfrac{1}{3}.$

(3) $\dfrac{19}{20} - \dfrac{3}{5}.$

(4) $\dfrac{20}{21} - \dfrac{5}{14}.$

(5) $\dfrac{1}{17} - \dfrac{1}{19}.$

(6) $\dfrac{9}{10} - \dfrac{8}{9}.$

(7) $\dfrac{11}{12} - \dfrac{5}{13}.$

(8) $\dfrac{10}{11} - \dfrac{7}{12}.$

(9) $\dfrac{15}{16} - \dfrac{2}{3}.$

(10) $\dfrac{11}{48} - \dfrac{5}{24}.$

(11) $\dfrac{47}{50} - \dfrac{2}{3}.$

(12) $8\dfrac{4}{5} - 3\dfrac{2}{3}.$

(13) $5\dfrac{3}{7} - 2\dfrac{1}{14}.$

(14) $7\dfrac{5}{9} - 2\dfrac{1}{12}.$

(15) $8\dfrac{11}{12} - 2\dfrac{2}{3}.$

(16) $9\dfrac{11}{13} - 3\dfrac{5}{12}.$

(17) $7\dfrac{8}{15} - 3\dfrac{1}{3}.$

(18) $9\dfrac{11}{100} - 3\dfrac{2}{75}.$

(19) $7\dfrac{3}{4} - 2\dfrac{5}{12}.$

(20) $8\dfrac{19}{24} - 6\dfrac{1}{3}.$

(21) $12\dfrac{31}{110} - 2\dfrac{1}{5}.$

(22) $5\dfrac{61}{96} - 2\dfrac{23}{72}.$

(23) $14\dfrac{3}{5} - 2\dfrac{8}{15}.$

Example 3.—Subtract $4\frac{4}{5}$ from $8\frac{1}{3}$.

Proceeding as before we get $8\frac{1}{3} - 4\frac{4}{5} = 4\frac{5-12}{15}$. Here we cannot take 12 from 5 ; so we get over the difficulty by taking 1 from the 4 and adding to the fractional part thus :—

$$8\frac{1}{3} - 4\frac{4}{5} = 4 + \frac{5-12}{15} = 3 + 1 + \frac{5-12}{15}$$

$$= 3\frac{15+5-12}{15} = 3\frac{20-12}{15} = 3\frac{8}{15}.$$

Example 4.—

$$\frac{5}{6} - \frac{3}{4} + \frac{7}{8} - \frac{2}{3} = \frac{20-18+21-16}{24} = \frac{41-34}{24} = \frac{7}{24}.$$

Example 5.—

$$4\frac{5}{12} - \frac{1}{2} - \frac{3}{4} - \frac{2}{3} = 4 + \frac{5-6-9-8}{12}$$

$$= 4 + \frac{5-23}{12}$$

$$= 2 + 2 + \frac{5-23}{12}$$

$$= 2\frac{24+5-23}{12}$$

$$= 2\frac{29-23}{12} = 2\frac{6}{12} = 2\frac{1}{2}.$$

EXERCISE 20.

Simplify—

(1) $8\frac{1}{2} - 4\frac{3}{4}$.   (2) $6\frac{2}{3} - 4\frac{4}{5}$.   (3) $7\frac{1}{11} - 2\frac{3}{7}$.

(4) $9\frac{3}{22} - 4\frac{8}{21}$.   (5) $15\frac{1}{8} - 3\frac{15}{16}$.   (6) $3\frac{10}{33} - 1\frac{57}{77}$.

(7) $4\frac{5}{12} - 2\frac{25}{42}$.   (8) $6\frac{1}{8} - 3\frac{17}{24}$.   (9) $5\frac{11}{32} - 2\frac{37}{48}$.

EXERCISE 20—*Continued.*

(10) $5\frac{7}{36} - 2\frac{41}{45}.$ **(11)** $\frac{5}{6} - \frac{1}{3} - \frac{1}{4}.$ **(12)** $2\frac{3}{4} - \frac{2}{5} - \frac{1}{3}.$

(13) $2\frac{3}{8} + \frac{5}{12} - \frac{1}{3} - \frac{3}{4}.$ **(14)** $\frac{1}{2} + \frac{1}{3} + \frac{1}{4} - \frac{1}{5} - \frac{1}{6}.$

(15) $2 + \frac{1}{6} - \frac{1}{2} - 1\frac{3}{4} + \frac{1}{4}.$ **(16)** $5 + \frac{1}{5} + \frac{1}{6} - \frac{1}{3} - \frac{3}{4}.$

(17) $5\frac{1}{4} + 2\frac{1}{8} - 3\frac{3}{4}.$ **(18)** $7\frac{1}{6} + 1\frac{1}{3} - 4\frac{7}{12}.$

(19) $8\frac{3}{5} + 2\frac{1}{3} - 9\frac{7}{15}.$ **(20)** $9\frac{5}{12} + 2\frac{7}{16} - 5\frac{1}{8}.$

(21) $15\frac{5}{16} - 3\frac{17}{48} + 2\frac{7}{24} - 5\frac{1}{8}.$ **(22)** $8\frac{1}{7} + 4\frac{3}{4} - 5\frac{5}{14} - 1\frac{15}{28}.$

(23) $7\frac{4}{5} - 2\frac{2}{3} + 5\frac{1}{2} - 2\frac{13}{15}.$

(24) $2\frac{1}{2} + 3\frac{1}{3} + 5\frac{1}{5} - 3\frac{1}{6} - 1\frac{1}{10} - 2\frac{1}{15}.$

(25) From $5\frac{1}{8} + 18\frac{1}{9}$ take $7\frac{5}{6} + 8\frac{7}{18}.$

(26) From $8\frac{1}{3} + 15\frac{2}{7}$ take $8\frac{5}{14} + 5\frac{2}{21}.$

(27) From $19\frac{5}{13} - 8\frac{1}{2}$ take $17\frac{3}{26} - 15\frac{1}{4}.$

(28) What must be added to $3\frac{1}{4} + 4\frac{1}{5} + 5\frac{1}{6}$ to obtain $14\frac{1}{2}$?

(29) Find the difference between $7\frac{1}{8} + 8\frac{1}{7}$ and $6\frac{3}{4} + 8\frac{13}{56}.$

(30) What must be subtracted from $6\frac{1}{5} + 5\frac{1}{4} + 4\frac{1}{3}$ to leave $10\frac{4}{15}$?

(31) What is the least fraction which must be added to the sum of $2\frac{7}{8}, 3\frac{6}{7}, 5\frac{1}{4}$ to make a whole number ?

(32) By how much does the difference between $12\frac{1}{3}$ and $3\frac{2}{5}$ exceed the sum of $2\frac{11}{20}$, $1\frac{1}{4}$, and $2\frac{13}{15}$?

Additional Examples.

(33) $8\frac{3}{4} - 1\frac{14}{15} - 2\frac{23}{24} - 1\frac{9}{10}$

(34) $7\frac{1}{6} - 3\frac{17}{20} + 2\frac{1}{16} - 3\frac{29}{32} - \frac{11}{12}$.

(35) $5\frac{1}{8} - 1\frac{15}{16} - 2\frac{25}{28} + 3\frac{1}{3} - 1\frac{19}{21}$.

(36) $11\frac{3}{8} - 2\frac{6}{7} - 1\frac{19}{20} + 1\frac{1}{3} - 3\frac{23}{24}$.

(*d*) MULTIPLICATION OF FRACTIONS.

To multiply $\frac{3}{4}$ by 5 we wish to get 5 times 3 **fourths**—that is, 15 **fourths** or $\frac{15}{4}$.

Thus to multiply a fraction by a *whole number* **we have merely to multiply the numerator by the number.**

If the multiplier and the denominator have a common factor, the resulting fraction will not be in its lowest terms. To reduce it to its lowest terms, we must divide numerator and denominator by their common factors, but this may be done before multiplying. This is called **cancelling**.

Example 1.—$\frac{5}{6} \times 4 = \frac{20}{6} = \frac{10}{3}$.

or $\qquad \frac{5}{\overset{}{\underset{3}{6}}} \times \overset{2}{4} = \frac{5}{3} \times 2$ (cancelling 4 and 6 by 2)

$$= \frac{10}{3} = 3\frac{1}{3}.$$

Mixed numbers should be converted into improper fractions before multiplying.

Example 2.—$3\frac{5}{12} \times 9 = \frac{41}{12} \times 9$

$$= \frac{41}{\overset{}{\underset{4}{12}}} \times \overset{3}{9} \quad \text{(cancelling by 3)}$$

$$= \frac{123}{4} = 30\frac{3}{4}.$$

To multiply $\frac{1}{2}$ by $\frac{1}{3}$ means to find $\frac{1}{3}$ of $\frac{1}{2}$. This is evidently $\frac{1}{6}$ of the whole. So to multiply $\frac{1}{2}$ by $\frac{2}{3}$ we take 2 *times* $\frac{1}{3}$ of $\frac{1}{2}$ = 2 times $\frac{1}{6} = \frac{2}{6}$. Thus $\frac{1}{2} \times \frac{2}{3} = \frac{2}{6}$.

Hence, to multiply one fraction by another we multiply the numerators together, and multiply the denominators together.

Example 3.

$$\frac{6}{35} \times \frac{14}{15} = \frac{\overset{2}{6}}{\underset{5}{35}} \times \frac{\overset{2}{14}}{\underset{5}{15}} = \frac{4}{25}. \quad \text{(cancelling before multiplying.)}$$

Example 4.—Find value of $\frac{2}{3} \times 3\frac{3}{5} \times 2\frac{1}{7}$.

$$\frac{2}{3} \times 3\frac{3}{5} \times 2\frac{1}{7} = \frac{2}{\cancel{3}} \times \frac{\cancel{18}}{\cancel{5}} \times \frac{\overset{3}{\cancel{15}}}{7} = \frac{36}{7} = 5\frac{1}{7}.$$

EXERCISE 21.

Simplify—

(1) $\frac{1}{3} \times 5$.   (2) $\frac{3}{4} \times 6$.   (3) $5\frac{1}{2} \times 4$.

(4) $3\frac{2}{7} \times 4$.   (5) $\frac{1}{2} \times \frac{1}{4}$.   (6) $\frac{2}{3} \times \frac{5}{7}$.

(7) $\frac{5}{9} \times \frac{3}{8}$.   (8) $\frac{6}{11} \times \frac{22}{27}$.   (9) $3\frac{1}{2} \times \frac{5}{7}$.

(10) $3\frac{4}{5} \times 2\frac{1}{2}$.   (11) $\frac{2}{3} \times \frac{3}{4} \times \frac{4}{5}$.   (12) $\frac{1}{2} \times 3\frac{1}{4} \times \frac{4}{13}$.

(13) $2\frac{7}{10} \times 1\frac{1}{9} \times 3\frac{1}{5}$.   (14) $\frac{16}{23} \times 4\frac{3}{5} \times 2\frac{1}{17}$.

(15) $2\frac{1}{5} \times \frac{5}{6} \times 14\frac{1}{3}$.   (16) $\frac{15}{16} \times 3\frac{1}{10} \times 4\frac{5}{31}$.

(17) $5\frac{1}{3} \times 2\frac{1}{4} \times 5\frac{1}{6}$.   (18) $7\frac{1}{8} \times 3\frac{1}{5} \times 1\frac{1}{19}$.

(19) $17\frac{8}{9} \times 2\frac{3}{4} \times 1\frac{7}{11}$.   (20) $6\frac{2}{3} \times 1\frac{7}{9} \times \frac{27}{40}$.

(21) $3\frac{1}{7} \times 3\frac{1}{11} \times 9\frac{2}{3}$.   (22) $4\frac{1}{5} \times 1\frac{7}{8} \times 3\frac{1}{3} \times \frac{13}{28}$.

(e) DIVISION OF FRACTIONS.

Division by an Integer.—To divide a number by 3 means to find $\frac{1}{3}$ of the number.

Thus $\frac{1}{2} \div 3$ means $\frac{1}{3}$ of $\frac{1}{2} = \frac{1}{6}$.

Hence, to divide a fraction by a whole number we multiply the denominator of the fraction by the number.

Example.—$2\frac{1}{3} \div 4 = \frac{7}{3} \div 4 = \frac{7}{3 \times 4} = \frac{7}{12}$.

Division by a Fraction.—To divide 6 by 3 is to find what 3 must be multiplied by to give 6. ($3 \times 2 = 6$.)

So to divide 1 by $\frac{2}{3}$ is to find what $\frac{2}{3}$ must be multiplied by to give 1.

Now, to give 1 we must multiply $\frac{2}{3}$ by $\frac{3}{2}$. $\therefore 1 \div \frac{2}{3} = \frac{3}{2}$. Thus to divide by $\frac{2}{3}$ is to multiply by $\frac{3}{2}$.

Two numbers whose product is 1 are called the **reciprocals** of each other. Thus $\frac{1}{3}$ is called the reciprocal of 3, because $\frac{1}{3} \times 3 = 1$. So $\frac{3}{2}$ is the reciprocal of $\frac{2}{3}$, because $\frac{3}{2} \times \frac{2}{3} = 1$.

Hence we have the general rule for division of fractions.

To divide by a fraction multiply by its reciprocal.

Example 1.— $\frac{3}{4} \div \frac{5}{7} = \frac{3}{4} \times \frac{7}{5} = \frac{21}{20} = 1\frac{1}{20}$.

Example 2.—$2\frac{4}{5} \div 3\frac{2}{3} = \frac{14}{5} \div \frac{11}{3} = \frac{14}{5} \times \frac{3}{11} = \frac{42}{55}$.

EXERCISE 22.

(1) $\frac{2}{3} \div 5$.   (2) $2\frac{1}{3} \div 4$.   (3) $5 \div \frac{2}{7}$.   (4) $\frac{3}{8} \div \frac{2}{3}$.

(5) $\frac{5}{8} \div \frac{3}{4}$.   (6) $1\frac{1}{8} \div \frac{4}{7}$.   (7) $3\frac{2}{5} \div 2\frac{1}{2}$.   (8) $6\frac{4}{7} \div 2\frac{7}{8}$.

(9) $\frac{2}{5} \div 3\frac{1}{4}$.   (10) $3\frac{1}{4} \div 4\frac{1}{3}$.   (11) $6\frac{11}{12} \div 3\frac{1}{4}$ (12) $3\frac{2}{5} \div 4\frac{9}{19}$.

EXERCISE 22—*Continued.*

(13) $6\frac{1}{5} \div 3\frac{7}{10}$ **(14)** $8\frac{3}{11} \div 4\frac{1}{3}$ **(15)** $10\frac{6}{13} \div 4\frac{6}{7}$ **(16)** $3\frac{1}{13} \div 2\frac{23}{26}$

(17) $\frac{55}{123} \div 3\frac{12}{41}$ **(18)** $8\frac{11}{15} \div 3\frac{37}{75}$ **(19)** $2\frac{23}{49} \div 8\frac{19}{21}$ **(20)** $4\frac{37}{62} \div 12\frac{27}{31}$

(*f*) BRACKETS AND ORDER OF PRECEDENCE OF SIGNS.

Two or more numbers enclosed within brackets are treated as one quantity.

Example 1. $2\frac{1}{4} \times \left(2\frac{1}{2} + \frac{1}{3}\right) = 2\frac{1}{4} \times \left(2\frac{3+2}{6}\right) = 2\frac{1}{4} \times 2\frac{5}{6}$

$$= \frac{\overset{3}{\cancel{9}}}{4} \times \frac{17}{\underset{2}{\cancel{6}}} = \frac{51}{8} = 6\frac{3}{8}$$

If the brackets were absent $2\frac{1}{4} \times 2\frac{1}{2} + \frac{1}{3}$ would mean that $2\frac{1}{4}$ had to be multiplied by $2\frac{1}{2}$ and $\frac{1}{3}$ added to the result. It is important to note that what is within the brackets must be worked first. This leads us to consider what we might call the order of precedence of the different signs.

Order of Precedence.—

    (1) " Of," brackets.
    (2) The signs :—" $\times$, $\div$."
    (3) The signs :—" $+$, $-$."

Example 2. $\frac{2}{3} \div \frac{5}{7}$ of $2\frac{1}{3} = \frac{2}{3} \div \left(\frac{5}{7} \text{ of } \frac{7}{3}\right)$ Here "of" takes precedence of " $\div$."

$$= \frac{2}{3} \div \frac{5}{3} = \frac{2}{3} \times \frac{3}{5} = \frac{2}{5}.$$

Example 3. $\frac{2}{3} \div \frac{5}{7} \times 2\frac{1}{3} = \frac{2}{3} \times \frac{7}{5} \times \frac{7}{3} = \frac{98}{45} = 2\frac{8}{45}.$

The signs $\div$ and $\times$ are in the same order of precedence, and in that case the sign coming first takes precedence—that is, $\frac{2}{3}$ is divided by $\frac{5}{7}$ only and the result multiplied by $2\frac{1}{3}$.

4

Example 4.—

$$3\frac{2}{3} + \frac{1}{2} \div \frac{3}{4} - \frac{1}{3} \times 2\frac{1}{4} = 3\frac{2}{3} + \left(\frac{1}{2} \times \frac{4}{3}\right) - \left(\frac{1}{3} \times \frac{9}{4}\right)$$
$$= 3\frac{2}{3} + \frac{2}{3} - \frac{3}{4}$$
$$= 3\frac{8 + 8 - 9}{12}$$
$$= 3\frac{16 - 9}{12} = 3\frac{7}{12}.$$

The last example consists of 3 terms separated by the + and —, and the terms have first to be simplified and then the addition or subtraction performed.

Notice in the following example the effect of having $3\frac{2}{3} + \frac{1}{2}$ enclosed in brackets.

Example 5.—

$$\left(3\frac{2}{3} + \frac{1}{2}\right) \div \frac{3}{4} - \frac{1}{3} \times 2\frac{1}{4} = \left(3\frac{4 + 3}{6}\right) \div \frac{3}{4} - \frac{1}{3} \times \frac{9}{4}$$
$$= \frac{25}{\overset{}{6}} \times \frac{\overset{2}{\cancel{4}}}{3} - \frac{3}{4}$$
$$= \frac{50}{9} - \frac{3}{4}$$
$$= \frac{200 - 27}{36}$$
$$= \frac{173}{36} = 4\frac{29}{36}.$$

EXERCISE 23.

(1) $\frac{1}{2} + \frac{2}{3} \times \frac{3}{4}.$ (2) $\frac{2}{3} \times \frac{1}{2} - \frac{1}{4}.$

(3) $\frac{2}{3} \times \left(\frac{1}{2} - \frac{1}{4}\right).$ (4) $\frac{3}{2} \div \frac{3}{4} - \frac{3}{5} \times 2\frac{1}{2}.$

(5) $\frac{3}{2} \div \left(\frac{3}{4} - \frac{3}{5}\right) + 1\frac{1}{4}.$ (6) $2\frac{1}{3} + \frac{1}{2} - \left(1\frac{1}{2} - \frac{1}{3}\right).$

(7) $3\frac{2}{3} \div \left(2\frac{1}{3} - 1\frac{1}{4}\right).$ (8) $5\frac{1}{6} \div \frac{1}{2}$ of $3\frac{1}{4}.$

EXERCISE 23—*Continued.*

(9) $\dfrac{3}{5} \div 1\dfrac{3}{4} \times \dfrac{5}{6} + \dfrac{1}{4} \div \dfrac{2}{3}.$

(10) $\dfrac{3}{5} \div 1\dfrac{3}{4}$ of $\dfrac{5}{6} + \dfrac{1}{4} \div \dfrac{2}{3}.$

(11) $\dfrac{3}{4} \div \dfrac{4}{7} \times 1\dfrac{1}{5} - \dfrac{1}{4} \times \dfrac{3}{2}.$

(12) $\dfrac{3}{4} \div \dfrac{4}{7} \times \left(1\dfrac{1}{5} - \dfrac{1}{4}\right) \times \dfrac{3}{2}.$

(13) $\dfrac{3}{5} \div \dfrac{7}{5} \times \dfrac{4}{9} + \dfrac{5}{8} \times 1\dfrac{1}{7}.$

(14) $\dfrac{3}{5} \div \dfrac{7}{6}$ of $\dfrac{4}{9} + \dfrac{5}{8}$ of $1\dfrac{1}{7}.$

(15) $3\dfrac{2}{5} \div 5\dfrac{2}{3} \times 4\dfrac{1}{5}.$

(16) $3\dfrac{2}{5} \div 5\dfrac{2}{3}$ of $4\dfrac{1}{5}.$

(17) $5\dfrac{1}{4} \div 3\dfrac{1}{2} \times 2\dfrac{1}{5}.$

(18) $5\dfrac{1}{4} \div 3\dfrac{1}{2}$ of $2\dfrac{1}{5}.$

(19) $5\dfrac{3}{4} \times 3\dfrac{1}{8} \div 4\dfrac{3}{5}.$

(20) $3\dfrac{1}{2} + \dfrac{1}{3}$ of $2\dfrac{1}{4} - \dfrac{4}{5} \div 1\dfrac{1}{3}.$

(21) $2\dfrac{3}{7} \times 3\dfrac{1}{2} \div 4\dfrac{1}{4} + 5\dfrac{1}{2} \div 3\dfrac{2}{3} \times \dfrac{6}{7}.$

(22) $5\dfrac{5}{7} + 3\dfrac{1}{4} \div 4\dfrac{1}{3} - 2\dfrac{4}{7} \times 1\dfrac{2}{5}.$

(23) $2\dfrac{2}{7} \div 5\dfrac{1}{3}$ of $3\dfrac{4}{7} + 4\dfrac{1}{8} \div 7\dfrac{5}{6} \times 4\dfrac{3}{11}.$

(24) $5\dfrac{1}{2}$ of $7\dfrac{1}{11} - 4\dfrac{1}{6} \div \dfrac{2}{3}$ of $6\dfrac{1}{4}.$

(25) $12\dfrac{2}{3} \div \dfrac{5}{7} \times 3\dfrac{3}{4} \div 2\dfrac{3}{8}.$

(26) $10\dfrac{4}{5} \times 5\dfrac{3}{7} \div 3\dfrac{4}{5}$ of $6\dfrac{3}{4}.$

(27) $\dfrac{2}{5} + \dfrac{1}{4} \div \dfrac{2}{3} \times \dfrac{3}{4} - \dfrac{1}{2}.$

(28) $\dfrac{2}{5} + \dfrac{1}{4} \div \dfrac{2}{3}$ of $\dfrac{3}{4} - \dfrac{1}{2}.$

(29) $\left(\dfrac{2}{5} + \dfrac{1}{4}\right) \div \dfrac{2}{3} \times \dfrac{3}{4} - \dfrac{1}{2}.$

(30) $\dfrac{2}{5} + \dfrac{1}{4} \div \dfrac{2}{3} \times \left(\dfrac{3}{4} - \dfrac{1}{2}\right).$

(31) $\dfrac{2}{5} + \dfrac{1}{4} \div \dfrac{2}{3}$ of $\left(\dfrac{3}{4} - \dfrac{1}{2}\right).$

(32) $\left(\dfrac{2}{5} + \dfrac{1}{4}\right) \div \dfrac{2}{3} \times \left(\dfrac{3}{4} - \dfrac{1}{2}\right).$

(33) $\left(\dfrac{2}{5} + \dfrac{1}{4}\right) \div \dfrac{2}{3}$ of $\left(\dfrac{3}{4} - \dfrac{1}{2}\right).$

(34) Divide the sum of $3\dfrac{2}{5}$ and $5\dfrac{1}{2}$ by the difference between $8\dfrac{1}{5}$ and $3\dfrac{2}{3}.$

(35) Divide the difference between $8\dfrac{3}{7}$ and $4\dfrac{5}{6}$ by the sum of $3\dfrac{5}{14}$ and $8\dfrac{2}{3}.$

(36) Divide the sum of $7\dfrac{3}{4}$ and $5\dfrac{5}{6}$ by their difference.

(37) Divide the product of $3\frac{2}{5}$ and $1\frac{2}{3}$ by the sum of $3\frac{3}{4}$ and $4\frac{1}{8}$.

(38) Divide the difference between $8\frac{1}{3}$ and $2\frac{5}{6}$ by the sum of $2\frac{1}{12}$ and $3\frac{3}{4}$.

(39) Multiply $\frac{3}{16}$ of $10\frac{2}{3}$ by the sum of $2\frac{1}{2}$ and $3\frac{1}{4}$.

(40) Multiply the sum of $9\frac{6}{35}$ and $2\frac{3}{7}$ by the difference between $8\frac{18}{29}$ and $5\frac{1}{2}$.

(41) Multiply $3\frac{1}{2} + 5\frac{1}{4} - 2\frac{1}{3}$ by $4\frac{1}{11} + 2\frac{1}{2} - 1\frac{3}{22}$.

(42) Add together $5\frac{1}{2} \times 3\frac{7}{11}$ and $4\frac{1}{6} \times 1\frac{3}{5}$.

(43) Find difference between $4\frac{3}{7} \times 5\frac{1}{4}$ and $2\frac{1}{8} \times 3\frac{1}{5}$.

(44) Multiply the sum of $8\frac{3}{7}$ and $2\frac{5}{21}$ by the difference between $11\frac{1}{4}$ and $2\frac{3}{8}$.

(*g*) COMPLEX FRACTIONS.

A fraction is **complex** when its numerator or denominator is a fraction.

Thus $\frac{\frac{2}{3}}{\frac{4}{5}}$ is a complex fraction.

Now, as $\frac{5}{3}$ means $\frac{1}{3}$ part of 5, or 5 divided by 3, so $\frac{\frac{2}{3}}{\frac{4}{5}}$ means

$$\frac{2}{3} \div \frac{4}{5} = \frac{2}{3} \times \frac{5}{4}.$$

Hence the rule :—

To simplify a complex fraction, divide numerator by denominator or multiply numerator by reciprocal of denominator.

Example 1. $\dfrac{3\frac{1}{2}}{\frac{4}{5}} = \dfrac{7}{2} \div \dfrac{4}{5} = \dfrac{7}{2} \times \dfrac{5}{4} = \dfrac{35}{8} = 4\dfrac{3}{8}.$

Example 2. $\dfrac{\frac{2}{3}+\frac{1}{5}}{2\frac{1}{2}-\frac{3}{4}} = \dfrac{\frac{10+3}{15}}{2\frac{2-3}{4}} = \dfrac{\frac{13}{15}}{\frac{7}{4}} = \dfrac{13}{15} \times \dfrac{4}{7} = \dfrac{52}{105}.$

Example 3.

$$\dfrac{3\frac{4}{5} \times 5\frac{2}{3}}{2\frac{3}{5} \times 11\frac{1}{2}} \div \dfrac{5\frac{2}{3} \times \frac{2}{23}}{\frac{4}{19} \times 1\frac{6}{7}} = \dfrac{\frac{19}{5} \times \frac{17}{3}}{\frac{13}{5} \times \frac{23}{2}} \times \dfrac{\frac{4}{19} \times \frac{13}{7}}{\frac{17}{3} \times \frac{2}{23}}$$

$$= \dfrac{19}{5} \times \dfrac{17}{3} \times \dfrac{5}{13} \times \dfrac{2}{23} \times \dfrac{4}{19} \times \dfrac{13}{7} \times \dfrac{3}{17} \times \dfrac{23}{2} = \dfrac{4}{7}.$$

In this example it would have been a mistake to have simplified each complex fraction first and then divided the one by the other. It is a good rule **never to multiply out till compelled to do so,** otherwise we lose the advantage of cancelling.

EXERCISE 24.

(1) $\dfrac{\frac{3}{5}}{\frac{2}{3}}.$

(2) $\dfrac{2\frac{1}{4}}{3\frac{1}{2}}.$

(3) $\dfrac{\frac{2}{3} \text{ of } 2}{\frac{1}{4} \times \frac{1}{3}}.$

(4) $\dfrac{2\frac{1}{3} - 1\frac{1}{2}}{\frac{2}{3} + \frac{1}{2}}.$

(5) $\dfrac{3\frac{1}{6} + \frac{2}{3}}{2\frac{1}{2} - 1\frac{1}{6}}.$

(6) $\dfrac{13\frac{1}{5} + 4\frac{1}{7}}{6\frac{1}{7} - 3\frac{1}{5}}.$

(7) $\dfrac{3\frac{1}{5} - 2\frac{1}{3}}{5\frac{1}{2} + 1\frac{2}{5}}.$

(8) $\dfrac{8\frac{2}{3} + 5\frac{1}{4}}{2\frac{1}{3} \times 3\frac{5}{8}}.$

(9) $\dfrac{10\frac{1}{5} - 6\frac{1}{3}}{7\frac{1}{4} \div 2\frac{2}{3}}.$

(10) $\dfrac{4\frac{2}{3} \times 2\frac{1}{7}}{3\frac{5}{14} - 1\frac{1}{6}}.$

(11) $\dfrac{6\frac{2}{3} \div 4\frac{4}{15}}{7\frac{1}{2} + 2\frac{1}{3} + 1\frac{3}{5}}.$

(12) $\dfrac{2\frac{1}{2} \div 3\frac{1}{3}}{3\frac{1}{4} \times 4\frac{1}{5}}.$

(13) $\dfrac{8\frac{1}{3} - 4\frac{1}{5}}{5\frac{1}{2} + 2\frac{1}{4}} \times 1\frac{7}{8}.$

(14) $\dfrac{1\frac{5}{8} + \frac{7}{12}}{2\frac{5}{6} - 1\frac{3}{4}} \div 3\frac{5}{16}.$

(16) $\dfrac{1\frac{2}{3} \times 3\frac{3}{4}}{3\frac{4}{5} \div 6\frac{1}{3}}.$

(16) $\dfrac{\frac{7}{9} + \frac{2}{3} + \frac{3}{4}}{2\frac{1}{4} + 4\frac{1}{2} + 5\frac{1}{3}}.$

(17) $\dfrac{3\frac{1}{2} + 2\frac{1}{4} + 1\frac{1}{5}}{4\frac{1}{2} + 2\frac{1}{3} - 1\frac{1}{6}}.$

(18) $\dfrac{\frac{1}{5} \text{ of } \frac{3}{4} + \frac{2}{3} \text{ of } \frac{6}{7}}{\frac{2}{5} \text{ of } \frac{1}{4} + \frac{1}{4} \text{ of } \frac{5}{7}}.$

(19) $\dfrac{(2\frac{3}{4} + 1\frac{5}{8}) \times 3\frac{3}{7}}{7\frac{1}{4} \div (1\frac{1}{2} + 5\frac{3}{4})}.$

(20) $\dfrac{2\frac{3}{4} + 1\frac{5}{8} \times 3\frac{3}{7}}{7\frac{1}{4} \div 1\frac{1}{2} + 5\frac{3}{4}}.$

(21) $\dfrac{3\frac{1}{2} \times 4\frac{1}{3} \times (1\frac{1}{2} + \frac{4}{5})}{(2\frac{1}{3} - 1\frac{1}{4}) \times (3\frac{1}{4} - 1\frac{1}{3})}$,

(22) $\dfrac{\frac{1}{15} + \frac{4}{9} - \frac{1}{4} \text{ of } (1\frac{2}{3} - \frac{3}{10})}{7\frac{1}{35} \div 5\frac{1}{7}}$.

(23) $\dfrac{3\frac{2}{5} \times 3\frac{1}{4}}{2\frac{1}{3} \times 2\frac{3}{5}} \times \dfrac{1\frac{1}{11} \times 1\frac{1}{3}}{2\frac{3}{7} \times 2\frac{2}{5}}$.

(24) $\dfrac{4\frac{1}{3}}{2\frac{1}{2}} \times \dfrac{1\frac{1}{6}}{4\frac{1}{4}} \div \dfrac{2\frac{1}{3} \times 2\frac{3}{5}}{3\frac{2}{5} \times 3\frac{3}{4}}$.

(25) $\dfrac{2\frac{4}{5} \div 5\frac{1}{4}}{7\frac{1}{5} \times 3\frac{2}{5}} \div \dfrac{6\frac{1}{2} \div 3\frac{1}{4}}{4\frac{1}{3} \times 2\frac{3}{4}}$.

(26) $\dfrac{4\frac{2}{7} \times 5\frac{4}{9}}{9\frac{3}{4} \div 7\frac{4}{5}} \div \dfrac{6\frac{1}{5} \div 2\frac{1}{4}}{5\frac{1}{6} \times 3\frac{1}{8}}$.

(27) $\dfrac{2\frac{1}{5} \times 2\frac{1}{2}}{4\frac{6}{7} \times 6\frac{1}{4}} \times \dfrac{2\frac{1}{8} \div 2\frac{1}{4}}{5\frac{1}{2} \times 1\frac{1}{6}}$.

(28) $\dfrac{2\frac{1}{3} \text{ of } 7\frac{1}{2} \text{ of } 1\frac{3}{5}}{4\frac{3}{8} \text{ of } 6\frac{3}{7} \text{ of } 1\frac{4}{9}} \times \dfrac{3\frac{1}{9} \text{ of } 6\frac{1}{4} \text{ of } 3\frac{2}{3}}{4\frac{2}{3} \text{ of } 3\frac{1}{9} \text{ of } 13\frac{1}{2}}$.

(29) $\dfrac{3\frac{1}{4} \times 1\frac{7}{8}}{4\frac{2}{3} \times 8\frac{4}{5}} \times \dfrac{4\frac{2}{3} \div 5\frac{1}{4}}{3\frac{1}{7} \times 2\frac{1}{3}}$.

(30) $\dfrac{2}{3\frac{1}{5}} - \dfrac{4\frac{1}{2}}{9} + 3\frac{5}{8} + \dfrac{1\frac{1}{7}}{4\frac{4}{7}}$.

(31) $\dfrac{1}{2\frac{1}{2}} + \dfrac{1}{3\frac{1}{3}} + \dfrac{1}{3\frac{3}{4}}$.

(32) $7\frac{1}{2} \div 3\frac{3}{4} \text{ of } \dfrac{2\frac{1}{4} \times 6\frac{1}{8}}{3\frac{1}{2} \div 2\frac{3}{4}}$.

(33) $8\frac{2}{5} \div 3\frac{1}{2} \text{ of } \dfrac{5\frac{1}{2} \div 2\frac{3}{4}}{1\frac{5}{13} \text{ of } 4\frac{1}{4}}$.

(34) $\dfrac{\frac{2}{3} + \frac{4}{7}}{\frac{4}{5} + \frac{1}{7}} \times \dfrac{\frac{3}{7} + \frac{3}{4}}{\frac{1}{2} + \frac{2}{3}}$.

(35) $\dfrac{\frac{2}{5} + \frac{3}{4}}{\frac{1}{2} + \frac{4}{5}} + \dfrac{\frac{2}{3} + \frac{3}{8}}{\frac{5}{6} + \frac{1}{4}}$.

(36) $\dfrac{3\frac{1}{2} - 2\frac{1}{3}}{3\frac{1}{2} + 2\frac{1}{3}} \div \dfrac{3\frac{1}{7} \times 2\frac{1}{7}}{\frac{11}{12} \text{ of } \frac{3}{5}}$.

(37) $\dfrac{6\frac{2}{3} - \frac{1}{5} \text{ of } 3\frac{1}{3}}{5\frac{1}{6} \times \frac{1}{4} \div 1\frac{1}{8}} \times \dfrac{3\frac{1}{7} - 1\frac{1}{5}}{1\frac{1}{7} \times 3\frac{1}{5}}$.

(38) $\dfrac{1}{2 + \dfrac{1}{3 + \frac{1}{4}}}$.

(39) $\dfrac{1}{3 + \dfrac{1}{4 + \frac{1}{5}}}$.

(40) $\dfrac{1}{2 + \dfrac{3}{4 + \frac{5}{6}}}$.

(41) $\dfrac{7}{3 + \dfrac{1}{4 + \frac{2}{3}}}$.

(42) $\dfrac{5}{3 + \dfrac{7}{2 + \frac{1}{4}}}$.

(43) $\dfrac{4}{6 + \dfrac{3}{2 + \dfrac{7}{2 + \frac{4}{5}}}}$.

(44) $\dfrac{\frac{1}{2}}{\frac{2}{3}} \div \dfrac{\frac{3}{4}}{\frac{4}{5}} \times \dfrac{\frac{5}{6}}{\frac{6}{7}}$.

(45) $\dfrac{\frac{1}{2}}{\frac{2}{3}} \div \dfrac{\frac{3}{4}}{\frac{4}{5}} \text{ of } \dfrac{\frac{5}{6}}{\frac{6}{7}}$.

(46) $\dfrac{\frac{1}{2}}{\frac{2}{3}} \times \dfrac{\frac{3}{4}}{\frac{4}{5}} \div \dfrac{\frac{5}{6}}{\frac{6}{7}}$.

(47) $\dfrac{\frac{1}{2}}{\frac{2}{3}} + \dfrac{\frac{3}{4}}{\frac{4}{5}} + \dfrac{\frac{5}{6}}{\frac{6}{7}}$.

(48) $\dfrac{7\frac{3}{8}}{5\frac{7}{12}} \div \frac{3}{7} \text{ of } \dfrac{4\frac{1}{5}}{13\frac{2}{5}}$.

EXERCISE 24—*Continued.*

(49) $\frac{2}{13}$ of $\dfrac{2\frac{1}{3} + 3\frac{1}{4}}{4\frac{1}{2} - 1\frac{3}{4}} \times 2\frac{1}{6}$ of $\dfrac{4\frac{4}{5} \times 2\frac{1}{8}}{7\frac{4}{11} - 5\frac{1}{3}}$.

(50) $\frac{4}{5}$ of $\dfrac{7\frac{1}{2} - 3\frac{3}{4}}{4\frac{1}{3} + 3\frac{1}{4}} \div \frac{4}{7}$ of $\dfrac{5\frac{1}{2} \div 3\frac{1}{7}}{\frac{1}{4} \text{ of } 10\frac{1}{9}}$.

(*h*) FRACTIONS OF CONCRETE QUANTITIES.

We append a few examples on finding fractions of concrete quantities.

Example 1.—Find the value of $\frac{2}{5}$ of £6 4s. 10d.

```
  £   s.  d.
  6   4  10        We multiply by 2 and divide by 5.
          2        We may first divide by 5 and then
5 ) 12  9  8       multiply by 2.
    ‾‾‾‾‾‾‾‾‾
    2   9  11⅕
```

Example 2.—Find the value of $\frac{3}{4}$ of 2s. 6d. $+$ $2\frac{1}{3}$ of 5s. $4\frac{1}{2}$d.
Find value of each part as in Example 1, and add, or thus :—

$$\frac{3}{4} \text{ of 2s. 6d.} + 2\frac{1}{3} \text{ of 5s. } 4\frac{1}{2}\text{d.} = \frac{3}{4} \text{ of 30d.} + \frac{7}{3} \text{ of } 64\frac{1}{2}\text{d.}$$

$$= \frac{45}{2}\text{d.} + \frac{301}{2}\text{d.}$$

$$= \frac{346}{2}\text{d.} = 173\text{d.} = 14\text{s. 5d.}$$

Example 3.—Find value of $1\frac{1}{3}$ of 1 yd. 2 ft. $-$ $\frac{2}{5}$ of 4 ft. 6 ins.

$$\text{Value required} = \frac{4}{3} \text{ of 5 ft.} - \frac{2}{5} \text{ of } 4\frac{1}{2} \text{ ft.} = \frac{20}{3} \text{ ft.} - \frac{9}{5} \text{ ft.}$$

$$= \frac{100 - 27}{15} \text{ ft.} = \frac{73}{15} \text{ ft.} = 4\frac{13}{15} \text{ ft.}$$

Example 4.—Divide 5 tons 7 cwts. 2 qrs. by $\frac{2}{3}$ of $3\frac{3}{4}$.

$\frac{2}{3}$ of $3\frac{3}{4} = \frac{2}{3} \times \frac{15}{4} = \frac{5}{2}$

$\therefore$ 5 tons 7 cwts. 2 qrs. $\div \frac{5}{2}$

$\quad = 5$ tons 7 cwts. 2 qrs. $\times \frac{2}{5}$

$\quad = 2$ tons 3 cwts.

```
              5 tons   7 cwts. 2 qrs.
                             2
    ‾‾‾‾‾‾‾‾‾‾‾‾‾‾‾‾‾‾‾‾‾‾‾‾‾‾‾‾‾‾‾‾‾‾
    5 ) 10 tons 15 cwts. 0 qrs.
        ‾‾‾‾‾‾‾‾‾‾‾‾‾‾‾‾‾‾‾‾‾‾‾‾‾‾
        2 tons   3 cwts.
```

EXERCISE 25.

Find the value of—

(1) $\frac{3}{4}$ of 4s. 8d.   **(2)** $\frac{2}{5}$ of 17s. 6d.   **(3)** $\frac{1}{4}$ of 5 ft. 8 ins.
(4) $4\frac{1}{3}$ of 15s. 3d.   **(5)** £2 7s. 6d. $\times \frac{3}{8}$.   **(6)** 3 lbs. 8 ozs. $\div \frac{4}{5}$.
(7) $\frac{2}{3}$ of £1 6s. 9d.   **(8)** $\frac{2}{11}$ of 1 mile.   **(9)** $\frac{2}{3}$ of 1s. $7\frac{1}{2}$d.
(10) $\frac{5}{7}$ of 4 miles 3 fur.   **(11)** $\frac{1}{7}$ of £1 1s. 9d.   **(12)** $\frac{5}{7}$ of £7 7s. $10\frac{1}{2}$d.
(13) £5 6s. 2d. $\div 6\frac{1}{2}$.   **(14)** $\frac{2}{3}$ of 5 tons 3 cwts. 2 qrs.
(15) $2\frac{1}{3}$ of 16s. $10\frac{1}{2}$d.   **(16)** $3\frac{2}{5}$ of £4 15s. $7\frac{1}{2}$d.
(17) $\frac{3}{4}$ of $3\frac{1}{5}$ of £1 17s. 11d.   **(18)** $\frac{3}{8}$ ton $+ \frac{3}{4}$ cwt.
(19) $\frac{1}{11}$ of 3 ac. 27 sq. poles $13\frac{3}{4}$ sq. yds.
(20) $\frac{7}{13}$ of £7 16s. $+ \frac{3}{11}$ of £9 19s. 10d.
(21) $\frac{2}{3}$ of $3\frac{3}{4}$ of 16s. 9d. $+ \frac{1}{5}$ of $6\frac{2}{3}$ of 15s. 3d.
(22) $3\frac{1}{4}$ of 5s. 6d. $+ \frac{2}{3}$ of 1s. $4\frac{1}{2}$d. $- \frac{1}{5}$ of 2s. 6d.
(23) $\frac{2}{3}$ of $\frac{3}{4}$ of 3s. 5d. $+ 2\frac{1}{3}$ of 1s. 3d. $+ \frac{3}{4}$ of 1s. 4d.
(24) $\frac{3}{7}$ of £1 8s. $- \frac{3}{5}$ of 3s. 4d. $+ \frac{1}{11}$ of 4s. 7d.
(25) $\frac{4}{7}$ of 12s. 10d. $+ \frac{3}{5}$ of £11 13s. $1\frac{1}{2}$d.
(26) $\frac{3}{11}$ of £6 7s. $2\frac{1}{4}$d. $+ \frac{5}{7}$ of £1 10s. $0\frac{1}{2}$d.
(27) $\frac{1}{3}$ of $\frac{3}{4}$ of £1 8s. 4d. $+ \frac{1}{2}$ of $\frac{4}{7}$ of £1 5s. 8d.
(28) $\frac{1}{4}$ of $1\frac{1}{5}$ of £5 16s. $6\frac{3}{4}$d. $- \frac{2}{3}$ of $1\frac{1}{3}$ of £1 11s. 10d.
(29) $\frac{2}{3}$ of $\frac{3}{4}$ of 7s. 1d. $+ 1\frac{1}{2}$ of 7s. $1\frac{1}{2}$d.
(30) $\frac{7}{16}$ of £18 8s. 4d. $+ \frac{1}{8}$ of £2 16s. 8d.
(31) $1\frac{1}{3}$ of £1 13s. $10\frac{1}{2}$d. $- 3\frac{1}{2}$ of 7s. 4d.
(32) $\frac{7}{20}$ of 46 lbs. 4 ozs. $- \frac{4}{5}$ of 15 lbs. 10 ozs.
(33) $\frac{4}{3}$ of 11 miles 5 fur. 6 poles $- \frac{3}{4}$ of 2 miles 5 fur. 24 poles.
(34) $\frac{5}{6}$ ton $- \frac{7}{8}$ cwt. $+ \frac{3}{7}$ qr.
(35) 18 tons 19 cwts. 2 qrs. $\div 1\frac{1}{10}$.
(36) 9 sq. yds. 1 sq. ft. 74 sq. ins. $\div 3\frac{1}{4}$.
(37) 12 yds. 1 ft. 6 ins. $\div 1\frac{2}{7}$.

(i) REDUCING ONE QUANTITY TO THE FRACTION

OF ANOTHER.

Example 1.—Find what part 3s. $5\frac{1}{2}$d. is of 17s. 8d.

$$\frac{3s.\ 5\frac{1}{2}d.}{17s.\ 8d.} = \frac{41\frac{1}{2}d.}{212d.} = \frac{83}{424}.$$

Example 2.—Reduce $\frac{2}{3}$ of 6s. $5\frac{1}{4}$d. $+ \frac{1}{4}$ of 17s. 2d. to the fraction of $\frac{4}{7}$ of £1 5s. 9d.

$$\frac{\frac{2}{3} \text{ of 6s. } 5\frac{1}{4}\text{d.} + \frac{1}{4} \text{ of 17s. 2d.}}{\frac{4}{7} \text{ of £1 5s. 9d.}} = \frac{\frac{2}{3} \times 77\frac{1}{4} + \frac{1}{4} \times 206}{\frac{4}{7} \times 309}$$

$$= \frac{\frac{2}{3} \times \frac{309}{4} + \frac{1}{4} \times 206}{\frac{4}{7} \times 309}$$

We express each quantity in pence and then simplify the fraction formed.

$$= \frac{\frac{103}{2} + \frac{103}{2}}{\frac{4}{7} \times 309}$$

$$= 1\emptyset3 \times \frac{7}{4} \times \frac{1}{\underset{3}{3\emptyset\emptyset}} = \frac{7}{12}.$$

EXERCISE 26.

What fraction is

(**1**) 4s. $5\frac{1}{2}$d. of 16s. 8d. ? (**2**) £2 15s. of £5 10s. ?

(**3**) £3 17s. 6d. of £5 12s. 6d. ? (**4**) 3s. $6\frac{1}{4}$d. of 14s. 2d. ?

(**5**) 4s. 9d. of 7s. $1\frac{1}{2}$d. ? (**6**) 3s. 8d. of 12s. 10d. ?

(**7**) £3 9s. 6d. of £11 13s. ? (**8**) £2 6s. $7\frac{1}{2}$d. of £11 13s. $1\frac{1}{2}$d. ?

(**9**) 11s. $11\frac{1}{4}$d. of 15s. 11d. ? (**10**) £6 18s. 9d. of £12 14s. $4\frac{1}{2}$d. ?

(**11**) £8 1s. $1\frac{3}{4}$d. of £9 4s. 2d. ? (**12**) 10s. $8\frac{3}{4}$d. of 15s. $0\frac{3}{4}$d. ?

(**13**) 4 yds. 2 ft. 7 ins. of 6 yds. 9 ins. ?

(**14**) 1 mile 1 fur. 3 poles of 1 mile 7 fur. 5 poles ?

(**15**) 3 miles 7 fur. 2 poles of 5 miles 6 fur. 23 poles ?

(**16**) 51 yds. of 1 mile 110 yds. ?

(**17**) 16 lbs. 3 ozs. of 23 lbs. 2 ozs. ?

(**18**) 4 tons 6 cwts. 1 qr. of 9 tons 9 cwts. 3 qrs. ?

(**19**) 12 sq. ft. 100 sq. ins. of 4 sq. yds. 5 sq. ft. 37 sq. ins. ?

(**20**) 3,780 sq. yds. of 2 ac. 3,550 sq. yds. ?

(**21**) 216 cub ins. of 1 cub. yd. ?

EXERCISE 26—*Continued.*

(**22**) 8 gallons 1 pint of 14 gallons 2 qts. 1 pint?

(**23**) 7 cwts. 3 qrs. of $\frac{2}{5}$ of 1 ton?

(**24**) 50 sq. yds. 3 sq. ft of $\frac{1}{11}$ of $\frac{1}{3}$ acre?

(**25**) From $\frac{5}{7}$ of 12s. 3d. take $\frac{2}{11}$ of £1 8s. 5d., and express result as a fraction of £1 12s. 3d.

(**26**) What fraction of £2 15s. is $\frac{1}{12}$ of £2 10s. + $\frac{1}{12}$ of 1 guinea + $\frac{2}{3}$ of 5s. ?

(**27**) Express the difference between $\frac{3}{5}$ of 12s. 6d. and $\frac{1}{7}$ of £1 1s. $10\frac{1}{2}$d. as the fraction of 15s.

(**28**) What fraction of $\frac{3}{5}$ of 11s. $10\frac{1}{2}$d. is $\frac{4}{7}$ of 2s. $4\frac{1}{2}$d. ?

(**29**) What fraction of $1\frac{3}{4}$ of 1s. 10d. is $\frac{3}{11}$ of 13s. 9d. ?

(**30**) Express the difference between $\frac{1}{3}$ of 2 cwts. 1 qr. 21 lbs. and $\frac{1}{7}$ of 1 cwt. 3 qrs. 14 lbs. as the fraction of 1 cwt. 2 qrs. 15 lbs.

(*k*) MISCELLANEOUS EXAMPLES IN FRACTIONS.

We shall conclude this chapter with a few miscellaneous examples.

Example 1.—Find the L.C.M. of $\frac{2}{3}$, $\frac{4}{5}$, $\frac{5}{6}$.

Reducing the fractions to the same denominator—viz., 30—we get 20, 24, 25 **thirtieths.** The L.C.M. of 20, 24, 25 is 600. The required L.C.M. is, therefore, 600 **thirtieths**—*i.e.*, $\frac{600}{30} = 20$.

In the same way the H.C.F. of fractions may be got by reducing the fractions to the same denominator.

Example 2.—Find the H.C.F. of $\frac{2}{3}$, $\frac{4}{5}$, $\frac{8}{9}$.

The fractions are $\frac{30}{45}$, $\frac{36}{45}$, $\frac{40}{45}$.

H.C.F. of 30, 36, 40 = 2

∴ H.C.F. of the fractions = $\frac{2}{45}$.

Reduce the fractions to common denominator 45. Then find H.C.F. of the numerators.

Example 3.—A person who owns $\frac{3}{7}$ of a ship worth £12,355, sells $\frac{1}{3}$ of his share to A and $\frac{1}{2}$ of remainder to B. What fraction of the ship does he now possess and what is it worth ?

First Method.—

He sells $\frac{1}{3}$ of $\frac{3}{7}$ or $\frac{1}{7}$ to A, leaving $\frac{2}{7}$.
He sells $\frac{1}{2}$ of $\frac{2}{7}$ or $\frac{1}{7}$ to B, leaving $\frac{2}{7} - \frac{1}{7}$ or $\frac{1}{7}$.
Now, $\frac{1}{7}$ of £12,355 $=$ £1,765.

Second Method.—

Sold.	Remainder.
To A, $\dfrac{1}{3}$ of $\dfrac{3}{7}$.	$\dfrac{2}{3}$ of $\dfrac{3}{7}$
To B, $\dfrac{1}{2}$ of $\dfrac{2}{3}$ of $\dfrac{3}{7}$	$\dfrac{1}{2}$ of $\dfrac{\overset{1}{2}}{\underset{1}{3}}$ of $\dfrac{\overset{1}{3}}{7}$
	$= \dfrac{1}{7}.$

$$\frac{1}{7} \text{ of } £12,355 = £1,765.$$

EXERCISE 27.

(1) If $\frac{1}{8}$ and $\frac{5}{12}$ of a sum of money are paid away, what fraction is left ?

(2) If a man owns $\frac{3}{14}$ of a ship and sells $\frac{1}{3}$ of his share, what is the value of the share remaining to him if the ship is worth £4,200 ?

(3) A man owns $\frac{7}{15}$ of a ship. If he sells $\frac{3}{4}$ of his share, what fraction of the ship will belong to him ?

(4) Three men paid a bill of £5 7s. 11d. If the first paid $\frac{2}{5}$ and the second $\frac{3}{7}$ of the bill, how much did the third pay ?

(5) Out of £15, $\frac{1}{4}$ is paid to A, and $\frac{1}{3}$ to B. Then $\frac{3}{5}$ of the remainder is paid to C. How much is left ?

(6) An army consisting of 9,800 is $\frac{1}{5}$ Irish, $\frac{2}{7}$ Welsh, and $\frac{3}{10}$ English. If the rest of the army is Scotch, find the number of Scotch in the army.

(7) What is the largest fraction that is contained an exact number of times in each of the fractions $\frac{3}{4}$, $\frac{9}{10}$, $\frac{12}{25}$?

(8) Find the smallest number which contains each of the fractions $\frac{4}{5}$, $\frac{7}{10}$, $\frac{8}{15}$ an exact number of times.

(9) 2 men, whose steps are $2\frac{3}{4}$ ft. and $2\frac{5}{6}$ ft., walk together. If they start in step, how far will they go before they are in step again, and how many steps will each have taken ?

(10) A man spent $\frac{1}{3}$ of his money in one shop, $\frac{3}{5}$ of what remained in a second, and $\frac{1}{2}$ of what still remained in a third. If he had £1 2s. left, what had he at first ?

(11) A man left his estate to his family of 4 sons and 2 daughters. Each of the sons received $\frac{1}{7}$ of the estate and the daughters received the remainder. If the daughters' share amounts to £3,300, what was the value of the estate ?

(12) The tenth part of a number exceeds its twelfth part by 3. What is the number ?

(13) A pole has $\frac{1}{3}$ of its length in mud, $\frac{2}{5}$ of the remainder in water, and the remainder, which is 12 ft. in length, is out of water. What is the length of the pole ?

(14) How many pieces of string $\frac{5}{6}$ ft. long can be cut from a piece of string 7 yds. 1 ft. in length, and how long is the portion left over ?

(15) A vessel holds $3\frac{2}{3}$ quarts. How many times can it be filled from a barrel which contains $18\frac{1}{2}$ gallons, and how much will then be left in the barrel ?

(16) A person dies, leaving one-fifth of his property to his wife, a sixth to each of his four sons, and the rest to his daughter, who gets £200. What is the value of the whole property ?

(17) One box contains $\frac{5}{7}$ of a cwt. of flour, another contains $\frac{11}{16}$ of a cwt. Find which contains most flour, and how many pounds it contains more than the other.

(18) A man left $\frac{1}{3}$ of his property to his wife, $\frac{1}{4}$ of the remainder to his son, and $\frac{1}{3}$ of what still remained to his daughter, and £350 remained. Find the amount of his property.

(19) In a school $\frac{2}{5}$ of the scholars are girls and the rest boys. If $\frac{2}{7}$ of the girls and $\frac{1}{3}$ of the boys be absent, what fraction of the whole number of scholars is present ?

(20) One-twentieth of an army are killed in battle, one-tenth of the remainder are wounded, leaving 17,100 fit men. What was the original size of the army ?

CHAPTER IV.

DECIMAL FRACTIONS.

I.—TERMINATING DECIMAL FRACTIONS.

(a) MEANING OF A DECIMAL FRACTION.

THE fractions we have dealt with in the previous chapter are Vulgar (*i.e.*, common) Fractions. **Decimal fractions** are written with a dot or point separating the whole number from the fractional part. The numerators of the fractions only are written. The denominators being all powers of 10 are not written, but only implied or understood.

For example, 3·475 means $3 + \dfrac{4}{10} + \dfrac{7}{100} + \dfrac{5}{1000}.$

The denominator corresponding to any particular numerator depends on its place relative to the point. Thus the " 5 " in the above example, being in the 3rd place to the right of the point, has for its denominator 1,000 or 10^3—*i.e.*, the third power of 10—the " 7 " being in the 2nd place has 100 or 10^2—*i.e.*, the second power of 10—for its denominator.

Thus, $\cdot 5 = \dfrac{5}{10}$; $\cdot 05 = \dfrac{5}{100}$; $\cdot 005 = \dfrac{5}{1000}$, and so on. From the meaning of a decimal fraction we see that it is easy to express it as a vulgar fraction.

Example 1.—Express ·237 as a vulgar fraction.

$$\cdot 237 = \frac{2}{10} + \frac{3}{100} + \frac{7}{1000} = \frac{200 + 30 + 7}{1000} = \frac{237}{1000}.$$

It is evident from the above example that it is necessary only to write down the figures of the decimal as numerator, and as denominator to write down 1 followed by as many 0's as there are figures after the point.

Example 2.— $6 \cdot 325 = 6\dfrac{325}{1000} = 6\dfrac{13}{40}.$

Example 3.— $\cdot 0105 = \dfrac{105}{10000} = \dfrac{21}{2000}.$

EXERCISE 28.

(1) What is the meaning of ·3, ·03, ·003, ·33, 3·3 ?
(2) Write ·375 as the sum of 3 vulgar fractions, and add them.
(3) Express as vulgar fractions in their lowest terms :—·75, ·125, ·25, ·625, ·875, ·0125, ·0375, ·0625, ·005, ·0035, ·0002, ·00045.
(4) Express as mixed numbers :—6·0875, 4·0025, 5·0005, 7·05, 16·325, 4·0025, 5·003.

(b) ADDITION OF DECIMALS.

The addition of decimals is performed in the same way as ordinary simple addition, the decimal points being placed below each other in the same column.

Example.—Add together 75·34, 19·215, 36·753, ·0312.

We are here adding in each column the numerators of fractions having same denominator— viz., 3, 2, 7 tenths ; 4, 1, 5, 3 hundredths ; 5, 3, 1 thousandths, etc. The carrying also is on same principle as simple addition—*e.g.*, the 13 hundredths in the 2nd column to the right of the

75·34
19·215
36·753
·0312
───────
131·3392

point $= \dfrac{13}{100} = \dfrac{10}{100} + \dfrac{3}{100} = 1$ tenth and 3 hundredths. Hence carry 1 to the tenths column.

EXERCISE 29.

Add together—

(1) 6·123, ·875, ·0736, ·00146, 3·0465.
(2) 24·0876, ·00463, 1·438, ·07625, 4·7.
(3) 9·8642, ·00014, ·036, 2·0045, ·9.
(4) ·0115, ·56125, 6·090909, ·003, 15·4.
(5) 6·2, 7·56, 11·0045, ·00782, 6·5, 11·853.
(6) ·0014, 717·6, ·056009, 10·853, ·0073.
(7) ·000425, ·078, ·3152, ·00723, ·652.
(8) 7·853, ·0054, 16·783, ·65, 25·873.
(9) ·0013, 3·07, ·014, 6·32, ·782, ·0009.
(10) ·015, 7·2, ·0004, 6·56, 7·3, ·423.
(11) 8·2, ·00045, ·32, 7·5, 4·365, ·7023.
(12) ·7, 6·352, ·0082, 16·734, ·65, 5·372.

(c) SUBTRACTION OF DECIMALS.

Subtraction of decimals is also performed in the same way as ordinary simple subtraction.

Example.—Subtract 13·0176 from 27·10963 and ·0357 from **1.**

```
  27·10963        1·0000
  13·01760         ·0357
  14·09203         ·9643
```

EXERCISE 30.

(1) Take ·075 from ·5.
(2) Take ·0875 from 3.
(3) Take 3·0725 from 6·005.
(4) Take 3·25 from 6·0235.
(5) Take ·0625 from ·725.
(6) Take 3·1625 from 17·5.
(7) Simplify 8·375 + ·0017 − ·03415.
(8) Take 1·75 from the sum of 3, ·2, ·02, and 1·034.
(9) Subtract the difference between ·5 and ·05 from the sum of 5 and ·005.
(10) By how much does the sum of 16·305 and 26·23 exceed the sum of 5·0825 and 15·25 ?
(11) Take the sum of 6·25, ·035, and 7·0025 from 15.
(12) Take the sum of ·025, 6·35, and ·0075 from 11.
(13) What is the difference between the sum of 5·035 and 11·6 and the sum of 5·235 and 6·52 ?
(14) What is the difference between the sum of ·0642 and ·78 and the sum of ·723 and ·15 ?

(d) MULTIPLICATION OF DECIMALS.

Multiplication of decimals is performed in the same way as ordinary simple multiplication of whole numbers.

Example 1.—Multiply 6·23 by 5.

```
  6·23
     5
 31·15
```
When we multiply 3 by 5 we are multiplying 3 hundredths. The 15 hundredths obtained make 1 tenth + 5 hundredths, hence we carry 1 to tenths' column as in addition, and so on.

Example 2.—Multiply 6·2 by ·7.

6·2
·7
4·34

Multiplying ·2 by ·7 $= \dfrac{2}{10} \times \dfrac{7}{10} = \dfrac{14}{100}$ = 1 tenth + 4 hundredths. The " 4 " must be in 2nd place from the point. Then $6 \times ·7 = 6 \times \dfrac{7}{10} = \dfrac{42}{10}$, *i.e.*, 42 tenths making 43 tenths with the 1 tenth which we carried. 43 tenths = 4 units + 3 tenths. ∴ 3 is in 1st place to the right of the decimal point. Thus result = 4·34, or thus :—

$$6·2 \times ·7 = \frac{62}{10} \times \frac{7}{10} = \frac{434}{100} = 4\frac{34}{100} = \mathbf{4·34}.$$

Example 3.—Multiply ·004 by ·02.

·004
·02
·00008

Here we are **not** multiplying 4 by 2, but $\dfrac{4}{1000}$ by $\dfrac{2}{100}$, and the product $= \dfrac{8}{100000}$, *i.e.*, ·00008, or, in other words, ·004 × ·02 = ·00008.

Hence we have the rule for multiplication of decimals.

Multiply the numbers as if there were no decimal points, and place the point in the product so that the number of decimal places = the sum of the number of decimal places in the two factors.

or

Move the figures one place to the right or the left for every place that the multiplying figure is to the right or the left of the units' column.

Example 4.—Multiply ·00325 by ·014.

First Method.—

·00325
·014
1300
325
·00004550
= ·0000455.

The sum of the number of decimal places in the factors = 8. We, therefore, " point off " 8 figures in the product, filling up with four 0's to make up the 8 figures. The 0 on extreme right is not needed.

Second Method.—

```
·00325
·014
_____
·0000325
·00001300
_____
·0000455.
```

Multiply by the left-hand figure first, placing each figure of the product in its proper column. Then multiply in the same way by each figure in turn.

EXERCISE 31.

Multiply—

(1) 3·125 by 6, 20, 200, 35.
(2) ·0125 by 5, 25, 250.
(3) 2·123 by 12, 1·2, ·12, ·012.
(4) ·025 by 5, ·5, ·05.
(5) ·05 by ·6.
(6) ·05 by ·06.
(7) ·005 × ·06.
(8) ·105 by ·23.
(9) ·045 × ·07.
(10) ·45 by ·035.
(11) ·123 by ·321.
(12) 5·023 by ·47.
(13) 3·27 by 4·01.
(14) ·0327 by 401.
(15) ·0247 by ·536.
(16) ·00426 by ·035.
(17) ·0426 by ·35.
(18) 42·6 by 3·5.
(19) 4,260 by ·0035.
(20) 6·1 by ·062.

Find continued product of—

(21) ·3, ·03, and ·003.
(22) ·5, ·25, and ·125.
(23) ·004, 2·4, and 3·05.
(24) ·14, ·014, ·0014.

To multiply by 10 or a power of 10, we have merely to shift the point to the right.

Example 1.—Multiply 3·2016 by 100.

```
  3·2016
100
_____
320·1600
= 320·16
```

Thus to multiply by 100 we shift the point 2 places to the right. So to multiply by 10 we shift the point 1 place to the right, and to multiply by 1,000 we shift the point 3 places to the right, and so on. We must supply 0's when necessary.

This rule may also be stated as follows :—

To multiply by 10 or a power of 10, move the figures in the multiplicand one place to the left for each 0 in the multiplier.

Example 2.—Multiply ·03706 by 1000.
·03706 × 1000 = 37·06.

5

EXERCISE 32 (Mental).

Multiply—

(**1**) 3·021 by 10.
(**2**) ·4016 by 100.
(**3**) ·00245 by 1,000.
(**4**) ·2016 by 10,000.
(**5**) ·001 by 100 and by 1,000.
(**6**) ·1 by 10 and by 100.
(**7**) ·01 by 1,000 and by 10,000
(**8**) 1·1 by 1,000.

(e) DIVISION OF DECIMALS.

Division of Decimals by a **whole number** is performed in the same way as ordinary simple division.

Example 1.—Divide 321·0648 by 24.

$$\frac{321\cdot0648}{24} = 13\cdot3777.$$

$$24 \begin{cases} 4 \\ 6 \end{cases} \begin{array}{|l} 321\cdot0648 \\ \hline 80\cdot2662 \\ \hline 13\cdot3777 \end{array}$$

Example 2.—Divide 162·445 by 53.

$$\frac{162\cdot445}{53} = 3\cdot065$$

```
      3·065
53 ) 162·445
     159
     ----
      344
      318
      ----
      265
      265
      ----
```

It is a good plan to place the answer above the dividend with the point directly above the point of the dividend. The place of each figure in the answer is directly above the right hand figure in the multiplicand obtained from it.

To divide by 10, or a power of 10, we have merely to shift the point as in multiplication, but in the opposite direction—that is, to the left.

Example 1.—421·5 ÷ 100 = 4·215.
Example 2.—·015 ÷ 10 = ·0015.

This rule may also be stated as follows :—

To divide by 10 or a power of 10, move the figures in the dividend one place to the right for every 0 in the divisor.

Example.—503·05 ÷ 100 = 5·0305.

EXERCISE 33.

Divide—

(**1**) 318·24 by 4, 8, 12, 16, 30, 100.   (**2**) 9·375 by 3, 15.
(**3**) ·1896 by 6, 24, 10.   (**4**) ·0864 by 36, 40.
(**5**) 2·06125 by 25, 100.   (**6**) 45·936 by 18.
(**7**) 3·9483 by 321.   (**8**) 23·6081 by 47.
(**9**) 14·91 by 426.   (**10**) 31·025 by 2,125

DIVISION BY A DECIMAL.

We know that a fraction is not altered when its numerator and denominator are both multiplied by the same number.

Thus $7·328 \div ·32 = \dfrac{7·328}{·32}$

$= \dfrac{732·8}{32}$ $\left(\begin{array}{l}\text{by multiplying both numer-}\\ \quad \text{ator and denominator by}\\ \quad 100.\end{array}\right)$

Thus we see that 7·328 ÷ ·32 is the same as 732·8 ÷ 32.

Hence the rule :—

To divide by a decimal, make the divisor a whole number by shifting the point to the end, and shift the point the same number of places in the dividend, and then divide.

Example 1.—·007328 ÷ ·032.

$$·007328 \div ·032 = \frac{·007328}{·032} = \frac{7·328}{32} = ·229.$$

$$32\left\{\begin{array}{l} 4 \\ 8 \end{array}\right. \begin{array}{|l} 7·328 \\ \hline 1·832 \\ \hline \quad ·229 \end{array}$$

Decimal Fractions.

Example 2.—

$$\cdot00068 \div \cdot0425$$
$$= 6 \cdot 8 \div 425$$
$$= \cdot016$$

```
        0·016
425 ) 6·800
      4 25
      2 550
      2 550
```

425 divided into 6 gives 0, into 68 gives 0. Then we attach 0 after the 8 making 6·80. We continue attaching 0's as required.

EXERCISE 34.

Divide—

(**1**) 3·6786 by ·6 and ·06.   (**2**) ·35427 by ·21, ·0021.

(**3**) ·025488 by ·36.   (**4**) ·96064 by 3·2.

(**5**) ·003782 by ·62.   (**6**) 2·36081 by 4·7.

(**7**) ·315 by ·45.   (**8**) 31·025 by ·2125, 21·25, 212·5.

(**9**) ·0031025 by ·02125.   (**10**) ·06205 by 7·3, ·073, ·00073.

(**11**) ·018615 by ·0438.   (**12**) ·0093075 by ·00876.

(**13**) 9·3075 by ·0876.   (**14**) ·031025 by 2·92.

(**15**) 2·36081 by 5·023.

Simplify, giving answers correct to 4 decimal places—

(**16**) ·03159 ÷ ·023.   (**17**) ·5713 ÷ 4·3.

(**18**) ·00375 ÷ ·059.   (**19**) ·00561 ÷ ·0021.

(**20**) ·007157 ÷ ·00351.   (**21**) ·01 ÷ 1·7.

(**22**) ·3 ÷ ·19.   (**23**) ·1 ÷ ·023.

(**24**) ·001 ÷ ·07.   (**25**) 3·125 × ·07 ÷ ·0037.

(**26**) ·6105 × 13·1 ÷ 6·1.   (**27**) (17·013 — ·00156) ÷ ·029.

(**28**) (51·01 + 16·713) ÷ (58·93 — 57·945).

(**29**) $\dfrac{6 \cdot 23 + \cdot 057}{8 \cdot 71 - 5 \cdot 84}.$ (**30**) $\dfrac{6 \cdot 5 \times 3 \cdot 8}{3 \cdot 45 + 2 \cdot 7}.$

(**31**) (7·45 + ·025) × (10·725 — 8·715).

(**32**) $\dfrac{9 \cdot 826 + 3 \cdot 794}{13 \cdot 21 - 9 \cdot 86}.$ (**33**) $\dfrac{10 \cdot 8 - 6 \cdot 94}{1 \cdot 27 + \cdot 056}.$

(**34**) $\dfrac{\cdot 203 \times \cdot 0016 \times 3}{\cdot 004 \times \cdot 0058}.$ (**35**) $\dfrac{7 \cdot 53 + 3 \cdot 325 - 4 \cdot 75}{4 \cdot 025 - 3 \cdot 75 + 2 \cdot 5}.$

(**36**) $\dfrac{\cdot 0038371 - \cdot 00366}{\cdot 035}.$

(**37**) $\dfrac{\cdot 5625 - \cdot 4375}{\cdot 1875 + \cdot 3125} \times \dfrac{\cdot 1875 + \cdot 0625}{\cdot 875 - \cdot 8125}.$

(f) CONVERSION OF A VULGAR FRACTION INTO A DECIMAL.

Example.—Convert $\frac{5}{8}$ into a decimal.

8 | 5·000
———
0·625

Thus $\dfrac{5}{8} = \cdot625$.

The fraction $\frac{5}{8}$ is equivalent to $5 \div 8$ or $5\cdot000 \div 8$. Thus to convert $\frac{5}{8}$ into a decimal we have merely to divide $5\cdot00\ldots$ by 8 in the ordinary way, using as many 0' as we require.

The vulgar fraction should first be reduced to its lowest terms.

EXERCISE 35.

Convert into decimals—

(1) $\dfrac{1}{2}, \dfrac{1}{4}, \dfrac{1}{5}, \dfrac{1}{8}.$

(2) $\dfrac{3}{4}, \dfrac{2}{5}, \dfrac{3}{8}.$

(3) $\dfrac{5}{4}, \dfrac{7}{5}, \dfrac{15}{8}.$

(4) $\dfrac{7}{16}, \dfrac{19}{16}, \dfrac{33}{16}.$

(5) $\dfrac{15}{32}, \dfrac{16}{25}, \dfrac{9}{125}.$

(6) $5\dfrac{5}{16}, 7\dfrac{13}{32}.$

(7) $\dfrac{19}{10}, \dfrac{19}{1000}.$

(8) $\dfrac{3017}{100}.$

(9) $\dfrac{13}{256}.$

(10) $\dfrac{594}{625}.$

(g) DECIMAL FRACTIONS OF CONCRETE QUANTITIES.

Example 1.—Find value of £3·6875.

£3·6875
20
————
13·75ø0̸
12
————
9·0̸0̸

Reduce the £·6875 to shillings by multiplying it by 20, leaving the £3 unreduced. Reduce the ·75 shillings to pence, leaving the 13 shillings unreduced.

∴ £3·6875 = £3 13s. 9d.

Example 2.—Find the value of ·125 of 7s. 6d. + ·875 of 1s. 4d.

·125 of 7s. 6d. + ·875 of 1s. 4d. = ·125 × 90d. + ·875 × 16d.
= 11·25d. + 14d.
= 25·25d. = 2s. 1¼d.

Example 3.—Simplify 3·4 tons + 5·3125 cwts. + 2·75 qrs.

3·4 tons
20
⎯⎯⎯⎯
8·0   cwts.
5·3125 cwts.
⎯⎯⎯⎯
13·3125 cwts.   ∴ 3·4 tons + 5·3125 cwts. + 2·75 qrs.
4   = 3 tons + 13 cwts. + 4 qrs.
⎯⎯⎯⎯   = 3 tons 14 cwts.
1·2500 qrs.
2·75   qrs.
⎯⎯⎯⎯
4 qrs.

EXERCISE 36.

(1) £1·875.   (2) £3·625.
(3) £·0375.   (4) ·1875 ton.
(5) ·3125 ton.   (6) ·8125 lb.
(7) ·9375 lb.   (8) ·5625 ac.
(9) ·0625 ac.   (10) ·4375 cwt. + ·25 qr.
(11) ·5625 ton + ·75 cwt.   (12) ·6875 ton + ·625 cwt. + ·5 qr.
(13) ·4375 ton — ·75 cwt.   (14) ·0625 lb. + ·75 oz.
(15) ·375 ac. + ·75 ro.   (16) ·125 ac. + ·875 ro.
(17) ·0625 of 17s. 6d.   (18) ·375 of £1 4s. 8d.
(19) 1·25 of £2 10s.   (20) 1·15625 of 6s. 8d.
(21) ·01625 of £18 6s. 8d.   (22) 1·146875 of £40.
(23) ·12425 of £129 3s. 4d.   (24) 2·825 of £5 8s. 4d.
(25) ·125 of 17s. 6d. + 1·375 of 8s. 6d.
(26) 2·75 of 3s. 4d. — 1·12 of 4s. 2s. + ·125 of 6s. 8d.
(27) 5·35 of 1s. 8d. — 1·45 of 7s. 6d. + 1·55 of 6s. 3d.
(28) ·625 of 2 guineas — ·5625 of 10s. + ·125 of 3s. 6d — ·3375
     of £1.
(29) ·625 of 1 ton — ·3375 of 10 cwts. + ·125 of 2 qrs. — 1·25
     of 24 lbs.
(30) ·01625 of £10 — ·875 of 22s. + ·9125 of £1 — ·125 of 7s. 6d.
(31) ·325 of £1 3s. 4d. — ·0013 of 2s. 6d. — ·031 of 2s. 7d.
(32) ·125 of a ton + ·175 of a cwt. + ·145 of a quarter, giving
     answer in pounds and decimals of a pound.

(h) REDUCING ONE QUANTITY TO THE DECIMAL OF
ANOTHER.

First Method.—

Example.—Reduce 13s. 4d. to the decimal of £5 6s. 8d.

$$\frac{13s.\ 4d.}{£5\ 6s.\ 8d.} = \frac{160d.}{1280d.} = \frac{1}{8} = ·125.$$

EXERCISE 37.

What decimal fraction is—

(1) 15s. 6d. of £1 ?

(2) 12s. 6d. of £2 ?

(3) 2s. 3d. of 9s. ?

(4) 1s. 10½d. of 3s. 9d. ?

(5) 1s. 5d. of 11s. 4d. ?

(6) 2s. 3¾d. of 11s 6¾d. ?

(7) 7s. 1d. of 11s. 4d. ?

(8) 19s. 3d. of £1 1s. 9½d.

(9) 8s. 0¼d. of £1 12s. 1d. ?

(10) 16s. 11¼d. of £2 5s. 2d. ?

(11) 2s. 7d. of £2 14s. ?

(12) 1s. 0¾d. of 5s. 6d. ?

(13) ½ fur. of 1 mile ?

(14) 2½ qrs. of 1 ton ?

(15) 3 qrs. 9 lbs. of 4 cwts. 1 qr. 20 lbs. ?

(16) 3 cwts. 27 lbs. of 17 cwts. 1 qr. 4 lbs. ?

(17) 3s. 6d. of 5s. 8d. ?

(18) ·3125 ton of ·875 of 1 ton 5 cwts. ?

(19) 440 sq. yds. of 1 ac. ?

(20) ⅔ of 7s. 6d. of ⅕ of £3 5s. ?

(21) Reduce ·5 of £1 + ·125 of 10s. + ·75 of 3s. to decimal fraction of £1.

(22) Reduce ·025 of 1 ton + ·375 of 3 cwts. to decimal fraction of 1 qr. 22 lbs.

(23) Express the difference between £6·125 and 50·25 shillings as decimal fraction of £3·75.

Second Method.—

A convenient method of expressing a sum of money in pounds and decimals of a pound is to first express the pence as the decimal of a shilling and then the shillings as the decimal of a pound.

Example 1.—Express £3 17s. 10½d. in pounds and decimals of a pound.

12) 10·5d.   20) 17·875s.

·875s.   ·89375£.

Thus, £3 17s. 10½d. = £3·89375.

The working may in practice be set down thus—

12) 10·5 pence

20) 17·875 shillings

£3·89375

This method may also be applied to the other tables.

Example 2.—Express 7 cwts. 3 qrs. 21 lbs. as a decimal of a ton.

28	21	lbs.
4	3·75	qrs.
20	7·9375	cwts.
	·396875	ton.

EXERCISE 37 (*a*).

Express the following sums in pounds and decimals of a pound :—

(**1**) 19s. 6d.	(**2**) 18s. 9d.	(**3**) £2 10s. 6d.
(**4**) £1 10s. 9d.	(**5**) £2 12s. 7½d.	(**6**) £4 15s. 8d.
(**7**) £3 14s. 10½d.	(**8**) £7 16s. 4½d.	(**9**) £9 18s. 6¾d.
(**10**) £11 11s. 11¼d.	(**11**) £2 13s. 3¾d.	(**12**) £5 7s. 2¼d.
(**13**) £4 9s. 5¼d.	(**14**) £5 11s. 8¼d.	(**15**) £7 18s. 2½d.

Additional Examples.—

(**16**) Express £6 18s. 4½d. as a decimal of £10.

(**17**) Express £3 15s. 8¼d. as a decimal of £5.

(**18**) What decimal of a ton is 15 cwts. 1 qr. 10½ lbs. ?

(**19**) What decimal of 5 tons is 3 tons 12 cwts. 1 qr. 1½ sts. ?

(**20**) Express 3 furs. 7 chains 5½ yards as the decimal of a mile.

EXERCISE 37—*Continued.*

(21) Express 8 chains 8 yards 9 inches as the decimal of a quarter of a mile.

(22) What decimal of a gallon is 3 qts. 1 pt. 3 gills ?

(23) What decimal of a week is 4 days 21 hours 36 mins. ?

(24) What decimal of an acre is 3 roods 605 sq. yards. ?

(25) Express 2 roods 25 sq. poles as the decimal of an acre

II.—RECURRING DECIMALS.

(a) MEANING OF RECURRING DECIMALS.

When we convert $\frac{1}{3}$ into a decimal we find $\frac{1}{3} = \cdot333 \ldots$ and never ending, the reason being evidently that 3 will not divide 10 or any power of 10. So also if we convert $\frac{9}{11}$ into a decimal we find $\frac{9}{11} = \cdot818181 \ldots$, the 81 always recurring. In these cases the process of division never comes to an end, and we have the same figure or same set of figures recurring over and over again. Such decimals are called **Recurring Decimals** or **Repeating Decimals,** and in writing such a decimal we do not repeat the recurring figures, but write them **once** with a dot placed above the **first** one and the **last** one.

Thus $$\frac{1}{3} = \cdot\dot{3}, \frac{9}{11} = \cdot\dot{8}\dot{1}.$$

So we will find that $\frac{1}{7} = \cdot\dot{1}4285\dot{7}$.

Example.—Convert $\frac{19}{44}$ into a decimal.

$$44 \begin{cases} 4 & | 19\cdot0 \\ 11 & | \overline{4\cdot75} \\ & \overline{\cdot4318 \ldots} \end{cases}$$

When we get the remainder 2 for the second time, we see that the figures 18 will recur over and over again. Hence we stop.

$$\therefore \frac{19}{44} = \cdot43\dot{1}\dot{8}.$$

The recurring part is called the **Period.** When the period begins immediately after the point, the fraction is called a **Pure Recurring Decimal,** as ·6̇ or ·2̇3̇. When the period does not begin immediately after the point, the fraction is called a **Mixed Recurring Decimal.** Thus ·431̇8̇ is a mixed recurring decimal.

The vulgar fractions which become recurring decimals are those whose denominators do not divide exactly into 10 or a power of 10, as $\frac{1}{3}$, $\frac{1}{7}$, $\frac{1}{11}$. Now, no number can divide 10 or a power of 10 if it contains any factor other than 2 or 5.

Thus all fractions in their *lowest terms* **whose denominators contain any prime factor other than 2 or 5 become recurring decimals.**

EXERCISE 38.

Convert into decimals :—

(1) $\frac{2}{3}$, $\frac{5}{9}$, $\frac{7}{9}$.   **(2)** $\frac{1}{11}$, $\frac{5}{11}$, $\frac{7}{11}$.   **(3)** $\frac{5}{13}$, $\frac{7}{13}$, $\frac{10}{13}$.   **(4)** $\frac{1}{7}$, $\frac{2}{7}$, $\frac{3}{7}$, $\frac{4}{7}$.

(5) $\frac{5}{22}$, $\frac{7}{26}$.   **(6)** $\frac{19}{52}$.   **(7)** $\frac{5}{27}$.   **(8)** $\frac{17}{11}$.

(9) $\frac{19}{7}$.   **(10)** $\frac{4}{35}$.   **(11)** $\frac{16}{27}$.   **(12)** $\frac{7}{65}$.

(b) CONVERSION OF RECURRING DECIMALS INTO VULGAR FRACTIONS.

(1) Pure Recurring Decimals.

Consider ·3̇.   ·3̇ = ·333 . . . to infinity.

Multiply by 10. ∴ 10 **times** ·3̇ = 3·333 . . . to infinity (by shifting the point).

     i.e. **10 times** ·3̇ = 3 + ·3̇

     ∴ **9 times** ·3̇ = 3.

     i.e.   ·3̇ = $\frac{1}{9}$ of 3 = $\frac{3}{9}$.

Consider also ·5̇16̇.   ·5̇16̇ = ·516516516 . . . to infinity.

     ∴ **1,000 times** ·5̇16̇ = 516·516516 . . . to infinity.

               = 516 + ·5̇16̇.

     999 times ·5̇16̇ = 516,

         ∴   ·5̇16̇ = $\frac{516}{999}$.

Hence the we have rule :—

To convert a pure recurring decimal into a vulgar fraction, write down the figures recurring for the numerator and the same number of 9's for the denominator.

Examples.—$\cdot 31\dot{7} = \dfrac{317}{999}$, $\cdot 0\dot{3}\dot{4} = \dfrac{34}{999}$, $\cdot 00\dot{1}\dot{1} = \dfrac{11}{9999} = \dfrac{1}{909}$.

EXERCISE 39.

Convert into vulgar fractions in their lowest terms :—

(1) $\cdot\dot{2}$, $\cdot\dot{6}$.   (2) $\cdot\dot{1}$, $\cdot 0\dot{1}$, $\cdot 00\dot{1}$.   (3) $\cdot\dot{1}\dot{8}$, $\cdot\dot{2}\dot{7}$.

(4) $\cdot\dot{3}6\dot{9}$.   (5) $\cdot 0\dot{2}\dot{4}$.   (6) $\cdot 008\dot{1}$.

(7) $\cdot\dot{6}11\dot{1}$.   (8) $\cdot\dot{2}8571\dot{4}$.

Additional Examples.—

(9) $\cdot 4\dot{0}\dot{5}$.   (10) $\cdot\dot{6}1538\dot{4}$.   (11) $\cdot\dot{7}9487\dot{1}$.

(12) $\cdot\dot{8}0246913\dot{5}$.

(2) Mixed Recurring Decimals.

Convert $\cdot 81\dot{3}2\dot{5}$ into a vulgar fraction.

$$\cdot 81\dot{3}2\dot{5} = 81325325325 \ldots$$

Multiply by 100,000. $\therefore$ 100,000 times $\cdot 81\dot{3}2\dot{5} = 81325\cdot 325325 \ldots$

Also   100 times $\cdot 81\dot{3}2\dot{5} = 81\cdot 325325 \ldots$

Subtract, $\therefore$ 99,900 times $\cdot 81\dot{3}2\dot{5} = 81325 - 81$

Hence $\cdot 81\dot{3}2\dot{5} = \dfrac{81325 - 81}{99900}$.

From a consideration of this example we deduce the following rule for converting a mixed recurring decimal into a vulgar fraction :—

To form the numerator, write down the difference between the whole number consisting of all the figures of the decimal and the number consisting of the non-recurring figures, and to form the denominator write down as many 9's as there are recurring figures and as many 0's as there are non-recurring figures.

Example 1.—Convert $\cdot 47\dot{3}6\dot{9}$ into a vulgar fraction.

$$\cdot 47\dot{3}6\dot{9} = \frac{47369 - 47}{99900} = \frac{47322}{99900} = \frac{2629}{5550}.$$

Example 2.—Convert ·5i̇4285ẏ into a vulgar fraction.

Here if we multiply and divide by 10 we get—

$$·5i̇4285ẏ = \frac{5·i̇42857}{10} = \frac{5\frac{1}{7}}{10} = \frac{18}{35}.$$

The following should be carefully noted :— $\frac{1}{7} = ·i̇4285ẏ$,

$\frac{2}{7} = ·2̇8571ẏ$, $\frac{3}{7} = ·4̇2857i̇$, $\frac{4}{7} = ·5̇7142ẏ$, $\frac{5}{7} = ·ẏ14285̇$, $\frac{6}{7} = ·8̇5714ẏ$.

In each case we have the same 6 figures in the same order.

£XERCISE 40.

Convert into vulgar fractions :—

(**1**) ·2̇3̇.   (**2**) ·4i̇5̇.   (**3**) ·2i̇8̇.

(**4**) ·16̇5̇4̇.   (**5**) ·2i̇8ȯ.   (**6**) ·03̇6̇.

(**7**) ·0i̇4̇5̇.   (**8**) ·32i̇6̇3̇.   (**9**) ·13̇4̇2857i̇.

Additional Examples.—

(**10**) ·19̇4̇.   (**11**) ·329̇5̇4̇.   (**12**) ·46527̇.

(**13**) ·548̇076923̇.   (**14**) ·54ẏ29̇.

(*c*) ADDITION AND SUBTRACTION OF RECURRING

DECIMALS.

The method is the same as for ordinary decimals. The sum or the difference will be a recurring decimal.

Example 1.—Add 2·32̇6̇, 5·73̇8̇, 6·45̇3̇.

2·326326326
5·738738738
6·453453453
——————
14·518518517

Evidently if we keep on repeating the periods in each line we keep on repeating the period 518 in the sum.

Sum = 14·5̇18̇.

Example 2.—Add $3\cdot6\dot{7}\dot{2}$ and $5\cdot\dot{1}0\dot{8}$.

3·6	727272	727272
5·1	081081	081081
8·7	808353	808353

Evidently there must be 6 figures in the period in the answer, the L.C.M. of 2 and 3, the numbers in the periods of the given decimals.

$$Sum = 8\cdot7\dot{8}0835\dot{3}.$$

Example 3.—Subtract $3\cdot\dot{1}42\dot{3}$ from $5\cdot1\dot{2}\dot{6}$.

5·	126126126126	126
3·	142314231423	142
1·	983811894702	984

Here the period in the answer contains 12 figures, the L.C.M. of 3 and 4.

$$Ans. = 1\cdot\dot{9}8381189470\dot{2}.$$

For practical purposes it is altogether unnecessary to extend the figures so as to obtain the recurring period in the answer if it is a long one, three or four figures after the decimal point being in most cases a sufficiently close approximation.

EXERCISES 41.

Add together—

(1) $5\cdot\dot{7}\dot{2}$, $3\cdot4\dot{5}$, $2\cdot\dot{1}\dot{8}$.

(2) $4\cdot\dot{3}$, $5\cdot0\dot{6}$, $3\cdot\dot{2}\dot{7}$.

(3) $\cdot3\dot{6}$, $\cdot\dot{7}$, $\cdot02\dot{5}$.

(4) $\cdot\dot{6}21\dot{3}$, $\cdot1\dot{2}$, $5\cdot\dot{3}$.

Subtract—

(5) $\cdot3\dot{6}$ from $\cdot6\dot{3}$.

(6) $1\cdot2\dot{5}\dot{4}$ from $3\cdot01\dot{6}$.

(7) $3\cdot1\dot{8}$ from $7\cdot5$.

(8) $1\cdot0\dot{2}$ from $3\cdot\dot{1}2\dot{5}$.

(d) MULTIPLICATION AND DIVISION OF RECURRING DECIMALS.

Convert the recurring decimals into vulgar fractions before multiplying or dividing, and then convert the result back into a decimal if required.

Example 1.—

$$\cdot43\dot{1}\dot{8} \times 3\cdot\dot{6} = \frac{4318 - 43}{9900} \times 3\tfrac{6}{9}$$

$$= \frac{4275}{9900} \times \frac{11}{3} = \frac{19}{12} = 1\cdot58\dot{3}.$$

Example 2.—$\cdot\dot{6}1428\dot{5}7 \div \cdot\dot{1}\dot{8} = \dfrac{6\frac{1}{7}}{10} \div \dfrac{18}{99} = \dfrac{43}{70} \times \dfrac{11}{2}$

$\qquad\qquad\qquad = \dfrac{473}{140} = 3\cdot37857142\dot{}.$

EXERCISE 42.

Simplify, giving the result as a vulgar fraction—

(**1**) $\cdot1\dot{5} \times 3.$ (**2**) $\cdot03\dot{6} \times \cdot3.$ (**3**) $4\cdot6\dot{1} \div 2\cdot\dot{4}.$

(**4**) $\cdot7\dot{2} \div \cdot\dot{6}.$ (**5**) $1\cdot1\dot{8} \times 1\cdot\dot{2}.$ (**6**) $\cdot41\dot{3} \div \cdot54\dot{5}.$

Simplify, giving the result as a decimal to 4 decimal places—

(**7**) $\cdot5\dot{3} \times 1\cdot\dot{1}.$ (**8**) $1\cdot6\dot{4} \div \cdot3\dot{2}.$ (**9**) $\cdot3 \times \cdot1\dot{8} \div \cdot6\dot{3}.$

(**10**) $\dfrac{1\cdot6 \times 2\cdot\dot{3}}{\cdot16}.$ (**11**) $\cdot42\dot{3} \div \cdot5\dot{1} \times \cdot\dot{6}.$ (**12**) $\dfrac{4\cdot7 \div 1\cdot0\dot{3}}{2\cdot01\dot{5}}.$

III.—MISCELLANEOUS EXAMPLES IN DECIMAL FRACTIONS.

Example 1.—How many pieces each ·375 ins. long can be cut from a rod 12·25 ins. long, and what is the length of the part remaining ?

Here we have to find how often ·375 is contained in 12·25.

The number of times $= \dfrac{12\cdot25}{\cdot375} = \dfrac{12250}{375} = 32\dfrac{250}{375} = 32\dfrac{2}{3},$

i.e., 12·25 ins. contains 32 whole pieces and $\frac{2}{3}$ of a piece,

$\qquad \dfrac{2}{3}$ of ·375 ins. $= \dfrac{\cdot750}{3} = \cdot25$ ins.

It should be noted that 250 is the remainder when 12,250 is divided by 375. If the rod = 12,250 ins. and a piece = 375 ins., then there would be 32 pieces and 250 ins. remaining over, but this is magnifying our quantities 1,000 times, so that the remainder 250 is 1,000 times too big ; ∴ the remaining piece $= \dfrac{250}{1,000} = \cdot250.$ Thus we get the bit left over by shifting the point in the remainder 250 as far to the left as it was shifted to the right in the divisor before dividing (*i.e.*, 3 places). So 250 becomes ·250.

EXERCISE 43.

(1) Reduce 1·1875 miles to feet.

(2) Take 8·7̇2̇ lbs. from ·6 cwt.

(3) Find the L.C.M. of 2·4, 2·5, 2·7.

(4) How many pieces, each 3·25 ins. long, can be cut from a wire 57·6 ins. long, and what is the length of the remaining part ?

(5) If the front wheel of a motor bicycle is 10·5 feet in circumference and the back wheel 9·6 feet, how far will it move from rest before the same points on the wheels are again in contact with the ground ?

(6) A bill of £4 16s. 8d. is paid by A, B, and C. If A pays ·3125 of the bill and B pays ·375 of it, how much does C pay ?

(7) A man leaves ·325 of his estate to his wife and ·125 of it to each of his three sons. If the estate is worth £20,000, what does his daughter receive ?

(8) A knife is 10·75 ins. long ; the blade is 6·25 ins. long. What fraction is the handle of the whole knife ?

(9) A ship is worth £15,000. What will the owner of ·4 of the ship get for ·475 of his share ?

(10) Reduce 1·0̇3̇ ozs. to decimal of ·85̇4̇ lb. to 4 decimal places.

(11) What fraction is ·0̇5̇ of £1 7s. of ·5 of 7s. 6d. ?

(12) A man left ·5 of his estate to one son and ·25 of remainder to another son, and ·4 of what still remained to his daughter, and what was left to his wife, whose share amounted to £900. What was the value of the whole estate ?

(13) Express ·5̇14285̇7̇ of £3 10s. as decimal fraction of ·4̇2857̇1̇ of £1 15s.

(14) Being given that 277·274 cubic inches = 1 gallon, find to 2 decimal places how many gallons there are in a cubic yard.

(15) Being given that the circumference of a circle = the diameter × 3·1416, find the circumference of a circle whose diameter is 2·5 ins.

(16) A man spent ·475 of his money and then had £1 3s. 4½d. more than he had spent. How much had he at first ?

(17) A debtor owed equal sums to three creditors. To the first he paid ·45 of what he owed him, to the second ·315, and to the third ·525. What decimal fraction of the total debt remained unpaid ?

CHAPTER V.

DECIMAL APPROXIMATIONS.

(a) APPROXIMATE ADDITION AND SUBTRACTION.

Example.—Add together ·701692, 1·500943, ·4523745, 4·302587, giving the result correct to 3 decimal places.

·701	69
1·500	94
·452	37
4·302	58
6·957	58

Retain two more decimal places than the number required in the result.

As the first of the rejected digits in the result is 5, the last retained (*i.e.*, the 7) is increased by 1. Thus the nearest 3 place approximation is 6·958.

Result = 6·958.

The necessity of working to 2 extra decimal places is apparent from this example, as the 2 carried from the 8 affects the result.

In all cases of addition and subtraction the work should be carried out to *two* decimal places more than the desired number.

EXERCISE 44.

Give the nearest approximation to 2 decimal places and to 4 decimal places of—

(1) 3·71248.　　　　(2) 15·43901.　　　　(3) ·45359.

Add together, giving the nearest 2-place decimal approximation in each case—

(4) 7·41235, 14·0716, ·021435, 1·007168.
(5) 6·3̇, ·04132, ·065184, ·36̇.
(6) 1·7, 17·6̇, ·01273, ·7̇2̇, 5·49134, ·0021375.

Find to 3 decimal places the difference between—

(7) 7·012364 and 6·94132.　　　　(8) ·019173 and ·027156.
(9) 5·83435 + ·079283 + 12·08795 − 8·796376 correct to 3 decimal places.
(10) 3·109728 − 4·735386 − 9·897254 + 1·934267 + 17·957 correct to 3 decimal places.
(11) 5·876324 + 13·901256 − (7·326971 + 2·09856) + 2·38798 correct to 2 decimal places.

(b) CONTRACTED MULTIPLICATION.

Example 1.—Consider the multiplication of ·643571 by 8·216.
The work may be set down thus—

·64357	1			
8·216				
5·14856	8	= ·643571	×	8
·12871	42 =	,,	×	·2
·00643	571 =	,,	×	·01
·00386	1426 =	,,	×	·006
5·28757	9336 =	,,	×	8·216

In this arrangement we observe that if the decimal points
are placed vertically below the decimal point of the multiplicand
each line obtained after the first is placed one place further to
the right than the one above it.

Now, if we wish to retain only 3 decimal places in the result,
we add up only 5 columns after the decimal points, so that the
work to the right of the vertical line may be omitted. This is
done by curtailing the multiplicand as follows :—

·643	571		
8·216			
5·148	56	= ·643571 ×	8
·128	71	= ·643571 ×	·2
·006	43	= ·643571 ×	·01
·003	85	= ·643571 ×	·006
5·287	55		

Result = 5·288.

As indicated above, we strike out the 1 before multiplying by
8. We then strike out the 7 and multiply by 2, carrying from the
rejected 7, and so on.

Thus the principle of the contracted method consists in this
that when multiplying by the successive digits of the multiplier
*instead of commencing each new line one place further to the right
than the one above it we strike out a digit from the multiplicand.*

6

Example 2.—Multiply ·34675 by 627·034 to 2 decimal places.

First Method.—

Arrange and curtail as before—

           ·3̷4̷ | 6̷7̷5̷
        627·03 | 4
        ──────────
        208·05 | 0   = ·34675 × 600
          6·93 | 50   = ·34675 × 20
          2·42 | 72   = ·34675 ×   7
           ·01 | 03   = ·34̷6̷7̷5̷ ×   ·03
           ·00 | 13   = ·34̷6̷7̷5̷ ×   ·004
        ──────────
        217·42 | 38

Result = 217·42.

The 6 being in the hundreds' place when we multiply by it we are really multiplying by 600, so that in order, as before, to keep our decimal points vertically below that of the multiplicand we have to shift the product obtained 2 places to the left—*i.e.*, when we say 6 times 5 = 30 the 0 is placed not below the 5 but below the 6 in the 3rd decimal place. After multiplying by the 6 we multiply by the 2, placing the 0 one place to the right of the line above—*i.e.*, in 4th decimal place. As we do not wish to retain the 5th decimal place we strike out 5 before multiplying by 7, but, of course, we " carry " 3 and place the 2 obtained below the 0 in 4th decimal place. Since 0 is the next digit of the multiplier we strike out 2 digits of multiplicand before multiplying by 3, and so on.

Second Method.—

In Example 2, as we have seen, the first figure of the multiplier being in the hundreds' place we had to shift the product obtained by it two places to the left, whereas in Example 1 there was no shifting, the first figure of the multiplier being in the units' place. As this shifting is necessary when the first figure of the multiplier is in any position other than the *units' place*, and as it is confusing to a beginner, it is a good plan before commencing the multiplication *to shift the point in the multiplier so that the first figure is in the units' place*, and to shift the point in the multiplicand the same number of places in the opposite direction. This does not affect the product. Thus, taking the example just worked—

·34675 × 627·034 = 34·675 × 6·27034.

Having made this adjustment, it would be also convenient to *place the first or units' figure of the multiplier under the last figure of the multiplicand* that we are retaining, as that is the figure on which it commences to operate. If in addition we *reverse* the digits of the multiplier we bring each under the figure of the multiplicand on which it commences to operate, and by so doing reduce the risk of error to a minimum. Let us treat Example 2 in this way.

Multiply ·34675 by 627·034 to 2 decimal places.

$$·34675 \times 627·034 = 34·675 \times 6·27034.$$

34·67	50
43 07	26
208·05	00
6·93	50
2·42	72
1	03
	13
217·42	38

Retaining 4 decimal places (*i.e.*, two more than the number required) we place the 6 under the 4th decimal place of multiplicand and reverse the multiplier, and on multiplying by 6 we place the product obtained directly below. We then strike off the 0 and multiply by 2, then strike off 5 and multiply by 7 and so on, the first figure obtained in each line or product being placed in the 4th decimal place.

Result = 217·42.

The advantage of this plan is apparent. It presents no difficulty, and after working a few examples the student will be able to apply it with great facility and considerable saving of time and labour.

Our method then is as follows :—

1. Adjust the factors so that the first digit of the multiplier is in the units' place.

2. Retain in the multiplicand two decimal places more than the number required in the result (affixing 0's if necessary).

3. Place the first (*i.e.*, units') digit of the multiplier under the last retained decimal place of the multiplicand and reverse the multiplier.

4. Multiply from right to left, commencing to operate with each digit of the multiplier on the digit of the multiplicand directly above it, " carrying " from the adjacent rejected digit on the right.

5. Set the first obtained figure of each line or product in the last decimal place retained.

6. After adding reject the two last digits in the result, and if the first rejected digit be 5 or more increase the last retained digit by 1.

We shall work out another example.

Example 3.—Multiply ·32045 by ·007156 to the nearest 5-place decimal approximation.

$$·32045 \times ·007156 = ·00032045 \times 7·156.$$

·00032̸	0̸4̸5̸
65	17
·00224	31
3	20
1	60
	19
·00229	30

Result = ·00229.

EXERCISE 45.

Multiply to 2 decimal places—

(1) 324·6105 by 2·143.

(2) 13·1243 by 7·2413.

(3) 13·1203 by 2·1326.

(4) 51·71426 by 3·421.

(5) 34·21425 by 6·54313.

(6) 7·014036 by 32·412.

Multiply to 3 decimal places—

(7) ·461235 by 410·423.

(8) 1·401356 by 21·4013.

(9) 32·52163 by ·41235.

(10) 516·1432 by ·04213.

(11) 732·10264 by ·00123.

(12) ·451342 by ·4632.

Multiply to 4 decimal places—

(13) 3·401365 by 1·1023.

(14) ·310236 by ·02413.

(15) 1·641023 by ·00324.

(16) ·0531264 by ·04123.

(17) ·01234156 by 324·6132.

(18) 123·10674 by ·023451.

(19) 3·41025 by 23·126.

(20) 243·01326 by ·005724.

Multiply to 5 decimal places.

(21) ·005319 by ·04236.

(22) 2·314132 by ·000425.

(23) ·006415 by ·002374.

(24) ·0324756 by ·05236.

(25) ·0312536 by ·00461345.

(26) ·0371426 by ·0043215.

Find the square to 3 decimal places of—

(27) 1·03125.   (28) ·04315.   (29) ·106342.

Find to the nearest unit the square of—

(30) 1·414.   (31) 1·732.   (32) 2·236.

(c) CONTRACTED DIVISION.

Let us consider a case of ordinary long division by a decimal.

Example 1.—Divide ·094476358 by 62·435 to 6 decimal places.

$$\frac{·094476358}{62·435} = \frac{94·476358}{62435}.$$

Placing the quotient above the dividend with the point directly above that of the dividend the work would appear thus :—

```
           ·001  513
62435 ) 94·476 | 358
        62 435 |
        ------
        32 041 | 3
        31 217 | 5
        ------
           823 | 85
           624 | 35
           ---
           199 | 508
           187 | 305
           ---
            12 | 203
```

A little examination will show that the work to the right of the vertical line may be omitted without affecting the result obtained. After getting the first remainder instead of "taking down" 3 from the dividend we may strike out 5 from the divisor and divide by 6243, and after obtaining the next remainder instead of attaching a figure to it use 624 as divisor, and so on.

The curtailed work would appear thus :—

```
                ·001513(2)
62435 ) 94·476358
        62 435
        ------
        32 041
        31 217
        ------
           824
           624
           ---
           200
           187
           ---
            13
```

Result = ·001513 (the nearest 6-place decimal approximation).

After obtaining the remainder 32041 we strike out 5 from the divisor but "carry" from it when multiplying the 6243 by the digit 5 obtained in the quotient. After getting remainder 824 we strike out 3 from the divisor and so on. When we divide the 6 (the last figure left in the divisor) into the 13 the 2 obtained being less than 5 indicates that the 3 is not to be increased by 1, and that the result is, therefore, ·001513 to 6 places.

We cannot proceed further, and it should be noted that the number of digits in the quotient obtained by " contraction " is three—*i.e., two fewer than the number of digits in the divisor.* The method is, therefore, limited, and in employing it we must first determine how many figures are required in the quotient and not commence " contracting " till the number of figures still to be found is **two** fewer than the number of figures in the divisor.

Our method of procedure then is as follows :—

1. Determine how many digits are required in the quotient.

2. Divide in the ordinary way till the number of digits still to be found is two fewer than the number of digits in the divisor.

3. In finding the remaining digits of the quotient strike out successively digits from the divisor (commencing with the units' digit) instead of attaching digits to the remainders.

4. Work to a digit more than the required number, and if this last digit is 5 or more than 5 increase by 1 the last digit retained.

Example 2.—Divide 9·2317506 by ·314725 to 4 decimal places.

$$9 \cdot 2317506 \div \cdot 314725 = 9231750 \cdot 6 \div 314725.$$

```
                    29·3327(6)
        314725 ) 9231750·6
                 629450
                 2937250
                 2832525
                  104725
                   94417
                   10308
                    9441
                     867
                     629
                     238
                     220
                      18
```

Here we must find two figures before commencing to abridge, as we cannot find more than four by abridgement, the number of figures in the divisor being 6.

Result 9= 2·3328.

Note.—In determining the number of digits required in the quotient it is not always necessary to make the divisor a whole number, and the method may be applied to division by a recurring decimal. When dividing by a recurring decimal we should retain one digit more in the divisor than the number required in the quotient, and find the first digit of the quotient before commencing to contract.

Example 3.—Divide ·354234 by ·043i̇ to 4 decimal places.

Adjust the divisor so as to have 1 digit before the decimal point.

Thus :—·354234 ÷ ·043i̇ = 35·4234 ÷ 4·31431431 . . .

From the integral parts we see that there is only 1 digit before the point in the quotient. We, therefore, require 5 digits in the result altogether, and therefore retain 6 digits in the divisor. Thus :—

$$
\begin{array}{r}
8\cdot2106(8) \\
4\cdot31431\ )\ \overline{35\cdot42340} \\
34\ 51448 \\
\hline
90892 \\
86286 \\
\hline
4606 \\
4314 \\
\hline
292 \\
258 \\
\hline
34
\end{array}
$$

Result = 8·2107.

EXERCISE 46.

Divide without unnecessary work to 4 decimal places—

(1) ·0253476 by ·12345.　　(2) 2·517834 by 3·0126.
(3) ·05013426 by ·49376.　　(4) 1·537016 by ·36425.
(5) ·00032456 by ·001234.　　(6) ·50316273 by 2·5036.

Divide to 5 decimal places—

(7) ·02401376 by ·37215.　　(8) ·90812713 by 8·2014.
(9) ·007302415 by ·51324.　　(10) ·024710453 by ·0543261.
(11) ·063124 by 8·324.　　(12) 2·0153267 by 312·45.

Divide to 6 decimal places—

(13) ·07810214 by 6·12324.   **(14)** ·04560236 by 6·3425.

(15) ·000860137 by ·79832.   **(16)** ·0871204 by 32·106.

(17) Divide 71·3$\overset{.}{2}\overset{.}{6}$ by 8·4$\overset{.}{3}$ to 4 decimal places.

(18) Divide ·35123 by ·043$\overset{.}{1}\overset{.}{4}$ to 3 decimal places.

Divide without shifting the decimal point of the Divisor—

(19) 39·21072 by 5·7203462 to 4 decimal places.

(20) 316·20145 by 24·102732 to 3 decimal places.

(d) DECIMALISATION OF MONEY.

To express a sum of money correct to the nearest 3-place decimal approximation of £1 (*i.e., correct to a farthing*).

To reduce shillings to the decimal of £1 we divide by 20 mentally. Thus :—

10s. = £·5 ; 17s. = £·85 ; 2s. = £·1 ; 1s. = £·05.

In dealing with the pence, since 1 farthing = £·001,* approximately, it will be convenient to reduce to farthings and multiply by ·001. Thus :—

2d. = 8f. = £·008 ; 2¾d. = 11f. = £·011.

These results are only approximate, though correct to 3 places, but for larger sums the approximation obtained by this rule will be so rough that the results will not be the nearest 3-place decimal approximation, as will be evident on comparing the values obtained in this way with the exact values in the following cases :—

3d. = 12f. = £·012 ; exact value = £·0125

6d. = 24f. = £·024 ;   ,,   = £·025

9d. = 36f. = £·036 ;   ,,   = £·0375

Thus, in dealing with 6d., after reducing it to farthings we must add 1 (making 25) to get the correct result, £·025.

Also, it is clear from the above that, to get the closest 3-place decimal approximation, we should on reducing to farthings *add 1 for the sums* 3d. *to* 8¾d. *and add 2 for the sums* 9d. *to* 11¾d.

Note.—The *exact* values of 3d. and 9d. should be noted. Thus :—

7d.=£·029 (7×4+1=29) ; 10½d.=£·044 (10½×4+2=44).

---

* 1 farthing = £·001$\frac{1}{24}$ = £·00104 . . .

Example 1.—Express £57 16s. 8½d. as the decimal of £1 to 3 places.

$$16s. = £·8 \atop 8½d. = £·035 \Big\} \quad ∴ £57 \ 16s. \ 8½d. = £57·835.$$

Example 2.—Express £5 13s. 10¾d. as the decimal of £1 to 3 places.

$$13s. = £·65 \atop 10¾d. = £·045 \Big\} \quad ∴ £5 \ 13s. \ 10¾d. = £5·695.$$

With a little practice the work can be performed mentally.

EXERCISE 47.

Express as decimals of £1 to the nearest 3-place decimal approximation—

(1) £1 10s. 2d.	**(2)** £2 12s. 6d.	**(3)** £5 8s. 5d.
(4) £7 15s. 1d.	**(5)** £13 17s. 2d.	**(6)** £14 9s. 2½d.
(7) £2 5s. 1¾d.	**(8)** £15 10s. 3¾d.	**(9)** £17 11s. 4½d.
(10) £1 19s. 10d.	**(11)** £2 16s. 9¾d.	**(12)** £4 7s. 10¾d.
(13) £3 1s. 6d.	**(14)** £5 1s. 7¾d.	**(15)** £25 1s. 11¾d.
(16) £2 0s. 8¼d.	**(17)** £1 1s. 9¼d.	**(18)** £2 13s. 4¾d.

Given a sum of money expressed in pounds as the nearest 3-place decimal approximation to express it in £. s. d.

In Example 1 above, where we got £·835 from 16s. 8½d., we find that £·8 gives 16s. (*i.e.,* 8 × 2) and £·035 gives 8½d.—*i.e.,* 34 f. or (35 − 1)f., and in Example 2 above, where we got £·695 from 13s. 10¾d., we find that £·65 = 13s. (6 × 2 + 1) and £·045 = 10¾d.—*i.e.,* 43f. or (45 − 2)f.

Hence it follows that :—

The number of shillings is double the 1st decimal figure (and 1 more if the 2nd decimal figure is 5 or more). And the number formed of the 2nd decimal figure (less 5 if it is 5 or more) and the 3rd decimal figure gives the rest of the sum in farthings, with this correction that 1 is subtracted if it is 13 or more, and 2 if it is 38 or more, *because* 3d. *was reckoned as* 13f. *and* 9d. *as* 38f. *in decimalising.*

Example 1.—£·378 = 7s. 6¾d. $\begin{cases} 3 \times 2 + 1 = 7\text{s.} \\ 28 - 1 = 27\text{f.} = 6\frac{3}{4}\text{d.} \end{cases}$

Example 2.—£6·847 = £6 16s. 11¼d. $\begin{cases} 8 \times 2 = 16\text{s.} \\ 47 - 2 = 45\text{f.} = 11\frac{1}{4}\text{d.} \end{cases}$

EXERCISE 48.

Express in £. s. d. to the nearest farthing—

(1) £·525	**(2)** £·618.	**(3)** £1·436.	**(4)** £3·549.
(5) £6·108.	**(6)** £4·658.	**(7)** £·765.	**(8)** £15·271.
(9) £2·884.	**(10)** £3·718.	**(11)** £16·079.	**(12)** £15·055.
(13) £1·008.	**(14)** £·075.	**(15)** £3·014.	**(16)** £·085.

CHAPTER VI.

PRACTICE AND INVOICES.

I. PRACTICE.

Aliquot Parts.—A quantity is called an **aliquot part** of another quantity when it is contained in that other quantity **an exact number of times without remainder.**

Thus 5s., 4s., 3s. 4d. are aliquot parts of £1, because they are contained in £1 exactly 4, 5, and 6 times respectively. These sums are, therefore, $\frac{1}{4}$, $\frac{1}{5}$, and $\frac{1}{6}$ of £1, so that an aliquot part of any quantity is a fraction of it having 1 for its numerator.

In the method of calculating known as **Practice,** aliquot parts are made use of.

The following aliquot parts of £1 should be carefully noted :—

10s. = $\frac{1}{2}$,   6s. 8d. = $\frac{1}{3}$,   5s. = $\frac{1}{4}$,   4s. = $\frac{1}{5}$,

3s. 4d. = $\frac{1}{6}$,   2s. 6d. = $\frac{1}{8}$,   2s. = $\frac{1}{10}$,   1s. 8d. = $\frac{1}{12}$,

1s. 4d. = $\frac{1}{15}$,   1s. 3d. = $\frac{1}{16}$.

(a) Simple Practice.

The nature of Simple Practice and the method of using aliquot parts are shown in the following examples :—

Example 1.—Find the price of 254 articles at £2 16s. **6d. each.**

	£	s.	d.				
	254	0	0	= price at £1 each.			
			2				
	508	0	0	=	,,	£2	,,
10s. = ½ of £1	127	0	0	=	,,	10s.	,,
5s. = ½ of 10s.	63	10	0	=	,,	5s.	,,
1s. = ⅕ of 5s.	12	14	0	=	,,	1s.	,,
6d. = ½ of 1s.	6	7	0	=	,,	6d.	,,
	£717	11	0	=	,,	£2 16s. 6d. each.	

To get the price at 10s. each, we take the ½ of £254 (price at £1).
To get the price at 5s. each, we take the ½ of £127 (price at 10s.), and so on.

Example 2.—Find the price of 346 articles at 19s. 6d. **each.**

	£	s.	d.			
	346	0	0 = price at £1 each.			
10s. = ½ of £1	173	0	0 =	,,	10s. ,,	
5s. = ½ of 10s.	86	10	0 =	,,	5s. ,,	
4s. = ⅕ of £1	69	4	0 =	,,	4s. ,,	
6d. = ⅛ of 4s.	8	13	0 =	,,	6d. ,,	
	£337	7	0 =	,,	19s. 6d. each.	

Example 3.—Find the cost of 366½ cwts. at £2 11s. 4½d. **each.**

First Method.	£	s.	d.			
	366	10	0	= price at £1 each.		
			2			
	733	0	0	=	,,	£2 ,,
10s. = ½ of £1	183	5	0	=	,,	10s. ,,
1s. = 1/10 of 10s.	18	6	6	=	,,	1s. ,,
3d. = ¼ of 1s.	4	11	7½	=	,,	3d. ,,
1½d. = ½ of 3d.	2	5	9¾	=	,,	1½d. ,,
	£941	8	11¼	=	,,	£2 11s. 4½d. each.

Second Method.

£366·5   = price at £1 each.
2

	733	=	,,	£2	,,
10s. = ½ of £1	183·25	=	,,	10s.	,,
1s. = 1/10 of 10s.	18·325	=	,,	1s.	,,
3d. = ¼ of 1s.	4·58125	=	,,	3d.	,,
1½d. = ½ of 3d.	2·290625	=	,,	1½d.	,,

£941·446875 = ,, £2 11s. 4½d. each.

£941·446875 = £941 8s. 11¼d.

EXERCISE 49.

Find, by Practice, the cost of each of the following number of articles at the price given for one :—

(1) 69 at 15s.

(2) 72 at 12s. 6d.

(3) 58 at 13s. 4d.

(4) 67 at 6s. 3d.

(5) 72 at 17s. 6d.

(6) 67 at 16s.

(7) 94 at 18s.

(8) 42 at 15s. 6d.

(9) 52 at 13s. 7d.

(10) 78 at 14s. 8½d.

(11) 34 at 12s. 3½d.

(12) 68 at 3s. 5¾d.

(13) 72 at 11s. 6½d.

(14) 89 at 13s. 5½d.

(15) 75 at 12s. 11½d.

(16) 67 at 13s. 1¼d.

(17) 42 at 6s. 5½d.

(18) 625 at £1 17s. 6d.

(19) 534 at £3 17s. 8d.

(20) 725 at £4 16s. 9½d.

(21) 525 at £3 12s. 3¼d.

(22) 673 at £4 11s. 9½d.

(23) 785 at £5 18s. 6¼d.

(24) 956 at £4 19s. 7½d.

(25) 698 at £3 17s. 9¼d.

(26) 548 at £4 16s. 7¾d.

(27) 756 at £5 13s. 10¾d.

(28) 623 at £4 17s. 11¼d.

(29) 897 at £2 13s. 7¾d.

(30) 756 at £3 11s. 9¼d.

(31) 653½ at £4 15s. 6½d.

(32) 2,843⅓ at £2 16s. 9d.

(33) 524¼ at £3 19s. 10d.

(34) 765⅔ at £6 18s. 6d.

(35) 753½ at £12 17s. 11½d.

(36) 483⅗ at £5 15s. 10d.

(37) 963 at £5 19s. 11¾d.

(38) 725¾ at £3 14s. 8d.

(39) 235⅙ at £5 18s. 9d.

(40) 245⅛ at £4 14s. 8d.

(b) **Compound Practice.**

The nature of **Compound Practice** and the method of calculating by aliquot parts are shown in the following examples :—

First Method.—*Example* 1.—Find the value of 2 tons 13 cwts. 2 qrs. 21 lbs. at £23 6s. 8d. per ton.

	£	s.	d.			
	23	6	8	= price of 1 ton.		
			2			

	£	s.	d.			
	46	13	4	=	,,	2 tons.
10 cwts. $= \frac{1}{2}$ of 1 ton	11	13	4	=	,,	10 cwts.
2 cwts. $= \frac{1}{5}$ of 10 cwts.	2	6	8	=	,,	2 cwts.
1 cwt. $= \frac{1}{2}$ of 2 cwts.	1	3	4	=	,,	1 cwt.
2 qrs. $= \frac{1}{2}$ of 1 cwt.	0	11	8	=	,,	2 qrs.
14 lbs. $= \frac{1}{4}$ of 2 qrs.	0	2	11	=	,,	14 lbs.
7 lbs. $= \frac{1}{2}$ of 14 lbs.	0	1	$5\frac{1}{2}$	=	,,	7 lbs.
	£62	12	$8\frac{1}{2}$	=	,,	2 tons 13 cwts.
						2 qrs. 21 lbs.

The aliquot parts are set down as above, and to get price of 10 cwts. we take $\frac{1}{2}$ of £23 6s. 8d (price of 1 ton), and to get price of 5 cwts. we take $\frac{1}{5}$ of £11 13s. 4d. (price of 10 cwts.), and so on.

Second Method.—*Example* 2.—Find the cost of 5 acres 3 roods 35 sq. poles at £2 11s. 7d. per acre.

12 | 7d.
20 | 11·58333s.
  | £2·57917

Express £2 11s. 7d. in pounds correct to the fifth decimal place.

	£2·57917 = cost of 1 acre.		
	5		
	12·89585		
2 roods $= \frac{1}{2}$ of 1 acre	1·28959	= cost of 2 roods.	
1 rood $= \frac{1}{2}$ of 2 roods	·64479	= ,,	1 rood.
20 sq. pls. $= \frac{1}{2}$ of 1 rood	·32240	= ,,	20 sq. pls.
10 sq. pls. $= \frac{1}{2}$ of 20 sq. pls.	·16120	= ,,	10 sq. pls.
5 sq. pls. $= \frac{1}{2}$ of 10 sq. pls.	·08060	= ,,	5 sq. pls.
	£15·39443	= ,,	5 acres 3 roods
			35 sq. pls.

= £15 7s. 11d. (correct to nearest penny).

Third Method.—

Example 3.—Find the cost of 3 miles 5 furs. 6 chs. 13 yds. at £7 16s. 9d. per mile.

$$22 \begin{cases} 2 \\ 11 \end{cases} \begin{array}{c|c} 2 & 13 \qquad \text{yds.} \\ 11 & \overline{6\cdot5} \\ 10 & \overline{6\cdot59090 \text{ chs.}} \\ 8 & \overline{5\cdot65909 \text{ furs.}} \\ & \overline{3\cdot70739 \text{ miles.}} \end{array}$$

Express 3 miles 5 furs. 6 chs. 13 yds. as miles correct to the fifth decimal place.

∴ 3 miles 5 furs. 6 chs. 13 yds. = 3·70739 miles.

£3·70739 = cost at £1 per mile.

7

	25·95173 =	,,	£7	,,
10s. = ½ of £1s.	1·85370 =	,,	10s.	,,
5s. = ½ of 10s.	·92685 =	,,	5s.	,,
1s. = ⅕ of 5s.	·18537 =	,,	1s.	,,
6d. = ½ of 1s.	·09269 =	,,	6d.	,,
3d. = ½ of 6d.	·04635 =	,,	3d.	,,
	£29·05669 =	,,	£7 16s. 9d. per mile.	

= £29 1s. 2d. (correct to nearest penny).

EXERCISE 50.

Find by Practice the cost of—

(1) 3 tons 15 cwts. 2 qrs. at £20 per ton.
(2) 3 tons 16 cwts. 3 qrs. at £16 per ton.
(3) 5 tons 17 cwts. 2 qrs. at £12 per ton.
(4) 4 tons 12 cwts. 3 qrs. at £16 6s. 8d. per ton.
(5) 10 yards 2 feet 6 inches at £1 5s. 6d. per yard.
(6) 5 yards 2 feet 7½ inches at £2 3s. 6d. per yard.
(7) 4 lbs. 10 ozs. 15 dwts, at £3 12s. per lb.
(8) 3 tons 12 cwts. 3 qrs. 14 lbs. at £9 6s. 8d. per ton.
(9) 4 tons 15 cwts. 3 qrs. 21 lbs. at £14 per ton.
(10) 7 tons 12 cwts. 1 qr. 21 lbs. at £25 13s. 4d. per ton.
(11) 6 ozs. 12 dwts. 15 grains at £2 10s. per oz.
(12) 15 cwts 3 qrs. 22 lbs. at £21 per ton.
(13) 17 cwts. 2 qrs. 21 lbs. 8 ozs. at £28 per ton.
(14) 3 tons 6 cwts. 3 qrs. 22 lbs. at £23 6s. 8d. per ton.

(15) 5 tons 13 cwts. 2 qrs. 17 lbs. at £14 per ton.
(16) 7 tons 18 cwts. 3 qrs. 10½ lbs. at £9 6s. 8d. per ton.
(17) 8 tons 15 cwts. 3 qrs. 25 lbs. at £23 6s. 8d. per ton.
(18) 6 miles 5 fur. 30 poles at £5 10s. per mile.
(19) 13 miles 7 fur. 110 yds. at £4 10s. per mile.
(20) 5 ac. 3 ro. 25 sq. poles at £1 12s. per acre.
(21) 3 ac. 2 ro. 32 sq. poles at £10 per acre.
(22) 32 gallons 3 qts. 1 pint at £1 6s. 6d. per gallon.
(23) 2 tons 13 cwts. 3 qrs. 22 lbs. 8 ozs. at £23 6s. 8d. per ton.
(24) 3 tons 16 cwts. 3 qrs. 16 lbs. at £12 per ton.

Work the remaining examples correct to the nearest penny by the decimal method.

(25) 5 tons 8 cwts. 3 qrs. 21 lbs. at £2 11s. 7d. per ton.
(26) 18 cwts. 1 qr. 7 lbs. at £14 7s. 11d. per ton.
(27) 7 acres 2 roods 16 sq. poles at £4 15s. 7d. per acre.
(28) 3 miles 5 furs. 4 chs. 11 yds. at £12 13s. 11d. per mile.
(29) 8 miles 3 furs. 170 yds. at £11 17s. 1d. per mile.
(30) 6 acres 2 roods 25 sq. poles at £3 19s. 5d. per acre.
(31) 3 tons 12 cwts. 1 qr. 16 lbs. at £17 12s. 5d. per ton.
(32) 4 acres 1 rood 380 sq. yds. at £7 12s. 9d. per acre.
(33) 8 cub. yds. 26 cub. ft. 360 cub. ins. at £5 18s. 4d. per cub. yd.
(34) 16 gals 3 qts. 1 pt. at £2 6s. 6d. per gallon.
(35) 5 sts. 11 lbs. 7 ozs. 6 drs. at £7 13s. 8d. per stone.
(36) 8 tons 3 cwts. 1 qr. 26 lbs. at £12 14s. 10d. per ton.
(37) 13 acres 3 roods 19 sq. poles at £7 4s. 6½d. per acre.
(38) Find the tax on a rental of £374 15s. at 12s. 7½d. per £1.
(39) Find the dividend on £1,387 5s. at 8s. 7¾d. per £1.
(40) Find the commission due on sales amounting to £1,327 12s. 4d. at 3s. 2½d. per £1.
(41) Find the rent of a farm containing 219 acres 3 roods 7 sq. poles at £2 12s. 10d. per acre.
(42) Find the cost of 7 tons 11 cwts. 1 qr. 18 lbs. at £2 11s. 8d. per ton. (*Use two aliquot parts only*).
(43) Find the cost of 9 tons 16 cwts. 2 qrs. 13 lbs. at £3 17s. 6d. per ton. (*Use three aliquot parts only*).

II. INVOICES.

When a buyer has completed his purchases at a shop, the seller presents him with a bill or **invoice** in the form of a written list of the articles bought with their prices set down, as in the following specimen :—

Specimen of a Bill or Invoice.

Glasgow, 20th March, 1919.

Mr. John Smith,

       Bought of M'Pherson Bros.,

           Queen Street.

	£	s.	d.
2 dozen knives at 3s. 6d. each, . .	4	4	0
3 dozen spoons at 15s. 6d. per half-dozen,	4	13	0
30 files at 17s. 6d. per dozen, . .	2	3	9
2 dozen cork screws at 1s. 6d. each, .	1	16	0
	£12	16	9

EXERCISE 51.

Make out the following invoices (with names and dates), and find the total cost of the following purchases :—

(1) 22 lbs. of sugar at 5¾d. per lb. ; 16 lbs. of beans at 6½d. per lb. ; 2 lbs. of butter at 2s. 4d. per lb. ; 5 lbs. of tea at 2s. 8d. per lb. ; 16 lbs. of flour at 4¾d. per lb.

(2) 15½ lbs. of currants at 7d. per lb. ; 14¼ lbs. raisins at 8d. per lb. ; 28½ lbs. of soap at 5d. per lb. ; 13½ lbs. margarine at 1s. 2d. per lb ; 15½ lbs. of rice at 9d. per lb.

(3) 18 yards of flannel at 3s. 4d. per yard. ; 15 yards of calico at 1s. 5½d. per yard ; 6 pairs of gloves at 5s. 11½d. per pair ; 35 yards of velvet at 8s. 9½d. per yard ; 17 yards of silk at 11s. 9½d. per yard.

(4) 4½ yards of cloth at 1s. 11d. per yard ; 16¼ yards of flannel at 4s. 4d. per yard ; 25½ yards of crape at 4s. 11d. per yard ; 17¼ yards of ribbon at 2s. 4d. per yard ; 50½ yards muslin at 1s. 10d. per yard.

(5) 16½ lbs. of jam at 10½d. per lb. ; 7¾ lbs. of currants at 10d. per lb. ; 15¼ lbs. of cheese at 11d. per lb. ; 6¾ lbs. of butter at 2s. 6d. per lb. ; 6½ lbs. of tea at 2s. 4d. per lb.

(6) 15¾ yards of cloth at 2s. 6d. per yard; 15¼ yards of calico at 1s. 7½d. per yard; 16¼ yards of velvet at 7s. 9d. per yard; 36¾ yards of flannel at 2s. 8d. per yard; 17½ yards of ribbon at 1s. 8½d. per yard.

(7) 2 lbs. of pepper at 3½d. per oz.; 3 stones of sugar at 5¼d. per lb.; 1 cwt. of potatoes at 10½d. per stone; 3 qrs. of flour at 1s. 10d. per half-stone; 6 ozs. of spice at 1½d. per dram.

(8) 12 bars of soap, each 7½ lbs., at 5¾d. per lb.; 6 bars of soap, each 9¾ lbs., at 5d. per lb.; 15 packets of candles, each 5½ lbs., at 6½d. per lb.; 126 candles at 1s. 1½d. per dozen.

(9) 2 lbs. 5 ozs. of pepper at 2½d. per oz.; 1½ stones of sugar at 5½d. per lb.; 2½ lbs. of butter at 1½d. per oz.; 2 cwts. of potatoes at 10½d. per stone; 2 qrs. 3 lbs. rice at 4½d. per lb.

(10) 16½ yards of linen at 5½d. per yard; 5 yards 2 feet cretonne at 2½d. per foot; 15¾ yards of velvet at 5s. 6d. per yard; 6 yards 2 feet 6 inches of tape at 4½d. per foot.

(11) 3 pieces of cloth, each 15 yards, at 1s. 5½d. per yard; 10 pieces of cloth, each 12½ yards, at 2s. 4½d. per yard.; 3 dozen skeins of silk at 1s. 10½d. per skein; 5 dozen reels of cotton at 5s. 10d. per half-dozen reels.

(12) 5 dozen knives at 7s. 9d. per half-dozen; 30 forks at 11s. 10d. per dozen; 2 dozen pairs scissors at 6s. 11½d. per pair; 6½ dozen spoons at 1s. 11½d. each.

(13) 5 dozen slates at 4 for 1s. 10d.; 7 score pencils at 1¾d. each; 150 pen holders at 1s. 11½d. per dozen; 2 gallons ink at 7¾d. per pint.

(14) 162 yards calico at 15s. 4d. per dozen yards; 2,550 buttons at 2s. 10d. per 100; 175 yards trimming at 7s. 10d. per 10 yards; 135 reels of silk at 1s. 10d. per 5 reels.

(15) 1 cwt. of sugar at 5¼d. per lb.; 2 cwts. 1 qr. 15 lbs. of rice at 6¼d. per lb.; 1 ton of flour at 1s. 11½d. per stone; 2 qrs. 3 lbs. of tea at 1½d. per oz.

(16) 2 dozen pairs of gloves at 5s. 11½d. per pair; 600 buttons at 1s. 8½d. per dozen; 550 yards of trimming at £1 16s. 8d. per 100 yards; 66 reels cotton at 5s. 10d. per dozen reels.

III. SHORT METHODS OF CALCULATING PRICES.

(a) When the Cost of 1 article is known, to find the cost of 12, 20, 240, 480, 960.

12.—Count the pence as shillings.
Example.—Find the cost of 12 articles at 1s. 3d. each.
  1s. 3d. = 15d.   ∴ Cost of 12 = 15s.

20.—Count the shillings as pounds.
Example.—Find the cost of 20 articles at 5s. 4d. each.
  5s. 4d. = $5\frac{1}{3}$s.   ∴ Cost of 20 = £$5\frac{1}{3}$ = £5 6s. 8d.

240.—Count the pence as pounds.
Example.—Find the cost of 240 articles at 1s. $4\frac{1}{2}$d. each.
  1s. $4\frac{1}{2}$d. = $16\frac{1}{2}$d.   ∴ Cost of 240 = £$16\frac{1}{2}$ = £16 10s.

480.—Count the halfpence as pounds.
Example.—Find the cost of 480 articles at 1s. $5\frac{1}{2}$d. each.
  1s. $5\frac{1}{2}$d. = 35 halfpence.   ∴ Cost of 480 = £35.

960.—Count the farthings as pounds.
Example.—Find the cost of 960 articles at 2s. $1\frac{1}{4}$d. each.
  2s. $1\frac{1}{4}$d. = 101 farthings.   ∴ Cost of 960 = £101.

(b) When the price is an aliquot part of £1.

Example.—Find the cost of 26 articles at 6s. 8d. each.
6s. 8d. = £$\frac{1}{3}$.   ∴ Cost of 26 = £26 × $\frac{1}{3}$ = £$8\frac{2}{3}$ = £8 13s. 4d.

(c) When the price is an aliquot part of £1 less than a whole number of pounds.

Example 1.—Find the cost of 24 articles at £3 17s. 6d. each.
 £3 17s. 6d. = £4 − £$\frac{1}{8}$.
∴   Cost of 24 = £24 × 4 − $\frac{1}{8}$ of £24 = £96 − £3 = £93.

Example 2.—Find the cost of 485 articles at £1 16s. 8d. each.

	£	s.	d.		
	485	0	0	= cost at £1.	
			2		
Subtract—	970	0	0	= ,,	£2.
3s. 4d. = £$\frac{1}{6}$.	80	16	8	= ,,	3s. 4d.
∴	£889	3	4	= ,,	£1 16s. 8d.

EXERCISE 52.

Find the cost of-

(1) 12 strings of glass beads at 1s. 5½d. each.
(2) 12 artificial silk scarves at 3s. 3½d. each.
(3) 36 coat hangers at 7d. each.
(4) 24 articles at 1s. 8d. each.
(5) 25 yards of print at 1s. 1d. per yard.
(6) 20 bulb bowls at 1s. 6d. each.
(7) 20 yards of velveteen at 2s. 1½d. per yard.
(8) 21 lbs. of apples at 9d. per lb.
(9) 240 yards of gingham at 9½d. per yard.
(10) 480 lbs. sugar at 7½d. per lb.
(11) 960 yards of cretonne at 1s. 1¼d. per yard.
(12) 24 chubby umbrellas at 5s. each.
(13) 37 blackboard pointers at 6s. 8d. each.
(14) 27 lbs. of Ceylon tea at 3s. 4d. per lb.
(15) 30 yards of marocain at 2s. 6d. per yard.
(16) 25 sponges at 1s. 8d. each.
(17) 33 lbs. of Canterbury lamb at 1s. 3d. per lb.
(18) 32 portable gramophones at £4 15s. each.
(19) 32 lawn mowers at £3 17s. 6d. each.
(20) 12 waterproof coats at £2 13s. 4d. each.
(21) 25 cameras at £2 18s. each.
(22) 36 Axminster carpets at £3 18s. 4d. each.
(23) 32 canteens of cutlery at £4 18s. 9d. each.
(24) 1 cwt. of beans at 1d. per lb.
(25) 1 cwt. of barley at 6d. per lb.
(26) 56 articles at 11¾d. each.
(27) 24 yards of Crawford tartan cloth at 8s. 4d. per yard.
(28) 22 dining room chairs at £1 4s. each.
(29) 168 stones Australian apples at 3s. 4d. per stone.
(30) 19 tons of coal at 35s. 6d. per ton.
(31) 40 yards Maltese lace at 1s. 3d. per yard.
(32) 369 model yachts at 6s. 8d. each.
(33) 1 ton salt at 1½d. per lb.
(34) 20 easy chairs at £3 12s. 6d. each.
(35) 60 yards of gaberdine at 6s. 6d. per yard.
(36) 960 lbs. flaked rice at 5½d. per lb.

CHAPTER VII.

THE METRIC SYSTEM.

(a) MEASUREMENT OF LENGTH.

The metric system gets its name from the **metre.**

The **metre** is the **unit of length,** and from it all other units of the system are derived. The length of the metre is approximately 39·37 inches.

The metre is subdivided into *tenths, hundredths, thousandths.* These subdivisions are named by prefixing to the word **metre** *deci-, centi-, milli-,* from the Latin.

Thus the tenth of a metre is called a decimetre.
,,   hundredth ,, ,, ,,   centimetre.
,,   thousandth ,, ,, ,,   millimetre.

There are also **multiples** of the metre, named by prefixing *Deka-, Hecto-, Kilo-,* from the Greek.

Thus the Dekametre   =   10 metres,
,,   Hectometre   =   100 metres,
,,   Kilometre   = 1,000 metres.

The tables of the Metric System are given on page 9.

In the Metric System, there is no Reduction, as in our British tables.

Example 1.—6 m. 7 dm. 5 cm. =   67 dm. 5 cm.
                              = 675 cm. = 6,750 mm.

Example 2.—5,347 mm. = 5 m. 3 dm. 4 cm. 7 mm.

Example 3.—5,347 mm. = 534·7 cm. = 53·47 dm. = 5·347 m.

Example 4.—6·47136 Km. = 64·7136 Hm.
                            = 647·136 Dm.
                            = 6471·36 m.
                            = 64713·6 dm.
                            = 647136 cm.

By comparison of the two systems it is found that—

1 metre   = 39·37 inches, or 1 cm. = ·3937 inch.
1 inch   =   2·54 cm.
1 Kilometre = 1,094 yards, or about $\frac{5}{8}$ mile.

Example 5.—Express 1 ft. 3 ins. as cm.

1 ft. 3 ins. = 15 ins. = 15 × 2·54 cm. = 38·1 cm.

EXERCISE 53.

Reduce—

(1) 6 m. 7 dm. to mm.
(2) 8 m. 9 dm. 7 cm. to mm.
(3) 5 m. 4 dm. 6 cm. 4 mm. to m.
(4) 7 m. 4 dm. 3 cm. to dm.
(5) 11 m. 5 dm. 7 cm. 6 mm. to cm.
(6) 3 Km. to m.
(7) 5 Km. 5 Hm. to cm.
(8) 7 Hm. 4 Dm. to mm.
(9) 5 Km. 7 Hm. 5 Dm. 4 m. to mm.
(10) 4,356 mm. to cm. and to m.
(11) 4,763 m. to Km.
(12) 5,324,638 mm. to Km. Hm., Dm., m., etc.
(13) Express 7,412,036 mm. as m., as Dm., as Hm., and as Km.
(14) Express 7,456·315 m. as Km. and as mm.
(15) Express ·56 m. as decimal of a Km.
(16) Express ·04136 Km. as m. and decimal of m.
(17) Express ·0056321 Km. as mm.
(18) Express 5 m. in yds. ft. ins.
(19) Express 20 ins. in cm.
(20) Express 3 ft. 6 ins. in mm.
(21) How many yards are there in 3 Km. ?
(22) How many miles in 8 Km. ?

(b) MEASUREMENT OF AREA.

Since 1 cm. = 10 mm. ∴ 1 sq. cm. = 100 sq. mm. Thus from the table of linear measure we derive the table for square measure given on page 10.

The square dekametre is also called the **are,** and is the unit used for land measurement.

Thus the are = 100 sq. metres.

The centiare (ca.) and the hectare (Ha.) are also used, see tables on page 10.

1 hectare = 2·471 acres.   1 sq. cm. = ·155 sq. in.
1 acre   = ·4047 hectare.   1 sq. in. = 6·452 sq. cm.

In this table also reduction is done away with.

Thus, *Example* 1.—46 sq. Km. 50 sq. Hm. 45 sq. Dm. 56 sq. m.
$$= 46 \cdot 504556 \text{ sq. Km.}$$
$$= 4,650 \cdot 4556 \text{ sq. Hm.}$$
$$= 465,045 \cdot 56 \text{ sq. Dm.}$$
$$= 46,504,556 \text{ sq. m.}$$

Example 2.—43,257 sq. cm. $= 432 \cdot 57$ sq. dm.
$$= 4 \cdot 3257 \text{ sq. m.}$$
$$= 4 \text{ sq. m. } 32 \text{ sq. dm. } 57 \text{ sq. cm.}$$

EXERCISE 54.

Express as square metres

(**1**) 6 sq. Km. 15 sq. Hm. 23 sq. Dm.
(**2**) 4 sq. Hm. 30 sq. Dm. 45 sq. m.
(**3**) 5 sq. Dm. 6 sq. m.
(**4**) 5 sq. Dm. 60 sq. m.
(**5**) 45 sq. Km. 8 sq. Hm. 9 sq. Dm.

Express as square metres and decimals of a sq. m.

(**6**) 536 sq. dm.
(**7**) 78,516 sq. cm.
(**8**) 8,604,305 sq. mm.

Express as sq. Kilometres and decimals of a sq. kilometre

(**9**) 95, 367 sq. Dm.
(**10**) 5,036,210 sq. metres.
(**11**) 5 sq. Km. 46 sq. Hm. 50 sq. Dm.
(**12**) 10 sq. Km. 6 sq. Hm. 5 sq. Dm.

Express as sq. Km., sq. Hm., sq. Dm., etc.

(**13**) 4,530,164 sq. m.
(**14**) 613,042,047 sq. dm.
(**15**) How many square metres are there in 15 ares ?
(**16**) Reduce 756 sq. metres to ares.
(**17**) Express 4,356 sq. metres in ares and centiares.
(**18**) Express 7 Ha. 45 a. 63 ca. as sq. metres.
(**19**) How many acres are equivalent to 50 hectares ?
(**20**) Express 5 acres as hectares.
(**21**) Convert 50 sq. cm. into sq. ins.
(**22**) Express 10 sq. ins. as sq. cm.

(c) MEASUREMENT OF VOLUME.

From the table of linear measure we derive the table for cubic measure :—

1,000 cubic millimetres (c.mm.)	= 1 cubic centimetre (c.cm.)
1,000 cubic centimetres	= 1 cubic decimetre (c.dm.)
1,000 cubic decimetres	= 1 cubic metre (c.m.)

The **cubic decimetre** is called a **litre,** which is used as a convenient unity of capacity and of volume for liquids more especially.

To the word **litre** the Latin and Greek prefixes are attached, as in the case of the metre, and with the same significance, the Latin prefixes *deci-, centi-, milli-* always denoting $\frac{1}{10}$, $\frac{1}{100}$, $\frac{1}{1000}$, and the Greek prefixes *Deka-, Hecto-, Kilo-* denoting, 10, 100, and 1,000. See tables on page 10.

Note that 1 litre being equal to 1 cubic decimetre contains 1,000 cubic centimetres.

Thus 1 litre = 1,000 c.cm. A litre is roughly equal to 1¾ pints = ·22 gallon, or 1 gallon = 4½ litres.

(d) WEIGHT.

The unit of weight adopted in this system is the weight of *a cubic centimetre of water* under certain conditions. This unit is called the **gram.** Starting with this unit and using the same significant prefixes as before, we get the Table of Weight which is given on page 11.

Note.—Since 1 gram is the weight of 1 c.cm. of water, and 1 litre = 1,000 c.cm. ∴ 1 litre of water weighs 1,000 grams, or 1 kilogram.

| **1 gram = 15·4 grains.** | **1 grain = ·06 gram.** |
| **1 kilogram = 2·2 lbs.** | **1 lb. = ·45 Kilogram.** |

For heavy weights the **quintal** and the **tonne** are used.

The quintal (Q.) =	100 Kg.
The tonne (T.) =	1,000 Kg.
1 tonne =	·98 ton.
1 ton =	1·016 tonne.

Example 1.—Add together 3 Dg. 5 g. 7 dg. ; 6 g. 2 dg. 6 cg. ; 7 g. 5 dg. 3 cg. ; 4 dg. 6 cg. 6 mg. ; 3 cg. 4 mg.

Express each quantity in grams and decimals of a gram.

Thus 3 Dg. 5 g. 7 dg.   = 35·7 g.

       6 g. 2 dg. 6 cg.   = 6·26 g.

       7 g. 5 dg. 3 cg.   = 7·53 g.

       4 dg. 6 cg. 6 mg. =   ·466 g.

            3 cg. 4 mg. =   ·034 g.

                      49·990 g.

Example 2.—If a litre of a certain liquid weighs 1 Kg. 41 g., find the weight of 36 decilitres.

      36 dl. = 3·6 litres, and 1 Kg. 41 g. = 1,041 g.

         Weight of 1 litre   = 1,041 g.

∴   ,,   3·6 litres = 1,041 × 3·6 gram.

                     = 3,747·6 g.

EXERCISE 55.

Express as grams

(1) 3 Kg.   **(2)** ·02 Kg.

(3) 4 Kg. 5 Hg. 3 Dg.   **(4)** 6 Dg. 3 g.

(5) 6 g. 4 dg. 3 cg.   **(6)** 3 cg. 6 mg.

(7) 6,324 mg.   **(8)** How many mg. are equal to 6 Kg. ?

(9) Express 6 g. as mg.

(10) Express 5 g. 6 dg. 3 cg. as mg.

(11) Reduce ·06 g. to mg.

(12) Reduce ·45 dg. to mg.

(13) Express 6,435 g. as Kg.

(14) Express 4,326 mg. as Kg.

(15) Add together 36 g. 432 dg. 364 cg. 1,205 mg., giving result in grams.

(16) Simplify 3·45 Kg. + 3·62 Dg. + 34·2 dg., giving result in grams.

(17) Express as litres 7 Kl + 3 Dl. + 6 l. + 17 cl.

(18) If 1 litre cost £3·26, what is the cost of 2 Kl. ?

(19) If 1 litre weighs 6 Kg. 36 g., what is the weight of 30 litres in Kg. ?

(20) If 30 litres of water flow into a cistern per minute, how many kilolitres flow into it in 6 hours ?

(21) If a litre of a certain liquid weighs 950 grams, find the weight of 15 litres in kilograms.

(22) If 6 litres of a liquid weigh 7·5 kilograms, find the weight of 1 litre in grams.

(23) Taking a litre as equivalent to ·22 gallon, convert 2 Kl. into gallons.

(24) A litre of hydrogen weighs ·0896 gram. Find the weight of 16 litres in grams and in grains.

(25) Find the weight of a Kl. of air, being given that a litre of air weighs 1·293 grams.

(26) Find in grams the weight of a litre of oxygen, being given that oxygen is 16 times as heavy as hydrogen, and that a litre of hydrogen weighs ·0896 gram.

(27) Being given that a kilogram = 2·2 lbs., convert 6,750 grams into lbs.

(28) If 1 lb. = ·45 Kg., convert 25 lbs. into grams.

(29) How many grains are equal to 5 g. 6 dg., if 1 grain = ·06 gram ?

(30) Convert 1 oz. Troy (480 grains) into grams, being given 1 grain = ·06 gram.

(31) Given 1 in. = 2·54 cm., convert 32·2 ft. into cm.

(32) If the velocity of a falling body increases every second by the rate of 32·2 ft. per second, express this rate of increase as cm. per second.

(33) If a metre of a certain wire weighs ·025 gram, find the weight of 75 m. 6 dm. 5 cm. of the same wire.

(34) If a piece of wire which weighs a gram is 2·5 metres in length, find the length of 15 g. 4 dg. 6 cg. of the same wire.

(35) 1 c.c. of methylated spirit weighs ·83 g. Find, in Kg., the weight of 1 Kl. 125 l.

(36) A block of brass whose volume is 7·25 c.dm. weighs 59·45 Kg. Find the weight of 1 c.c. of the brass.

CHAPTER VIII.

MEASUREMENT OF RECTANGULAR AREAS.

(a) TO FIND THE AREA OF A RECTANGLE WHEN ITS LENGTH AND BREADTH ARE KNOWN.

Let A B C D represent a rectangle 5 inches in length and 4 inches in breadth.

Divide the sides into inches, and draw parallel lines as in the diagram.

Then it is obvious that the number of square inches in the area of the rectangle is 5 × 4 = 20.

Hence, Area of a rectangle = its length × its breadth.
The length and breadth must be expressed in the **same unit.**

Example 1.—Find area of a rectangle 4 ft. long and 7 ins. wide.

Length = 48 ins., breadth = 7 ins.
∴　Area = 48 × 7 = 336 sq. ins.
= 2 sq. ft. 48 sq. ins.

Example 2.—A metal plate is 1 yd. 2 ft. 6 ins. square. Find its weight if a square foot of it weighs 30 lbs.

Area = $5\frac{1}{2}$ × $5\frac{1}{2}$ sq. ft. = $30\frac{1}{4}$ sq. ft.
Weight of 1 sq. ft. = 30 lbs.
∴　Weight of $30\frac{1}{4}$ sq. ft. = 30 × $30\frac{1}{4}$ lbs. = $907\frac{1}{2}$ lbs.

Example 3.—A field is 16 chains 25 links long and 8 chains 40 links broad. Find its area in acres, roods, sq. poles.

Length = 16·25 chains, breadth = 8·40 chains.
∴　Area = 16·25 × 8·40 square chains.
= 136·5 square chains
= 13·65 acres
= 13 acres 2 roods 24 square poles.

EXERCISE 56.

Find the areas of the following rectangles :—

(1) Length 2 ft., width 9 ins.
(2) Length 3 ft. 2 ins., width 2 ft. 3 ins.
(3) Length 3 yds., width 3 ft.,
(4) Length 1 yd. 2 ft., width 2 ft.
(5) Length 367 yds., width 42 yds.
(6) Length 2 miles, width 40 yds.

Find the areas of the squares whose sides are

(7) 2 ft. 9 ins.   **(8)** 13·5 cms.
(9) 5 yds. 1 ft.   **(10)** 10 chains 5 links.

Find the areas in acres, etc., of the fields

(11) Length 60 chains 40 links, breadth 50 chains 20 links.
(12) Length 56 chains 15 links, breadth 32 chains 5 links.
(13) Length 16 chains 50 links, breadth 10 chains 5 links.
(14) Find the weight of a steel plate 9·25 ft. long and 3·4 ft. wide, if 1 sq. ft. weighs 35 lbs.
(15) If a carpet measures 18 ft. by 15 ft., find its cost at 4s. per sq. yard.
(16) A piece of glass measures 2 ft. 6 ins. by 1 ft. 9 ins. What will it cost at 8d. per sq. ft. ?
(17) The floor of a room is 15 ft. square. Find the cost of covering it with carpet at 7s. per sq. yd.
(18) A field is 80 yds. by 60 yds. What would it cost if an acre cost £121 ?
(19) If a carpet 12 ft. long and 10 ft. wide cost £5, what is the price per sq. yd. ?
(20) If it cost £5 10s. to lay linoleum on a floor 16 ft. 6 ins. by 15 ft., find the price per sq. yd.

(b) WHEN THE AREA AND ONE OF THE DIMENSIONS OF A RECTANGLE ARE KNOWN TO FIND THE OTHER.

Since the area of a rectangle = length × breadth

∴   length = $\dfrac{\text{area}}{\text{breadth}}$, and breadth = $\dfrac{\text{area}}{\text{length}}$.

Example 1.—The area of a rectangle is 1 sq. yd. 7 sq. ft. 128 sq. ins., and its length is 5 ft. 4 ins. Find its breadth.

$$\text{Area} = 2{,}432 \text{ sq. ins.}$$
$$\text{Length} = 64 \text{ ins.}$$
$$\therefore \quad \text{Breadth} = \frac{2432}{64} \text{ ins.}$$
$$= 38 \text{ ins.} = 3 \text{ ft. 2 ins.}$$

Example 2.—The area of a field is 33·165 acres. Its length is 20 chains 10 links. Find its breadth.

$$\text{Area} = 331\cdot65 \text{ sq. chains.}$$
$$\text{Length} = 20\cdot1 \text{ chains.}$$
$$\therefore \quad \text{Breadth} = \frac{331\cdot65}{20\cdot1} \text{ chains.}$$
$$= 16\cdot5 \text{ chains} = 16 \text{ chains 50 links.}$$

EXERCISE 57.

(1) The area of a rectangle is 135 sq. ft. Its length is 15 ft. Find its width.

(2) The area of a rectangle is 4 sq. ft. 64 sq. ins. Its width is 1 ft. 8 ins. Find its length.

(3) The area of a rectangle is 3 sq. ft. 108 sq. ins., and its length is 2 ft. 3 ins. Find its width.

(4) Find the length of a rectangle whose area is 5 sq. ft. 30 sq. ins. and width 2 ft. 1 in.

(5) The width of a rectangle is 1 ft. 9 ins., and its area is 4 sq. ft. 75 sq. ins. Find its length.

(6) The area of a field is 5 ac. 4,550 sq. yds. and its length is 230 yds. Find its breadth in yds.

(7) The area of a field is 3 ac. 894 sq. yds. Its width is 42 yds. Find its length.

(8) The area of a field is 21·73 ac. Its length is 20 chains 50 links. Find its width.

(9) The area of a field is 5·757 ac. Its breadth is 5 chains 5 links. Find its length.

(10) A square and a rectangle have the same area. If the side of the square be 8 yds. and the rectangle be 16 yds. long, what is its breadth ?

(c) TO FIND THE AREA OF A BORDER.

Example 1.—A lawn measuring 100 yds. by 60 yds. has a path 4 ft. wide all round and enclosing it. Find the area of the path.

The inner rectangle represents the lawn. The outer rectangle represents lawn + path, and its length = length of lawn + 2 width of path, and its breadth = breadth of lawn + 2 width of path.

∴   Total area   = 308 × 188 sq. ft. = 57,904 sq. ft.
    Area of lawn = 300 × 180 sq. ft. = 54,000 sq. ft.
∴   Area of path = 3,904 sq. ft.
                  = 433 sq. yds. 7 sq. ft.

Example 2.—A room is 15 ft. by 14 ft. The floor is covered with a carpet leaving a border 15 ins. wide all round. Find the area of the border.

Here the dimensions of the carpet are less than those of the floor by twice the width of border (*i.e.*, $2\frac{1}{2}$ ft.).

∴   Area of floor   = 15 × 14 sq. ft.   = 210 sq. ft.
    Area of carpet = $12\frac{1}{2}$ × $11\frac{1}{2}$ sq. ft. = $143\frac{3}{4}$ sq. ft.
∴   Area of border = 210 − $143\frac{3}{4}$ sq. ft. = $66\frac{1}{4}$ sq. ft.

EXERCISE 58.

(1) The floor of a room is 18 ft. by 15 ft. It is covered with a carpet leaving a stained border 1 ft. wide all round. Find the area of the border.

(2) A path 3 ft. wide encloses a lawn 70 yds. by 60 yds. Find the area of the path.

(3) A garden plot is 20 yds. by 15 yds. and is surrounded by a path 2 ft. wide. Find the area of the path and the cost of laying it with gravel at the rate of $\frac{1}{2}$d. per sq. foot.

(4) If the total area of ground taken up by a rectangular hall be 80 ft. long and 40 ft. wide, and if the width of the walls be $2\frac{1}{2}$ ft., find the area of the flooring of the hall.

(5) If the frame of a picture be 2 ins. wide, and the picture measure 20 ins. by 16 ins., find the total area of the picture and frame.

(6) If the mount of an upright photograph measure $11\frac{1}{2}$ ins. by 9 ins., and if the margin of the mount be $1\frac{1}{2}$ ins. at the sides and top and 2 ins. at the bottom of the picture, find the area occupied by the picture itself.

(7) The picture on an oblong enlargement is 9 ins. in length and 5 ins. in height. If the margin round the picture is 3 ins. wide, except at the bottom of the picture, where it is 4 ins. wide, find the total area of the mount.

(8) A door is 6 ft. $10\frac{1}{2}$ ins. high and 2 ft. 9 ins wide. The facings at the sides and top are $4\frac{1}{2}$ ins. wide. Find the total area of the door and facings, and the area of the facings alone.

(9) A garden plot is 35 ft. by 24 ft. It is surrounded by a path 3 ft. wide. Find the area of the path and the cost of covering it with gravel at 3d. per sq. yd.

(10) A garden plot is 35 ft. by 30 ft. It is surrounded by a path $3\frac{1}{2}$ ft. wide. Find the area of the path and the cost of making it at 10d. per sq. yd.

(d) CARPETING OF FLOORS.

A carpet for a floor is made from a long roll which is cut into strips, the strips being sewn together to form a carpet of the required size.

Example 1.—If a roll of carpet is 2 ft. 3 ins. wide, how many strips, each 15 ft. long, would be required to form a carpet 15 ft. long and 13 ft. 6 ins. wide.

$$\text{The number of strips required} = \frac{\text{width of carpet}}{\text{width of roll}}$$
$$= \frac{13\frac{1}{2}}{2\frac{1}{4}} = 6.$$

If the width of the carpet does not contain the width of the roll an exact number of times, and if the pattern is to be properly matched, there will be so much waste, because a whole number of strips must be cut from the roll and one of them slit along its length to the required width.

Example 2.—A roll of carpet is 2 ft. wide. What length of it must be used to form a carpet to exactly cover a floor 15 ft. by 13 ft. 6 ins., the strips to be cut the length of the floor, and the pattern to be matched ? What area of carpet will be wasted ?

$$\text{Number of strips} \quad = \frac{13\frac{1}{2}}{2} = \frac{27}{4} = 6\frac{3}{4}.$$

∴   Number to be cut   = 7.

∴   Length of roll used = 15 ft. × 7

= 105 ft. = 35 yds.

As $\frac{3}{4}$ of the last strip only is used—

∴   Amount wasted = $\frac{1}{4}$ of 2 × 15 sq. ft. = $7\frac{1}{2}$ sq. ft.

If there is no pattern to be matched, there would be no waste, and the exact $6\frac{3}{4}$ strips only would be cut from the roll, the $\frac{3}{4}$ of strip being cut up and sewn together as required. Again, if the width of the carpet required contained the width of the roll an exact number of times, there would be no waste, and in that case the usual method of finding the length of roll required is shown in the following example :—

Example 3.—If a roll of carpet is 21 ins. wide, what length of it would be required to make a carpet to cover a floor 16 ft. 6 ins. long and 14 ft. wide ? What would it cost at 3s. 9d. per yard ?

$$\text{Total area} \quad = 16\frac{1}{2} \times 14 \text{ sq. ft.}$$

$$\text{Width of roll} \quad = \frac{21}{12} \text{ ft.}$$

∴   Length of roll $= \frac{33}{2} \times 14 \times \frac{12}{21}$ ft.

= 132 ft. = 44 yds.

Cost of 1 yd.   = 3s. 9d.

∴   Cost of 44 yds. = 3s. 9d. × 44 = £8 5s.

EXERCISE 59.

(1) If a roll of carpet is 2 ft. wide, how many strips would be required to make a carpet 9 ft. by 10 ft., the strips to be 9 ft. long ?

(2) If a roll of carpet is 2 ft. wide, what length of it would be required to make a carpet 16 ft. by 14 ft., and what would it cost at 5s. 6d. per yd. of length ?

(3) If a roll of carpet is 2 ft. 3 ins. wide, what length of it will be required to carpet a floor 16 ft. by 13½ ft., and what will it cost at 6s. per yd. ?

(4) If a carpet 15 ft. by 11 ft. is to be made and properly matched from a roll 2 ft. wide, what length would require to be cut from the roll, and what would be the waste (1) if the strips were made 15 ft. long and (2) if the strips were made 11 ft. long ?   (3) What length of roll would suffice if there were no pattern to match ?

In the Examples 5 to 11 there will be no waste, and the method of the worked Example 3 should be used.

(5) How much carpet 27 ins. wide will cover a floor 33 ft. 9 ins. long by 20 ft. wide, and what will it cost at 3s. 6d per yard ?

(6) A room is 27 ft. by 18 ft.   Find the cost of carpeting it with carpet 27 ins. wide and costing 4s. per yd.

(7) If it requires 32 yds. 2 ft. of carpet to cover a floor 15 ft. 9 ins. long and 14 ft., wide, find the width of the roll of carpet used.

(8) Find the cost of carpeting a floor 14 ft. by 12 ft. with carpet 21 ins. wide at 5s. per yd.

(9) If it require 24 yds. of a roll of carpet which is 2 ft. 6 ins. wide to cover a floor whose length is 15 ft., find the width of the floor.

(10) If it costs £7 10s. to carpet a floor with carpet 2 ft. wide and costing 3s. a yd., find the length of the room if its width is 15 ft.

(11) A room is 18 ft. by 18 ft.   Find the cost of carpeting the floor with carpet 27 ins. wide and costing 4s. 6d. a yd.

(12) A room is 19 ft. long and 15 ft. wide.   If a carpet be made for it by sewing together strips whose length equals the length of the room, find what length of carpet must be cut from a roll 21 ins. wide, there being a pattern to match.   What will it cost at 6s. per yd., and what is the amount of waste ?

(13) Which of the following carpets can be made without waste from a roll 2 ft. 3 ins. wide :—(1) 18 ft. by 16 ft., (2) 20 ft. 3 ins. by 17 ft. 6 ins., (3) 19 ft. by 13 ft.   Find least waste, if any.

(e) STANDARD SIZES OF CARPETS AND BORDERS.

Carpets are usually made up in rectangles and squares of different sizes, and do not cover the whole area of a floor.

Example 1.—A floor 18 ft. by 14 ft. is covered with a carpet leaving a border $1\frac{1}{2}$ ft. wide all round. Find area of carpet and its cost at 4s. 6d. a sq. yd., also cost of staining the border at $4\frac{1}{2}$d. per sq. yd.

Area of carpet $= (18 - 3) \times (14 - 3) = 15 \times 11$ sq. ft.
$= 165$ sq. ft.

Cost of 1 sq. ft. $= 6$d.

∴ Cost of 165 sq. ft. $= 6$d. $\times 165 = £4$ 2s. 6d.

Area of border $= 18 \times 14 - 15 \times 11 = 252 - 165$ sq. ft.
$= 87$ sq. ft.

Cost of 1 sq. ft. $= \frac{1}{2}$d.

∴ Cost of 87 sq. ft. $= \frac{1}{2} \times 87$d. $= 3$s. $7\frac{1}{2}$d.

EXERCISE 60.

(1) A room is 18 ft. long and 15 ft. wide. It is covered with a carpet leaving a border 15 ins. wide all round. Find (1) area of the floor, (2) area of the carpet, (3) area of the border.

(2) A room measures 16 ft. by 14 ft. The floor is covered with a carpet leaving a stained border 1 ft. wide all round it. If the carpeting cost 5s. per sq. yd., and the staining $1\frac{1}{2}$d. per sq. yd., find the total cost.

(3) A room is 18 ft. 6 ins. long and 13 ft. 6 ins. wide. It is covered with a carpet leaving a border 21 ins. wide all round. Find the area of the carpet and its cost at 5s. per sq. yd.

(4) A floor is 18 ft. by 15 ft. There is a carpet on it whose area is 15 ft. by 12 ft. If the uncovered part is the same width all round, find its width and the cost of staining it at 4d. per sq. yd.

(5) If the carpet in Example 4 was made from a roll 2 ft. 3 ins. wide and costing 3s. per yd., what was the price of the carpet ?

(6) A floor is 20 ft. square, and has a square carpet in the centre. If the carpet cost £6 8s. at 4s. 6d. per sq. yd., how much of the floor is left uncovered, and if the uncovered portion be uniform in width, what is its width ?

8

(f) AREA OF THE WALLS OF A ROOM.

As the four walls of a room are all of the same height, they may be treated as one rectangle whose **breadth** is the **height** of the room, and whose **length** is equal to **twice the length of the room + twice the breadth of the room,** as shown in the diagram.

h	side wall	end wall	side wall	end wall
	l	b	l	b

If $l =$ length, $b =$ breadth, and $h =$ height of room,

Then area of walls = area of rectangle $2(l + b)$ by h
$$= 2(l + b) \times h.$$

Example.—Find the area of the walls of a room 17 ft. 9 ins. long, 15 ft. 6 ins. wide, and 11 ft. high.

$$\text{Area} = 2(17\tfrac{3}{4} + 15\tfrac{1}{2}) \times 11 \text{ sq. ft.}$$
$$= 2 \times 33\tfrac{1}{4} \times 11 \text{ sq. ft.}$$
$$= 731\tfrac{1}{2} \text{ sq. ft.}$$

EXERCISE 61.

Find the areas of the walls of the following rooms :—

(1) Length 18 ft., breadth 15 ft., height 11 ft.

(2) Length 20 ft., breadth 16 ft., height 10 ft.

(3) Length 20 ft., breadth 16 ft., height 12 ft.

(4) Length 19 ft., breadth 16 ft., height 12 ft.

(5) Length 18 ft. 6 ins., breadth 15 ft. 6 in., height 10 ft.

(6) Length 20 ft. 9 ins., breadth 17 ft. 9 ins., height 12 ft.

(7) Find cost of painting the walls of a room 20 ft. long, 16 ft. wide, and 12 ft. high, allowing 70 sq. ft. for door, window, and fireplace, at $4\tfrac{1}{2}$d. per sq. yd.

(8) Find the cost of painting the walls of a room 18 ft. long, 15 ft. wide, and 12 ft. high, allowing for a door $6\tfrac{1}{2}$ ft. by 3 ft., a fireplace 6 ft. by 5 ft., and a window 6 ft. by 6 ft., at 3d. per sq. yd.

(9) Find the cost of painting and decorating a room at the average rate of 1s. 6d. per sq. yd. of wall area, the room being 15 ft. by 13 ft. and 11 ft. high.

(10) A room is 15 ft. long and 14 ft. wide, and the area of the walls is 638 sq. ft. Find the height of the room.

(11) A room is 17 ft. long and 16 ft. 6 ins. wide. When allowance is made for a door 7 ft. by $3\frac{1}{2}$ ft., a window 8 ft. by 5 ft., and a fireplace 4 ft. 6 ins. by 4 ft. 4 ins., the area of the walls covered by paper is 80 sq. yds. Find the height of the room.

(g) PAPERING THE WALLS OF A ROOM.

As the walls of a room are papered by means of **strips of paper,** whose pattern is usually 21 inches wide and priced at so much per linear yard or **piece** of 12 yards ; therefore, in order to find the cost of papering the walls we have to find the length of paper or the number of pieces required in the same way as we did in the carpeting of floors. There will be a certain amount of waste in matching the paper, and a certain amount of saving owing to doors, windows, and fireplaces.

Example 1.—Assuming that the waste is balanced by the saving, find the cost of papering the walls of a room 18 ft 4 ins. long, 15 ft. 8 ins. wide, and 12 ft. high, if the paper is 21 ins. wide and costs $3\frac{1}{2}$d. per yard.

$$\text{Area of walls} = 2 \left(18\tfrac{1}{3} + 15\tfrac{2}{3} \right) \times 12 \text{ sq. ft.}$$
$$= 24 \times 34 \text{ sq. ft.}$$
$$\text{Width of paper} = \frac{21}{12} \text{ ft.}$$
$$\therefore \text{ Length of paper required} = 24 \times 34 \times \frac{12}{21} \text{ ft.}$$
$$= \frac{24 \times 34 \times 12}{21 \times 3} \text{ yds.}$$
$$\therefore \text{ Cost} = \frac{24 \times 34 \times 12}{21 \times 3} \times \frac{7d}{2}.$$
$$= 544\text{d.} = £2 \text{ 5s. 4d.}$$

In practice paper is bought by the **piece** of 12 yards. and pieces must be bought whole. Thus if $7\frac{1}{4}$ are required 8 must be paid for.

Example 2.—A room is 20 ft. 8 ins. long, 19 ft. 6 ins. wide, and 12 ft. high. It has 2 doors, each 6 ft. by $3\frac{1}{2}$ ft., a fireplace 6 ft. by 5 ft., and a window 9 ft. by 5 ft. A piece of paper being 21 ins. wide and 12 yds. long, and 1 piece being allowed for waste, find how many pieces must be bought to paper the walls, and find the cost at 2s. 6d. per piece.

$$\text{Area of walls} = 2\,(20\tfrac{2}{3} + 19\tfrac{1}{2}) \times 12 \text{ sq. ft.}$$
$$= 964 \text{ sq. ft.}$$
$$\text{Area of doors} = 2 \times 6 \times \frac{7}{2} = 42 \text{ sq. ft.}$$
$$\text{Area of fireplace} = 6 \times 5 \quad = 30 \text{ sq. ft.}$$
$$\text{Area of window} = 9 \times 5 \quad = 45 \text{ sq. ft.}$$
$$\therefore \qquad \text{Area not to be papered} = 117 \text{ sq. ft.}$$
$$\therefore \quad \text{Area to be papered} = 964 - 117 = 847 \text{ sq. ft.}$$
$$\text{Area of 1 piece of paper} = 36 \times \frac{21}{12} = 63 \text{ sq. ft.}$$
$$\therefore \quad \text{Number of pieces} = \frac{847}{63} + 1 \text{ for waste}$$
$$= 13\tfrac{4}{9} + 1 = 14\tfrac{4}{9}.$$

$$\therefore \quad \text{Number requiring to be bought} = 15$$
$$\text{Cost of 1 piece} = \text{2s. 6d.}$$
$$\therefore \qquad \text{Cost of 15 pieces} = \text{2s. 6d.} \times 15$$
$$= \text{£1 17s. 6d.}$$

EXERCISE 62.

Assuming that the waste balances the saving by doors, etc., find the cost of papering the walls of the rooms :—

(1) 19 ft. long, 16 ft. wide, and 12 ft. high with paper 21 ins. wide and costing $2\frac{1}{2}$d. per yd.

(2) 14 ft. by 14 ft. and 10 ft. high, with paper 21 ins. wide, at 3d. per yd.

(3) 15 ft. by 13 ft. and 10 ft. high, with paper 21 ins. wide, at $4\frac{1}{2}$d. per yd.

(4) $14\frac{1}{2}$ ft. by $13\frac{1}{2}$ ft. and 10 ft. high, with paper 21 ins. wide, at $1\frac{1}{2}$d. per yd.

EXERCISE 62—*Continued*.

Assuming that the waste balances the saving, but that the pieces must be bought whole, and that a piece is 21 ins. by 12 yds., find the cost of papering the walls of the following rooms :—

(5) 15 ft. 8 ins. long and 13 ft. 10 ins. wide, and 10 ft. 6 ins. high, at 2s. per piece.

(6) 20 ft. 9 ins. long, 16 ft. 3 ins. wide, and 12 ft. high, at 3s. 6d. per piece.

(7) 18 ft. by 16 ft. and 10 ft. high, at 1s. 9d. per piece.

(8) 20 ft. 6 ins. by 14 ft. 9 ins. and 10 ft. high, at 3s. 3d. per piece.

Allowing 1 piece for waste, and that a whole number of pieces must be bought, find the cost of papering the following rooms :—

(9) 18 ft. 8 ins. by 13 ft. 4 ins. and 10 ft. high with 2 doors, each $6\frac{1}{2}$ ft. by 3 ft., a window 8 ft. by 5 ft. 9 ins., and a fireplace 5 ft. by 5 ft., at 3s. per piece.

(10) 19 ft. 9 ins. long, 16 ft. 6 ins. wide, and 12 ft. high, with door 7 ft. by $3\frac{1}{2}$ ft., window 7 ft. by 6 ft., and fireplace 7 ft. by $5\frac{1}{2}$ ft., at 3s. 6d. per piece.

(11) 13 ft. 6 ins. by 13 ft. 6 ins. and 10 ft. high, allowing $\frac{1}{6}$ of the total wall area for doors, window, etc., paper to cost 2s. 6d. per piece.

(12) 17 ft. 5 ins. by 14 ft. 4 ins. and 10 ft. high, with 2 doors 7 ft. 2 ins. by 3 ft. 4 ins., a window 8 ft. by 7 ft., and a fireplace 7 ft. 6 ins. by 6 ft., paper to cost 2s. 9d. per piece.

(*h*) MISCELLANEOUS EXAMPLES IN RECTANGULAR AREAS.

EXERCISE 63.

(1) A rectangular steel plate weighs 1,540 lbs. If the weight per sq. ft. be 35 lbs., find the length of the plate, its width being 5 ft. 6 ins.

(2) A rectangular steel plate 6 ft. 3 ins. by 5 ft. 9 ins. weighs 1,150 lbs. Find the weight per sq. ft.

(3) A hearth measuring 4 ft. 6 ins. by 16 ins, is laid with tiles measuring 4 ins. by 2 ins. Find the number of tiles used.

(4) A court 80 yds. by 50 yds. is paved with stone slabs 4 ft. by 3 ft. Find the number of slabs.

(5) A hall is 84 ft. by 30 ft., and the flooring consists of slabs of wood each 9 ins. by 3 ins. Find the number used in making the floor.

(6) A rectangular court is paved with square slabs of slate, each 3 ft. 6 ins. by 3 ft. 6 ins. If the number of slabs is 3,312, and if the court is 98 yds. long, find its width.

(7) Find the cost of laying tiles on a floor which is 24 ft. by 15 ft., each tile being $4\frac{1}{2}$ ins. by 6 ins., and the cost of laying them being 3s. per dozen.

(8) Find the cost of papering the walls of a room 17 ft. 6 ins. by 14 ft. and 10 ft. high with paper 21 ins. wide at 2s. 6d. per piece of 12 yds., assuming waste balanced by saving due to door, etc.

(9) A cistern measures 4 ft. by 3 ft., and 2 ft. 6 ins. deep. How many sq. ft. of sheet lead would be required to line the sides and bottom ?

(10) Find the cost of lining a cistern 3 ft. 4 ins. long, 2 ft. 8 ins. wide, and 2 ft. 6 ins. deep, with lead sheeting weighing 9 lbs. per sq. ft., and costing $3\frac{1}{2}$d. per lb., supposing there is no lid. (Find the 4 sides in same way as the walls of a room.)

(11) Find to the nearest penny the cost of painting the outside of a box (top and sides) 3 ft. by 2 ft. 4 ins. and 1 ft. 10 ins. deep at $1\frac{1}{2}$d. per sq. ft.

(12) An open cistern is 10 ft. 6 ins. long, 7 ft. wide, 6 ft. 6 ins. deep externally. It is made of wood 3 ins. thick. Find the cost of lining it inside with lead at 2s. 3d. per sq. yd.

(13) Find the cost of slating a roof 24 ft. long and 10 ft. 3 ins. wide at 4s. 6d. per sq. yd.

(14) If it cost 16s. 8d. to lay gravel on a path 30 yds. long and 10 ft. wide, what was charged per sq. yd. ?

(15) A room is 15 ft. by 14 ft. and 10 ft. high. The walls are papered with paper 21 ins. wide and costing 2s. per piece of 12 yds., leaving a frieze 1 ft. wide round the top. If the frieze cost 1s. per linear yd., find the total cost, supposing a whole number of pieces of wall paper must be bought and a whole number of yards of frieze, but ignoring waste.

(16) Find the cost of turfing a piece of ground 140 ft. by 80 ft. with pieces of turf, each $3\frac{1}{2}$ ft. by 2 ft., at the rate of 5s. per 100.

(17) Find the cost to the nearest 1d. of painting the walls of a room 17 ft. 6 ins. by 15 ft., and 10 ft. high, at $3\frac{1}{2}$d. per sq. yd., allowing for 2 doors 7 ft. by 3 ft., a window 6 ft. by 5 ft., and a fireplace 4 ft. by 4 ft. 6 ins.

(18) A square lawn, whose side is 34 ft., is surrounded by a path 4 ft. wide. Find the cost of gravelling the path at $4\frac{1}{2}$d. per sq. yd.

(19) What length of a roll of carpet 21 ins. wide would be required to make a carpet for a room 25 ft. by 20 ft., if a margin 2 ft. wide all round is left uncovered and there is no pattern to be matched.

(20) If a hall 42 ft. 6 ins. long and 29 ft. wide is to be paved with square tiles, find the largest size of tile that can be used if the side of the tile is to measure a whole number of inches.

(21) If 30 yds. of a roll of carpet 2 ft. 3 ins. wide are used to make a carpet for a room 17 ft. 6 ins. long and 16 ft. wide, find the area of the floor left uncovered, and the cost of staining it at 1d. per square foot.

(22) The area of a rectangular field is 3 acres 4,680 sq. yds. Its length is 160 yds. Find the cost of fencing it at 3s. 3d. per linear yard of fencing.

(23) If it cost £5 5s. to make a path 120 ft. long and $4\frac{1}{2}$ ft. wide, what price was charged per square yard ?

(24) The roller for a lawn is 6 ft. in circumference and 2 ft. 6 ins. long. It turns 10 times in passing from one end of the lawn to the other. Find the area rolled when it has passed 15 times from end to end of the lawn, assuming that the strips rolled meet but do not overlap

(25) If the length of a rectangle were increased by $5\frac{1}{2}$ ft., its area would be increased by $71\frac{1}{2}$ sq. ft. What is its width ?

Examples involving Metric Measurements.

(26) A carpet is 5·6 metres long and 4·25 metres wide. Find its area in square metres.

(27) Find the area in *ares* of a rectangular field 230 metres long and 150 metres wide.

(28) How many *ares* are there in a rectangular piece of land ·75 Km. long and 200 metres wide ?

(29) A rectangular field contains 864 *ares*. If its length is 360 metres, what is its breadth ?

(30) A floor 35·2 metres long and 16 metres wide is laid with tiles, each measuring 22 cm. by 10 cm. Find the number of tiles.

(31) The floor of a hall is 22·5 metres long and 14·8 metres wide. If it is floored with planks, each 2·5 metres long and ·2 metres wide, find the number of planks.

(32) A rectangular field contains 700 *ares*. Its length is 350 metres. Find its breadth and the time it takes to walk round it at the rate of 6 kilometres per hour.

(33) A rectangular field is 19,800 sq. metres in area. If it takes a man 6 minutes to walk round it, and if the length of the field is 165 metres, find the man's rate of walking in kilometres per hour.

(34) A window contains 4 panes of glass, each 62 cm. by 75 cm., and one pane 1·3 m. by 1·6 m. Find in sq. metres the total area of glass in the window and its cost in francs and centimes (100 centimes = 1 franc) at 5 francs per sq. metre.

<hr>

CHAPTER IX.

Measurement of Rectangular Solids.

A **rectangular solid** or prism is a solid bounded by 6 rectangular surfaces like an ordinary box. It has three dimensions—length, breadth, and thickness.

A **cube** is a rectangular solid whose dimensions are all equal. It is bounded by 6 equal square faces.

A cubic inch is a cube in which each dimension is equal to 1 inch.

In measuring rectangular solids the unit used is the **cubic inch** or **cubic foot,** etc.—that is, the **size** or **volume** or **cubical contents** of a rectangular solid is the number of cubic inches or cubic feet, etc., which it contains.

(a) TO FIND THE VOLUME OF A RECTANGULAR SOLID.

A rectangular slab of wood 4 ins. long and 3 ins. broad contains 4 × 3 or 12 sq. ins. on its surface. If it is 1 inch thick, then it can be divided up into 12 cubic inches ; if it is 2 inches thick, we get other 12 cubic inches—that is, 4 × 3 × 2 cubic inches—and so on.

Thus, to find the number of cubic inches in a rectangular solid we multiply together the numbers of inches in its length, breadth, and thickness.

∴ **Volume of rectangular solid = length × breadth × thickness.**

Example 1.—Find the volume of a brick 10 ins. by 5 ins. by 4 ins., and the number of bricks in a stalk 15 ft. long, 10 ft. broad and 6 ft. high.

Volume of brick   = 10 × 5 × 4 cub. ins. = 200 cub. ins.
Volume of stalk   = 15 × 10 × 6 × 1,728 cub. ins.
∴ Number of bricks = $\dfrac{15 \times 10 \times 6 \times 1,728}{200}$ = 7,776.

Example 2.—A wooden box is 4 ft. long, 2 ft. 6 ins. wide, and 2 ft. deep externally. If the sides, lid, and bottom are all 1 inch thick, find the internal volume and the volume of the wood.

The internal dimensions are each 2 ins. shorter than the external dimensions, since the wood is 1 inch thick.

∴ Total space occupied by box = 48 × 30 × 24 cub. ins.
                              = 34,560 cub. ins.
      Internal volume of box = 46 × 28 × 22 cub. ins.
                              = 28,336 cub. ins.
                              = 16 cub. ft. 688 cub. ins.
          Volume of wood = 34,560 − 28,336 cub. ins.
                         = 6,224 cub. ins.
                         = 3 cub. ft. 1,040 cub. ins.

EXERCISE 64.

Find the volumes of the rectangular solids whose dimensions are

(1) 6 ins by 5 ins. by 3 ins.   (2) 7 ins. by 8 ins. by 4 ins.

(3) 9 ins. by 8 ins. by $7\frac{1}{2}$ ins.   (4) 1 foot by 10 ins. by $6\frac{1}{4}$ ins.

(5) $6\frac{1}{2}$ ft. by $3\frac{1}{4}$ ft. by 8 ft.

(6) 4 ft. 6 ins. by 3 ft. 4 ins. by 2 ft.

(7) 6 ft. 4 ins. by 5 ft. 6 ins. by 3 ft.

(8) 8 ft. 3 ins. by 7 ft. 4 ins. by 6 ft. 6 ins.

(9) 2 ft. 5 ins. by 3 ft. 4 ins. by 1 ft. 3 ins.

(10) 6 ft. 7 ins. by 8 ft. 9 ins. by 10 ft. 5 ins.

(11) Find the number of cubic feet in a block of stone 6 ft. long, 1 ft. 6 ins. broad, and 10 ins. thick.

(12) Find volume of a beam of wood 15 ft. long, the section of the end being 10 ins. by $2\frac{1}{2}$ ins.

(13) Find in cubic yards and cubic feet the volume of a wall 200 yds. long, 6 ft. high, and 1 ft. 2 ins. thick.

(14) Find the cubical contents of a cistern 14 ft. long, 6 ft. 6 ins broad, and 4 ft. 6 ins. deep internally.

(15) Find the weight of water in a tank 6 ft. long, 5 ft. 6 ins. wide, if the depth of the water be 3 ft. and 1 cub. ft. weigh 1,000 ozs.

(16) Find the cost of digging a trench 30 yds. long, 10 ft. wide, and 6 ft. deep at 1s. 2d. per cubic yard.

(17) A path 120 ft. long and 4 ft. wide is covered with gravel to the depth of 3 ins. Find the volume of the gravel and the cost of laying it at 2s. 6d. per cubic yard.

(18) A path 6 ft. wide goes round and encloses a grass plot 120 yds. by 80 yds. Find the cost of covering the path with gravel to the depth of 2 ins., if the gravel cost 1s. 6d. per cubic yard.

(19) A pond 30 yds. long and 20 yds. wide is frozen to the depth of 3 ins. Find the weight of the ice on it if a cubic ft. weighs $57\frac{1}{4}$ lbs.

(20) If steel weighs 7,800 ozs. per cubic foot, find the weight of a steel plate 7 ft. 6 ins. long, 4 ft. wide, and $\frac{3}{4}$ in. thick.

(21) During the rainfall of 1 inch, what volume of water would be added to a pond which is 150 ft. square ?

(22) Find the volume of water falling during the rainfall of 1·2 ins. on an area of 500 sq. yds., and find its weight if 1 cub. ft. weighs 62 lbs.

(23) If in a school room 120 cub. ft. of air space must be provided for each child, what is the maximum number of children allowed in a classroom 24 ft. long, 20 ft. wide, and 15 ft. high ?

(24) Find correct to a gallon the number of gallons of water in a tank 8 ft. long, 6 ft. 6 ins. wide, and 5 ft. deep, if 277·274 cub. ins. = 1 gallon.

(25) If water flows through an orifice whose area is 2 sq. ins. at the rate of 16 ft. per minute, find the weight of the water that flows through in an hour if 1 cub. ft. weighs 1,000 ozs.

(26) A stream 1½ ins. square in section pours into a cistern at the rate of 20 ft. per minute. How many gallons would enter the cistern in 1 hour if 277·274 cub. ins. = 1 gallon ?

(27) If a brick is 9 ins. by 4 ins. by 3 ins., how many are required to build a wall 600 yds. long, 9 ft. high, and 3 ft. thick ?

(28) How many cubes, each 1½ ins. in edge, can be cut out of a large cube, each of whose edges is 9 inches long ?

(29) How many tiles, each 5 ins. square and 1 inch thick, can be put together in a stalk 20 ft. long and 10 ft. wide and 6 ft. high ?

(30) A box with a lid is made of wood 1 in. thick. If its external dimensions be 21 ins. by 16 ins. by 13 ins. deep, find its internal volume and also the volume of the wood.

(31) A rectangular garden is enclosed by a wall 5 ft. high and 1 ft. thick. If the garden is 140 yds. long and 80 yds. wide internally, find cost of the wall at 13s. 6d. per cub. yd., allowing for a gateway 3 ft. wide.

(b) KNOWING THE VOLUME OF A RECTANGULAR SOLID AND TWO OF THE DIMENSIONS, TO FIND THE THIRD.

Since   volume = length × breadth × thickness,

∴ **Length** = $\dfrac{\textbf{volume}}{\textbf{breadth} \times \textbf{thickness}}$.

Example.—A tank is 6 ft. 8 ins. long and 5 ft. wide. Water flows into it from a pipe whose section is 5 sq. ins. at the rate of 20 ft. per minute. How far will the water have risen in the tank after 1 hour ?

Volume of water run in in 1 min. $= 5 \times 20 \times 12$ cub. ins.

$\therefore$ Volume after 1 hour $= 5 \times 20 \times 12 \times 60$ cub. ins.

Area of bottom of tank $= 80 \times 60$ sq. ins.

$\therefore$ Height of water required $= \dfrac{5 \times 20 \times 12 \times 60}{80 \times 60}$ ins.

$= 15$ ins.

So, also, if the volume and one dimension be given, we can find the product of the other two (that is, the area of a surface) by dividing the volume by the given dimension.

Example.—If a bar of iron 18 ft. long weighs $168\frac{3}{4}$ lbs., and if a cubic foot of iron weighs 450 lbs., find the area of its section (*i.e.*, product of its breadth and thickness).

Number of cubic feet in the bar $= \dfrac{168\frac{3}{4}}{450} = \dfrac{675}{4 \times 450}$

$\therefore$ Volume in cubic inches $= \dfrac{675 \times 1728}{4 \times 450}$ cub. ins.

Length $= 18$ ft. $= 216$ ins.

$\therefore$ Area of end $= \dfrac{675 \times 1728}{4 \times 450 \times 216}$ sq. ins.

$= 3$ sq. ins.

EXERCISE 65.

(1) A rectangular block is 7 ft. long, 6 ft. wide, and contains 168 cub. ft. Find its height.

(2) A box contains 50 cub. ft. It is 5 ft. long and 4 ft. wide internally. Find its depth.

(3) A box whose cubic content is 84 cub. ft. is 3 ft. deep. Find the area of its bottom.

(4) A rectangular beam of wood, with a section 5 ins. by 4 ins., has a volume of 2 cub. ft. 144 cub. ins. What is its length ?

(5) A beam of wood 20 ft. long has a volume of 2 cub. ft. 864 cub. ins. Find the area of its section.

(6) A tank, 2 ft. by $1\frac{1}{2}$ ft. by $2\frac{1}{2}$ ft., is full of water. If the water is poured into another tank, which is 4 ft. long and 2 ft. wide, to what height would the water rise ?

(7) If a volume of 10 gallons of water, when poured into a tank, rises in the tank to a height of 5 ins., find the area of the bottom of the tank in sq. ins., assuming that a gallon is equal to $277\frac{1}{4}$ cub. ins.

(8) Water flows through an orifice at the rate of 20 ft. per minute. If a volume of 8 cub. ft. 846 cub. ins. flows through the orifice in 30 minutes, find the area of the orifice.

(9) If a volume of 6 cub. ft. 882 cub. ins. flows through an orifice 2 sq. ins. in area in 45 minutes, find the rate of flow in feet per minute.

(10) The air space in a room is 3,200 cub. ft. The height of the room is 10 ft. Find the cost of laying the floor with linoleum at 2s. 3d. per sq. yd.

(11) A cistern is 8 ft. long and 5 ft. wide. The weight of the water in it is 2 tons 15 cwts. 1 qr. 12 lbs. Assuming that a cubic foot weighs 62 lbs., find the depth of the water in the cistern.

(12) A wall 135 ft. long, $5\frac{1}{2}$ ft. high contains 34 cub. yds. 10 cub. ft. 216 cub. ins. Find the thickness of the wall.

(13) A rectangular stack of bricks contains 8,160 bricks. If each brick is 9 ins. by 5 ins. by 4 ins., and if the stack is 8 ft. 4 ins. wide and 5 ft. 8 ins. high, find its length.

(14) A log of wood whose section is 1 ft. 4 ins. by 8 ins. costs £2. If this price works out at 1s. 3d. per cubic foot, find the length of the log.

(15) A cistern 2 yds. 2 ft. 6 ins. long, 2 yds. 1 ft. 3 ins. wide contains a volume of water equal to 5 cub. yds. 19 cub. ft. 108 cub. ins., find the depth of the water.

(16) A lake, whose surface is 15 acres in area, is frozen all over to a uniform depth. If the weight of the ice is 5,566 tons 10 cwts. 3 qrs. 6 lbs., find its thickness, assuming that a cubic foot of ice weighs 57·25 lbs.

(17) A tank 6 ft. long, 4 ft. 6 ins. wide, and 4 ft. deep is full of water. Water is transferred from it to a smaller tank 3 ft. long, 2 ft. 6 ins. wide, and 2 ft. deep. When the latter tank has been completely filled, find how far the surface of the water in the first tank has fallen.

Examples involving Metric Measurements.

(18) Find the volume of a rectangular block measuring 1·65 m. by 8 dm. by 9 cm. in cubic metres.

(19) Find the volume of a plank of wood 6·5 metres long, 4 dm. broad, and 3·4 cm. thick in c.c. If 1 c.c. of the wood weighs ·54 gram, find the weight of the plank in Kg.

(20) A tank is 2·5 metres long, 1·75 metres broad, and 1·48 metres deep. Find its volume in cubic metres, and also in litres (1 c.m. = 1,000 litres).

(21) A cistern is 3·5 metres long, 2·8 metres wide, and 1·25 metres deep. Find its volume in litres.

(22) A cistern, which is 4·5 metres long and 4 metres wide, is filled with water to the depth of 3·6 metres. Find the weight of the water in Kg., being given that 1 c.c. of water weighs 1 gram.

(23) A stack of bricks is 9 metres long, 6 metres broad, and 3 metres high. If each brick is 22·5 cm. by 12·5 cm. by 7·5 cm., find the number of bricks.

(24) Express in Kg. the weight of water in a tank 2 metres long, 90 cm. broad, and 56 cm. deep (weight of 1 c.c. = 1 gram).

(25) A tank is 4 metres long and 3·5 metres wide. If 33,600 litres of water are poured into it, how high will the water rise in the tank ?

(26) A tank 3·45 m. long, 2·8 m. wide, and 2·4 m. deep is full of water. If this water is poured into a cistern which is 5·6 m. long and 4·6 m. wide, to what height will the water rise in the cistern ?

(27) A tank 1·8 metres long, 1·2 m. wide, and 1·75 m. deep is filled from a cistern which is 4·5 metres long. If the surface of the water in the cistern is thereby lowered by ·3 m., find the breadth of the cistern.

(28) A plank is 3·2 m. long, ·5 m. broad, and 4 cm. thick. If the wood weighs ·8 g. per c.c., find the weight of the plank in kilograms.

(29) A sheet of iron is 2·8 m. long, 1·2 m. broad, and ·5 cm. thick. If the iron weighs 7·5 g. per c.c., find the total weight of the sheet in Kg.

CHAPTER X.

SQUARE ROOT.

(a) MEANING OF SQUARE ROOT.

When a number is multiplied by itself, the product is called the **square** of the number.

Thus 25 is the square of 5, since $5 \times 5 = 25$. The square of 5 is indicated thus :—5^2, so that $5^2 = 5 \times 5 = 25$.

A number is said to be the **square root** of its **square.**

Thus 5 is the square root of 5^2 or 25.

The symbol $\sqrt{}$ is used to indicate " **square root,**" so that

$$\sqrt{25} = \text{the square root of } 25 = 5.$$

It is essential to know the squares of the first 12 natural numbers.

The squares of 1, 2, 3, 4, 5, 6, 7, 8, 9, 10, 11, 12, are respectively 1, 4, 9, 16, 25, 36, 49, 64, 81, 100, 121, 144.

EXERCISE 66.

Find the squares of

(1) 13   **(2)** 14.   **(3)** 15.   **(4)** 16.   **(5)** 25.   **(6)** 100.

Write down the square root of

(7) 16.   **(8)** 64.   **(9)** 121.   **(10)** 2,500.   **(11)** 8,100.
(12) 10,000.   **(13)** 196.   **(14)** 256.   **(15)** 25,600.

(b) SQUARE ROOT OF A PERFECT SQUARE BY FACTORISING.

Only those numbers which are **perfect squares,** like 4, 16, etc., can have an **exact square root,** and where a number is a perfect square the square root can be found by reducing the number to its prime factors.

Example.—Find the square root of 3,969.

Breaking 3,969 up into prime factors, we find

$$3969 = 3^4 \times 7^2$$
$$\therefore \quad \sqrt{3969} = 3^2 \times 7 = 9 \times 7 = 63.$$

EXERCISE 67.

Find the square root of the following by breaking them up
into prime factors :—

(1) 324.	(2) 576.	(3) 225.	(4) 1,764.
(5) 784.	(6) 1,225.	(7) 11,025.	(8) 44,100.
(9) 5,929.	(10) 53,361.	(11) 148,225.	(12) 1,016,064.

(c) GENERAL METHOD OF FINDING THE SQUARE ROOT.

The method of finding the square root by factorising is only
applicable to numbers which are perfect squares. We shall
now give a method applicable to all numbers.

Since the **square** of 10 = 100 and the **square** of 100 = 10,000,
it follows that the square of a number consisting of **2 digits** lies
between 100 and 10,000, and, therefore, contains either **3 or 4
digits.** Conversely, the **square root** of a number of **3 or 4 digits**
will contain **2 digits.** Further consideration of this principle
shows us that **we can tell the number of digits in the square
root of any number by marking it off into periods of 2 digits.**

Thus the square root of 10,56,25 will contain 3 digits.

Example 1.—Find the square root of 105,625.

```
3  | 10,56,25 ( 325
3  | 9
62 | 156
2  | 124
645| 3225
   | 3225
```

First mark off periods containing 2
digits each, counting from the units'
place.

The highest square below the period
10 is 9. We place 3, the square root
of 9, in the answer, and placing 9
itself below 10 we subtract, getting
remainder 1. We then bring down
the next period " 56," making 156.

Now place 3 (the first figure in the answer) to the left of the top
line, and add 3 to itself, making 6. This is the " trial divisor "
for the second figure in the answer. Trying 6 into 15 we get 2.
Place 2 in the answer and also place 2 after the 6 to make " the
complete divisor " 62. Divide 156 by 62, giving 2 with 32 for a
remainder. Now bring down the next period 25, thus obtaining
3225. On the left place 2 below 2 and add, getting 64 (or twice
32, the part of the answer found).

Then proceed as before. Try 64 into 322, giving 5. Place 5 in the answer and also after the 64, giving " the complete divisor " 645, and divide 3225 by 645, obtaining 5 without remainder. The square root is 325.

Example 2.—Find the square root of 564,917,824.

2	5,64,91,78,24 (23768	
2	4	
43	164	
3	129	
467	3591	
7	3269	
4746	32278	
6	28476	
47528	380224	
	380224	

We merely set down the working, leaving the student to follow the process from the explanation given under Example 1. He will note that the trial divisor at any stage formed by adding the last figure obtained in the answer to the previous divisor is double the part of the answer found.

EXERCISE 68.

Find the square root of

(1) 1,369. (2) 2,916. (3) 1,296.
(4) 9,604. (5) 7,921. (6) 45,369.
(7) 186,624. (8) 281,961. (9) 254,016.
(10) 498,436. (11) 1,993,744. (12) 408,321.
(13) 1,127,844. (14) 1,016,064. (15) 2,537,649.
(16) 10,150,596. (17) 40,602,384. (18) 162,409,536.
(19) 1,461,685,824. (20) 5,846,743,296.

(d) SQUARE ROOT OF DECIMALS.

In finding the square root of a decimal the method is the same, but it should be noted that **the decimal point is a point of separation between two periods,** and the marking off of the periods should be commenced at the decimal point.

9

Example 1.—Find the square root of 384·16.

```
  1  | 3,84,·16, ( 19·6
  1  | 1
 ——  | ———
 29  | 284
  9  | 261
 ——  | ————
386  | 2316
     | 2316
     | ————
```

The process is the same as if there were no decimal point, because

$$384 \cdot 16 = \frac{38416}{100}$$

and ∴ Square root $= \dfrac{196}{10} = 19 \cdot 6$.

Example 2.—Find the square root of ·003136.

```
  5  | ·00,31,36 ( ·056
  5  |     25
 ——  |    ———
106  |    636
     |    636
     |    ———
```

∴ Square root = ·056.

As the first period consists of the two 0's, the first figure in the answer after the decimal point is evidently 0, and the other two are got by extracting the square root of 3136.

$$\cdot003136 = \frac{3136}{1,00,00,00}$$

$$\therefore \text{ square root} = \frac{56}{1000}.$$

EXERCISE 69.

Extract the square root of

(**1**) 3·1684.   (**2**) 316·84.   (**3**) 1·1664.
(**4**) ·011664.   (**5**) ·038416.   (**6**) ·005476.
(**7**) ·005184.   (**8**) ·181476.   (**9**) ·04511376.
(**10**) ·0001993744.   (**11**) ·0001633284.   (**12**) 406·4256.

In cases where there is *no exact square* root, we can find the square root approximately to any number of decimal places.

Example 1.—Find the square root of ·561 correct to 3 decimal places.

```
    7   | ·56,10,00, ( ·7489
    7   |  49
  ————  |  ———
  144   |  710
    4   |  576
  ————  |  ————
 1488   | 13400
    8   | 11904
 ————   | —————
14969   |  149600
        |  134721
        |  ————
        |  14879
```

∴ Square root = ·749.

To get the *closest approximation* with 3 *figures* after the decimal point, we should work for 4, because if the fourth figure is 5 or more we should increase the third figure by 1 as in the example. It should be noted that if we try 9 for the third figure we get $1,489 \times 9 = 13,401$, so that the root is almost ·749 exactly. Note also that in finding the square root the *remainder at any step may be greater than the divisor*—*e.g.*, the remainder 1,496 is greater than 1,488.

Example 2.—Find the square root of 6 to 3 decimal places.

2	6·00 (2·4494
2	4
44	200
4	176
484	2400
4	1936
4889	46400
9	44001
48984	239900
	195936

∴ Square root = 2·449.

Here, as the decimal point is after the 6, the first period is 6. and each period after the first is 00.

EXERCISE 70.

Find to 3 decimal places the square root of

(1) 5·413. (2) 3·14159. (3) 133·4. (4) 3·5.
(5) 35. (6) 7. (7) ·7. (8) 3.
(9) 2. (10) 11. (11) 1·1. (12) 8.
(13) 15. (14) ·5. (15) 3·25.

(e) SQUARE ROOT OF VULGAR FRACTIONS.

A vulgar fraction should be converted into a decimal fraction before we extract its square root, unless the denominator is a square number, and in this case a mixed number may be first converted into an improper fraction.

Example 1.—**Denominator a Square.**

Find the square root of $1\frac{8}{9}$ to 3 decimal places.

$$\sqrt{1\frac{8}{9}} = \sqrt{\frac{17}{9}} = \frac{\sqrt{17}}{3} = \frac{4·1231}{3}$$
$$= 1·374.$$

When worked out the square root of 17 will be found to be 4·1231 ...

Example 2.—**Denominator not a Square.**

Find the square root of $5\frac{1}{3}$ to 3 decimal places.

$$5\frac{1}{3} = 5\cdot3333 \ldots$$

2	5·33,33, . . . (2·3094
2	4
43	133
3	129
4609	43333
9	41481
46184	185233
	184736

When finding the 3rd figure in the answer the trial divisor " 46 " into 43 gives " 0." So we take down the next period 33, and place 0 in the answer and after the 46, getting 460 for the next trial divisor.

$$\therefore \quad \sqrt{5\frac{1}{3}} = 2\cdot309.$$

EXERCISE 71.

Find the square root of

(1) $\dfrac{25}{4}$. (2) $\dfrac{64}{25}$. (3) $\dfrac{196}{9}$. (4) $10\dfrac{6}{25}$.

(5) $7\dfrac{21}{25}$. (6) $14\dfrac{1}{16}$. (7) $5\dfrac{19}{25}$. (8) $5\dfrac{1}{9}$.

(9) $7\dfrac{1}{4}$. (10) $2\dfrac{1}{7}$. (11) $3\dfrac{1}{5}$. (12) $\dfrac{5}{6}$.

(13) $\dfrac{1}{5}$. (14) $\dfrac{3}{2}$. (15) $3\dfrac{15}{56}$. (16) $34\dfrac{7}{15}$.

(*f*) MISCELLANEOUS EXAMPLES ON SQUARE ROOT.

Example 1.—The length of a rectangle is three times its breadth and its area is 4 sq. ft. 99 sq. ins. Find its breadth.

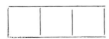

Evidently if the length be divided into 3 equal parts and straight lines be drawn through the points of division parallel to the breadth, the rectangle is divided into 3 squares, each equal to the square of the breadth. We therefore, *divide the area by 3 and extract the square root.*

4 sq. ft. 99 sq. ins. = 675 sq. ins.

$$675 \div 3 = 225 = \text{square of the width.}$$

$\therefore$ Width $= \sqrt{225} = 15$ ins. $= 1$ ft. 3 ins.

Or, thus :—   Let x ins. represent breadth,

then $3x$ ins. represents length,

$\therefore$ $x \times 3x$ sq. ins. represents area,

$\therefore$ $3x^2 = 675$,

$\therefore$ $x^2 = 225$, $\therefore$ $x = 15$,

$\therefore$ breadth $= 15$ ins. $= 1$ ft. 3 ins.

Example 2.—If the fifth part of a number multiplied by its fourth is equal to 980, find the number.

Note.—This does not mean $\frac{1}{5}$ of $\frac{1}{4}$ of the number. It will be convenient to represent the number by the symbol " x ."

Thus $\dfrac{x}{5} \times \dfrac{x}{4} = 980$,

$\therefore$ $\dfrac{x^2}{20} = 980$,

$\therefore$ $x^2 = 980 \times 20 = 19{,}600$,

$\therefore$ $x = \sqrt{19{,}600} = 140$.

EXERCISE 72.

(1) A square field contains 10 acres 2,225 sq. yds., find the length of its side.

(2) A square field contains 11 acres 1,985 sq. yds., find the length of a side.

(3) A square piece of metal contains 2 sq. ft. 153 sq. ins., find the length of a side.

(4) A square field contains 8 acres 3,305 sq. yds., find the cost of putting a fence all round it at 2s. 6d. per yd.

(5) Find the length of side of a square whose area is 6 sq. ft. 36 sq. ins.

(6) A square contains $156\frac{1}{4}$ sq. ft., find the length of its side.

(7) A square field contains 40 acres, find length of its side in yards.

(8) The area of a square field is 7·225 acres, find the length of its side in chains and links.

(9) The length of a rectangular field is 3 times its width, and it contains $7\frac{1}{2}$ acres, find the length and width of field, and the cost of fencing it at 2s. 6d. per yard.

(10) A square field contains $\frac{5}{8}$ acre, find the cost of fencing it at 1s. 2d. per yard.

(11) A field, whose length is twice its width, contains $11\frac{1}{4}$ acres. Find its width and the cost of fencing it at 1s. 3d. per yard.

(12) A square field contains 10 acres. It is surrounded by a roadway of uniform width whose area is 4,500 sq. yds. Find the width of the roadway.

(13) The length of a rectangle is twice its breadth, and the area is 3 sq. ft. 80 sq. ins., find its breadth.

(14) If a square metal plate weighs 722 lbs., being 32 lbs. per square foot, find the length of its side.

(15) How many yards of fencing are required for a square field containing 9 acres 540 sq. yds. ?

(16) A square is equal to a rectangle whose length is 11 ft. 8 ins. and width 2 ft. 11 ins., find the side of the square.

(17) How long will it take a man to walk round the boundary of a square field containing 40 acres at the rate of 4 miles an hour ?

(18) How long will it take a man to walk round the boundary of a square field containing 250 acres at $3\frac{1}{2}$ miles per hour ?

(19) A square field occupies $2\frac{1}{2}$ acres. A pathway goes right round the field to a width of 6 feet. Find the area of the pathway.

(20) If the half of a number multiplied by a fifth of the number is equal to 640, find the number.

(21) What is the number whose fifth part multiplied by its third part gives 735 ? What is a fifth of a third of the number equal to ?

(22) If $\frac{1}{6}$ of a number multiplied by $\frac{1}{7}$ of double the number is equal to 2,100, find the number.

(23) If $\frac{3}{4}$ of a number $\times \frac{5}{7}$ of the number = 1,680, find the number.

CHAPTER XI.

THE UNITARY METHOD.

In the *unitary method*, as its name implies, problems are solved through the medium of *unity* or 1. Thus, for example, when the value of a certain number of articles is known, the value of *one* article is first found, and then from that the value of any number required may be found.

(a) QUANTITIES DIRECTLY PROPORTIONAL TO ONE ANOTHER.

Two changing quantities may be so related that when one of them increases the other also increases in the same proportion. Such quantities are said to be *directly proportional* or simply *proportional* to one another. Thus, for example, a wage-earner's pay is proportional to the time he works. If the time he works is *doubled* his pay is *doubled*, and so on. The unitary method may be applied to quantities related in this way.

Example 1.—Find the cost of 5 lbs. of tea if 9 lbs. cost 21s.

Cost of 9 lbs. = 21s.

$\therefore$,, 1 lb. $= \dfrac{21s.}{9}$

$\therefore$,, 5 lbs. $= \dfrac{21s.}{9} \times 5 = \dfrac{35s.}{3} = 11s.\ 8d.$

Example 2.—If 1 cwt. 18 lbs. of tea cost £13, how much tea can be bought for £5 12s.?

Reduce the sums of money to shillings, and the weight to lbs.

Then 260 shillings buy 130 lbs.

$\therefore$ 1 shilling buys $\dfrac{130}{260}$ lbs.

$\therefore$ 112 shillings buy $\dfrac{130}{260}$ lbs. $\times$ 112, *i.e.*, 56 lbs.

Example 3.—If a man earns 18s. 8d. in 7 hours, how many hours must he work to earn 24s. ?

$$18/8 = 224d. \text{ and } 24/- = 288d.$$

Thus, Time required to earn 224d. = 7 hours.

∴   ,,   ,,   1d. = $\dfrac{7}{224}$ hours.

∴   ,,   ,,   288d. = $\dfrac{7}{224} \times 288$ hours

                            = 9 hours.

EXERCISE 73.

(1) If 5 lbs. of tea cost 9s. 2d., find the cost of 3 lbs.

(2) If a man earns 6s. 8d. in 4 hours, find what he earns in 5 hours.

(3) If an apprentice earns 4s. 6d. in 6 hours, how long does he take to earn 3s. ?

(4) If a man saves £6 5s. in 25 weeks, how much will he save in 52 weeks at the same rate ?

(5) If 8 men reap 6 acres of corn in a certain time, how many acres would 10 men reap in the same time, all working at same rate ?

(6) If 2 yards of cloth cost 7s. 6d., find the cost of 1 yard 2 feet.

(7) What is the cost of 5 tons 15 cwts. if 2 tons 10 cwts. cost 30s. ?

(8) If 3 tons 10 cwts. of metal cost £7 3s. 6d., what quantity can be bought for £4 12s. 3d. ?

(9) How long will a man take to earn £16 10s., if he earns £12 in 32 days ?

(10) If it cost £6 5s. to lay 50 yds. of an electrical cable, what will it cost to lay 1 mile of it ?

(11) If a glazier charges 2s. 6d. for 5 sq. ft. of glass, what would he charge for 6 sq. ft. 72 sq. ins. ?

(12) If a man earns £156 in 8 months, how long will he take to earn £58 10s. ?

(b) QUANTITIES INVERSELY PROPORTIONAL TO ONE ANOTHER.

If two changing quantities are so related that when one of them *increases* the other *decreases* in the same proportion, they are said to be *inversely proportional* to one another. Thus, for example, the time required to do a job is inversely proportional to the number of men put on the job. If the number of men were *doubled* the time would be *halved*, and so on.

The unitary method may also be applied to quantities related in this way.

Example 1.—If three men require 10 hours to do a piece of work, how long will 5 men require to do the same at the same rate ?

3 men require 10 hours.

∴   1 man requires 10×3 hours.

∴   5 men require $\dfrac{10 \times 3}{5}$ hours.

i.e., 6 hours.

Example 2.—If a man working 6 hours a day takes 4 days to do a certain work, how many days would he take to do it if he worked 8 hours a day ?

When he works 6 hours a day the time taken $= 4$ days.

,,   1 hour   ,, $= 4 \times 6$ days.

,,   8 hours ,,   ,, $= \dfrac{4 \times 6}{8}$ days.

$= 3$ days.

Example 3.—How many yards of cloth worth 5s. a yard should be given in exchange for 10 yards worth 7s. a yard ?

When the cloth costs 7s. a yard the number of yards $= 10$.

,,   ,,   1s.   ,,   ,, $= 10 \times 7$

,,   ,,   5s.   ,,   ,, $= \dfrac{10 \times 7}{5}$

$= 14$ yds.

EXERCISE 74.

(1) If 18 men require 10 days to do a certain piece of work, how long should it take 12 men to do it ?

(2) If sixteen men can finish a job in 15 days, how many men would be required to do it in 12 days ?

(3) If a man takes 6 days to do a job working 8 hours every day, how long would he take if he worked 12 hours a day ?

(4) If a man working 6 hours a day take 20 days to do a piece of work, how many hours a day must he work in order to do it in 12 days ?

(5) If with a certain sum of money I can buy 60 articles at 3s. 6d. each, how many articles can I buy at 5s. each with the same sum of money ?

(6) A garrison of 1,400 men has provisions for 105 days, how long would the provisions last 1,750 men ?

(7) A garrison of 2,000 men has provisions for 12 months. If 400 men were added to the garrison, how long would the provisions last ?

(8) A fort was provisioned for a garrison of 800 men for 10 months, but owing to the fact that a smaller number of men was sent to garrison the fort the provisions lasted for 16 months. How many men were sent ?

(9) How many articles worth 7s. 6d. each should be given in exchange for 60 articles worth 10s. 6d. each ?

(10) The carriage of 2 cwts. for 15 miles is a certain sum (2s. 6d.). How far will 84 lbs. be carried for the same money ?

(11) A train travelling at the rate of 45 miles an hour takes 32 minutes to go a certain distance. How long would it take to travel the same distance if it travelled 48 miles an hour ?

(12) What is the rate of a train which travels in 2 hours 12 minutes a distance which a train whose rate is 30 miles per hour takes 3 hours 40 minutes to travel ?

(13) If 56 men can do a job in 160 days, how many more men must be employed in order to complete the job 20 days sooner ?

(14) A contractor estimates that it would take 16 men 65 days to complete a job. How many men must he employ if he wishes the job finished in 52 days ?

We now give an exercise of mixed examples, and in dealing with each separate example the pupil must consider whether the quantities involved are so related that they increase together or whether the one decreases while the other increases.

EXERCISE 75.

(1) If 2 cwts. 36 lbs. of tea cost £26, find the cost of 84 lbs.

(2) If 6 men require 15 hours to do a job, how long would 10 men take to do it ?

(3) If a man whose house rent is £20 pays £2 6s. 8d. for rates, what amount would a man pay whose house rent is £18, the amount of rates being proportional to the rent ?

(4) If a man whose house rent is £20 pays £3 10s. for rates, what rent does a man pay whose rates amount to £4 7s. 6d. ?

(5) If 15 yds. of cloth worth 4s. per yd. are exchanged for 12 yds. of another cloth, what is this other cloth worth per yard ?

(6) If a train travels $26\frac{2}{3}$ miles in 40 minutes, how far will it travel in an hour ?

(7) If a cyclist takes 2 hours 10 minutes to cycle 26 miles, how long will he take to go 30 miles at the same rate ?

(8) If a brick whose volume is 108 cub. ins. weighs 9 lbs., what is the volume of a similar brick which weighs 11 lbs. 4 ozs. ?

(9) If a block of wood whose volume is 150 cub. ins. weighs 12 lbs., find the weight of a block of the same wood whose volume is 1 cubic foot 22 cubic inches.

(10) If a garrison of 5,600 men have provisions for 60 days, how long would the same provisions last 4,200 men ?

(11) A certain quantity of corn will suffice 8 horses for 9 weeks, how many horses should the same quantity suffice for 12 weeks.?

(12) How much will a man earn in 16 days if he earns 17s. 6d. in 3 days ?

(13) If a man whose salary is £750 pays £93 15s. of income tax, what income tax would a man pay whose salary is £1,050 if they are taxed at the same rate ?

(14) If the income tax on a salary of £525 is £65 12s. 6d., what is the income of a man who pays £225 of income tax ?

EXERCISE 75—*Continued.*

(15) How far will a railway company carry 8 tons for the same money as they charge for carrying 3 tons 10 cwts. a distance of 160 miles ?

(16) A man performs a journey in 5 days when he walks for 6 hours every day. Walking at the same rate, how many hours a day would he need to walk in order to do the same journey in 4 days ?

(17) Walking for 5 hours every day a man took 9 days to go from A to B. On the return journey from B to A he walked for $7\frac{1}{2}$ hours each day. How long did he take to return ?

(18) If a furnace consumes $5\frac{1}{2}$ tons of coal in $38\frac{1}{2}$ hours, how much would be consumed in 24 hours at the same rate ?

(19) If the rent of 360 acres of land be £480, what would be the rent of a farm of 560 acres ?

(20) If an account is discharged by the payment of 14 crowns, how many florins would be required to pay the same account ?

(21) If £5 8s. is the amount of the rates paid on a house rent of £27, find the rent of a house on which the rates amount to £2, the rates being proportional to the rent.

(22) A sum of money is sufficient to pay the weekly wages of 10 men, each of whom is paid £2 2s. per week. How many men who earn £3 per week can be paid with the same sum of money for their week's work ?

(23) If $6\frac{1}{2}$ lbs. of butter cost 9s. 9d., how much can be bought for £1 2s. 6d. ?

(24) If 60 gallons of water flow through an orifice in 1 hour 20 minutes, how long will it take 150 gallons to flow through it ?

(25) If a pipe discharges 24 gallons of water in 10 minutes 40 seconds, what volume will it discharge in 17 minutes 20 seconds ?

(26) 168 men were employed to complete a contract in 12 months. After 3 months 56 men were withdrawn. How many additional months must be allowed to the remaining men to complete the contract ?

(27) If 15 boxes of tea, each containing $7\frac{1}{2}$ lbs., cost £13 2s. 6d., what would 24 boxes, each containing $10\frac{1}{2}$ lbs., of the same tea cost ?

(c) PROBLEMS WITH MORE THAN TWO CHANGING QUANTITIES.

One quantity may depend on several other quantities, and this gives rise to more complicated problems, to which the unitary method is applicable. The nature of these problems and the method of their solution by the unitary method are shown in the following examples :—

Example 1.—If 6 men in 20 days reap 5 acres of corn, how many acres would 10 men reap in 18 days working at the same speed ?

Amount reaped by 6 men in 20 days = 5 acres.

∴   „   1 man in 20 days = $\dfrac{5}{6}$ acres.

∴   „   1 man in 1 day = $\dfrac{5}{6 \times 20}$ acres.

∴   „   10 men in 1 day = $\dfrac{5 \times 10}{6 \times 20}$ acres.

∴   „   10 men in 18 days = $\dfrac{5 \times 10 \times 18}{6 \times 20}$ acres.

$\qquad\qquad\qquad\qquad\qquad = 7\frac{1}{2}$ acres.

There are 4 steps in the above working, but the first two steps may be performed in one operation, and the remaining two steps in another, thus involving only two steps as in the simple cases already considered.

Thus, Amount reaped by 6 men in 20 days = 5 acres.

∴   „   „   1 man in 1 day = $\dfrac{5}{6 \times 20}$ acres.

∴   „   „   10 men in 18 days = $\dfrac{5 \times 10 \times 18}{6 \times 20}$ acres.

$\qquad\qquad\qquad\qquad\qquad = 7\frac{1}{2}$ acres.

Example 2.—If 25 men in 9 days of 8 hours each dig a trench 300 yards long, what length of a similar trench could 16 men dig in 12 days of 6 hours each ?

25 men in 9 days of 8 hrs. dig 300 yds.

$\therefore$ 1 man in 1 day of 1 hr. digs $\dfrac{300}{25 \times 9 \times 8}$ yds.

$\therefore$ 16 men in 12 days of 6 hrs. dig $\dfrac{300 \times 16 \times 12 \times 6}{25 \times 9 \times 8}$ yds.

$= 192$ yds.

When a quantity depends on several other quantities it may be *directly* proportional to some of them and *inversely* proportional to others, and in each particular case we must consider carefully whether it will be *increased* or *decreased* as the other increases.

Example 3.—If 5 men working 6 hours each day plough 12 acres in $4\frac{1}{2}$ days, how many hours a day must 4 men work at the same rate in order to plough 16 acres in 5 days ?

To do 12 ac. in $4\frac{1}{2}$ days 5 men need day of 6 hours.

$\therefore$,, 1 ,, 1 day 1 man needs ,, $\dfrac{6 \times 5 \times 4\frac{1}{2}}{12}$ hours.

$\therefore$,, 16 ,, 5 days 4 men need ,, $\dfrac{6 \times 5 \times 4\frac{1}{2} \times 16}{12 \times 4 \times 5}$

i.e., 9 hours.

In this case the length of day is inversely proportional to the number of men and to the number of days, but directly proportional to the number of acres. Thus 1 man requires 5 times as long a day as 5 men, and to do it in 1 day requires $4\frac{1}{2}$ times as long a day as to do it in $4\frac{1}{2}$ days, whereas to do 1 acre requires only $\frac{1}{12}$ of the length of day required for 12 acres. Similarly for the second step.

EXERCISE 76.

(1) If a man earns £4 in 12 days working 8 hours a day, what will he earn in 10 days working 6 hours a day ?

(2) If 5 lbs. of bread cost $7\frac{1}{2}$d. when wheat is 45s. a quarter, what would 6 lbs. cost when wheat is 50s. per quarter ?

(3) If goods weighing 56 lbs. can be carried 30 miles for 1s. 6d., what will be the carriage of 168 lbs. for 90 miles ?

(4) If 20 men need 10 days to mow 12 acres, how long will 15 men need to mow 9 acres ?

(5) If 12 men can reap $7\frac{1}{2}$ acres in 15 hours, how many men would be required to reap 12 acres in 9 hours ?

(6) If 15 men take 12 hours to reap 8 acres, how many acres would 35 men reap in 18 hours ?

(7) If it costs 30s. to keep a horse for 2 weeks when oats are at 25s. per quarter, what will it cost to keep the horse 6 weeks when oats are 30s. per quarter ?

(8) If 20 men build a wall 30 ft. long in 8 days, how long will it take 16 men to build a wall 24 ft. long of the same height and thickness ?

(9) If a carpet 6 yds. long and 4 yds. 2 ft. wide costs £4 14s. 6d. find the cost of a carpet 6 yds. 2 ft. long and 4 yds. wide ?

(10) If 12 men require 21 days to remove 660 yds. of an embankment, how many men would be required to remove 880 yds. of the embankment in 12 days ?

(11) If 6 men working 9 hours a day can mow $22\frac{1}{2}$ acres in 5 days, how many acres could 8 men mow in 4 days working 10 hours a day ?

(12) At a boarding house the board of 16 persons for 5 weeks amounted to £70. What would the board of 10 persons for 12 weeks amount to ?

(13) If the cost of printing 500 booklets of 16 pages be £2 10s., what would be the cost of printing 750 booklets of 12 pages ?

(14) If 30 men working 6 hours a day earn £63 in 7 days, how much will 24 men earn in 12 days working 8 hours a day ?

(15) If the carriage of 2 cwts. 28 lbs. for 16 miles be 2s. 3d., find the weight of goods which would be carried 56 miles for £4 4s.

(16) If 15 men working 8 hours a day can do a piece of work in 7 days, how long will 10 men take to do 3 times the amount of work, working 7 hours a day ?

(17) If 20 men working 7 hours a day take 30 days to dig a trench 1,800 yds. long, find how long 35 men would take to dig a trench 6,000 yds. long working 10 hours a day.

(18) If 15 men build a wall 25 ft. long and 5 ft. high in 12 days, how long will it take 20 men to build a wall 125 ft. long and 6 ft. high of the same thickness ?

(19) If 50 men take 56 days to dig a trench 250 yds. long, 10 ft. wide, and 7 ft. deep, how long will 80 men take to dig a trench 350 yds. long, 8 ft. wide, and 5 ft. deep ?

(20) If 40 men dig a trench 300 yds. long, 5 ft. wide, and 8 ft. deep in 18 days working 10 hours a day, how long would 60 men take to dig a trench 250 yds. long, 6 ft. wide, and 9 ft. deep if they work 9 hours a day ?

CHAPTER XII.

THE RATIO METHOD.

I. MEANING OF RATIO.

The word **Ratio** is used when we are comparing one quantity with another, and we speak of the **Ratio of the one to the other.**

The ratio of one quantity to another is best defined as **the fraction that the one is of the other.**

Thus the ratio of 3 to 4 $= \frac{3}{4}$, the ratio of 4 to 3 $= \frac{4}{3}$. The ration of 2s. 3d. to 2s. 9d. $= \frac{2s.\ 3d.}{2s.\ 9d.} = \frac{27}{33} = \frac{9}{11}$.

The **numerator** and **denominator** are called the **terms** of the ratio.

The ratio or fraction is not a concrete quantity like money, etc., but merely a number. When we say that the ratio of 2s. 3d. to 2s. 9d. is $\frac{9}{11}$, we mean that 2s. 3d. is $\frac{9}{11}$ of 2s. 9d., or that 2s. 9d. is $\frac{11}{9}$ of 2s. 3d.

The quantities compared in this way must be of the same kind—that is, **the terms of the ratio must be of the same kind.**

We do not speak of the ratio of 2s. 3d. to 2 ft. 9 ins., because 2s. 3d. cannot be a fraction of 2 ft. 9 ins. We may speak of the ratio of the circumference of a circle to its radius, because both are lengths, but we do not speak of the ratio of the area of the circle to its radius, because an area cannot be a fraction of a length. We can compare one area to another area. So we may speak of the ratio of the area of a circle to the area of the square on its radius.

The following are important ratios :—

$$\frac{\text{circumference of circle}}{\text{its diameter}} = \frac{22}{7} \text{ (approximately).}$$

$$\frac{\text{area of circle}}{\text{square on its radius}} = \frac{22}{7} \qquad \text{,,}$$

We see, then, from the meaning of the word ratio, that to find the ratio of one quantity to another is just to *express the one quantity as a fraction of the other.*

Example 1.—Find the ratio of 10s. 7½d. to 19s. 1½d.

$$\frac{10\text{s. }7\frac{1}{2}\text{d.}}{19\text{s. }1\frac{1}{2}\text{d.}} = \frac{127\frac{1}{2}}{229\frac{1}{2}} = \frac{255}{2} \times \frac{2}{459} = \frac{5}{9}.$$

Example 2.—Find what sum of money bears to 6s. 5½d. the ratio of 4 to 5.

As we have seen, to say that the ratio of the required sum to 6s. 5½d. is $\frac{4}{5}$ means that the required sum is $\frac{4}{5}$ of 6s. 5½d.

Now, $\frac{4}{5}$ of 6s. 5½d. $= 77\frac{1}{2}$d. $\times \frac{4}{5} = \frac{155}{2} \times \frac{4}{5} = 62$d. $= 5$s. 2d.

EXERCISE 77.

Find the ratio of

(1) 90 to 120.

(2) 6½ to 7¼.

(3) ·05 to ·5.

(4) ·0625 to ·125.

(5) $\frac{3}{8}$ to $\frac{2}{3}$.

(6) 5·7 to 3·24.

(7) £3 15s. to £4 5s.

(8) 4 ft. 9 ins. to 3 ft. 6 ins.

(9) 2s. 5d. to 3s. 7½d.

(10) 4 miles 316 yds. to 6 miles 80 yds.

Express the following ratios in their simplest form

(11) $\dfrac{6 \text{ days}}{16 \text{ hours}}$ **(12)** $\dfrac{456 \text{ grams.}}{2 \text{ Kg.}}$ **(13)** $\dfrac{6\text{s. } 10\frac{1}{2}\text{d.}}{8\text{s. } 1\frac{1}{2}\text{d.}}$

(14) $\dfrac{18\text{s. } 7\frac{1}{2}\text{d.}}{\pounds 1 \text{ 1s. } 8\frac{3}{4}\text{d.}}$ **(15)** $\dfrac{\pounds 1 \text{ 1s. } 11\frac{1}{4}\text{d.}}{17\text{s. } 0\frac{3}{4}\text{d.}}$ **(16)** $\dfrac{4 \text{ yds. } 2 \text{ ft. } 7 \text{ ins.}}{3 \text{ yds. } 1 \text{ ft. } 5 \text{ ins.}}$

(17) Prove that $\dfrac{5\text{s. } 10\frac{1}{2}\text{d.}}{9\text{s. } 9\frac{1}{2}\text{d.}} = \dfrac{7 \text{ ft.}}{11 \text{ ft. } 8 \text{ ins.}}$

(18) Prove that $\dfrac{3 \text{ yds. } 2 \text{ ft. } 3 \text{ ins.}}{6 \text{ yds.}} = \dfrac{3 \text{ tons } 16 \text{ cwts. } 1 \text{ qr.}}{6 \text{ tons } 2 \text{ cwts.}}$

(19) Find the sum of $\dfrac{3 \text{ yds. } 2 \text{ ft. } 6 \text{ ins.}}{2 \text{ yds. } 1 \text{ ft. } 8 \text{ ins.}}$ and $\dfrac{3 \text{ tons } 5 \text{ cwts.}}{3 \text{ tons } 18 \text{ cwts.}}$

(20) What sum of money bears to 18s. 9d. the ratio of 2 to 3 ?

(21) The ratio of a certain sum to 16s. 3d. is $\frac{4}{5}$. Find the sum.

(22) What quantity bears to 4 yds. 0 ft. 6 ins. the ratio of 7 to 10 ?

(23) The ratio of 21s. 9d. to a certain sum is equal to the ratio of 6 to 7. Find the sum.

(24) What sum has the same ration to 6s. 5d. as 4 tons 1 cwt. has to 2 tons 14 cwts. ?

(25) The population of a town consists of 12,500 males and 10,600 females. Find the ratio of the females to the whole population.

(26) Knowing that the ratio of the circumference of a circle to its diameter is equal to the ratio $\frac{22}{7}$, find the circumference of a circle whose diameter is 1 ft. 9 ins.

(27) Knowing that the ratio of the diameter of a circle to the circumference is $\frac{7}{22}$, find the diameter of a circle whose circumference is 9 ft. 2 ins.

(28) Knowing that the ratio of the area of a circle to the square of its radius is equal to the ratio of 22 to 7, find the area of a circle whose radius is 1 ft. 2 ins.

(29) In a school the ratio of boys to girls is 4 to 3. If there are 546 pupils, how many boys are there ?

(30) If the ratio of A's salary to B's salary is 8 to 9, and if B's salary is £308 5s., what is A's salary ?

II. THE RATIO METHOD.

Reverting to Example 2, on p. 145—viz., to find what sum of money bears to 6s. 5½d. the ratio of 4 to 5—we saw that it meant finding $\frac{4}{5}$ of 6s. 5½d. Now, this leads to a convenient method of solving questions like the following :—

" If 5 lbs. of tea cost 6s. 5½d., find the cost of 4 lbs."

Since the price of the tea is proportional to the amount of the tea,

∴ $\dfrac{\text{Cost of 4 lbs.}}{\text{Cost of 5 lbs.}} = \dfrac{4}{5}$, which, as we have seen, means that

Cost of 4 lbs. $= \frac{4}{5}$ of cost of 5 lbs.

$= $ 6s. 5½d. $\times \frac{4}{5} = $ 5s. 2d.

This is the type of question dealt with under the **Unitary Method,** and all these questions can be solved by multiplying by the **ratio** without using the medium of unity.

In using the **Ratio Method,** the above example may be set down thus :—

Cost of 5 lbs. $= $ 6s. 5½d.

∴ Cost of 4 lbs. $= $ 6s. 5½d. $\times \dfrac{4}{5} = $ 5s. 2d.

We shall now apply the **Ratio Method** to the examples worked out under the **Unitary Method.**

(a) Quantities Directly Proportional to One Another.

(*See page* 135.)

Example 1.—Find the cost of 5 lbs. of tea if 9 lbs. cost 21s.

Cost of 9 lbs. $= $ 21s.

∴ Cost of 5 lbs. $= $ 21s. $\times \dfrac{5}{9} = $ 11s. 8d.

Example 2.—If 1 cwt. 18 lbs. of tea cost £13, how much tea can be bought for £5 12s. ?

$$£13 \quad \text{buys } 130 \text{ lbs.}$$

$$\therefore \quad £5 \; 12s. \quad ,, \quad 130 \text{ lbs.} \times \frac{£5 \; 12s}{£13}.$$

$$= 130 \text{ lbs.} \times \frac{112}{260} = 56 \text{ lbs.}$$

Example 3.—If a man earns 18s. 8d. in 7 hours, how many hours must he work to earn 24s. ?

$$\text{Time required to earn 224d.} = 7 \text{ hours.}$$

$$\therefore \quad ,, \quad ,, \quad 288d. = 7 \times \frac{288}{224} \text{ hours} = 9 \text{ hours.}$$

At this stage the examples under Exercise 73 on page 136 should be worked out by the **Ratio Method,** and **additional** examples will be found in the following exercise :—

EXERCISE 78.

(1) If a man earns 37s. 6d. in 3 days, what will he earn in 2 days ?

(2) If 28 lbs. cost £2 16s., find the cost of 65 lbs.

(3) If a man saves £13 in 26 weeks, how much will he save in 25 weeks ?

(4) If it cost £787 10s. to make a road $5\frac{1}{4}$ miles long, what would it cost to make a road 7 miles long ?

(5) If a cyclist takes 3 hours 15 minutes to cycle 39 miles, how long would he take to go 15 miles at the same rate ?

(6) If a train goes 20 miles in 30 minutes, how far will it go in 2 hours ?

(7) If a brick whose volume is 135 cub. ins. weighs 11 lbs. 4 ozs., find the weight of a brick of the same material whose volume is 162 cub. ins.

(8) If a glazier charges 3s. 9d. for 7 sq. ft. 72 sq. ins. of glass, what should he charge for 13 sq. ft. ?

(9) How long will a man take to earn £24 15s., if he earn £15 in in 40 days ?

(10) If 6 yards of cloth cost £1 2s. 6d., what length of cloth can I buy for 12s. 6d. ?

The Ratio Method.

(11) If 1 ton 15 cwts. of metal cost £3 11s. 9d., find the cost of 2 tons 5 cwts.

(12) If 75 yards of cable can be laid for £9 7s. 6d., what would it cost to lay $1\frac{1}{2}$ miles ?

(13) If it cost £275 to lay 1 mile of cable, what length of cable would it cost £7 16s. 3d. to lay ?

(14) Knowing that the circumference of a circle is proportional to its diameter, and that the circumference of a circle of 3-inch diameter is 9·42 ins., find the circumference of a circle of 1 foot diameter ?

(15) A picture on a lantern slide measures $2\frac{1}{2}$ ins. in length and 2 ins. in width, what will be the width of the picture projected on the screen if its length is 10 feet ?

(16) If a pole 10 ft. high casts a shadow 12 ft. in length, what is the height of a steeple which casts a shadow 138 ft. in length ?

(*b*) Quantities Inversely Proportional to One Another.

If 2 men require a certain time to do a job, 1 man would require twice as long to do it.

Thus $\dfrac{\text{time taken by 1 man}}{\text{time taken by 2 men}} = \dfrac{2}{1}$ $\left[\text{not } \dfrac{1}{2}\right]$.

So $\dfrac{\text{time taken by 3 men}}{\text{time taken by 2 men}} = \dfrac{2}{3}$ $\left[\text{not } \dfrac{3}{2}\right]$.

That is, time taken by 3 men $= \dfrac{2}{3}$ of that taken by two

Thus, if 2 men take 15 days to do a job, then

the time taken by 3 men $= \dfrac{2}{3}$ of 15 = 10 days.

Thus, we see that the ratio method can be applied equally well to questions involving quantities which are *inversely proportional* to one another—that is, two quantities so related that if the one increases the other decreases.

The above illustration should be set down thus :—

Time taken by 2 men = 15 days.

$\therefore$,,   3 ,, = $15 \times \frac{2}{3}$ days = 10 days.

Before multiplying by the ratio, the pupil must ask himself whether 3 men require more days or fewer days than the 2 men.

If more, the multiplying ratio is greater than 1.
If less,   ,,   ,,   less than 1.

We shall now apply the ratio method to the worked examples under Section (*b*) of the unitary method, page 137.

Example 1.—If 3 men require 10 hours to do a piece of work, how long will 5 men require to do the same work at the same rate ?

Time required by 3 men = 10 hours.

$\therefore$,,   5 ,, = $10 \times \frac{3}{5}$ hours = 6 hours.

Note.—As 5 men require *less* time than 3 men, we must multiply by $\frac{3}{5}$ (a ratio *less* than 1), and not by $\frac{5}{3}$.

Example 2.—If a man working 6 hours a day takes 4 days to do a certain work, how many days would he take to do it if he worked 8 hours a day ?

Working 6 hours a day, the time taken = 4 days.

   ,,   8   ,,   ,,   = $4 \times \frac{6}{8}$ days

                                           = 3 days.

Example 3.—How many yards of cloth worth 5s. a yard should be given in exchange for 10 yards worth 7s. a yard ?

Length of cloth at 7s. a yard = 10 yards.

$\therefore$ Length of same value at 5s. a yard = $10 \times \frac{7}{5}$ = 14 yards.

Evidently the multiplying ratio must be greater than 1, because a greater length than 10 yards is required of the cheaper cloth to be equivalent to the 10 yards of the dearer cloth.

The pupil should now work out by the *Ratio Method* Exercise 74, on page 138, but we add here a few more examples :—

EXERCISE 79.

(1) If 8 men require 20 days to do a piece of work, how long will 5 men require to do it ?

(2) If 10 men require 16 days to do a certain work, how long will 40 men require to do it ?

(3) If 15 men require 8 days for a job, how many men would be needed to do it in 6 days ?

(4) If 10 men can do a work in 12 days, how many could do it in 15 days ?

(5) If a garrison of 8,400 men have provisions for 4 months, how long would the same provisions last a garrison of 5,600 men ?

(6) A man working at the rate of 9 hours a day takes 16 days to finish a task. How many days would it have taken him if he had worked only 6 hours a day ? If the time taken had been 18 days, how many hours a day would he have worked ?

(7) A cyclist, whose rate is 15 miles an hour, takes 8 minutes to cycle round a circular track, How long will it take a cyclist whose rate is 12 miles an hour ?

(8) If a cyclist going 10 miles an hour takes 8 minutes to go a certain distance, what must have been the rate of a cyclist who went the same distance in 5 minutes ?

(9) If 15 men can do a certain work in 68 days, how many men should be employed when 85 days are allowed to do the work ?

(10) If 70 men need 18 days to do a job, how long would it have taken 42 men ?

(11) If a certain amount of corn can feed 18 horses for 64 days, how long would the same amount feed 72 horses ?

(12) How many horses could feed for 30 days on a quantity of corn that could feed 74 horses for 45 days ?

(13) If 25 men require 3 weeks 4 days to do a certain work, how many more must be employed to do the work in 1 week 4 days, taking a week to be 6 days ?

(14) A garrison of 4,500 is provisioned for 9 months. After 1 month 1,500 men leave. For how many more months will the provisions last the men that remain ?

(15) An encampment of 2,500 men have 30 months' provisions. After 10 months have passed 500 men join the encampment. How much longer will the provisions last ?

(16) If 30 yards of carpet $1\frac{1}{3}$ yards wide are required to cover the floor of a room, how many yards would have sufficed if the carpet had been 2 yards wide ?

(17) If a floor require 44 yards of a carpet whose width is $1\frac{1}{2}$ yards, what must be the width of a carpet if 33 yards of it are sufficient ?

N.B.—In using this method or the Unitary Method, we must be sure that the quantities involved are proportional or inversely proportional to one another.

For example, the *area of a circle* is not proportional to its radius, but to the *square on its radius.*

The distance a stone falls under gravity is not proportional to the time of falling, but to the *square of the time.*

Example.—If a stone falls 64 feet in 2 seconds, how far does it fall in 3 seconds ?

The distance is *not* $64 \times \dfrac{3}{2}$, but $64 \times \dfrac{3^2}{2^2} = 64 \times \dfrac{9}{4} = 144$ ft.

Exercise 75 on page 139 may be worked at this stage by the Ratio Method, but we give here an exercise of additional miscellaneous examples.

In working each example, the pupil must ask himself whether the quantities are directly or inversely proportional, whether the multiplying ratio should be greater or less than unity, whether the given quantity should be increased or decreased.

EXERCISE 80.

(1) If 2 tons 12 cwts. cost £3 5s., find the cost of 10 tons 10 cwts.

(2) If 12½ yards of cloth cost £2 3s. 9d., find the cost of 10⅝ yards.

(3) If a man walking 3½ miles an hour takes 52 minutes to go round a circular track, how long will a man walking 3¼ miles an hour take to go round it ?

(4) If a man walking 4 miles an hour takes 50 minutes to go a certain distance, how many miles an hour does a man walk who takes an hour to go the same distance ?

(5) If 5 tons 5 cwts. of coal cost £6 11s. 3d., how much will £6 10s. buy ?

(6) If 7½ lbs. cost 11s. 3d., find the cost of 18 lbs.

(7) If the rates on a rental of £12 amount to £2 8s., find the amount of the rates on a £15 rental.

(8) A rectangular piece of ground is 360 yards long and 200 yards wide. Find the length of another rectangular piece of ground of the same size. whose width is 240 yards.

(9) If 16 articles cost £1 16s., what number of the same articles can I buy for £5 17s. ?

(10) If a furnace consumes 6 tons 15 cwts. of coal in 36 hours, how much coal would it consume in 32 hours ?

(11) If 5 yards 2 feet cost 18s. 5d., find the cost of 7 yards 1 foot.

(12) If a cyclist whose rate is 10 miles an hour takes 6 hours to go a certain distance, how long will another cyclist, who goes 12 miles per hour, take to go the same distance ?

(13) The area of a circle of 1 in. radius is 3·1416 sq. ins. Find the area of a circle of 2 ins. radius, knowing that the area of a circle is proportional to the *square on its radius*.

(14) If a body falls under gravity 64·4 ft. in 2 seconds, find the height from which a stone was dropped if it reached the ground in 1 second (knowing that the distance is proportional to the square of the time).

(15) If 80 men can do a certain work in 18 days, how long will it take 120 men to do the same work ?

(16) If 35 men take 54 days to do a job, how many would be required to do it in 14 days ?

(17) If a piece of work is given to 66 men which would take them 18 months to do, how many more men must be employed to get the work done in 6 months ?

(18) If it cost £787 10s. to make a road 5¼ miles long, what would it cost to make a road 7 miles long ?

(19) If 500 men have provisions for 150 days, how long would these provisions last 750 men ?

(20) If 600 men have provisions for 8 months, how many men would the same provisions last for 10 months ?

(21) Being given that the circumference of a circle is proportional to its diameter, and that the circumference of a circle of 3 ins. diameter is 9·42 ins., find the circumference of a circle 1 ft. in diameter ?

(22) If the front wheel of a carriage is 8·5 ft. in circumference and the hind wheel 10·2 ft. in circumference, and if the hind wheel makes 595 revolutions when the carriage goes a certain distance, how many revolutions does the front wheel make in the same distance ?

(23) How many yards of cloth worth 3s. 6d. per yard should be given for 60 yards worth 4s. 8d. per yard ?

(24) The rent of a farm of 130 acres is £295, find the size of a farm whose rent is £354.

(25) If 11 yards of cloth cost £1 14s. 4½d., how many yards can be bought for £1 8s. 1½d. ?

(26) A boy received 9s. 2d. In seven days he had spent 6s. 5d. If he continues to spend at the same rate per day, in how many more days will the whole 9s. 2d. be spent ?

(27) A train is 220 yards long. If it is travelling 45 miles per hour, how long will it take to pass a person standing near the line ?

(28) If 1 litre of water weighs 2·205 lbs., and a pint of water weighs 1¼ lbs., express 7·056 pints in litres.

(29) A housewife received £2 1s. 5½d. as dividend. If her purchases amounted to £16 11s. 8d., at what rate per £ was dividend paid ?

(30) A merchant bought 36 cases of fruit at 13s. 4d. per case. 4 cases proved unfit to be used. At what price per case had he to sell the rest so as not to lose on the deal ?

(c) **Problems with more than Two Changing Qualities.**

We shall now apply the Ratio Method to the examples, worked out under the above head of the Unitary Method on page 141.

Let us consider Example 1, *viz.* :—

If 6 men in 20 days reap 5 acres of corn, how many acres would 10 men reap in 18 days working at the same speed ?

If the time were the same in both cases, then to find the number of acres reaped by the 10 men as against 6 men, we would multiply the 5 acres by $\frac{10}{6}$. This would give the result if the 10 men worked for the 20 days. If we now consider the time, 18 days as against 20 days, to get the number of acres reaped in the 18 days, we multiply by the ratio $\frac{18}{20}$.

That is to say, the method is precisely as before ; we consider the men and the time separately, multiplying by the *appropriate ratios.*

The working is set down thus—

Acres reaped by 6 men in 20 days = 5.

$$\therefore \quad ,, \quad 10 \; ,, \quad 18 \; ,, \quad = 5 \times \frac{10}{6} \times \frac{18}{20}$$
$$= 7\tfrac{1}{2} \text{ acres.}$$

Example 2.—If 25 men in 9 days of 8 hours each dig a trench 300 yards long, what length of trench could 16 men dig in 12 days of 6 hours each ?

25 men in 9 days of 8 hours dig 300 yards.

$$\therefore \quad 16 \; ,, \quad 12 \; ,, \quad 6 \quad ,, \quad 300 \text{ yards} \times \frac{16}{25} \times \frac{12}{9} \times \frac{6}{8}$$
$$= 192 \text{ yards.}$$

Example 3.—If 5 men working 6 hours each day plough 12 acres in $4\frac{1}{2}$ days, how many hours a day must 4 men work at the same rate in order to plough 16 acres in 5 days ?

To do 12 ac. in $4\frac{1}{2}$ days 5 men need 6 hours a day.

$$\therefore \text{ ,, } \quad 16 \text{ ,, } \quad 5 \text{ ,, } \quad 4 \text{ ,, } \quad \text{,, } \quad 6 \times \frac{16}{12} \times \frac{4\frac{1}{2}}{5} \times \frac{5}{4} \text{ hours.}$$

$$= 9 \text{ hours.}$$

16 acres require a longer day than 12, hence we multiply by $\frac{16}{12}$.

With 5 days a shorter day is required than with $4\frac{1}{2}$ days, hence we multiply by $\frac{4\frac{1}{2}}{5}$.

4 men require to work a longer day than 5 men, hence we multiply by $\frac{5}{4}$.

In using the Ratio Method we should set down *the same quantities in the same column, one below the other*, and it is not necessary to put last what is asked. If there is a number of multiplying ratios, it would be convenient to use the symbol " x " for what is required, and do the working in a separate line, as in the following examples :—

Example 4.—If the carriage of 1 cwt. 14 lbs. for 32 miles be 1s. 6d. by goods train, how far will 3 cwts. 42 lbs. be carried for 5s. 3d. by passenger train, the ratio of the charge by goods train to that by passenger train being 3 to 4 ?

By goods,   1 cwt. 14 lbs. carried 32 miles for 1s. 6d. at rate 3.
By passenger, 3 cwts. 42 lbs. carried x miles for 5s. 3d. at rate 4.

$$\therefore x = 32 \text{ miles} \times \frac{1 \text{ cwt. 14 lbs.}}{3 \text{ cwts. 42 lbs.}} \times \frac{5s. \ 3d.}{1s. \ 6d.} \times \frac{3}{4}$$

$$= 32 \text{ miles} \times \frac{126}{378} \times \frac{63}{18} \times \frac{3}{4} = 28 \text{ miles.}$$

Note.—(1) As 3 cwts. 42 lbs. would be carried a *shorter* distance than 1 cwt. 14 lbs. for same money, we multiply by $\frac{1 \text{ cwt. 14 lbs.}}{3 \text{ cwts. 42 lbs.}}$ (a ratio less than unity).

(2) As goods would be carried a *longer* distance for 5s. 3d. than for 1s. 6d., we multiply by $\dfrac{5s.\ 3d.}{1s.\ 6d.}$ (a ratio *greater* than unity).

(3) As the passenger train rate is higher than the goods train rate, goods would be carried a *shorter* distance for same money by passenger than by goods train, and so we multiply by ¾ (a ratio *less* than unity).

Example 5.—If 8 men working 10 hours a day can dig a trench 30 yards long, 10 feet wide, and 4 feet deep in 6 days, how long will it take 6 men working 8 hours a day to dig a trench 80 yards long, 9 feet wide, and 5 feet deep ?

8 men working 10 hours a day dig 30 yards by 10 feet by 4 feet in 6 days.

6 men working 8 hours a day dig 80 yards by 9 feet by 5 feet in x days.

$$\therefore x = 6 \text{ days} \times \frac{8}{6} \times \frac{10}{8} \times \frac{80}{30} \times \frac{9}{10} \times \frac{5}{4} = 30 \text{ days.}$$

The pupil should now work out by the Ratio Method the examples under Exercise 76 on page 142.

The following are additional examples :—

EXERCISE 81.

(1) If 15 men working 8 hours a day do a job in 7 days, how long will 10 men take to do the same job working 7 hours a day ?

(2) If 18 men can do a certain piece of work in 5 hours, how long will it take 24 men to do twice the amount of work ?

(3) If 12 men take 7½ hours to do a certain amount of work, how many men would be required to do 3 times the amount in 5 hours ?

(4) If 20 men take 9 hours to do a certain amount of work, how many men would be needed to do ⅔ of the amount in 6 hours ?

(5) If a certain amount of provisions last 4,500 men for 20 months, how long would ⅘ of the amount last 6,000 men ?

EXERCISE 81—*Continued.*

(6) An engine making 154 strokes per minute travels 160 miles in 4 hours. How many strokes per minute must the same engine make to travel 260 miles in 7 hours ?

(7) If 20 men take 30 days to dig a trench of a certain length 4 feet deep and 6 feet wide, how long will it take 15 men to dig the same length of trench but 6 feet deep and 10 feet wide ?

(8) If a trench 120 yards long, 2 yards wide, and 3 feet deep can be dug by 50 men in 6 days working 8 hours a day, how many men would be required to dig a trench 300 yards long, 3 yards wide, and 4 feet deep in 15 days of 10 hours each ?

(9) If 40 men dig a trench 300 yards long, 5 feet wide, and 8 feet deep in 18 days working 10 hours a day, what length of trench 6 feet wide and 9 feet deep would 60 men dig in 15 days working 9 hours a day ?

(10) At a certain boarding-house the board of 32 persons for 5 weeks amounted to £140, what would be the board of 12 persons for 8 weeks at another boarding-house where the rate of charge was $\frac{5}{4}$ of that of the first boarding-house ?

(11) If the carriage of 1 cwt. 56 lbs. by goods train for 20 miles be 1s. 3d., what would be the carriage of 84 lbs. for 64 miles by passenger train if the passenger train rate be $\frac{3}{2}$ of that of the goods train ?

(12) If the carriage of 63 lbs. for 64 miles be 3s. by passenger train, how far would 1 cwt. be carried by goods train for 1s. 8d., the goods rate being to the passenger rate as 2 to 3 ?

(13) If 18 tons of coal are carried 250 miles by rail for £7 10s., how much will it cost to send 280 tons a distance of 360 miles by a ship whose charges are $\frac{3}{10}$ of the charges by rail ?

(14) If 2,000 copies of a book of 180 leaves require 60 reams of paper, how many reams of paper would be required for 5,000 copies of a book of 120 leaves of the same size ?

(15) If 10,000 copies of a book of 320 pages require 280 reams of paper, how many copies of a book of 400 pages of the same size could be made from 350 reams of paper ?

(16) If 3,000 copies of a book of 160 pages require 45 reams of paper, how many reams would be required for 2,000 copies of a book of 480 pages, the size of a page of the latter being $\frac{4}{3}$ of the size of a page of the former ?

(17) If a man takes 4 days, walking 5 hours every day, to perform a journey of 120 miles, how many days would he take to go 180 miles, walking 6 hours a day at the same rate ?

(18) Walking 4 hours every day, a man goes 168 miles in 14 days. How many days must another man walk to go a journey of 140 miles if he walk for 5 hours every day and his rate of walking is $\frac{4}{3}$ of that of the first man ?

(19) If a garrison of 2,800 men consume 2 tons 15 cwts. of a certain foodstuff in 22 days, how long would 5 tons of the same foodstuff last another garrison of 3,500 men if the latter consumed per man per day $\frac{8}{7}$ of the amount consumed per man per day by the former garrison ?

(20) If 3,600 men consume 9 tons of a certain foodstuff in 20 days how much of the same foodstuff would 4,000 men consume in 25 days, the ration allowed to the latter being to that of the former as 4 to 5 per man per day ?

(21) A garrison of 2,500 men has provisions for 12 weeks, allowing each man 8 ozs. per day. How much would the daily allowance per man be if the same amount of provisions had to last 4,800 men for 8 weeks ?

(22) If 20 men in 35 days of 8 hours each excavate 3,500 tons of earth, how much would 24 men, working at same speed excavate in 30 days of 9 hours each ?

(23) If 10 men in 35 days of 9 hours each excavate 1,750 tons of earth, in how many days would 15 men excavate 2,500 tons working 6 hours a day ?

(24) If it takes 15 men 28 days of 6 hours each to excavate 1,800 tons of earth, how many men would be required to excavate 2,400 tons in 16 days working 10 hours a day ?

(25) If 12 men working 8 hours a day build a wall in 6 days, how many men working 9 hours a day would be required to build in 4 days a wall twice as long as the first, $\frac{2}{3}$ of its height, and $\frac{3}{4}$ of its width ?

(26) A builder employs a squad of men on a job at the rate for each man of 6s. a day for a 10 hours' day. When the job is finished he finds that his wages bill has amounted to £180. If he had employed the same squad at the rate for each man of 5s. a day for an 8 hours' day for the same job, what would have been his wages bill ?

(27) If it takes a clerk 20 days of 8 hours each to copy 240 pages of 24 lines, how many days would it take him to copy 360 pages of 28 lines of same length if he work 10 hours a day ?

(28) If 4 compositors in 18 days of 9 hours each set up in type 450 pages, how many pages of the same size would 6 compositors set in type in 15 days of 8 hours each ?

(29) If an engine of 20 horse-power raise 60,000 lbs. to a height of 11 feet in 1 minute, how long will it take an engine of 30 horse-power to pump up 88,000 cub. feet of water to a height of 18 feet, being given that 1 cubic foot of water weighs 1,000 ozs. ?

(30) If 4 pumps, each with a stroke of $2\frac{1}{2}$ feet length, working 12 hours a day for 9 days, empty the water out of a mine, how many pumps with a stroke of $2\frac{1}{4}$ feet working 10 hours a day will empty the same amount of water in 8 days, the stroke of the latter set of pumps working twice as quickly as that of the former ?

(31) The charge for conveying 28 people by motor bus a distance of 72 miles was £8 2s. What should be charged for conveying 63 people a distance of 160 miles at the same rate ?

(32) A rectangular vessel 2 dm. long, 11·5 cm. broad and 6 cm. deep contains 18·768 Kg. of mercury when full. What is the depth of the mercury in a similar vessel 2·5 dm. long, and 8 cm. broad if the weight of the mercury is 6·528 Kg. ?

(33) A contractor undertook to complete a contract in 72 days, and employed 36 men. After 63 days he found that only $\frac{4}{5}$ of the work was finished. How many more men had he to employ to complete his contract in time ?

(34) During one year a man covered 2,688 miles in a car which gave him 24 miles to the gallon of petrol. The cost of petrol for the year was 1s. $4\frac{1}{2}$d. per gallon. The following year in a new car he covered 3,520 miles, and though the

price of petrol was increased by 2d. per gallon, the total increase in his outlay was only 15s. 7d. How many miles to the gallon did he get out of the second car ?

(35) 12 men working 8 hours a day for 30 days managed to complete $\frac{3}{5}$ of a contract. 20 additional men were sent in order to finish the work in the remaining 6 days of the contract. How many hours a day did all the men work during these 6 days ?

III. THE RATIO METHOD APPLIED.

RATES, TAXES, BANKRUPTCY, INSURANCE, AND FOREIGN EXCHANGE.

We shall deal briefly with these subjects, because all questions on them are merely examples on the Ratio Method, and, therefore, require no new rule for their solution.

(a) Rates and Taxes.

Example 1.—What rates does a householder pay on a rental of £12 10s., if rents are assessed at 5s. 6d. in the pound.

Rate on £1   rent = 5s. 6d.

,,   £12 10s. ,, = 5s. 6d. $\times \dfrac{£12\ 10s}{£1}$.

              = 5s. 6d. $\times 12\frac{1}{2}$ = £3 8s. 9d.

Example 2.—If a man pays £10 13s. 9d. of income tax when the rate is 2s. 3d. in the pound, find the net income taxed, and his total income if there is a total abatement of £205 (that is, £205 not taxed).

When tax is   2s. 3d. net income taxed = £1.

,,   £10 13s. 9d.   ,,   = £1 $\times \dfrac{£10\ 13s.\ 9d.}{2s.\ 3d.}$

                              = £1 $\times \dfrac{2,565}{27}$ = £95.

∴ Total income   = £95 + £205

                          = £300.

11

EXERCISE 82.

Rates and Taxes.

(1) A man has an income of £250. If £210 of this income is not taxed, find the tax paid on the remainder when the rate is 2s. 3d. in the pound.

(2) When the income-tax rate is 2s. in the pound a man's income tax amounts to £5 12s. What was the amount of the income taxed ?

(3) After paying income tax at the rate of 2s. 6d. in the pound, a man's net income was £1,400. What was his gross income if the whole of it was taxed ?

(4) The income tax having been raised from 5s. in the pound to 6s., a man now pays £210 5s. more tax than formerly. What is his income, the whole of it being taxed ?

(5) The rates in a burgh being assessed at 4s. 6d. in the pound of rental, what rates does a householder pay whose rent is £15 10s. ?

(6) The rates in a town being assessed at 5s. 3d. in the pound on the tenant, what is the rental of a house the tenant of which pays £4 14s. 6d. ?

(7) A man pays £25 for house rent. If the rates amount to 3s 6d. in the pound, and are calculated on $\frac{4}{5}$ of the rent, what is the amount charged for rates ?

(8) A man who owns his dwelling-house pays rates at 3s. 6d. in the pound as owner and 5s. 6d. in the pound as tenant. If the house is valued at £30 and the rates are charged on $\frac{5}{6}$ of this value, what is the total amount of the rates that he has to pay ?

(9) The total rateable value of a town is £50,000. If it is desired to raise £8,125 by rates, at what rate per pound must the rates be charged ?

(10) If a rate of 3s 4d. in the pound in a parish produced £5,000, what was the rateable value of the parish ?

(11) If a parish whose rateable value is £30,000 produces £5,000 in rates, what amount would be produced by a parish whose rateable value is £35,000, the same rate per pound being charged in both ?

(b) **Bankruptcy.**

Example 3.—A bankrupt's debts amount to £560, and his assets are worth £210, how much can he pay in the pound, and what will a creditor receive to whom he owes £30 ?

(1)   Amount paid on £560 = £210.

$$\therefore \quad \text{''} \quad \text{''} \quad £1 = 210 \times \frac{1}{560}$$

$$= £\frac{3}{8} = 7\text{s. } 6\text{d.}$$

(2)   Amount paid on £560 = £210.

$$\therefore \quad \text{''} \quad \text{''} \quad £30 = £210 \times \frac{30}{560}$$

$$= £\frac{90}{8} = £11 \text{ } 5\text{s.}$$

EXERCISE 82.

Bankruptcy.

(**12**) A bankrupt's debts are £850, and his assets (the amount he can pay) are £340.   How much can he pay in the pound ?

(**13**) A bankrupt whose assets amounted to £240 was able to pay 13s. 4d. in the pound.   What was the amount of his debts ?

(**14**) A bankrupt whose debts amounted to £680 10s. paid 6s. 8d. in the pound.   What were his assets ?

(**15**) A bankrupt's debts amounted to £481, of which he could only pay £360 15s.   How much did he pay to a creditor to whom he owed £60 ?

(**16**) A bankrupt has 3 creditors, to whom he owes £480, £560, and £840 respectively.   If his assets total £564, how much does each creditor receive ?

(**17**) A man owes his creditors £1,328.   If he can only pay 8s. 7½d. in the pound, how much money has he ?

(**18**) If a bankrupt pays £104 3s. 5d. to a creditor to whom he owes £500, and if his total debts are £4,075, what are his assets ?

(**19**) A bankrupt fails and pays 13s. 4d. in the pound on a total debt of £15,320 15s.   What are his assets ?

(20) A bankrupt whose assets were £760 10s. failed for £1,901 5s. If one of his creditors received £85 15s., how much was owing to him ?

(21) A bankrupt fails and pays 12s. 6d. in the pound after paying the cost of liquidation, which amounted to £90 3s. 8d. If his total indebtedness was £8,320 15s. 4d., what did his assets amount to at the time of failure ?

(22) A bankrupt fails and pays 6s. 8d. in the pound. How much did he owe to a creditor who lost £76 13s. 4d. by the bankruptcy ?

(23) A bankrupt pays 11s. 6d. in the pound. How much did a creditor lose who received £17 5s. ?

(c) Insurance.

Example 4.—When an insurance premium is at the rate of £3 10s. on £100, what premium does a fisherman pay who insures his drifter for £3,050 ?

Premium paid on £100 = £3 10s.

$$\therefore \quad \text{,,} \quad\quad £3,050 = £3\ 10s. \times \frac{3,050}{100} = £106\ 15s.$$

Example 5.—A shipowner paid £6,500 for a vessel. At what figure must he insure it in order that in case of loss he may recover both the price paid for the vesssel and a year's cost of insurance, the insurance premium being at the rate of £2 10s. for £100 insured ?

£100 = £2 10s. + £97 10s. ∴ If property worth £97 10s. is insured for £100, the cost of insurance would be £2 10s., and if lost, £100 received would cover both the £97 10s. lost and the £2 10s. paid for a year's insurance.

Hence £97 10s. is insured £100,

$$\therefore \quad\quad £6,500 \quad\quad \text{,,} \quad\quad £100 \times \frac{6,500}{97\frac{1}{2}} = £6,666\ 13s.\ 4d.$$

or as $2\frac{1}{2}°/_\circ = \frac{1}{40}$ ∴   Required sum = £6,500 $\times \frac{40}{39}$.

EXERCISE 82.

Insurance.

(24) A man insures his life for £1,200. What premium does he pay at the rate of £3 12s. 6d. per £100 ?

(25) A vessel cost £10,500. Find the amount of the insurance premium on it at £2 10s. per £100.

(26) A drifter is worth £2,800. If it is insured for that sum at £3 5s. per £100, what is the amount of the premium paid by a man who owns $\frac{1}{4}$ of the drifter ?

(27) A trawler which cost £4,500 is insured for its full value at the rate of £2 15s. per £100. What share of the trawler does a shareholder own who pays as insurance premium £41 5s. ?

(28) The owner of a drifter insured it at £2,666 13s. 4d. What premium did he pay if the rate was £2 10s. per £100 ? If in case of loss the insured sum covers both the value of the drifter and the year's insurance, what is the value of the drifter ?

(29) A man owns a vessel worth £5,820. If the rate of insurance is £3 per £100, at what figure must he insure it in order that, in case of loss, he may recover the value of the vessel and the cost of the year's insurance ?

(30) A man owns a vessel worth £7,840. He insures it for £8,000 If this covers both the value of the ship and the insurance premium, at what rate per £100 was the premium charged ?

(d) Foreign Exchange.

Example 6.—In 1919 when £1 = 61·5 marks of German money an Englishman in Cologne ran up a bill of 2,091 marks. Find the equivalent in English money.

$$61 \cdot 5 \text{ marks} = £1.$$

$$\therefore \ 2,091 \text{ marks} = £1 \times \frac{2,091}{61 \cdot 5} = £\frac{20,910}{615} = £34.$$

Example 7.—If an article cost a British soldier £1 14s. in Cologne in 1919 when £1 = 61·5 marks, what would it have cost him if the rate of exchange had been £1 = 20·4 marks ?

Evidently if £1 were about ⅓ of its value, the amount in English money would be trebled.

Thus,

If £1 is worth 61·5 marks, amount reqd. = £1 14s.

,, £1   ,,   20·4   ,,   ,, $= £1\ 14s. \times \dfrac{61·5}{20·4}$

$= £\dfrac{34}{20} \times \dfrac{615}{204}$

$= £5\ 2s.\ 6d.$

EXERCISE 82.

Foreign Exchange.

(31) If a man owes 240 dollars 50 cents in New York, what must he pay in English money if a dollar = 4s. 2d. ? (100 cents = 1 dollar.)

(32) How many dollars must an American merchant pay who owes a London merchant £72 18s. 4d., if 1 dollar = 4s. 2d. ?

(33) If a franc = 9½d., find to the nearest 1d. the amount in English money required to pay 2,640 francs 40 centimes ? (100 centimes = 1 franc).

(34) A merchant owes 3,780 francs in Paris. Find the equivalent in English money if 25·2 francs = £1.

(35) A Paris merchant owes £141 11s. in London, how many francs must he pay if a franc = 9½d. ?

(36) If I wish to send £145 to Berlin, for what sum in marks must I buy a bill if £1 = 20·4 marks ?

(37) A British officer paid 49 marks 24 pfennige in Cologne in 1919 for an article when £1 = 61 m. 55 pf. Find the cost in English money. (100 pfennige = 1 mark).

(38) If 17s. was paid in Germany by a British soldier in 1919 when £1 = 61·55 marks, what would it have cost at the rate of £1 = 20·4 marks, the pre-war rate ?

Additional Examples.

(39) A man's income is £450. He receives a personal allowance of £150, $\frac{1}{5}$ of his gross income for earned income, £90 for his two children. He is also allowed £15 for life assurance. What tax does he pay at the rate of 2s, 6d. per £ ?

(40) A married man with 3 children under 16 years of age has an income of £840, $\frac{5}{6}$ of which is earned. His personal allowance is £150 with $\frac{1}{5}$ of his earned income. £60 is allowed for the first child, and £40 for each of the others. He is also allowed £45 for life assurance at half the standard rate. If the standard rate is 5s. per £, and he is charged half the standard rate on the first £225 of taxable income, how much tax does he pay ?

(41) A company became bankrupt for £14,386 and the sale of its stock and property yielded £8,614. If a dividend of 11s. 6d. per £ was paid, what was the cost of winding up the company ?

(42) A debtor's liabilities amount to £1,295 10s., and his assets to £820 9s. 8d. If he owes £285 to A, £387 10s. to B, and £178 15s. to C, what share of the assets should each of these creditors receive ?

(43) A town treasurer wishes to raise £18,250 from the rates and levies a rate of 5s. $5\frac{1}{2}$d. per £. If the rateable value of the town is £67,285, what is the value of his surplus ?

(44) A man who owns $\frac{3}{5}$ of a property pays £87 as his share of the insurance premium at the rate of £3 12s. 6d. per £100. For what sum is the whole property insured ?

(45) If a dollar is worth 4s. 2d. and a rupee is worth 1s. 6d., how many dollars must be sent from New York to Calcutta to pay an account of 1,250 rupees ?

(46) An Englishman on entering Italy changed £36 into lire when the rate of exchange was 92·75. He spent 2,226 lire and on leaving changed the remainder into English money, the rate of exchange being 87·5. Find to the nearest penny how much he gained or lost in the transaction.

CHAPTER XIII.

PROPORTIONAL DIVISION.

Proportional Division or **Proportionate Division** means dividing a quantity into parts which are **proportional** to certain given numbers.

Thus, for example, we may wish to divide 370 into 3 parts proportional to 2, 3, and 5. To do this we would divide 370 into 10 equal parts, because $2 + 3 + 5 = 10$, and then take 2, 3, and 5 respectively of these equal parts.

The required parts would, therefore, be $\frac{2}{10}$, $\frac{3}{10}$, and $\frac{5}{10}$ of 370— that is, 74, 111, and 185.

The following is a useful notation :—A ratio like $\frac{2}{3}$ may be written 2 : 3, and so the statement that 3 quantities, A, B and C are proportional to 2, 3, and 5 may be written thus :—A : B : C $= 2 : 3 : 5$.

This would read " A to B to C $=$ 2 to 3 to 5."

It should also be noted that the proportions are not altered if each quantity is multiplied or divided by the same number.

Thus $2 : 3 : 5 = 20 : 30 : 50 = \frac{2}{10} : \frac{3}{10} : \frac{5}{10}$, etc.

(a) SIMPLE PROPORTIONAL PARTS.

Simple proportional parts are illustrated by the following examples :—

Example 1.—The ages of 4 boys are 4, 5, 7, and 10 years respectively. Divide £799 10s. between them in the proportion of their ages.

$$4 + 5 + 7 + 10 = 26.$$

∴ 1st boy gets $\frac{4}{26}$ of £799 10s. $=$ £30 15s. $\times$ 4 $=$ £123

2nd ,, $\frac{5}{26}$ of £799 10s. $=$ £30 15s. $\times$ 5 $=$ £153 15s.

3rd ,, $\frac{7}{26}$ of £799 10s. $=$ £30 15s. $\times$ 7 $=$ £215 5s.

4th ,, $\frac{10}{26}$ of £799 10s. $=$ £30 15s. $\times$ 10 $=$ £307 10s.

If we add the results, their sum is equal to   £799 10s.

Example 2.—Divide an estate of 495 acres into 3 parts proportional to the fractions $\frac{1}{2}$, $\frac{3}{4}$ and $\frac{2}{5}$.

In dealing with fractions, we convert them into fractions with the same common denominator. The fractions are then proportional to their numerators. Or, thus, using the notation explained above :—

$$\frac{1}{2} : \frac{3}{4} : \frac{2}{5} = \frac{10}{20} : \frac{15}{20} : \frac{8}{20} = 10 : 15 : 8.$$

And $10 + 15 + 8 = 33.$

$$\therefore \text{ 1st part} = \frac{10}{33} \text{ of } 495 = 10 \times 15 = 150 \text{ acres.}$$

$$\text{2nd ,, } = \frac{15}{33} \text{ of } 495 = 15 \times 15 = 225 \text{ ,,}$$

$$\text{3rd ,, } = \frac{8}{33} \text{ of } 495 = 8 \times 15 = 120 \text{ ,,}$$

Example 3.—A, B and C form a business. A's capital is £2,000, B's £3,000, and C's £5,000. Divide a profit of £750 between them in proportion to their capital.

$$2,000 : 3,000 : 5,000 = 2 : 3 : 5, \text{ and } 2 + 3 + 5 = 10.$$

$$\therefore \text{ A's profit} = \frac{2}{10} \text{ of £750} = £150.$$

$$\text{B's ,, } = \frac{3}{10} \text{ of £750} = £225.$$

$$\text{C's ,, } = \frac{5}{10} \text{ of £750} = £375.$$

EXERCISE 83.

(1) Divide 56 into 2 parts proportional to 3 and 4.

(2) Divide 65 into 2 parts in the ratio of 2 to 3.

(3) Divide 315 into 3 parts proportional to 3, 5, and 7.

(4) Divide £50 10s. into 3 parts proportional to 1, 2, and 3.

(5) Divide £20 5s. into 3 parts proportional to 2, 3, and 5.

(6) Divide £29 8s. into 3 parts proportional to 3, 5, and 6.

(7) Divide £156 17s. 3d. into 3 parts proportional to 2, 3, and 4.

(8) Divide £49 3s. 6d. into 3 parts proportional to 1, 2, and 4.

(9) Divide £34 8s. into 4 parts proportional to 1, 3, 5, and 7.

(10) Divide £10 15s. into 2 parts proportional to $\frac{1}{2}$ and $\frac{1}{3}$.

(11) Divide £40 6s. into 3 parts proportional to $\frac{1}{2}$, $\frac{1}{3}$, and $\frac{1}{4}$.

(12) Divide 1 ton 6 cwts. into 3 parts proportional to $\frac{1}{2}$, $\frac{2}{3}$, and 1.

(13) Divide £2 13s. into 3 parts proportional to $\frac{1}{2}$, $\frac{2}{3}$, and $\frac{3}{5}$.

(14) Divide £3 1s. 6d. into 3 parts proportional to $\frac{1}{2}$, $\frac{3}{4}$, and $\frac{4}{5}$.

(15) Divide £302 10s. into 3 parts proportional to $2\frac{1}{2}$, $3\frac{1}{3}$, and $4\frac{1}{4}$.

(16) Divide £196 7s. into 4 parts proportional to $1\frac{3}{8}$, $2\frac{1}{2}$, $4\frac{2}{5}$, and $5\frac{3}{4}$.

(17) Divide £81 18s. between A and B so that for every half-crown that A gets B gets a florin.

(18) Divide £38 19s. between A, B, and C so that for every crown that A gets B gets half-a-crown and C a florin.

(19) A and B are partners in a business, to which A contributes £450 and B £600 as capital. How should a year's profit of £70 15s. 9d. be divided between them ?

(20) A invested £2,500 in a business, B invested £2,000, and C £1,500. Divide a profit of £360 18s. among them.

(21) A and B rent a park for a month for £12 10s. If 75 sheep belonging to A and 50 belonging to B are grazed in it, what proportion of the rent should each pay ?

(22) A levy of 3,500 is made on 3 towns, whose populations are 40,000, 55,000, and 45,000, the number from each town being in proportion to its population. How many should each contribute ?

(23) Four boys, whose ages are 8, 10, 12, and 15 years, receive a sum of £3 15s. to be divided among them in proportion to their ages. Find the amount which each should receive.

(24) Three towns, whose populations are 20,000, 25,000 and 30,000, agree to raise a fund of £5,250. If their contributions are to be in proportion to their populations, how much should each pay ?

(25) Divide £29 8s. among A, B, C, and D so that for every 1s. A gets B may get 1s. 6d., C 2s., and D 2s. 6d.

(b) **COMPOUND PROPORTIONAL PARTS.**

Compound porportional parts are illustrated by the following examples :—

Exanple 1.—A and B are set a piece of work for which they are to receive 20s. 6d. A spends 5 hours and B 7 hours on the work, but the work done by A in an hour is to the work done by B in an hour as 4 is to 3. How should the money be divided between them ?

As we have learned under the Ratio Method, Section (c), page 155.

A's share = B's share $\times \dfrac{5}{7} \times \dfrac{4}{3}$ = B's share $\times \dfrac{20}{21}$.

That is,   A's share : B's share = 20 : 21 or $5 \times 4 : 7 \times 3$.

Therefore, we divide 20s. 6d. into parts proportional to 20 and 21.

$$\therefore \quad \text{A's share} = \frac{20}{41} \text{ of 20s. 6d.} = 10\text{s.}$$

$$\text{B's share} = \frac{21}{41} \text{ of 20s. 6d.} = 10\text{s. 6d.}$$

Example 2.—A starts a business with a capital of £600. Four months later B joins him with a capital of £650. At the end of the year the profits amount to £254 4s. How should the profits be divided ?

As in the last example, their shares are jointly proportional to their capital and to the time it is in the business.

Thus, by Ratio Method,

$$\text{A's share} = \text{B's share} \times \frac{£600}{£650} \times \frac{12 \text{ months}}{8 \text{ months}},$$

or A's share : B's share = $600 \times 12 : 650 \times 8$

$$= 7,200 : 5,200 = 18 : 13.$$

$$\therefore \quad \text{A's share} = \frac{18}{31} \text{ of £254 4s.} = £147 \text{ 12s.}$$

$$\text{B's share} = \frac{13}{31} \text{ of £254 4s.} = £106 \text{ 12s.}$$

Example 3.—A starts a business with a capital of £800. **After** 2 months he is joined by B with a capital of £600, and after other 4 months by C with a capital of £1,000. The profit at the end of the year amounts to £378. What share of this should A receive ?

As in Example 2—

$$\text{A's share : B's : C's} = 800 \times 12 : 600 \times 10 : 1000 \times 6$$
$$= 8 : 5 : 5, \text{ and } 8 + 5 + 5 = 18.$$
$$\therefore \ \text{A's share} = \frac{8}{18} \text{ of £378} = £168.$$

Example 4.—Divide £300 among 4 men, 5 women, and 10 children so that a man's share is to a woman's share as 5 is to 4, and a woman's share is to a child's share as 3 is to 2.

A man's share : woman's $\quad\quad = 5 : 4 = 15 : 12$

$\quad\quad\quad\quad$ woman's : child's $\quad = 3 : 2 = \quad\quad 12 : 8$

$\therefore$ Man's share : woman's : child's $\quad = \quad\quad 15 : 12 : 8$

$\therefore$ 4 men's share : 5 women's : 10 children's $= 15 \times 4 : 12 \times 5 : 8 \times 10$

$\quad\quad\quad\quad\quad\quad\quad\quad\quad\quad = 60 : 60 : 80$

$\quad\quad\quad\quad\quad\quad\quad\quad\quad\quad = 3 : 3 : 4.$

$\therefore$ 4 men get $\frac{3}{10}$ of £300 $\quad = £90.$ $\quad \therefore$ 1 man gets £22 10s.

$\quad$ 5 women get $\frac{3}{10}$ of £300 $\quad = £90.$ $\quad \therefore$ 1 woman gets £18.

$\quad$ 10 children get $\frac{4}{10}$ of £300 $= £120.$ $\quad \therefore$ 1 child gets £12.

Note.—In the above we multiply the terms of the ratio 5 : 4 by 3 and the terms of the ratio 3 : 2 by 4 in order to get the same number (viz., 12) representing a woman's share in both ratios, and thus the three shares are represented by the numbers 15, 12, 8.

EXERCISE 84.

(1) A and B are set a piece of work for which they are to receive 15s. A spends 3 hours and B 5 hours on the work, but the work done by A in an hour is to the work done by B in an hour as 4 is to 3. How much should each receive ?

(2) Two workmen, A and B, are employed on a job. A works at it for 6 hours and B 8 hours, but B only does in an hour $\frac{3}{4}$ of what A does in the same time. If they are paid 30s. for the job, how much should each receive ?

(3) A and B enter into partnership, A investing £850 in the business and B £900. After 8 months B withdraws his capital. At the end of the year the profits amount to £870. How should this be divided between them ?

(4) A commences a business with a capital of £500. After 3 months B joins him with a capital of £400, and after 3 months more C is admitted as a partner with a capital of £600. At the end of the year the profits amounted to £1,540. How should this be divided among them ?

(5) A, B, and C jointly rent a field for £31 9s. A puts into it 35 sheep for 10 months, B 30 sheep for 8 months, and C 25 sheep for 6 months. How much should each pay ?

(6) If £50 15s. be divided among 16 boys and 18 girls so that a boy gets half as much again as a girl, what does a boy get ?

(7) Divide £5 8s. among 6 boys and 10 girls giving a boy 4s. for every 3s. given to a girl.

(8) If £4 9s. 5d. be divided among 5 women, 4 boys, and 6 girls so that a woman's share : boy's share : girl's share = 3 : 2 : 1, what does each get ?

(9) Divide 106 yards into 3 parts so that 1st : 2nd = 5 : 3, and 2nd : 3rd = 4 : 7.

(10) A and B hire a park for a month. A puts into it 35 sheep for 20 days, and B 40 sheep for 25 days. If the rent be £8 10s., what part should each pay ?

(11) Divide £12 6s. among 6 men, 10 women, and 16 boys so that a man may get as much as 2 women and a woman as much as 3 boys.

(12) Divide £10 16s. among 12 men, 20 women, and 32 boys so that a man may get as much as 3 women and a woman as much as 2 boys.

(13) Divide £120 5s. among A, B, and C so that A's share = $\frac{2}{3}$ of B's share, and C's = $\frac{4}{5}$ of B's.

(14) Divide a legacy of £8,550 among A, B, and C so that for every £5 which A gets B may get £4, and for every £5 which B gets C may get £3.

(15) Divide £70 10s. among A, B, and C so that B's share = $\frac{3}{4}$ of A's share, and C's = $\frac{4}{5}$ of B's.

(16) Three boys, A, B, and C, divide 55 marbles among them so that for 2 given to A, B gets 3, and for 1 that B gets C gets 2. How many does each get?

(17) A, B, and C start a piece of work together. After 4 hours A leaves off, and after 2 hours more B leaves off. If C takes 3 more hours to finish the work, and if 3 hours of A = 4 of B = 5 of C, and the amount paid for the work be 23s. 2d., what should each receive?

[A's hour : B's hour : C's hour = $\frac{4}{3} : 1 : \frac{4}{5}$.

∴ A's share : B's share : C's share = $\frac{4}{3} \times 4 : 1 \times 6 : \frac{4}{5} \times 9$, etc.]

(18) Divide £68 5s. among A, B, C, and D so that A's share : B's = 3 : 2, B's : C's = 3 : 5, and C's : D's = 4 : 3.

(19) Divide £5 11s. among A, B, C, and D so that A's share : B's = 1 : 2, B's : C's = 3 : 4, and C's : D's = 2 : 5.

(20) A starts a business with a capital of £2,000. After 4 months he is joined by B with a capital of £2,500, and after 2 more months C joins them with a capital of £3,000. If A's share of the profits at the end of the year is £900, what was the total profit for that year, and what was B's share?

CHAPTER XIV.

PERCENTAGES.

Per cent. means per hundred (*Latin, centum = a hundred*), and a percentage is a ratio or fraction whose denominator is 100. Thus 60 per cent. $= \dfrac{60}{100}$.

The symbol % is used for per cent. Thus, 2% **means 2 per cent.**

(a) TO EXPRESS A PERCENTAGE AS A FRACTION.

Example 1.—Express 40% as a fraction in its lowest terms.

$$\text{By our definition } 40\% = \frac{40}{100} = \frac{2}{5}.$$

Example 2.—What is 30% of 350 ?

$$30\% \text{ of } 350 = \frac{30}{100} \text{ of } 350 = 105.$$

Example 3.—What is 5% of £3 10s. ?

$$5\% \text{ of £3 10s.} = \frac{5}{100} \text{ of £3 10s.} = \frac{1}{20} \text{ of 70s.} = \text{3s. 6d.}$$

The following special cases should be noted :—

$2\% = \frac{1}{50}$;	$2\frac{1}{2}\% = \frac{1}{40}$;	$5\% = \frac{1}{20}$;	$6\frac{1}{4}\% = \frac{1}{16}$;
$8\frac{1}{3}\% = \frac{1}{12}$;	$10\% = \frac{1}{10}$;	$12\frac{1}{2}\% = \frac{1}{8}$;	$16\frac{2}{3}\% = \frac{1}{6}$;
$20\% = \frac{1}{5}$;	$25\% = \frac{1}{4}$;	$33\frac{1}{3}\% = \frac{1}{3}$;	$50\% = \frac{1}{2}$.

EXERCISE 85.

Express as fractions in their lowest terms :—

(1) 20%.	**(2)** 60%.	**(3)** 25%.	**(4)** $33\frac{1}{3}\%$.
(5) $16\frac{2}{3}\%$.	**(6)** $22\frac{1}{2}\%$.	**(7)** $13\frac{3}{4}\%$.	**(8)** 32%.
(9) 85%.	**(10)** 36%.	**(11)** $5\frac{1}{4}\%$.	**(12)** $7\frac{1}{2}\%$.
(13) $8\frac{2}{3}\%$.	**(14)** $7\frac{1}{7}\%$.	**(15)** $2\frac{3}{11}\%$.	**(16)** $6\frac{2}{13}\%$.

Find the value of

(17) 10%. of 50 and 650. **(18)** 25% of 16 and 1,780.
(19) 30% of 150 and 2,750. **(20)** 6¼% of 4,096.
(21) 3 1/11% of 550. **(22)** 8⅔% of 6,600.
(23) 6⅖% of 1,550. **(24)** 8⅓% of 240.
(25) 7 3/11% of 660. **(26)** 5% of £4.
(27) 2½% of £7 10s. **(28)** 15% of 10 tons 5 cwts.
(29) 16⅔% of £3 18s. **(30)** 12½% of 1 yd. 1 ft.
(31) 140% of 5s. 10d. **(32)** 215% of £560.
(33) 18% of £840. **(34)** 124% of £760 10s.
(35) 4% of £27 10s. **(36)** 5 3/11% of £4 11s. 8d.
(37) 17¾% of £9 3s. 4d. **(38)** 235% of 2 tons 2 cwts.
(39) 55% of 25 yds. 1 ft. 3 ins. **(40)** 2½% of 6 tons 1 cwt. 8 lbs.
(41) 112½% of 9 lbs. 5 ozs.
(42) 3 3/13% of 11 cwts. 2 qrs. 12 lbs.

(b) TO EXPRESS A FRACTION AS A PERCENTAGE.

Example 1.—What percentage is equal to ¾?
This means :—What number bears to 100 the ratio ¾?
This is evidently equivalent to finding what number is ¾ of 100.

$$\therefore \frac{3}{4} = \frac{3}{4} \times 100 \text{ per cent.} = 75 \text{ per cent.}$$

∴ **To convert a fraction into a percentage we merely multiply by 100.**

Example 2.—Express $\frac{22}{30}$ as a percentage.

$$\frac{22}{30} \text{ of } 100 = \frac{220}{3} = 73\frac{1}{3}. \qquad \therefore \frac{22}{30} = 73\frac{1}{3}\%.$$

EXERCISE 86.

Express the following fractions as percentages :—

(1) ½. **(2)** ⅓. **(3)** ¼. **(4)** ⅕.
(5) ⅙. **(6)** ⅛. **(7)** ⅖. **(8)** ⅗.
(9) ⅚. **(10)** ⅞. **(11)** 21/40. **(12)** ⅗.
(13) 23/50. **(14)** 7/6. **(15)** 2/7. **(16)** ⅘.
(17) 33/35. **(18)** 35/72. **(19)** 11/75. **(20)** 13/40.
(21) 15/32. **(22)** 56/160. **(23)** 34/80. **(24)** 14/55.
(25) 5/16. **(26)** 13/18.

(c) TO EXPRESS ONE QUANTITY AS A PERCENTAGE OF ANOTHER.

To express one quantity as a percentage of another we express it as a fraction of the other and then convert the fraction into a percentage.

Example 1.—What percentage of 75 is 15 ?

$$\frac{15}{75} = \frac{1}{5} = 20\% \text{—}i.e., \text{ 15 is } 20\% \text{ of 75.}$$

Example 2.—What percentage is 220 yards of 1 mile ?

$$\frac{220 \text{ yds.}}{1 \text{ mile}} = \frac{220}{1760} = \frac{1}{8} = 12\frac{1}{2}\%.$$

EXERCISE 87.

What percentage is

(1) 9 of 10.

(2) 200 of 300.

(3) 75 of 225.

(4) 20s. of 30s.

(5) 7s. 6d. of £1 2s. 6d.

(6) 1 yd. 1 ft. of 4 yds.

(7) 440 yds. of 2 miles.

(8) 2 cwts. 2 qrs. of 1 ton 5 cwts.

(9) 6d. of £1.

(10) 1s. 3d. of £1.

(11) £1 of 15s.

(12) 5 ozs. of 1 lb.

(13) 880 sq. yds. of 1 acre.

(14) 5s. 6d. of £1 8s. 6d.

(15) £1 8s. 4d. of £6.

(16) £2 3s. 6d. of £17 7s.

(17) £3 11s. 6d. of £18.

(18) 3 ft. 2 ins. of 4 yds.

(19) 4 yds. of 3 ft. 2 ins.

(20) 5 lbs. 2 ozs. of 16 lbs.

(21) £3 10s. of £18.

(22) £3 18s. 5d. of £15 13s. 8d.

(23) £1 8s. 3d. of £8 9s. 6d.

(24) 2 ft. 7 ins. of 2 yds. 1 ft. 9 ins.

(25) 7 cwts. 3 lbs. of 18 cwts. 19 lbs.

(d) KNOWING THAT A GIVEN QUANTITY IS A CERTAIN PERCENTAGE OF ANOTHER QUANTITY, TO FIND THAT OTHER QUANTITY.

Example 1.—9s. 6d. is 24% of a certain sum. Find the sum.

Here $\frac{24}{100}$ of the sum = 9s. 6d.

$$\therefore \text{ Sum} = 9s. 6d. \times \frac{100}{24} = \text{£1 19s. 7d.}$$

12

EXERCISE 88.

Find the quantity of which
(**1**) 15 is 20%.   (**2**) 16 is 25%.   (**3**) 18 is 50%.
(**4**) 17 is 33⅓%.   (**5**) 11 is 12½%.   (**6**) 9 is 5%.
(**7**) 3 is 4%.   (**8**) 10 is 2½%.   (**9**) 7½ is 25%.
(**10**) 22 is 40%.   (**11**) 24 is 60%.

Find the sum of which
(**12**) 2s. 6d. is 40%.   (**13**) 9s. 6d. is 24%.
(**14**) £15 7s. 6d. is 7½%.   (**15**) 17s. 11½d. is 12½%.
(**16**) £4 1s. 6d. is 15%.   (**17**) £6 is 25%.
(**18**) £2 10s. is 15%.   (**19**) £3 17s. 6d. is 30%.
(**20**) £1 2s. 3d. is 60.%   (**21**) £5 10s. 7½d. is 62½%.

Find the quantity of which
(**22**) 3 cwts. is 9%.   (**23**) 6 cwts. 3 qrs. is 27%.
(**24**) 7 lbs. 12 ozs. is 62%.   (**25**) 1 yd. 2 ft. 5 ins is 13%.
(**26**) 9 bush. 3 pks. is 26%.   (**27**) 20 minutes is 40%.
(**28**) 10 minutes 15 seconds is 41%.   (**29**) 2 ft. 8 ins. is 16%.
(**30**) 3 gallons 2 qts. is 28%.   (**31**) 2 sq. yds. 6 sq. ft. is 15%.

(e) MISCELLANEOUS EXAMPLES.

Example 1.—The population of a town was 15,000 in 1891. In 1901 it became 20,000. What was the increase per cent. ?
The increase on the 15,000 = 20,000 − 15,000 = 5,000.

$$\therefore \text{ Increase } \% = \frac{5,000}{15,000} \times 100$$
$$= \frac{100}{3} = 33\tfrac{1}{3}.$$

Example 2.—If the population of a town increased 12½% between 1891 and 1901, and if the population was 17,550 in 1901, what was it in 1891 ?
An increase of 12½% = an increase of ⅛.
Since the population increased by ⅛ of itself, it becomes 9/8 of itself.

$$\therefore 17,550 = \frac{9}{8} \text{ of population of 1891.}$$

That is, the population of 1891 = $\frac{8}{9}$ of 17,550 = 15,600.

EXERCISE 89.

(1) If the population of a town increase from 20,000 to 25,000, what is the rate of increase per cent. ?

(2) If the population of a town decrease from 25.000 to 20,000, what is the rate of decrease per cent. ?

(3) If a town of 16,000 inhabitants increase at the rate of 25 %, what does it become ?

(4) If a town increased $33\frac{1}{3}$ % between 1891 and 1901, find the population in 1891, its population in 1901 having been 20,000.

(5) A population decreased 15 % between 1891 and 1901. If the population in 1901 was 17,000, what was it in 1891 ?

(6) The population of a town is 10,000 ; if it increases 10 % every year, what will the population be in 2 years ?

(7) Sixty candidates sat an examination. If 15 % failed, how many passed ?

(8) Out of 200 candidates who sat an examination 160 passed, what was the percentage of failures ?

(9) At an examination consisting of three subjects there were 400 candidates. Of these 15 % passed in all the subjects. 20 % in 2 subjects, 25 % in 1 subject. How many failed in all 3 subjects ?

(10) A proprietor owns property whose annual rental is £300. If he has to pay an agent 5 % for collecting it, and then pay $2\frac{1}{2}$ % on the remainder for insurance, what is his net income from the property ?

(11) If a shopkeeper allows $7\frac{1}{2}$ % off his accounts for ready money, what do I pay for goods amounting to £7 10s. ?

(12) In a battle an army lost $12\frac{1}{2}$ % of its numbers. If it numbered 17,500 after the battle, how many were lost ?

(13) An army 25,000 strong lost 5 % in killed, $7\frac{1}{2}$ % in wounded, and 10 % in prisoners. What was the total number of casualties ?

(14) An agent receives $1\frac{1}{2}$ % commission for selling a house. What was the house sold for if his commission amounted to £18 ?

(15) A collector gets $2\frac{1}{2}\%$ on all rents which he collects. How much does he get for collecting £3,750 ?

(16) If a house-owner raises his rents by $7\frac{1}{2}\%$, what will the rent of a house become whose present rent is £35 ?

(17) After an engagement the casualties in an army were 2,275. If this was equal to $3\frac{1}{2}\%$ of the army. what was the original strength of the army ?

(18) The total number of pupils in a school is 180. On a certain day 5% of the number were absent. How many were present ?

(19) The number of boys in a class is 1 more than the number of girls. If the girls are 48% of the whole class, what does the class number ?

(20) The boys in a class number 18, and the number of girls is 40% of the whole class. What does the class number ?

(21) The population of a town is 1,500,000. It increases at the rate of 10% every year for three years. What will be the population at the end of the third year ?

(22) A certain number of candidates were entered for an examination. Of them 20% were absent and 15% of those present failed. If the number that passed was 17, how many were entered altogether ?

(23) The total output of a colliery is 600 tons per day. $2\frac{1}{2}\%$ of this output is burnt at the boiler fire, 1% is taken off the picking tables as dirt, 19% is dross. What is the output of coal ?

(24) $9\frac{1}{11}\%$ was deducted from a sum of money, and then $12\frac{1}{2}\%$ of the remainder was deducted. If £764 3s. 4d. was left, what was the original sum ?

(25) A man's salary was £410, but was reduced by $8\frac{1}{3}\%$. In addition he had to pay 5% on the money he received for superannuation. If he received his salary in 12 equal instalments, what did each instalment amount to ?

(26) The number on roll in a school was 450 and on a certain day $13\frac{1}{3}\%$ were absent. Of those present $53\frac{1}{3}\%$ were girls. How many boys were present on that day ?

CHAPTER XV.

PROFIT AND LOSS.

I. ACTUAL PROFIT OR LOSS.

When goods are sold for more than they cost they are said to be sold at *a profit*, and

The *Profit* = the *Selling Price* — the *Cost Price*.

When goods are sold for less than they cost they are said to be sold *at a loss*, and

The *Loss* = the *Cost Price* — the *Selling Price*.

Example 1.—A merchant bought 1 cwt. of sugar for 30s. and sold it at 4½d. per lb. Find his profit.

Selling Price = 4½d. × 112 = 504d.
Cost Price = 30s.   = 360d.
∴   Profit = 504 — 360 = 144d. = 12s.

Example 2.—A man bought 80 lbs. of tea at 2s. 6d. per lb. and sold the whole for £9 10s. Find his loss.

Cost of 1 lb. = 2s. 6d.
 „   80 lbs. = 2s. 6d. × 80 = £10
 Selling Price = £9 10s.
∴   Loss = 10s.

Example 3.—A grocer pays £11 4s. for 1 cwt. of tea. Find what he must sell it at per lb. in order to make a profit of £2 16s. on the transaction.

Cost Price of 1 cwt. = £11 4s.
Profit = £2 16s.
∴ Selling Price of 1 cwt. = £14.

∴ „   „   „ 1 lb. = $£\dfrac{14}{112} = £\dfrac{1}{8}$ = 2s. 6d.

EXERCISE 90.

(1) A grocer buys 200 lbs. of tea at 2s. per lb. and sells the whole at 2s. 3d. per lb. Find his profit.

(2) A farmer buys 6 horses for £144 and sells them at £28 each. Find his profit.

(3) A draper paid £120 for 600 yards of cloth and sold the whole at 6s. per yard. Find his profit.

(4) A merchant bought 3 bales of cloth, each containing 80 yards, for £30 and sold the cloth at 3s. 6d. per yard. Find his profit.

(5) A draper bought 200 yards of cloth for £25, and on selling out at a certain price per yard he found he had lost £5 on the whole transaction. Find what price he charged.

(6) A grocer purchased 2 cwts. of sugar for £2 17s. 6d. He sold the whole at 3d. per lb. Find his gain or loss.

(7) A grocer purchased 3 cwts. of sugar for £3 15s. If 20 lbs. were wasted and the remainder sold at $3\frac{1}{2}$d. per lb., find his profit.

(8) A retailer pays £10 10s. for 120 lbs. of tea. If he wishes to make a profit of £1 10s. on the whole, find what price per lb. he must charge.

(9) A merchant bought 180 lbs. of tea at 1s. 9d. per lb. and sold the whole at 2s. 2d. per lb. Find his profit.

(10) A horse dealer bought 6 horses for £108. He sold 3 of them for £20 each, 2 for £22 each, and the remaining one for £25. If the expenses were 15s. on each horse, find his profit.

II. PERCENTAGE RATE OF PROFIT OR LOSS.

The common and universal method of estimating the rate of profit or loss is to find the amount gained or lost on £100 *of expenditure*. This is known as *profit per cent.* or *loss per cent.*

It must be noted that this percentage of profit or of loss is calculated on the *outlay*, not on the income, *on the cost price*, not on the selling price, of an article.

Let us consider different types of questions that may arise.

(a) When the Cost Price and the Selling Price are known, to find the Profit or Loss per cent.

We have merely to find what fraction the actual profit or loss is of the outlay or cost price, and then express that fraction as a percentage.

Example 1.—A man paid £350 for certain goods and sold them for £420. Find his profit per cent.

$$\text{Cost Price} = £350.$$
$$\text{Selling Price} = £420.$$
$$\text{Profit on } £350 = £70.$$
$$\text{Thus the Profit} = \frac{70}{350} \text{ or } \frac{1}{5} \text{ of the cost.}$$
$$\therefore \text{Profit per cent.} = \frac{1}{5} \times 100 = 20.$$

Example 2.—A man paid £2 for an article and sold it for £1 15s. Find his loss per cent.

$$\text{Cost Price} \quad = £2.$$
$$\text{Selling Price} = £1 \ 15s.$$
$$\therefore \quad \text{Loss on } £2 \quad = 5s.$$
$$\therefore \quad \text{Loss per cent.} = \frac{5}{40} \text{ of } 100 = 12\tfrac{1}{2}.$$

EXERCISE 91.

Find the profit per cent. in the following cases (*may be done mentally*) :—

(1) Cost price = £4,   selling price = £5.

(2) ,,   = £5,   ,,   = £6.

(3) ,,   = £2 10s., ,,   = £3.

(4) ,,   = £1 10s., ,,   = £1 15s.

(5) ,,   = £2,   ,,   = £2 13s. 4d.

(6) ,,   = £1 6s. 8d., ,,   = £1 13s. 4d.

Find the loss per cent. in the following cases (*may be done mentally*) :—

    (7) Cost price = £4,   selling price = £3.
    (8)   ,,   = £5,   ,,   = £4.
    (9)   ,,   = £3 10s.,   ,,   = £3.
    (10)   ,,   = £1 7s. 6d.,   ,,   = £1 2s. 6d.
    (11)   ,,   = £1 17s. 6d., ,,   = £1 2s. 6d.

Find the profit or loss per cent. in the following cases :—

    (12) Cost price = £3 15s., selling price   = £4 2s. 6d.
    (13)   ,,   = 13s. 4d.,   ,,   = 3s. 4d.
    (14)   ,,   = £4 4s.,   ,,   = £2 12s. 6d.
    (15)   ,,   = £7 10s.,   ,,   = £9 10s. 6d.
    (16)   ,,   = £17 10s.,   ,,   = £20.
    (17)   ,,   = £10 7s. 6d.,   ,,   = £9 10s 6d.
    (18)   ,,   = £8 5s.,   ,,   = £7 10s.

(*b*) To find the Profit or Loss per cent. when the Cost Price and the Selling Price of Different Quantities are known.

In this case we must find first the cost price and the selling price of the *same quantity*.

Example 1.—A grocer bought 1 cwt. of sugar for £1 3s. 4d. and sold it at the rate of $3\frac{1}{2}$d. per lb. Find his profit per cent.

        Selling Price of 1 lb. = $3\frac{1}{2}$d.
              ,,   1 cwt. = $3\frac{1}{2} \times 112$ = 392d.
       Cost Price of 1 cwt. = £1 3s. 4d. = 280d.
  ∴   Profit on 280d. = 112d.
  ∴   Profit per cent. = $\dfrac{112}{280} \times 100 = 40$.

Here we have got the cost price and the selling price of 1 cwt., but we might have got the cost price and selling price of 1 lb. It will be found that the cost price of 1 lb. is $2\frac{1}{2}$d.

    Thus,   Cost price of 1 lb. = $2\frac{1}{2}$d.
          Selling price of 1 lb. = $3\frac{1}{2}$d.
            Profit on $2\frac{1}{2}$d. = 1d.
  ∴   Profit per cent. = $\dfrac{1}{2\frac{1}{2}} \times 100 = \dfrac{2}{5} \times 100 = 40$.

Example 2.—A woman bought oranges at the rate of 8d. per dozen and sold them at the rate of 10 for 9d. Find her profit per cent.

Here we know the cost price of 12 and the selling price of 10, but to find the profit per cent. we must know the prices of the same number. Now, we might choose the number 1, but in examples of this kind it is usually most convenient to choose the L.C.M. of the two numbers, because by so doing we avoid fractions. The L.C.M. of 10 and 12 is 60.

Thus, Cost price of 12 = 8d. ∴ C.P. of 60 = 40d.

Sale price of 10 = 9d. ∴ S.P. of 60 = 54d.

∴ Profit on 40d. = 14d.

∴ Profit per cent. $= \dfrac{14}{40} \times 100 = 35$.

EXERCISE 92.

Find the gain or loss per cent. in the following 8 cases :—

(1) Cost price per cwt. = 18s. 8d., selling price per lb. = 3d.
(2) ,, ,, = 28s., ,, ,, = 4½d.
(3) ,, ,, = £11 4s., ,, ,, = 2s. 6d.
(4) ,, ,, = £14, ,, ,, = 2s.
(5) ,, ,, = £10, ,, ,, = 2s. 3d.
(6) ,, per lb. = 2s. 6d., ,, per cwt. = £12 12s.
(7) ,, ,, = 2s. 3d., ,, ,, = £10 10s.
(8) ,, ,, = 2s., ,, ,, = £9 16s.
(9) A draper pays £7 10s. for a bale containing 60 yards of cloth. If he sells it at 3s. 6d. per yard, find his profit per cent.
(10) A dealer bought 5 horses for £120 and sold them for £30 each. Find his total gain and his gain per cent.
(11) A cattle dealer sold 2 cows for £15 each and 3 cows for £18 each. If the 5 cows cost him £80, find his gain per cent.
(12) A woman bought a gross of eggs for 8s. and sold them at 10d. per dozen. Find her profit per cent.
(13) A woman bought eggs at 100 for 12s. 6d. sold them at 1s. 9d. per dozen. Find her gain per cent.
(14) If oranges are bought at 1s. 3d. per score and sold at 11d. per dozen, find the profit per cent.

(15) If oranges are bought at 5 for 4d. and are sold at 4 for 5d.,
find the profit per cent.

(16) If oranges are bought at 4 for 5d. and sold at 5 for 4d., find
the loss per cent.

(17) If a man buys oranges at 8s. per gross and sells them at 1d.
each, find his gain per cent.

(18) If eggs cost 15s. per gross and are sold at $1\frac{1}{2}$d. each, find the
gain per cent.

(19) If a dairyman buys milk at 1s. 4d. a gallon and sells it at
$2\frac{1}{2}$d. a pint, find his gain per cent.

(20) If a coal merchant pays 27s. 6d. per ton for his coal and
sells it in bags of 1 cwt. at 2s. 6d. each, find his gain per cent.

(c) When the Cost Price and the Profit or Loss per cent. are known, to find the Selling Price.

Example 1.—If an article cost £3 10s. and was sold at a profit
of 15 per cent., find the selling price.

Bearing in mind that " 15 per cent." means " 15 per cent. of
the cost price," we see that to give a profit of 15 per cent. the
selling price must be equal to the cost price + 15 per cent. of
the cost price—that is, 115 per cent. of cost price.

Thus,   Cost price = £3 10s.
              Selling price = 115% of £3 10s.
                            $= \dfrac{115}{100}$ of 70s. $= \dfrac{23}{2} \times 7$s.
                            $= \dfrac{161\text{s.}}{2} = $ £4 0s. 6d.

Example 2.—An article which cost £5 was sold at a loss of
$7\frac{1}{2}$ per cent. Find the selling price.

                    Loss $= 7\frac{1}{2}\%$.
        ∴ Selling price $= 92\frac{1}{2}\%$ of cost price.
        ∴   ,, $= \dfrac{92\frac{1}{2}}{100}$ of £5
                              $= \dfrac{185}{200}$ of £5 = £4 12s. 6d.

Example 3.—If a grocer buys tea at £9 6s. 8d. per cwt., find what price he must charge per lb. for it in order to gain 20 per cent.

$$\text{Profit} = 20\%.$$

∴ Selling price = 120% of cost price.

∴ Selling price of 1 cwt. = £9 6s. 8d. $\times \dfrac{120}{100}$

$$= 2{,}240\text{d.} \times \frac{120}{100} = 224\text{s.}$$

∴ Selling price of 1 lb. = $\dfrac{224\text{s.}}{112} = 2\text{s.}$

Or, we might have found the cost price of 1 lb. (20d.) and then multiplied by $\dfrac{120}{100}$, giving 2s.

EXERCISE 93.

(1) If tea cost 2s. per lb., find the selling price in order to gain 25 per cent.

(2) If an article cost 3s. 6d. and was sold at a profit of $33\frac{1}{3}$ per cent., find the selling price.

(3) If sugar cost 2d. per lb., find what it must be sold at to gain $12\frac{1}{2}$ per cent.

(4) An article which cost 8s 4d. was sold at a loss of 10 per cent. Find the selling price.

(5) If a grocer buys tea at 1s. 9d. per lb., find what he must sell it at per lb. so as to gain $33\frac{1}{3}$ per cent.

(6) If tea cost 1s. 6d. per lb., find at what rate it must be sold per lb. so as to gain $16\frac{2}{3}$ per cent.

(7) Tea which cost 1s. 6d. per lb. was sold at a loss of $16\frac{2}{3}$ per cent. What was the selling price ?

(8) A farmer paid £25 for a horse, and on selling it lost 20 per cent. What did he sell it for ?

(9) If a grocer pays 28s. for 1 cwt. of sugar, find what price he must charge per lb. for it in order to gain 25 per cent.

(10) A merchant paid £13 10s. for 120 lbs. of tea, and sold it so as to gain $33\frac{1}{3}$ per cent. What did he charge per lb. for it ?

(11) A merchant who paid for his potatoes at the rate of 8d. per stone sold a sack of 12 stones at a profit of 50 per cent. What price did he charge for the sack ?

(12) A merchant bought goods at £25 per ton. If he wishes to make a profit of 40 per cent., what price must he sell them at per lb. ?

(13) A house which cost £850 was sold at a profit of $11\frac{13}{17}$ per cent. What was the selling price ?

(14) If a grocer paid £1 3s. 4d. for 1 cwt. of sugar, what must he sell it at per lb. in order to gain 20 per cent. ?

(15) If an article cost £5 15s. 10d., what must it be sold for in order to gain 15 per cent. ?

(d) When the Selling Price and the Profit or Loss per cent. are known, to find the Cost Price.

Example 1.—An article was sold for 9s. 7d. at a profit of 15 per cent. Find the cost price.

$$\text{Selling price} = 115 \text{ per cent. of cost price}$$
$$= \frac{115}{100} \text{ of cost price.}$$

$$\therefore \frac{115}{100} \text{ of cost price} = 9s. 7d.$$

$$\therefore \quad \text{Cost price} = 9s. 7d. \times \frac{100}{115} = 8s. 4d.$$

Example 2.—A grocer, who charged 2s. 0½d. for 7 lbs of sugar, found that he had lost thereby $12\frac{1}{2}$ per cent. Find what the sugar cost him per lb.

$$\text{Selling price} = 87\frac{1}{2}\% \text{ of cost price} = \frac{7}{8} \text{ of cost price.}$$

$$\therefore \quad \frac{7}{8} \text{ of cost price of 7 lbs.} = 2s. 0\frac{1}{2}d.$$

$$\therefore \quad \text{Cost price of 7 lbs} = 2s. 0\frac{1}{2}d. \times \frac{8}{7}$$
$$= \frac{49d.}{2} \times \frac{8}{7} = 28d.$$

$$\therefore \quad \text{Cost price of 1 lb.} = 4d.$$

EXERCISE 94.

(1) Find the cost of an article which was sold for 5s. at a profit of 25 per cent.

(2) An article was sold for £6 at a profit of 20 per cent. Find the cost.

(3) When sugar is sold at $3\frac{1}{2}$d. per lb. the profit is $16\frac{2}{3}$ per cent. Find the cost price.

(4) An article was sold for £3 10s. at a loss of $12\frac{1}{2}$ per cent. Find the cost.

(5) A farmer sold a horse for £26 and gained 30 per cent. Find what he paid for it.

(6) When tea is sold at 2s. 10d. per lb. the profit is at the rate of $13\frac{1}{3}$ per cent. Find the cost price.

(7) A man lost $6\frac{2}{3}$ per cent. by selling an article for 2s. 4d. What did it cost him?

(8) On selling a sack of potatoes containing 12 stones for 13s. 3d. a merchant made a profit of $32\frac{1}{2}$ per cent. Find what he paid per stone for them

(9) A dairyman gained $13\frac{1}{3}$ per cent. by selling butter at 1s. 5d. per lb. How much per lb. did it cost him?

(10) If 15 per cent is lost by selling an article for £34, what did the article cost?

(11) If 17 per cent. is lost by selling goods for £166, what did they cost?

(12) If $12\frac{1}{2}$ per cent. is gained by selling 12 lbs. of tea for 27s., find what the tea cost per lb.

(13) By selling tea at 2s. 6d. per lb. a merchant made a profit of 25 per cent. How much did 1 cwt. of the tea cost him?

(14) If 26 per cent. is gained by selling tea at 2s. 3d. per lb., what did it cost per cwt.?

(15) By selling coal at 1s. 10d. per cwt. bag, a coal merchant made a profit of $37\frac{1}{2}$ %. At what price per ton had he bought the coals?

(16) A dairyman sold his milk at 3d. per pint, making a profit of 60 %. At what price per gallon had he bought the milk?

(17) A merchant sold a ton of potatoes at $1/2\frac{1}{2}$ per stone, making a profit of 45 %. What had he paid for the ton?

(*e*) **When the Selling Price and the Profit or Loss per cent. is known, to find the Profit or Loss per cent. on any other Selling Price, or the Selling Price which would yield any other Rate of Profit or Loss.**

Example 1.—When an article is sold for 7s. 6d. the profit is 25 per cent. What would have been the profit per cent. if it had been sold for 8s. ?

$$7s. \ 6d. = 125\% \text{ of the cost.}$$

$$\therefore \ 8s. \quad = 125 \times \frac{8s.}{7s. \ 6d.}\% \text{ of the cost (*ratio method*)}$$

$$= 125 \times \frac{16}{15}\% \text{ of the cost}$$

$$= 133\tfrac{1}{3}\% \text{ of the cost.}$$

∴ Profit gained by selling at 8s. $= 33\tfrac{1}{3}$ per cent.

Example 2.—If tea were sold at 1s. 10d. per lb. there would be a loss of $8\tfrac{1}{3}$ per cent. What would be the gain per cent. if it were sold for 2s. 6d. per lb. ?

$$1s. \ 10d. = 91\tfrac{2}{3}\% \text{ of the cost.}$$

$$\therefore \ 2s. \ 6d. = 91\tfrac{2}{3} \times \frac{2s. \ 6d.}{1s. \ 10d.}\% \text{ of the cost (*ratio method*)}$$

$$= \frac{275}{3} \times \frac{30}{22}\% \text{ of the cost}$$

$$= 125\% \text{ of the cost.}$$

∴ On selling at 2s. 6d. profit $= 25\%$.

Example 3.—On selling a horse for £40 a dealer gained $11\tfrac{1}{9}$ per cent. on his outlay. If he wished to gain 25 %, what price should he have sold it at ?

Thus,　　　　$111\tfrac{1}{9}\%$ of cost = £40.

$$\therefore \quad 125\% \quad ,, \quad = £40 \times \frac{125}{111\tfrac{1}{9}} = £45.$$

A similar type of question to the above is the following :—

Example 4.—A man sold an article at a profit of 25 per cent. If he had charged 7s. 6d. more for it its profit would have been 40 per cent. Find the price he sold it for.

Here 7s. 6d. is equivalent to a profit of 15 per cent. (40 — 25).

Thus, $\qquad$ 15% of cost = 7s. 6d.

and $\qquad$ selling price = 125% of cost = 7s. 6d. $\times \dfrac{125}{15} = 62\frac{1}{2}$s.

∴ $\qquad$ Selling price = £3 2s. 6d.

EXERCISE 95.

(1) If 25% is gained when an article is sold for 7s. 6d., what would have been the profit per cent. if it had been sold for 10s. ?

(2) If a selling price of 5s. 6d. gives a gain of 10 per cent., what gain per cent. would a selling price of 6s. give ?

(3) When an article was sold for £3 10s. the profit was 40 per cent. What would have been the profit per cent. if it had been sold for £4 ?

(4) On selling an article for 8s. 6d. a man gained $6\frac{1}{4}$ per cent. What selling price would have gained 25 per cent. ?

(5) If 5 per cent. was lost by selling an article for 9s. 6d., what selling price would have given a profit of 5 per cent. ?

(6) If 20 per cent. is gained by selling a horse for £42, what would have been gained per cent. if it had been sold for £49 ?

(7) If 4 per cent. was lost by selling a horse for £48, what would have been the gain per cent. if it had been sold for £54 ?

(8) A grocer gains $16\frac{2}{3}$ per cent. by selling his sugar at $3\frac{1}{2}$d. per lb. What per cent. would he have gained if he had sold it at 4d. per lb. ?

(9) If $3\frac{1}{3}$ per cent. is lost by selling a cart for £14 10s., what selling price would have gained $3\frac{1}{3}$ per cent. ?

(10) By selling a carriage for £57 15s. a carriage-builder made a profit of $15\frac{1}{2}$ per cent. What would have been his profit per cent. if he had sold it for £68 10s. ?

(11) If a selling price of $2\frac{1}{2}$d. per lb. gives a profit of 25 per cent., what selling price would give a profit of 50 per cent. ?

(12) A merchant sold an article at a profit of 25 per cent. If he had sold it for 4s. more his profit would have been 50 per cent. What did he sell it for ?

(13) A man made a profit of $8\frac{1}{3}$ per cent. by selling a sack of potatoes. If he had charged 6d. more for it his profit would have been $11\frac{1}{9}$ per cent. What did he sell it for ?

(14) If $6\frac{2}{3}$ per cent. more be gained by selling an article for £10 than by selling it for £9 10s., find the cost of the article.

(15) If 25 per cent. more be gained by selling an article for 12s. than by selling it for 10s., what was the cost of the article ?

(16) A man sold an article at a profit of 20%. If he had sold it for 10s. more his profit would have been 40%. What did he sell it for ?

(17) A man sold an article at a profit of 25 per cent. If he had sold it for 8s. more his profit would have been 45 per cent. What did he sell the article at ?

(18) If a difference of 1s. 6d. in the selling price of an article means a difference of 5 per cent. in the profit obtained, what did the article cost ?

(19) A man gained $12\frac{1}{2}$ per cent. by selling an article for £36. What profit per cent. would he have made if he had charged £2 more for it ?

(*f*) When the Original Cost of an Article is known, to find the Final Selling Price after it has passed through the hands of several Middlemen, or to find the Original Cost when the Final Selling Price is known.

Example 1.—A buys an article for £40 and sells it to B at a profit of 20 per cent. B sells it to C at a profit of 30 per cent. C sells it to D at a profit of 25 per cent. Find what D paid for it.

Let S.P. denote selling price and C.P. denote cost price.

A's S.P. = his C.P. $\times \dfrac{120}{100} = £40 \times \dfrac{120}{100}$ [see Section (*c*)].

B's S.P. = his C.P. $\times \dfrac{130}{100} = \left(40 \times \dfrac{120}{100}\right) \times \dfrac{130}{100}.$

C's S.P. = his C.P. $\times \dfrac{125}{100} = \left(£40 \times \dfrac{120}{100} \times \dfrac{130}{100}\right) \times \dfrac{125}{100} = £78.$

Profit and Loss.

In practice the operation is in one step.

Thus, Price paid by D = £40 $\times \frac{120}{100} \times \frac{130}{100} \times \frac{125}{100}$ = £78.

Example 2.—A sells an article to B at a profit of 20 per cent. B sells it to C at a profit of 30 per cent. C sells it to D for £78, making a profit of 25 per cent. Find what it cost A.

C's C.P. = $\frac{100}{125}$ of his S.P. = £78 $\times \frac{100}{125}$ [see Section (*d*)].

B's C.P. = $\frac{100}{130}$ of his S.P. = £78 $\times \frac{100}{125} \times \frac{100}{130}$.

A's C.P. = $\frac{100}{120}$ of his S.P. = £78 $\times \frac{100}{125} \times \frac{100}{130} \times \frac{100}{120}$ = £40.

As in the last example, this also may be done in one operation.

EXERCISE 96.

(1) A buys an article for £10 and sells it to B at a profit of 15 per cent. B sells it to C at a profit of 10 per cent. What did C pay for it?

(2) A sells an article to B at a profit of 20 per cent. B sells it to C for £31 4s., making a profit of 30 per cent. What did it cost A?

(3) A pays 18s. for an article and sells it to B at a profit of $16\frac{2}{3}$ per cent. B sells it to C at a profit of $33\frac{1}{3}$ per cent. What did C pay for it?

(4) A pays £3 for an article and sells it to B at a profit of $12\frac{1}{2}$ per cent. B sells it to C at a profit of 20 per cent. C sells it to D at a profit of 25 per cent. Find what D paid for it.

(5) A sold an article to B at a profit of 20 per cent. B sold it to C at a profit of $12\frac{1}{2}$ per cent., and D bought it from C for £4 4s. $4\frac{1}{2}$d. If C's profit was 25 per cent., find what the article cost A.

(6) An article cost a manufacturer £15. He sold it to a merchant at a profit of 30 per cent. The merchant sold it to an agent at a profit of 45 per cent. The agent sold it to a customer at a profit of 50 per cent. Find what the customer paid for it.

(7) A tea dealer sells his tea to a wholesale merchant at a profit of 25 per cent. The wholesale merchant sells it to a retailer at a profit of 20 per cent. The retailer sells it to his customers at a profit of $33\frac{1}{3}$ per cent. If this retail price is 3s. 6d. per lb., find what the tea cost the tea dealer per lb.

(8) A tea dealer pays 2s. 1d. per lb. for his tea. He sells it at a profit of 25 per cent. to a wholesale merchant, who sells to a retailer at a profit of 40 per cent. What must the retailer charge per lb. for it if he wishes to make a profit of 60 per cent. ?

(g) Miscellaneous Examples.

Example 1.—A merchant buys a quantity of oranges at 12 for 5d., and an equal quantity at 20 for 1s. If he sells the whole indiscriminately at the rate of 9d. per dozen, find his profit per cent.

As 60 is the L.C.M. of 12 and 20, it will be convenient to find the cost price of 60 of each kind.

Thus,   When cost of 12 = 5d., cost of 60 = 25d.
            ,,   20 = 12.,   ,,   60 = 36d.
                      ∴ Cost of 120 = 61d.
When selling price of 12 = 9d., S.P. of 120 = 90d.
                  ∴ Profit on 61d. = 29d.
∴ Profit per cent. $= \dfrac{29}{61} \times 100 = 47\dfrac{33}{61}$, *i.e.*, Profit $= 47\dfrac{33}{61}\%$.

Example 2.—If a dairyman buys his milk at 6d. per gallon and adds $1\frac{1}{2}$ pints of water for every gallon of milk and then sells it at 1d. per pint, find his profit per cent.

To 8 pints of milk which cost 6d., there is added $1\frac{1}{2}$ pints of water.

     ∴ Cost of $9\frac{1}{2}$ pints   = 6d.
   and   Selling price of $9\frac{1}{2}$ pints = $9\frac{1}{2}$d. (at 1d. per pint).
      ∴ Profit on 6d.   = $3\frac{1}{2}$d.
        ∴ Profit per cent. $= \dfrac{3\frac{1}{2}}{6} \times 100 = 58\dfrac{1}{3}$.

Example 3.—If a merchant sells 5 eggs for the price he paid for 6, find his profit per cent.

Here the price he charges for 5 eggs = the price he paid for them + the price he paid for 1 egg.

$$\text{Thus his profit} = \frac{1}{5} = 20\%.$$

It may make it clearer if we imagine he paid 1d. for each egg. Then he would be charging 6d. for what cost him 5d.

Example 4.—A merchant marks his goods 20 per cent. above what they cost him, but deducts 5 per cent. from the marked price for immediate cash payment. Find the actual cash he charges for goods marked £3. Also find the cost price and the net profit per cent.

(1) Cash payment   = marked price − 5 per cent. of M.P.

$$= £3 - \frac{5}{100} \text{ of } £3$$

$$= £3 - 3s. = £2 \ 17s.$$

(2) Marked price   = 120 per cent. of cost price

$$= \frac{120}{100} \text{ of cost price.}$$

∴ $\frac{120}{100}$ of cost price = £3.

∴   Cost price $= £3 \times \frac{100}{120} = £2 \ 10s.$

(3) Net profit   = cash price − cost price

$$= £2 \ 17s. - £2 \ 10s.$$

i.e.,   Profit on £2 10s. = 7s.

∴   Profit per cent. $= \dfrac{7s.}{£2 \ 10s.} \times 100$

$$= \frac{7}{50} \times 100 = 14, \ i.e., \textbf{Profit} = 14\%.$$

EXERCISE 97.

(1) A grocer buys a certain number of eggs at 1s. 6d. per dozen and the same number at 2s. per dozen. He mixes them and sells them at 1s. 10d. per dozen. Find his gain or loss per cent.

(2) A grocer buys 1 gross of oranges at 5d. per dozen and 2 gross at 6d. per dozen. He sells the whole at the uniform rate of 9d. per dozen. Find his total gain and his gain per cent.

(3) A grocer bought 20 dozen eggs at 1s. 8d. a dozen. He lost 4 dozen by breakages. Find what he must charge per dozen for the rest in order to get a profit of 20 per cent on the transaction.

(4) A merchant sells 2 cabbages for the price he paid for 3. Find his profit per cent.

(5) A grocer sold oranges so as to get for 10 the price he paid for 12. Find his gain per cent.

(6) If a grocer were to charge for 12 oranges the price he paid for 10, what would be his loss per cent. ?

(7) A woman charged for a dozen eggs the price she paid for 20. What was her gain per cent. ?

(8) A dairyman buys milk at 10d. per gallon. He adds 1½ pints of water to every gallon. Find his gain per cent. if he sells it at 2d. per pint.

(9) A dairyman pays 11d. per gallon for his milk. To every gallon he adds 2 pints of water. If he then sells it at 2½d. per pint, find his profit per cent.

(10) A merchant paid £10 for an article and marked it at a selling price of £13, but on selling it to a customer he took 5 per cent. off the marked price. What price did the customer pay, and what was the percentage of profit which the merchant made ?

(11) A merchant marked his goods so as to give a profit of 33⅓ per cent., but deducted 4 per cent. from the marked price for ready payment. Find (1) the cost price of an article marked at £20 (2) the ready cash payment, and (3) the net profit per cent.

(12) If a merchant marks his goods 25 per cent. above cost price, and then deducts 4 per cent. from the marked price for ready cash payment, find his actual profit per cent.

(13) If a merchant marks his goods at 30 per cent. above cost price and allows a discount of 5 per cent. of the marked price for ready payment, find (1) the marked price of goods for which the ready payment was £3 1s. 9d. (2) the cost price, and (3) the actual profit per cent.

(14) A merchant who paid 8s. for an article marked it at $37\frac{1}{2}$ per cent. above cost price, but sold it to a customer for 10s. 1d. ready cash. What percentage did he deduct from the marked price, and what was the actual rate of his profit per cent. ?

(15) A grocer buys a number of oranges at 1s. 4d. per score, and double that number at 6d. per dozen. He mixes them and sells them indiscriminately at 9d. per dozen. Find his gain per cent.

(16) A grocer buys a number of oranges at 1s. 1d. per score, and 3 times that number at 5d. per dozen. He mixes them all together and sells them so as to gain $66\frac{2}{3}$ per cent. on his outlay. Find the price per dozen at which he sold them.

(17) A man pays £72 for certain goods. He sells $\frac{1}{3}$ of them at a gain of 25 per cent., and another $\frac{1}{3}$ at a loss of $12\frac{1}{2}$ per cent. If he sells the remaining $\frac{1}{3}$ for £28, find his profit or loss per cent. on the whole.

We shall now add a number of examples of all kinds for revision

EXERCISE 98.

(1) Find the cost of a horse which was sold for £44 at a gain of 10 per cent.

(2) On selling a horse which cost him £110 a man lost 18 per cent. What did he sell it for ?

(3) By selling tea at the rate of 2 lbs. for 4s. 6d. a merchant lost 10 per cent. Find what he paid per cwt. for the tea.

(4) A coal merchant pays 18s. 3d. per ton for his coal, and his expenses for carriage and cartage amount to 4s. 3d. per ton. Find what he must charge per ton in order to make a profit of 40 per cent. on his total outlay.

(5) A grocer bought 1 cwt. 3 qrs. 11 lbs. of tea for £18 and sold the whole at 2s. per lb. Find (1) his total profit, and (2) his profit per cent.

(6) A grocer by charging 4½d. per lb. for sugar makes a profit of 50 per cent. How much must he sell in order to make a total profit of £3 5s. 6d. ?

(7) A grocer makes a profit of 30 per cent. by selling tea at 3s. 3d. per lb. What would be his total profit on a box containing 32 lbs. ?

(8) Oranges are bought at 20 for 1s. 2d. and sold at 5 for 4d. Find the profit per cent.

(9) A grocer buys 60 eggs at 1s. 3d. a dozen and 144 at 1s. 4d. a dozen. He sells the whole at the uniform rate of 1s. 6d. a dozen. Find his total gain and his gain per cent.

(10) On selling sugar at 3½d. per lb. a man lost 12½ per cent. What did it cost him per cwt. ?

(11) By selling an article for £63 a man gained 12½ per cent. What did the article cost him ?

(12) If 12½ per cent. is gained by selling an article for £45, what would have been the gain per cent. if it had been sold for £50 ?

(13) If eggs are bought at 1s. per score and sold at 10d. per dozen, find the gain per cent.

(14) A farmer paid £90 for 6 horses. Taking them to a market he sold 3 of them at £20 each, 2 of them at £22 each, and the remaining 1 at £25. If a market fee of 1s. 3d. per horse is deducted from the proceeds of the sale find his net profit, and his profit per cent.

(15) If 12½ per cent. was lost by selling an article for £2 9s., what should it have been sold for in order to have gained 12½ per cent. ?

(16) Find the cost price of an article if a difference of 12s. 9d. in the selling price means a difference of 7½ per cent. in the profit.

(17) An article was sold for 35 per cent. profit. It if had been sold for 10d. more, the profit would have been 40 per cent. What was it sold for.?

(18) A grocer sold a certain amount of tea at 3s. 6d. per lb. at a profit of 40 per cent. If his total profit was £5 12s., find the amount of tea sold.

(19) If a grocer makes a profit of 12½ per cent. by selling tea at 2s. 3d. per lb., what profit would he make by the sale of 2 cwts. 10 lbs. ?

(20) If a stationer makes a profit of $1\frac{1}{2}$d. on every dozen of pencils which he sells, and if he charges 6d. per dozen, find his profit per cent.

(21) By selling pencils at 5s. $2\frac{1}{2}$d. per 100, a stationer makes a profit of 2d. on every dozen sold. Find the cost price per dozen, and his profit per cent.

(22) A farmer bought two cows, paying the same price for each. He sold one for £18 at a profit of 20 per cent. The other he sold for £20. Find the profit per cent. on the latter.

(23) A grocer buys 5 cwts. 3 qrs. of sugar for £6 6s., and pays 8s. 2d. for expenses. Find what price he must charge per lb. for it in order to make a profit of 40 per cent. on his whole outlay.

(24) A spirit merchant mixes 70 gallons of whisky at 27s. 6d. per gallon with 50 gallons at 25s. per gallon. Find at what price per gallon he sells the mixture if he makes a profit of 60 per cent.

(25) A merchant makes a profit of $12\frac{1}{2}$ per cent. by selling 1 cwt. of tea for £12 12s. What price must he charge per lb. in order to gain 25 per cent. ?

(26) A grocer mixes 3 lbs. of tea at 2s. 9d. per lb. with 5 lbs. at 1s. 9d. per lb. If he wishes to make a profit of $33\frac{1}{3}$ per cent., how much per lb. must he charge for the mixture ?

(27) A man pays £36 for certain goods. He sells $\frac{2}{3}$ of them at a loss of $12\frac{1}{2}$ per cent. What must he charge for the remaining $\frac{1}{3}$ in order to gain $33\frac{1}{3}$ per cent. on the whole ?

(28) A man pays £40 for certain goods. He sells $\frac{3}{4}$ of them at a loss of 10 per cent. If he gets £21 for the remaining $\frac{1}{4}$, find his gain per cent. on the whole.

(29) A merchant mixes tea which cost him 2s. per lb. with tea which cost him 1s. 10d. per lb. in the proportion of 2 lbs. of the former to 3 lbs. of the latter. Find his profit per cent. if he sold the mixture at 2s. 3d. per lb.

(30) A merchant paid £8 a ton for potatoes, and by selling them at 15s. a sack he makes 25 per cent. profit, find the weight of potatoes in the sack.

(31) If a merchant allows 2½ per cent. off his selling price for cash payment, what was the selling price of goods for which he received £2 8s. 9d. cash payment, and what did the goods cost him if they were priced so as to give a profit of 25 per cent., and what was his net profit per cent. ?

(32) A merchant marked his goods at a profit of 50 per cent., but on selling for ready cash his net profit was only 44 per cent. Find how much per cent of the selling price was deducted. Find also the cost of goods for which he received 36s. cash.

(33) A woman bought a certain number of eggs at 9d. per dozen and the same number at 11d. per dozen. She mixes them and sells them at 1s. per dozen. Find her profit per cent.

(34) A woman bought a certain number of eggs at 8d. a dozen and double the number at 9½d. a dozen. She mixes them and sells them indiscriminately at 1s. per dozen. Find her profit per cent.

(35) A woman bought a number of eggs at 1s. per score and the same number at 10d. per dozen. If she mixes them and sells them at 1s. per dozen, find her gain per cent.

(36) When certain goods were sold for £6 18s. 6½d. a profit of 25 per cent. was made. What selling price would have given a profit of 20 per cent. ?

(37) If a sale price of £1,000 for a house realises a profit of 33⅓ per cent., find what per cent. would have been gained or lost if it had been sold (1) for £800 and (2) for £700.

(38) A grocer mixes tea which cost 1s. 8d. per lb. with tea which cost 2s. 2d. per lb. in the proportion of 1 to 2. At what rate must he sell the mixture to gain 75 per cent. ?

(39) A sold an article to B at a profit of 20 per cent. B sold it to C at a profit of 30 per cent. C sold it to D at a profit of 40 per cent. If D paid £109 4s. for the article, find what it cost A.

(40) A sold an article to B at a profit of 50 per cent. B sold it to C at a profit of 33⅓ per cent. If the price that B paid to A for it was £60, find (1) what it cost A and (2) what B sold it to C for ?

(**41**) A dairyman buys milk at 1s. 4d. per gallon, and after diluting it with water sells it at 2d. a pint, making a profit of 25 per cent. How much water did he add to a gallon of milk ?

(**42**) A dairyman adds $1\frac{1}{3}$ pints of water to every gallon of milk, and then sells it at $1\frac{1}{2}$d. per pint, making a profit of 40 per cent. Find what price per gallon he paid for his milk.

(**43**) A dairyman pays 9d. per gallon for milk. After adding 1 pint of water to every gallon of milk, what should he now sell it for per pint if he wishes to make a profit of 50 per cent. ?

<hr>

CHAPTER XVI.

SIMPLE INTEREST.

Interest is the name given to the money which is paid for the loan of money. The amount of the **interest** which is paid for the loan or use of money depends on the amount of money loaned and on the time for which it is loaned, and is reckoned at so much **per cent. per annum.**

Thus, when we say that the **rate of interest** is 4 **per cent. per annum** we mean that £4 is paid for the loan of £100 for 1 year.

The sum of money loaned is called the **Principal,** and the sum of the Principal and the Interest is called the **Amount.**

The Interest is directly proportional to the Principal, and in " **Simple Interest** " it is also **directly proportional to the time.** In what is known as " **Compound Interest** " the interest earned the first year is added to the Principal, and this sum is the new Principal for the second year, and so on, so that the interest increases each year, whereas in **Simple Interest** the interest on any given principal at any given rate is the same during every year of the loan.

In this chapter we shall deal with Simple Interest only.

Questions under Simple Interest involve no new principles, as they can all be worked by the **unitary** or **ratio methods,** with which the pupil is already familiar.

We shall divide the chapter into three sections.

(a) **TO FIND THE SIMPLE INTEREST ON ANY SUM OF MONEY FOR A GIVEN TIME AT A GIVEN RATE.**

Example 1.—Find the simple interest on £650 for 7 years at 3 per cent. per annum.

The interest on £100 for 1 year $= £3$

$\therefore$,, £1 for 1 year $= £\dfrac{3}{100}$.

$\therefore$,, £650 for 7 years $= £\dfrac{3 \times 650 \times 7}{100}$

$= £136$ 10s.

Or thus:—

As the interest for **1** year is **3** per cent. of the Principal,

$\therefore$ Interest on £650 for 1 year $= 3\%$ of £650

$= £650 \times \dfrac{3}{100}$.

$\therefore$ Interest on £650 for 7 years $= £\dfrac{650 \times 3 \times 7}{100}$.

Thus, we see that :—

$$\textbf{Interest} = \frac{\textbf{Principal} \times \textbf{Rate} \times \textbf{Time}}{\textbf{100}}.$$

In using the rule thus found, we must remember that " **time** " means the number of **years.**

Example 2.—Find the interest on £480 for 2 years 8 months at 5 per cent. per annum.

Here the " Time " $= 2\frac{2}{3}$ years, Rate $= 5$, Principal $= £480$.

$\therefore$ Interest $= \dfrac{\text{Principal} \times \text{Rate} \times \text{Time}}{100}$.

$= \dfrac{£480 \times 5 \times 2\frac{2}{3}}{100} = £64.$

If the **amount** is required, we first find the **interest** as above, and then add it to the principal.

Thus **the amount** of £480 in 2 years 8 months at 5 per cent. $= £480 + £64 = £544.$

EXERCISE 99.

Find the simple interest on

(**1**) £840 for 3 years at 5 per cent.
(**2**) £450 for 4 years at 2 per cent.
(**3**) £750 for $5\frac{1}{2}$ years at 4 per cent.
(**4**) £1,250 for $7\frac{1}{2}$ years at 3 per cent.
(**5**) £3,570 for 10 years at $4\frac{1}{2}$ per cent.
(**6**) £140 for 5 years at $4\frac{2}{5}$ per cent.
(**7**) £750 for 2 years 8 months at 4 per cent.
(**8**) £650 10s. for 1 year 5 months at 5 per cent.

Find the amount of

(**9**) £1,260 for 12 years at $1\frac{5}{6}$ per cent.
(**10**) £18 4s. for $7\frac{1}{2}$ years at 5 per cent.
(**11**) £800 10s. for 3 years 9 months at 4 per cent.
(**12**) £975 15s. for 2 years 10 months at 5 per cent.

When the time is expressed in days, it must be noted that a day $= \frac{1}{365}$ of a year.

Also, in calculating the number of days from one date to another, the first date is not counted. Thus, from 1st January to 2nd January is one day. From 4th January to 7th January is three days $(7 - 4 = 3)$. And in working examples, where the result does not come out to be an exact sum, fractions of a penny may be neglected.

Example 1.—Find the simple interest on £912 10s. for 150 days at 5 per cent. per annum.

$$\text{Interest} = \frac{\text{Prin.} \times \text{Rate} \times \text{Time}}{100}$$
$$= \text{£}\frac{912\frac{1}{2} \times 5 \times \frac{150}{365}}{100} = \text{£18 15s.}$$

Example 2.—A sum of £75 is lent out on the 10th of March at 4 per cent. Find how much interest is due on the 8th of June following.

Number of days $= (31 - 10)$ in March $+ 30$ in April $+ 31$ in May $+ 8$ in June $= 21 + 30 + 31 + 8 = 90$ days.

$$\therefore \text{ Interest} = \frac{\text{Prin.} \times \text{Rate} \times \text{Time}}{100}$$

$$= £75 \times 4 \times \frac{90}{365} \times \frac{1}{100}$$

$$= £\frac{54}{73} = 14s.\ 9d.\ \text{(neglecting fractions of a}$$
$$\text{penny).}$$

EXERCISE 100.

Find the simple interest on
(1) £350 for 73 days at $2\frac{1}{2}$ per cent.
(2) £850 for 146 days at 4 per cent.
(3) £182 10s. for 100 days at 6 per cent.
(4) £912 10s. for 150 days at 5 per cent.
(5) £638 15s. for 80 days at $3\frac{1}{2}$ per cent.
(6) £273 15s. from 8th June to 23rd August at $2\frac{1}{2}$ per cent.
(7) £25 from 26th July to 7th October at 4 per cent.
(8) £51 2s. from 12th May to 20th August at $2\frac{1}{2}$ per cent.

In these examples fractions of a penny may be neglected :—

(9) A man deposited £124 2s. in a bank on the 5th of May and withdrew it on the 2nd of September. If the average bank rate during that time was 3 per cent., find the amount of interest which he received on withdrawing his deposit.

(10) If £75 is deposited in a bank on 2nd October, 1917, and withdrawn on 14th December, 1918, find the amount of interest received, the bank rate being 2 per cent.

(11) On the 1st of January a man deposited £40 in a savings bank. Three months later he deposited £25. If the rate of interest was $2\frac{1}{2}$ per cent., how much interest was due to him at the end of the year?

(12) A man borrowed £50 on 1st April at 5 per cent. simple interest. What is the total amount which he must repay on 6th November?

(13) A man borrowed £60 from the bank on May 11th. The bank rate was $6\frac{1}{4}$ per cent. per annum. What was the total amount due to the bank on 18th October?

(14) A sum of £132 10s. was deposited in a bank on 15th March and withdrawn on 20th November. If the bank rate during that time was $1\frac{1}{2}$ per cent., what interest was due?

(b) TO FIND ANY ONE OF THE THREE—PRINCIPAL, RATE, TIME—WHEN THE OTHER TWO AND THE INTEREST ARE KNOWN.

We give an example of each case, omitting details of the working.

First Method.

These questions all lend themselves to the **ratio method.**

Example 1.—Find what Principal will gain £84 interest in 6 years at 4 per cent.

Here £100 gains £4 × 6, and we have to find what sum will gain £84.

Thus, Prin. which gains £4 × 6 = £100.

,, ,, £84 = £100 × $\frac{84}{4 \times 6}$ = £350.

or, £100 gains £4 in 1 year.   ∴ x = £100 × $\frac{84}{4}$ × $\frac{1}{6}$.
£x ,, £84 ,, 6 years.

Example 2.—At what rate per cent. per annum will £350 gain £84 of interest in 6 years?

Here £350 gains £84 in 6 years.

Thus, Int. gained by £350 in 1 year = $\frac{£84}{6}$.

∴ ,, £100 in 1 year = £$\frac{84}{6}$ × $\frac{100}{350}$ = 4°/₀.

or, £350 gains £84 in 6 years.   ∴ x = £84 × $\frac{100}{350}$ × $\frac{1}{6}$.
£100 ,, £x ,, 1 year.

Example 3.—In what time will £350 gain £84 interest at 4 per cent. per annum?

Here the time taken by £100 to gain £4 is 1 year.

Thus, To gain £84, £100 takes $\frac{84}{4}$ years.

or,
£100 gains £4 in 1 year.
£350 ,, £84 ,, x years.
∴ x = 1 yr. × $\frac{100}{350}$ × $\frac{84}{4}$.

∴ £350 ,, $\frac{84}{4}$ × $\frac{100}{350}$ years = 6 years.

Second Method.

We have seen that interest $= \dfrac{\text{Prin.} \times \text{Rate} \times \text{Time}}{100}$.

$\therefore$ Prin. $\times$ Rate $\times$ Time $=$ Interest $\times$ 100.

Apply this fact to each of the foregoing examples.

Thus, in Example 1, we have to find Prin. when Rate $= 4$, Time $= 6$, Int. $= 84$. But Prin. $\times$ Rate $\times$ Time $=$ Int. $\times$ 100.

$\therefore$ Prin. $\times 4 \times 6 = $ £84 $\times$ 100.

$\therefore$ Prin. $= $ £$\dfrac{84 \times 100}{4 \times 6} = $ £350.

In Example 2, we have to find Rate when Prin. $= 350$, Time $= 6$, Int. $= 84$. But Prin. $\times$ Rate $\times$ Time $=$ Int. $\times$ 100.

$\therefore$ Rate $\times 350 \times 6 = 84 \times 100$.

$\therefore$ Rate $= \dfrac{84 \times 100}{350 \times 6} = 4°/_{\circ}$.

In Example 3, we have to find Time when Prin. $= 350$, Rate $= 4$, Int. $= 84$. But Prin. $\times$ Rate $\times$ Time $=$ Int. $\times$ 100.

$\therefore$ Time $\times 350 \times 4 = 84 \times 100$.

$\therefore$ Time $= \dfrac{84 \times 100}{350 \times 4} = 6$ years.

Note.—Time is expressed in **years** ; Prin., Rate, Int., in **pounds.**

EXERCISE 101.

Find what Principal will gain

(1) £90 of interest in 4 years at 5 per cent.

(2) £96 of interest in 5 years at 3 per cent.

(3) £247 10s. of interest in $5\frac{1}{2}$ years at 4 per cent.

• **(4)** £126 of interest in 6 years at $2\frac{1}{2}$ per cent.

(5) £169 of interest in 4 years at $7\frac{1}{2}$ per cent.

(6) £11 12s. 6d. of interest in 15 years at $2\frac{1}{2}$ per cent.

Find the rate per cent. per annum when

(7) £750 gains £150 of interest in 4 years.

(8) £1,000 gains £440 of interest in $5\frac{1}{2}$ years.

(9) £1,260 gains £189 of interest in 6 years.

(10) £210 gains £46 4s. of interest in 8 years.

(11) £700 gains £77 of interest in $2\frac{1}{2}$ years.

(12) £150 gains £30 of interest in 5 years.

Find in what time

(**13**) £750 will gain £330 of interest at 4 per cent.

(**14**) £150 will gain £60 of interest at 4 per cent.

(**15**) £70 will gain £15 8s. of interest at 2 per cent.

(**16**) £280 will gain £61 12s. of interest at 2 per cent.

(**17**) £420 will gain £63 of interest at 2½ per cent.

(**18**) £560 will gain £91 of interest at 2½ per cent.

(**19**) Find what sum of money will gain £184 16s. of interest in 6 years at 3⅔ per cent.

(**20**) If £1,750 gains £110 of interest in 2 years 9 months, find the rate per cent.

(**21**) In what time will £15 gain £5 12s. 6d. of interest at 5 per cent. ?

(**22**) In what time will £15 10s. amount to £21 6s. 3d. at 2½ % ?

(**23**) At what rate will £360 amount to £454 10s. in 7½ years ?

(**24**) What principal will gain £15 8s. of interest in 4 years at 5½ per cent. ?

(**25**) How long will £940 take to gain £376 of interest at 4 % ?

(**26**) At what rate will £188 amount to £263 4s. in 8 years ?

(**27**) What sum of money will gain £9 9s. in 3 years at 3½ per cent. ?

(**28**) At what rate will £18 4s. gain £6 16s. 6d. of interest in 7½ years ?

(**29**) What principal would gain £6 of interest in 100 days at 6 per cent. ?

(**30**) At what rate will £456 5s. gain £18 15s. of interest in 150 days ?

(**31**) £150 was deposited in a savings bank at 2½ per cent. simple interest. When the deposit was withdrawn the interest received was 15s. How many days had the money lain in the bank ?

(**32**) A sum of £25 11s. was deposited in a savings bank on the 6th of May. If the rate of interest was 2½ per cent., and if, when withdrawn, the total amount received was £25 14s. 6d., find on what date the deposit was withdrawn.

(**33**) The sum of £54 15s. was deposited in a savings bank on the 8th of September, 1915, and withdrawn on the 6th of March, 1916. If the total amount received on withdrawal was £55 8s. 6d., what was the bank rate ?

(34) A sum of money lay in a bank from 2nd January, 1917, to 3rd March, 1918. If the bank rate was 4 per cent., and if the amount of interest earned was £1 14s., what was the amount of the sum of money ?

(c) TO FIND THE PRINCIPAL WHEN THE RATE, TIME AND AMOUNT ARE KNOWN.

The formula

" Prin. × Rate × Time = Int. × 100 "

cannot be used in this case, because the Interest is not known. So we use the Ratio Method.

Example 1.—Find the sum of money which will amount to £728 in $7\frac{1}{2}$ years at 4 per cent. per annum.

The interest on £100 for $7\frac{1}{2}$ years at 4 per cent. = £4 × $7\frac{1}{2}$ = £30

∴. £100 amounts to £130 at the given rate in the given time.

Thus, Principal which amounts to £130 = £100.

∴.   ,,   ,,   £728 = £100 × $\dfrac{728}{130}$ = £560.

Example 2.—A sum of money was lent from 7th October, 1917, to the 19th December, 1918, at 2 per cent. per annum simple interest. If the amount returned was £153 12s., what was the amount lent.?

Time from 7th October, 1917, to 7th October, 1918 = 365 days.

Time from 7th October, 1918, to 19th December, 1918

= (31 − 7) in Oct. + 30 in Nov. + 19 in Dec.
= 73 days.

∴. Total time = 438 days = $\dfrac{438}{365}$ = $\dfrac{6}{5}$ years.

∴. Interest on £100 = 2 × $\dfrac{6}{5}$ = $\dfrac{12}{5}$ = £$2\frac{2}{5}$.

∴. £100 amounts to £$102\frac{2}{5}$.

∴. Principal which amounts to £$102\frac{2}{5}$ = £100.

∴.   ,,   ,,   £$153\frac{3}{5}$ = 100 × $\dfrac{153\frac{3}{5}}{102\frac{2}{5}}$ = £150.

EXERCISE 102.

Find what Principal will amount to

(1) £85 8s. in 4 years at 5½ per cent.
(2) £180 in 10 years at 2 per cent.
(3) £316 15s. in 10 years at 4 per cent.
(4) £341 12s. in 5½ years at 4 per cent.
(5) £1,080 in 11 years at 4 per cent.
(6) £99 9s. in 6 years at 1¾ per cent.
(7) £25 0s. 6d. in 15 years at 2½ per cent.
(8) £63 18s. 9d. in 7½ years at 5 per cent.
(9) £512 8s. in 3 years at 7⅓ per cent.
(10) £1,372 10s. in 5¼ years at 4 per cent.
(11) A sum of money was deposited in a bank for 219 days, the bank rate being 2½ per cent. If at the end of that time the money was withdrawn and amounted to £355 5s., what was the amount deposited?
(12) A certain sum of money was lent from 30th July till the 11th October following at the rate of 4 per cent. If the total amount paid back was £50 8s., how much was lent?
(13) A sum of money was deposited in a bank on 5th October, 1917, and withdrawn on 17th December, 1918. If the total amount withdrawn was £76 16s., and if the rate was 2 per cent., what was the amount deposited?
(14) A man borrowed a certain sum of money at 6 per cent. per annum simple interest. After 3 years and 8 months he discharged his debt by the payment of £1,024 16s. What was the amount of the sum which he borrowed?
(15) A man borrowed a certain sum of money at 2¼ per cent. per annum simple interest. At the end of 2 years 8 months he repaid a sum of £164 6s. How much money had he borrowed?
(16) A debtor had to repay to a moneylender £5 0s. 6d. for the loan of a sum of money for 4 months. If interest was charged at 35 per cent. per annum, how much had the debtor borrowed?
(17) A certain sum of money was deposited in a bank for 1 year 4 months at 1¼ per cent. per annum. If the total amount repaid was £190 12s. 6d., what was the sum deposited?

14

We close this chapter with a few examples of the various
questions that may arise and with a revisal exercise.

Example 1.—A sum of £58 8s. was deposited in a Savings
Bank on the 5th of January, 1919, at $2\frac{1}{4}$ per cent. It was withdrawn when it amounted to £58 17s. Find the date on which it
was withdrawn.

Here we have to find the Time when the

Prin. $= 58\frac{2}{5}$, Rate $= 2\frac{1}{4}$, and Int. $= 9s. = \frac{9}{20}$.

Now,   Prin. $\times$ Rate $\times$ Time $=$ Int. $\times$ 100.

∴   Time $\times 58\frac{2}{5} \times 2\frac{1}{4}$ $= \frac{9}{20} \times 100 = 45.$

∴ Time $= \dfrac{45}{58\frac{2}{5} \times 2\frac{1}{4}}$ years

$= \dfrac{100}{292}$ years   Days in January $= 26$

                          ,,   February $= 28$

$= \dfrac{\overset{5}{100}}{\underset{4}{292}} \times 365$ days   ,,   March $= 31$

                          ,,   April $= \underline{30}$

                                        $\overline{115}$

$= 125$ days   ∴ Days in May $= \underline{10}$

$=$ time from 5th $\overline{125}$

Jan. to 10th May.

∴ Date of withdrawal $=$ 10th May.

Example 2.—If the interest on a certain sum for $5\frac{1}{2}$ years at
4 per cent. is £132, what would be the interest on the same sum
for 4 years at $3\frac{1}{2}$ per cent. ?

We may work this example by finding the sum of money, but
it may be done by the ratio method, thus :—

Int. on the sum for $5\frac{1}{2}$ years at 4 per cent. $=$ £132.

∴   ,,   ,,   4   ,, $3\frac{1}{2}$,, $= £132 \times \dfrac{4}{5\frac{1}{2}} \times \dfrac{3\frac{1}{2}}{4}$

              $= £84.$

Example 3.—Find what Principal will gain in 8 months at
$2\frac{1}{2}$ per cent. the same interest as £350 gains in 2 years 4
months at 3 per cent.

Here again we may find the interest, but it may be worked in one operation, thus :—

Since   Prin. × Rate × Time   = Interest × 100

∴ Reqd. Prin. × $2\frac{1}{2}$ × $\frac{2}{3}$ =   ,,   × 100

So also   £350   × 3   × $2\frac{1}{3}$ =   ,,   × 100

∴ Reqd. Prin. × $2\frac{1}{2}$ × $\frac{2}{3}$ = £350 × 3 × $2\frac{1}{3}$

∴ Reqd. Prin. $= \dfrac{350 \times 3 \times 2\frac{1}{3}}{2\frac{1}{2} \times \frac{2}{3}} = £1,470.$

Or, better still, by the *Ratio Method* :—

The Reqd. Prin. = £350 × $\dfrac{3}{2\frac{1}{2}}$ × $\dfrac{2\frac{1}{3}}{\frac{2}{3}}$ = £1,470.

It requires a larger principal to gain the interest in less time, and a larger principal to gain it at a lower rate. Hence both ratios are greater than unity.

EXERCISE 103.

(1) Find the simple interest on £210 in 4 years at $5\frac{1}{2}$ per cent.

(2) Find the simple interest on £400 5s. in 3 years 9 months at 3 per cent.

(3) Find the simple interest on £325 5s. in 2 years 10 months at 5 per cent.

(4) What principal will gain £123 15s. of interest in 11 years at 4 per cent. ?

(5) At what rate will £452 10s. gain £181 of interest in 10 years ?

(6) At what rate will £31 amount to £42 12s. 6d. in $7\frac{1}{2}$ years ?

(7) In what time will £420 amount to £512 8s. at $7\frac{1}{3}$ per cent. ?

(8) In what time will £70 gain £15 8s. of interest at $5\frac{1}{2}$ per cent. ?

(9) What principal will amount to £126 in 15 years at 4 per cent. ?

(10) What sum of money will amount to £1,449 in 6 years at $2\frac{1}{2}$ per cent. ?

(11) A man borrowed £1,000 at 4 per cent. simple interest. He discharged his debt after it had accumulated to £1,440. How long was he in discharging it ?

(12) A sum of £94 was borrowed for an indefinite time at the rate of $2\frac{1}{2}$ per cent. simple interest. What would be the total indebtedness at the end of 16 years ?

(13) How long will £282 take to amount to £394 16s. at $3\frac{1}{3}$ per cent. simple interest ?

(14) A man borrowed a sum of money at 4 per cent. simple interest. The total amount repaid at the end of 5 years was £1,240 16s. Find the amount of the sum borrowed.

(15) Find the simple interest on £273 15s. for 150 days at 6 per cent.

(16) If £456 5s. amounts to £460 18s. 9d. in 75 days, find the rate per cent.

(17) What sum of money would gain £4 18s. of interest in 40 days at $1\frac{3}{4}$ per cent. ?

(18) In how many days will £175 gain 17s. 6d. of interest at $2\frac{1}{2}$ per cent. ?

(19) At the beginning of the year a man deposited £50 in a savings bank. Four months later he deposited £30, and two months after that he withdrew £20. If interest is at the rate of $2\frac{1}{2}$ per cent., what would be the interest due to him at the end of the year ?

(20) If £75 is deposited in a bank on 12th October, 1917, and withdrawn on 24th December, 1918, find the interest on the deposit, the rate being $2\frac{1}{2}$ per cent.

(21) £50 is deposited in a savings bank on 29th July and withdrawn on 10th October following. If the total amount withdrawn is £50 8s., find the bank rate.

(22) A sum of money was lent out at $3\frac{1}{2}$ per cent. from 26th October, 1916, till 14th January, 1917. If the interest was £1 8s. what was the amount of the sum ?

(23) A man deposited £91 5s. in a bank on the 29th of October, 1916. On withdrawing it he received 14s. as interest. On what date was the deposit withdrawn, the rate of interest being $3\frac{1}{2}$ per cent. ?

(24) A sum of £18 5s. was deposited in a bank on the 5th of January, 1917, and withdrawn on the 6th of March, 1918. If the interest received was 17s., find the rate of interest.

(25) A man who had a deposit of £273 15s. in a bank withdrew it on the 10th of December, 1918, receiving as interest on the deposit £1 8s. $1\frac{1}{2}$d. If the bank rate was $2\frac{1}{2}$ per cent., on what date was the money deposited ?

(26) A certain sum gains £65 of interest in $2\frac{1}{2}$ years at 4 per cent. What would be the interest on it in $7\frac{1}{2}$ years at the same rate ?

(27) A certain sum gains £130 of interest in 5 years at 2 per cent. What would be the interest on it in $7\frac{1}{2}$ years at 3 per cent. ?

(28) A man deposited £54 15s. in a bank at 4 per cent. simple interest on the 3rd of January, 1917. When he withdrew the deposit the total amount received was £57 6s. On what date was the deposit withdrawn ?

(29) £27 7s. 6d. was deposited at $2\frac{1}{2}$ per cent., and when withdrawn on 16th March, 1916, the total amount received was £27 14s. 3d. Find the date on which it was deposited in the bank.

(30) Find to the nearest penny the simple interest on £441 13s. from 20th April to 27th September following at $2\frac{1}{2}$ per cent.

(31) A sum of money was deposited in a savings bank on 20th July and withdrawn on 1st October following. If the total sum withdrawn was £25 4s., and the rate 4 per cent., find the sum deposited.

(32) A sum of money was lent from 18th May to 26th August at $2\frac{1}{2}$ per cent. If the amount repaid was £51 9s., what was the amount lent.?

(33) A man deposited a sum of money in a bank on the 2nd of November, 1916, and withdrew it on the 21st of January, 1917, receiving altogether £91 19s. If the rate of interest was $3\frac{1}{2}$ per cent., what was the amount deposited ?

(34) What principal will gain in 9 years at 4 per cent. the same interest as £720 gains in 6 years at $2\frac{1}{2}$ per cent. ?

(35) A certain sum gains £126 of interest in 3 years at 5 per cent. What interest will it gain in 3 years 8 months at 6 per cent. ?

(36) What principal will in $6\frac{1}{4}$ years at 2 per cent. gain the same interest as £150 gains in 5 years at 4 per cent. ?

(37) What principal will in $6\frac{1}{4}$ years at 2 per cent. amount to the same sum as £150 amounts to in 5 years at 4 per cent. ?

CHAPTER XVII.

COMPOUND INTEREST.

In **Compound Interest,** the first year's interest is added to the Principal, giving a larger Principal for the second year. To this Principal the second year's interest is again added, giving a still larger Principal for the third year, and so on.

The most convenient method for finding compound interest is shown in the following examples :—

Example 1.—Find the compound interest on £560 15s. for 3 years at 6 per cent.

$$
\begin{array}{ll}
\qquad\qquad £560 \cdot 75 & = \text{Prin. for 1st year.} \\
6\,°/_\circ = \tfrac{6}{100} = 33 \cdot 6450 & = \text{Int. for 1st year.} \\
\cline{1-1}
 594 \cdot 3950 & = \text{Prin. for 2nd year.} \\
6\,°/_\circ = \tfrac{6}{100} = 35 \cdot 6637 & = \text{Int. for 2nd year.} \\
\cline{1-1}
 630 \cdot 0587 & = \text{Prin. for 3rd year.} \\
6\,°/_\circ = \tfrac{6}{100} = 37 \cdot 8035 & = \text{Int. for 3rd year.} \\
\cline{1-1}
 667 \cdot 8622 & = \text{Amount in 3 years.} \\
 560 \cdot 75 & = \text{Original capital.} \\
\cline{1-1}
 107 \cdot 1122 & = \text{3 year's interest.}
\end{array}
$$

Int. = £107 2s. 3d. to nearest penny.

Note that in the above we find $\tfrac{6}{100}$ of the principal in one step by multiplying by 6 and placing our figures **two places to the right.**

Also, the work is carried no further than 4 decimal places. This is sufficient to get the answer correct to within a penny of the true result. In the case of 5 per cent., instead of multiplying by 5 we may (as 5 per cent. $= \tfrac{1}{20}$) divide by 2 and place our figures **one place** to the right. So for $2\tfrac{1}{2}$ per cent. we may divide by 4 and shift one place to the right.

In some cases it will be convenient to break the rate up into 2 or more parts. Thus $7\tfrac{1}{2}$ may be taken as $5 + 2\tfrac{1}{2}$.

It should be noted also that for $\tfrac{1}{2}$ a year we take $\tfrac{1}{2}$ the rate, and the corresponding fraction for any fraction of a year.

Example 2.—Find the amount in $2\frac{1}{2}$ years of £651 2s. 6d. at $7\frac{1}{2}$ per cent. compound interest.

$$£651\cdot125$$

$7\frac{1}{2}\,°/_\circ \begin{cases} 5\,°/_\circ = \frac{1}{20} & = 32\cdot5562 \\ 2\frac{1}{2}\,°/_\circ = \frac{1}{2}\text{ of }5\,°/_\circ = 16\cdot2781 \end{cases}$ = Int. for 1st year.

$\overline{699\cdot9593}$ = Amount in 1 year.

$7\frac{1}{2}\,°/_\circ \begin{cases} 5\,°/_\circ = \frac{1}{20} & = 34\cdot9979 \\ 2\frac{1}{2}\,°/_\circ = \frac{1}{2}\text{ of }5\,°/_\circ = 17\cdot4989 \end{cases}$ = Int. for 2nd year.

$\overline{752\cdot4561}$ = Amount in 2 years.

$3\frac{3}{4}\,°/_\circ \begin{cases} 2\frac{1}{2}\,°/_\circ = \frac{1}{40} & = 18\cdot8114 \\ 1\frac{1}{4}\,°/_\circ = \frac{1}{2}\text{ of }2\frac{1}{2}\,°/_\circ = 9\cdot4057 \end{cases}$ = Int. for $\frac{1}{2}$ year.

$\overline{780\cdot6732}$ = Amount in $2\frac{1}{2}$ years.

$\therefore$ Amount required = £780 13s. 6d. to nearest penny.

EXERCISE 104.

Find to the nearest penny the amount at compound interest of
(1) £800 in 2 years at 4 per cent.
(2) £1,000 in 3 years at 2 per cent.
(3) £1,200 in 3 years at 3 per cent.
(4) £600 in $2\frac{1}{2}$ years at 4 per cent.
(5) £850 in 3 years at 5 per cent.
(6) £950 in $2\frac{1}{2}$ years at 2 per cent.
(7) £860 in 3 years at $2\frac{1}{2}$ per cent.
(8) £870 10s. in 2 years at $4\frac{1}{2}$ per cent. $(3 + 1\frac{1}{2})$.
(9) £800 in $2\frac{1}{4}$ years at 4 per cent.
(10) £840 10s. in 3 years at 6 per cent.

Find to the nearest penny the compound interest on
(11) £560 15s. in 3 years at 5 per cent.
(12) £720 7s. 6d. in $2\frac{1}{2}$ years at 5 per cent.
(13) £1,760 12s. 6d. in 2 years at $7\frac{1}{2}$ per cent.
(14) £1,850 12s. in 3 years at $2\frac{1}{2}$ per cent.
(15) £530 17s. 6d. in $2\frac{1}{2}$ years at $7\frac{1}{2}$ per cent.
(16) £670 16s. in 2 years at $1\frac{1}{2}$ per cent. $(1 + \frac{1}{2})$.

(17) £351 4s. in 2 years at $3\frac{1}{2}$ per cent.
(18) £743 11s. in 2 years at $3\frac{3}{4}$ per cent. $(2\frac{1}{2} + 1\frac{1}{4})$.
(19) £546 18s. in 3 years at 3 per cent.
(20) £400 in 2 years at $2\frac{3}{4}$ per cent. $(2\frac{1}{2} + \frac{1}{4})$.

CHAPTER XVIII.

MISCELLANEOUS PROBLEMS.

(*a*) AVERAGES.

IF the sum of 20s. were divided equally among 4 boys, each would get 5s. If the money were divided unequally we would then say they received an **average** of 5s. each, although the amounts received might be, say, 3s., 4s., 6s., and 7s.—that is, the average of 3, 4, 6, and 7 is 5, and is equal to $(3 + 4 + 6 + 7) \div 4$.

Thus we have the following definition of **average** :—
The average of any number of quantities is the sum of the quantities divided by their number.

Example 1.—The ages of 5 boys are 7, 8, 9, 11, and 15. What is their average age ?

$$\text{Their average age} = (7 + 8 + 9 + 11 + 15) \div 5$$
$$= 50 \div 5 = 10.$$

Example 2.—A boat's crew consists of a coxswain and 8 oarsmen. If their average weight is 11 stones, and the weights of the 8 oarsmen are 9, $9\frac{1}{2}$, 10, $10\frac{1}{2}$, 11, 12, $12\frac{1}{2}$, and 13 stones, find the coxswain's weight.

Total weight of crew $= 11 \text{ stones} \times 9 = 99 \text{ stones}.$
Weight of oarsmen $= 9 + 9\frac{1}{2} + 10 + 10\frac{1}{2} + 11 + 12 + 12\frac{1}{2} + 13$
$= 87\frac{1}{2} \text{ stones}.$
∴ Weight of coxswain $= 99 - 87\frac{1}{2} \text{ stones}$
$= 11\frac{1}{2} \text{ stones}.$

EXERCISE 105.

(1) Find the average of 6, 14, 19, 23, and 33.

(2) The ages of 6 boys are 7, 8, 11, 12, 13, and 15. What is their average age ?

(3) What is the average weight of 5 men whose weights are 10 stones, 10 stones 8 lbs., 10 stones 6 lbs., 11 stones 9 lbs., and 12 stones 5 lbs. ?

(4) A cyclist in going a distance of 5 miles notes that he takes 5 minutes 30 seconds, 5 minutes 40 seconds, 5 minutes 20 seconds, 5 minutes, and 5 minutes 10 seconds to the successive miles. What is the average time taken per mile, and what is his average speed in miles per hour ?

(5) What is the average of 1·201, ·934, 1·112, ·976, and ·854 ?

(6) The rainfall for a certain district for the first 6 months of the year was 4·00, 12·09, 6·54, 20·79, 27·40, and 3·73. What was the average monthly rainfall during that period ?

(7) A boat's crew consists of 8 oarsmen and a coxswain. The average weight of the crew is $10\frac{3}{4}$ stones, and the average weight of the oarsmen is $10\frac{1}{2}$ stones. What is the weight of the coxswain ?

(8) The average age of 4 men is 31 years, and the average age of 3 of them is 28 years. What is the age of the 4th man ?

(9) A boat's crew consists of the coxswain and 6 oarsmen. If the crew's age averages 25 years, and if the coxswain's age is 31 years. what is the average age of the oarsmen ?

(10) The average daily attendance during 3 days of a bazaar was 650. The attendances on the first two days were 500 and 580. What was the attendance on the 3rd day ?

(11) In a school consisting of 12 classes the total number of pupils present on a certain day was 420. If the average number present in 11 of the classes was 36 per class, find the number present in the remaining class.

(12) In a class of 20 pupils, with 10 meetings in the week, 3 were absent on Tuesday afternoon, 2 on Thursday morning, and 5 on Friday afternoon. What was the average number present per meeting during that week ?

(b) TIME AND WORK.

Example 1.—A can do a piece of work in 12 hours, B can do it in 8 hours. Find how long they would take to do the work if they worked at it together.

A does it in 12 hours.   ∴ A does $\frac{1}{12}$ in 1 hour.

B   ,,   8 hours.   ∴ B does $\frac{1}{8}$ in 1 hour.

∴ A and B together do $\frac{1}{12} + \frac{1}{8}$, *i.e.*, $\frac{2+3}{24}$ or $\frac{5}{24}$ in 1 hour.

∴ A and B together do the whole work in $\dfrac{24}{5}$ hours $= 4\frac{4}{5}$ hours.

Example 2.—Two pipes run water into a cistern. If empty, one of them could fill it in 40 minutes and the other in 60 minutes. There is a waste pipe which could empty the cistern (if full) in 80 minutes. If the cistern is empty and all the pipes are open, how long would the cistern be in filling ?

The filling pipes fill $(\frac{1}{40} + \frac{1}{60})$ of cistern in 1 minute.

The waste runs away at $\frac{1}{80}$ of cistern in 1 minute.

∴ The amount filled in 1 minute $= \dfrac{1}{40} + \dfrac{1}{60} - \dfrac{1}{80} = \dfrac{7}{240}$.

∴ Time of filling $= \dfrac{240}{7}$ minutes $= 34\frac{2}{7}$ minutes.

EXERCISE 106.

(1) A can mow a lawn in 4 hours, B can mow it in 5 hours. How long would they take to do it if they work together ?

(2) A can do a work in 10 days and B in 12 days. If B works at it for 3 days alone, how long would it take A to finish it alone ?

(3) A man can do a job in 6 hours. It would take a boy twice as long to do the work. If they work at the job together, how long would they take to do it ?

(4) A man and a boy working together can do a piece of work in 8 hours. If the man alone can do it in 12 hours, how long would it take the boy to do the work alone ?

(5) A can mow a field in 8 days and B in 10 days. They work at it together for 4 days. A then leaves off. How long will it take B to finish it alone ?

(6) A can do a piece of work in 5 days, B in 6 days, and C in $7\frac{1}{2}$ days. How long would they take all working together ?

(7) A, B, C, and D could separately do a piece of work in 5 hours, $4\frac{1}{2}$ hours, $3\frac{1}{4}$ hours, and $3\frac{3}{5}$ hours respectively. How long would it take them if they all worked at it together ?

(8) A cistern can be filled by one pipe in $13\frac{1}{3}$ minutes, and by another in $7\frac{1}{2}$ minutes, and emptied by a waste pipe in 8 minutes. If all are opened when the cistern is empty, find how long it will take before it is filled.

(9) A cistern can be filled by 3 pipes in 20, 30, and 24 minutes respectively. How long will they take to fill it when they are all running together ?

(10) Three taps, A, B, and C, can fill a cistern in 12, 15, and 10 minutes respectively. All are opened together for 3 minutes. Then A is turned off. How much longer will B and C take to fill it ?

(11) A can do a job in 6 hours, B in 8 hours, and C in 10 hours. They are all put on to the job together till it is finished. If £1 11s. 4d. is paid for the job, how should the money be divided between them ?

(12) A and B working together can finish a job in $6\frac{6}{7}$ hours. The job is finished by 6 hours' work from A and 8 hours' work from B. Find how long each of them would take to do the job separately.

(c) TIME AND DISTANCE.

Example 1.—A cycles off from a certain place at the uniform rate of 10 miles an hour. B follows him from the same place in the same direction 15 minutes afterwards at the uniform rate of 12 miles an hour. How long will it take B to overtake A ?

Distance cycled by A in 15 minutes $= 2\frac{1}{2}$ miles.

∴. B has to gain $2\frac{1}{2}$ miles.

But B gains 2 miles in 60 minutes.

∴ B gains $2\frac{1}{2}$ miles in $60 \times \dfrac{2\frac{1}{2}}{2}$ minutes $= 75$ minutes.

Example 2.—An express train, 130 yds. long, travelling 45 miles an hour passes a goods train 200 yds. long and travelling 30 miles an hour in the same direction on parallel rails. How long will it take the express train to pass the goods train ?

A point on express train (say the face of the engine) has to gain 330 yds. (lengths of the trains), and it gains 15 miles an hour (45 − 30).

Thus, 15 × 1,760 yds. are gained in 60 minutes.

$$\therefore \quad 330 \text{ yds. are gained in } 60 \times \frac{330}{15 \times 1,760} \text{ minutes}$$
$$= \tfrac{3}{4} \text{ minutes} = 45 \text{ seconds.}$$

Example 3.—At what time between 6 and 7 o'clock are the hands of a watch together ?

In questions on the hands of a watch we have to consider **how many minute-spaces** the minute-hand has to gain. Now, the minute-hand gains 55 minute-spaces in an hour.

At 6 o'clock the minute-hand is 30 spaces behind the hour-hand, and has, therefore, to gain 30 spaces in order to overtake the hour-hand.

Hence, M.H. gains 55 spaces in 60 minutes.

$$\therefore \qquad\qquad \text{,,} \quad 30 \quad \text{,,} \quad \text{in } 60 \times \frac{30}{55} \text{ mins.} = 32\tfrac{8}{11} \text{ mins.}$$

EXERCISE 107.

(1) A cycles off from a certain place at the uniform rate of 12 miles an hour. B follows him 20 minutes afterwards at 15 miles an hour. How long will B be in overtaking A ?

(2) A sets out to cycle from home at 12 noon at the uniform rate of 10 miles an hour. B follows him at 1.30 p.m. on a motor bicycle at 16 miles an hour. At what o'clock will B overtake A, and at what distance from home ?

(3) Two trains start at the same time from stations 28 miles apart, towards each other at 22 miles and 20 miles an hour respectively. When will they meet, and where ?

(4) A train going at the rate of 30 miles an hour passes a telegraph post in 12 seconds. What is the length of the train ?

(5) If a train 170 yds. long, travelling 30 miles an hour, takes 18 seconds to pass completely a station platform, what is the length of the platform ?

(6) A train travelling 30 miles an hour passes a platform 90 yds. long in 12 seconds. Find the length of the train.

(7) A train 200 yds. long passes a train 160 yds. long moving in the opposite direction. If their rates are 25 miles and 35 miles an hour, how long are they in passing each other ?

(8) If a train 120 yds. long passes a platform 100 yds. long in 10 seconds, find its speed.

(9) When will the hands of a watch be together between 2 and 3 o'clock ?

(10) At what times between 1 and 2 o'clock will the hands of a watch be at right angles ?

(11) At what time between 2 and 3 will the hands of a watch be opposite one another ?

(12) At what times between 6 and 7 will the hands of a watch be at right angles ?

(13) If a man who rows at the rate of 7 miles an hour in still water takes 40 minutes to row 2 miles up stream, at what rate is the stream flowing ?

(14) A man rows 6 miles down stream in 36 minutes. If the stream is flowing at the rate of $3\frac{1}{2}$ miles an hour, at what rate can the man row in still water ?

(d) RACES AND GAMES.

Example 1.—If A can beat B by 20 yds. in a 200 yds. race, and B can beat C by 10 yds. What start could A give C in the same race so that they may make a dead heat ?

C runs 190 yds. while B runs 200 yds. (*i.e.*, $\frac{190}{200}$ of what B runs) and B runs 180 yds. while A runs 200 yds. (*i.e.*, $\frac{180}{200}$ of what A runs)

$$\therefore \text{ C runs } \frac{190}{200} \text{ of what B runs}$$

$$= \frac{190}{200} \text{ of } \frac{180}{200} \text{ of what A runs}$$

$$= \frac{171}{200} \text{ of what A runs}$$

$$= \frac{171}{200} \text{ of 200 yds.} = 171 \text{ yds.}$$

$\therefore$ A can give C a start of 29 yds.

Example 2.—In a game of skill A can give B 1 point in 9, B can give C 1 point in 10, C can give D 1 point in 16. By how many points can A beat D in a game of 100 points ?

D scores 15 points while C scores 16,
and C ,,   9   ,,   B ,,   10,
and B ,,   8   ,,   A ,,   9.

$$\therefore \text{ D's score} = \frac{15}{16} \text{ of } \frac{9}{10} \text{ of } \frac{8}{9} \text{ of A's score}$$
$$= \tfrac{3}{4} \text{ of } 100 = 75.$$

$\therefore$ A can beat D by 25 points in 100.

EXERCISE 108.

(1) When A runs 150 yds. B runs 145, and when B runs 200 yds C runs 180 yds. How far does C run when A runs 400 yds. ?

(2) A can beat B by 80 yds. in a 480 yds. race, and B can beat C by 60 yds. By how much could A beat C in the same race ?

(3) A can beat B by 40 yds., and C by 62 yds. in a 400 yds. race. What start can B give C in a race of 420 yds. so that they may make a dead heat ?

(4) A gives B 20 yds. start in a 200 yds. race, and is beaten by B by 11 yds. If they start level in the same race by how much could A beat B ?

(5) A gives B a start of 60 yds. in a race of 880 yds., and is beaten by 30 yds. What start can A give B in a race of 680 yds. so that they may run a dead heat ?

(6) In a 100 yds. race A can beat B by 20 yds., B can beat C by 10 yds., and C can beat D by 5 yds. By how much can A beat D in a 250 yds. race ?

(7) If in a game of skill A scores 50 points while B scores 45, and B scores 50 points while C scores 40, what will C score while A scores 200 ?

(8) If A can give B 1 point in 5, and B can give C 1 point in 4 in a game of skill, how many points can A give C in a game of 100 points ?

(9) If in a game A can give B 1 point in 5, and C can give B 1 point in 10, show that A can give C 1 point in 9.

(10) If A scores 100 points while B scores 90, and B scores 100 while C scores 85, and C scores 100 while D scores 80, what will D score while A scores 500 ?

(11) In a game A can give B 1 point in 8, B can give C 1 point in 9, and C can give D 1 point in 10. How many points can A give D in 50 ?

(e) CHAIN RULE.

The method in Chain Rule is similar to the method we used in "Races and Games."

Example 1.—If 6 chickens are equivalent to 4 ducks, and 8 ducks to 3 geese, and 10 geese to 7 turkeys, find the price of a turkey if a chicken cost 3s. 6d.

7 turkeys = 10 geese.	∴ 1 turkey	$= \frac{10}{7}$ goose.
3 geese = 8 ducks.	∴ 1 goose	$= \frac{8}{3}$ duck.
4 ducks = 6 chickens.	∴ 1 duck	$= \frac{6}{4}$ chicken.
and	Cost of 1 chicken = 3s. 6d.	

$$\therefore \text{ Cost of 1 turkey} = \frac{10}{7} \text{ of } \frac{8}{3} \text{ of } \frac{6}{4} \text{ of 3s. 6d.}$$
$$= \frac{10}{7} \times \frac{8}{3} \times \frac{6}{4} \times \frac{7s.}{2} = 20s.$$

Example 2.—If B copies 7 pages while A copies 6, and C copies 8 while B copies 9, and D copies 15 while C copies 14, and if A copies a page in 5 minutes, how long does D take to copy a page ?

D does 15 while C does 14.

∴ D takes $\frac{14}{15}$ of time taken by C to do a page.

C does 8 while B does 9.

∴ C takes $\frac{9}{8}$ of time taken by B to do a page.

B does 7 while A does 6.

∴ B takes $\frac{6}{7}$ of time taken by A to do a page.

And A takes 5 minutes to a page.

$$\therefore \text{ Time taken by D} = \frac{14}{15} \text{ of } \frac{9}{8} \text{ of } \frac{6}{7} \text{ of 5 minutes}$$
$$= 4\frac{1}{2} \text{ minutes.}$$

EXERCISE 109.

(1) If 5 fowls cost as much as 4 ducks, and 10 ducks cost as much as 3 turkeys, and if a fowl cost 4s., find the cost of a turkey.

(2) If 4 fowls are equivalent to 3 ducks, and 15 ducks are equivalent to 4 turkeys, find the cost of a fowl if a turkey cost 20s.

(3) If 3 sheep cost as much as 2 pigs, and 8 pigs cost as much as 3 cows, find the cost of a cow if a sheep costs £2.

(4) If a fowl costs 3s., and if 6 fowls are equivalent in price to 4 ducks, and 8 ducks to 3 geese, and 12 geese to 8 turkeys, find the price of a turkey.

(5) If 5 lbs. of tea are equivalent in value to 6 lbs. of cocoa, and if 9 lbs. of cocoa are equivalent to 10 lbs. of coffee, and if 1 lb. of coffee cost 2s., find the price of 3 lbs of tea.

(6) If the cost of 6 apples = cost of 4 pears, and cost of 9 pears = cost of 7 oranges, and cost of 8 oranges = cost of 6 peaches, and if a peach cost $1\frac{1}{2}$d., find cost of 1 dozen of apples.

(7) If 5 Egyptian cigarettes are worth 18 Woodbines, and 7 cheroots are worth 12 Egyptian cigarettes, and 8 Marcella cigars are worth 15 cheroots, and 9 Habanas are worth 25 Marcellas, find the price of 100 Habanas if 10 Woodbines cost $3\frac{1}{2}$d.

(8) If A copies 7 pages while B copies 5, and C copies 13 while B copies 12, and D 14 while C copies 13, and if D takes 6 minutes to copy a page, how long does A take ?

(9) If B takes 15 hours to do what A does in 14 hours, and if C takes 11 hours to do what B does in 10 hours, and if D takes 10 hours to do what C does in 9 hours, find how long A will take to do a job which D takes 55 hours to do.

(10) If 1 in. = $2\frac{1}{2}$ cm., and 1 Kg. = 2·2 lbs., express a pressure of 30 lbs. per sq. in. in Kg. per sq. cm.

(f) **ALLIGATION.**

Example 1.—In what proportion must tea worth 3s. 6d. per lb. be mixed with tea worth 2s. 8d. a lb. so that the mixture may be worth 3s. per lb. ?

In selling 3s. 6d. tea at 3s. the loss on 1 lb. = 6d.
In selling 2s. 8d. tea at 3s. the gain on 1 lb. = 4d.
L.C.M. of 6 and 4 is 12, and 6d. × 2 = 12d., and 4d. × 3 = 12d.
Thus, loss of 6d. × 2 would balance gain of 4d. × 3.
∴. 3s. 6d. tea is mixed with 2s. 8d. tea in proportion of 2 to 3.

The working may be set down thus :—

$$\left.\begin{matrix}\text{3s. 6d.}\\\text{2s. 8d.}\end{matrix}\right\rangle \text{3s.} \quad \begin{matrix}\text{loss}=\text{6d., 6d.}\times 2=\\\text{gain}=\text{4d., 4d.}\times 3=\end{matrix}\left.\right\rangle \text{12d.}$$

$$\therefore \quad \frac{\text{Amount of 3s. 6d. tea}}{\text{Amount of 2s. 8d. tea}} = \frac{2}{3}.$$

Example 2.—In what proportions must tea at 3s. 4d. per lb. be mixed with teas at 2s. 6d. and 2s. 9d. per lb. to make a mixture worth 2s. 10d. per lb., taking equal quantities of the cheaper teas ?

$$\left.\begin{matrix}\text{3s. 4d.}\\\text{2s. 6d.}\\\text{2s. 9d.}\end{matrix}\right\rangle \text{2s. 10d.} \quad \begin{matrix}\text{loss on 1 lb.}=\text{6d.,}\\\text{gain on 1 lb.}=\text{4d.,}\\\text{gain on 1 lb.}=\text{1d.,}\end{matrix}\quad \left.\begin{matrix}\text{6d.}\times 5\\\text{5d.}\times 6\end{matrix}\right\rangle \text{30d.}$$

∴. 5 lbs. of 3s. 4d. tea is mixed with 6 lbs. each of 2s. 6d. and 2s. 9d. tea.

EXERCISE 110.

(1) In what proportion must tea worth 2s. 10d. per lb. be mixed with tea worth 2s. 4d. a lb. to give a mixture worth 2s. 6d. a lb. ?

(2) In what proportion must tea worth 3s. per lb. be mixed with tea worth 2s. 2d. per lb. to make a mixture worth 2s. 9d. per lb. ?

(3) In what proportion must tea worth 3s. per lb. be mixed with tea worth 2s. 2d. per lb. in order that 10 per cent. profit may be gained by selling the mixture at 2s. 9d. per lb. ?

(4) In what proportions must teas at 3s. and 2s. 10d. per lb. be mixed with tea at 2s. to make a mixture worth 2s. 6d. per lb., taking equal quantities of the two dearer teas ?

(5) In what proportions can tea worth 2s. 10d. per lb. be mixed with teas worth 1s. 8d. and 2s. per lb. to make a mixture worth 2s. 4d. per lb., taking equal proportions of the two cheaper teas ?

(6) In what proportion should wine which cost 18s. a gallon be mixed with wine which cost 28s. a gallon so that when the mixture is sold at 25s. a gallon there may be a profit of 25 per cent. ?

(7) In what proportion should spirits costing 4s. 6d. a bottle be blended with spirits costing 10s. a bottle so that when the blend is sold at 10s. a bottle there may be a profit of $33\frac{1}{3}$ per cent. ?

Additional Examples—

(8) Spirits costing 16s. per gallon were mixed with spirits costing 12s. per gallon, and the mixture was sold at 15s. per gallon, making a profit of $11\frac{1}{9}$ per cent. In what proportions were they mixed ?

(9) Sugar costing $3\frac{1}{4}$d. per lb. was mixed with another quality which cost $\frac{3}{4}$d. per lb. less. If 1 cwt. of the mixture was sold for £1 17s. 4d., making a profit of 25 per cent., what weight of the dearer quality must be mixed with a ton of the cheaper to give the correct mixture ?

(10) A milkman bought 80 gallons of milk at 11d. per gallon and added water to it. He sold the whole at $2\frac{1}{2}$d. per pint, and made a profit of 100 per cent. How much water did he add ?

(11) A grocer mixed coffee costing £8 8s. per cwt. with coffee costing 2s. 4d. per lb. He sold the mixture at 2s. 1d. per lb., making a profit of 25 per cent. What weight of the dearer quality did he mix with 1 cwt. of the cheaper to give the correct mixture ?

CHAPTER XIX.

PRESENT WORTH AND DISCOUNT, STOCKS AND SHARES.

I.—PRESENT WORTH AND DISCOUNT.

THE class of questions usually treated under this head is precisely the same as those coming under **Interest,** so that this subject introduces no new operations, and can be dealt with very briefly.

(a) Bankers' Discount.

In business life, when one merchant buys goods of another, instead of paying **ready cash,** the buyer usually signs what is known as a **Bill of Exchange,** by which he is bound to pay the debt at the end of a certain given time. The creditor gets this bill, and if he needs the money before that time is up, he may sell the Bill to a Banker. The Banker does not pay the total amount or "**face value**" of the Bill, but as a **fee** deducts from it what is known as **Bankers' Discount.** The fee which the Banker charges is just the **interest** on the bill for the time he has to wait till the bill is due, the rate of interest being the current rate of the Bank. When the time is up (*i.e.*, when the bill **matures**), the Banker can demand payment of the full "face value" from the debtor.

Example 1.—A merchant who received a bill for £40 discounted it at a bank 73 days before the money was due. Find the discount charged by the banker and the amount (*i.e.*, **present value**) which the merchant received for the bill, the bank rate of interest being 5 per cent.

The Bankers' discount = the interest on £40 for 73 days at 5 per cent.

$$\therefore \text{ Bankers' discount} = £40 \times \frac{73}{365} \times \frac{5}{100} = 8\text{s}.$$

$$\therefore \text{ Present value} \quad = £40 - 8\text{s}. = £39 \ 12\text{s}.$$

Days of Grace.—By law **three days of grace** are allowed the debtor for the paying of the bill, and are taken into account by the banker.

Example 2.—Find the bankers' discount on a bill of £730 due on 30th July but discounted on May 4th at 4 %, allowing for the days of grace.

Time = (31 − 4) May + 30 June + 30 July + 3 grace = 90 days.

$$\therefore \text{ Bankers' Discount} = £730 \times \frac{90}{365} \times \frac{4}{100} = £7 \ 4s.$$

EXERCISE 111.

(1) Find the banker's discount on £760 due in 12 months at 4 per cent.

(2) Find the banker's discount and the present worth of £250 due 9 months hence at 2 per cent.

(3) Find banker's discount on £80 due 3 months hence at $2\frac{3}{4}$ %.

(4) Find banker's discount on £750 due 2 months hence at 3 %.

(5) Find the banker's discount on a bill for £65 which he discounts 73 days before it is *legally due* (*i.e.*, including days of grace) at $2\frac{1}{2}$ per cent.

In the following the days of grace should be allowed for :—

(6) Find banker's discount on a bill for £401 10s. due on August 21st and discounted on June 5th at 5 per cent.

(7) Find banker's discount on a bill for £450 due on 15th September, and discounted on 7th July at 4 per cent.

(8) Find to the nearest 1d. the banker's discount on a bill for £76 13s. due on 26th October and discounted on 10th August at 5 per cent.

Additional Examples—

(9) A three months' bill for £1,022, drawn on 23rd February, was discounted on 7th March at 5 per cent. per annum. What was the banker's discount ?

(10) What was received for a bill for £875 drawn at 3 months from 5th July, and discounted on 27th July, at $3\frac{1}{2}$ per cent. interest ?

(11) A bill for £292 was dated 20th June at 6 months, and it was discounted on 14th September at 4 per cent. How much was received for it ?

EXERCISE 111—*Continued.*

(12) A bill for £273 15s. is drawn at 4 months from 12th May, and is discounted on 27th June at $3\frac{1}{3}$ per cent. What sum is received for it ?

(13) The banker's discount for cashing on 7th July a 6 months' bill for £1,250 drawn on 15th March was £10. What was the rate of interest charged ?

(14) A banker gave £867 for a 4 months' bill for £876 drawn on 14th July. If the rate of interest was 5 per cent., on what date was the bill discounted ?

(b) " True " Discount.

The " true " or theoretical present value of a bill is the sum of money which would amount to the face value of the bill in the given time at the given rate, and the " true " or theoretical discount is equal to the interest on the true present value.

Thus, since £100 amounts to £105 in 1 year at 5 per cent., £100 is the true present value of £105 due 1 year hence, and ∴ £5 is the true discount—the interest on £100—whereas the banker's discount is £5 5s.—the interest on £105.

" **True** " **discount** is only of theoretical interest, as it is not used in business practice.

Example.—Find the " true " present value and " true " discount on £61 due 8 months hence at $2\frac{1}{2}$ per cent. This is just a **simple interest** sum—viz., " Find what sum will amount to £61 in 8 months at $2\frac{1}{2}$ per cent."

Interest on £100 for 8 months $= \dfrac{8}{12} \times 2\frac{1}{2} = 1\frac{2}{3}$.

$$\therefore \text{ £100 amounts to } £101\tfrac{2}{3}.$$

$$\therefore \text{ P.V. of } £101\tfrac{2}{3} = £100.$$

$$\therefore \quad \text{P.V. of } £61 = £100 \times \frac{61}{101\frac{2}{3}} = £60.$$

$$\therefore \qquad \text{T.D.} = £61 - £60 = £1.$$

Note that the T.D. may be found without first finding the P.V., because " interest " is proportional to the " amount."

Thus,   T.D. on £101$\frac{2}{3}$ = £1$\frac{2}{3}$.

$$\therefore \quad \text{T.D. on } £61 = £1\tfrac{2}{3} \times \frac{61}{101\frac{2}{3}} = £1.$$

EXERCISE 112.

(1) Find the " true " present value on £455 5s. due $3\frac{1}{2}$ months hence at 4 per cent.

(2) Find the " true " discount on £66 1s. 8d. for 4 months at 5 per cent.

(3) Find the " true " discount on £163 6s. 8d. due 10 months hence at $2\frac{1}{2}$ per cent.

(4) Find the " true " discount on £347 13s. due in 6 months at $4\frac{1}{2}$ per cent.

(5) Find the " banker's " discount on a bill for £350 due in 3 months at 3 per cent.

(6) Find the " banker's " discount on a bill for £766 10s. discounted 65 days before it is legally due at 5 per cent.

(7) Find the " banker's " discount and the " true " discount on £489 due 9 months hence at $2\frac{1}{2}$ per cent.

(8) Find the difference between the " banker's " discount and " true " discount on £302 10s. due in $2\frac{1}{2}$ months at 4 %.

Additional Examples—

(9) How many months hence is a bill for £382 10s. due, if its " true " present worth at 4 per cent. is £375 ?

(10) The " true " discount on a bill for £640 10s. is £10 10s., interest being at 5 % per annum. When is the bill due ?

(11) The " true " present worth of a bill for £652 6s. 8d. due in 4 months' time is £643 15s. At what rate per cent. is the discount calculated ?

(12) The " true " discount on a certain sum of money due 73 days hence at $3\frac{1}{3}$ per cent. is £10. Find the sum and the banker's discount.

(13) The banker's discount on a sum of money for 4 months is £20 6s. 8d., and the " true " discount for the same time and at the same rate is £20. Find the sum of money and the rate per cent. of discount.

(14) The difference between the banker's discount and the " true " discount on a certain bill due 8 months hence at 4 per cent. is £1 1s. 4d. What is the amount of the bill ?

(15) Find to the nearest penny the difference between the true discount and the banker's discount on a bill for £1,350 due in 146 days at $3\frac{3}{4}$ per cent.

II.—STOCKS AND SHARES.

We shall treat **Stocks** very briefly, because questions on Stocks or Shares are solved by the Ratio Method, and, therefore, involve no new operations. The distinction, however, between the **Amount of the Stock** and the **Price of the Stock** must be carefully noted.

Thus, the phrase, " **the 4 per cent. Victory Loan at 80,**" means that £80 is the price of £100 stock, and that £4 is the annual income or dividend derived from £100 stock. The " **per cent.**" means " **for £100 stock.**" It does not mean " for £100 of money " invested in the stock. In the above example an investment of £80 cash buys an annual income of £4, which is equivalent to 5 per cent. on the money invested, because $\frac{4}{80} = \frac{1}{20} = 5$ per cent.

Example 1.—What annual income would a man receive by investing £1,955 in the Government 4 per cent. Victory Loan of 1919 at 85, and how much stock would he hold ?

(1) Income from £85 invested = £4.

$\therefore$,,   £1,955   ,, $= £4 \times \dfrac{1,955}{85} = £92.$

(2)   Stock bought by £85 = £100.

$\therefore$,,   £1,955 $= 100 \times \dfrac{1,955}{85} = £2,300.$

Example 2.—If a man receives an annual income of £54 from 4% stock, how much stock does he hold ? At what price did he buy the stock if the amount of money he invested was £1,080 ?

(1)   The stock yielding £4 inc. = £100.

$\therefore$,,   £54 inc. $= £100 \times \dfrac{54}{4} = £1,350.$

(2) Amount invested to buy £54 inc. = £1,080.

$\therefore$,,   ,,   £4 inc. $= 1,080 \times \dfrac{4}{54} = £80.$

Note.—Stock is bought or sold through the agency of a broker. If the broker's charge or " brokerage " is $\frac{1}{8}$, and a certain stock were quoted at 80, a man employing a broker to buy stock for him would have to pay altogether £80$\frac{1}{8}$ for £100 stock, while a man employing a broker to sell stock for him would receive from the broker £79$\frac{7}{8}$ for stock selling at £80.

Example 3.—A man bought £1,500 stock. If the price was 86¾ and the brokerage ⅛, what was the total amount which the stock cost him ?

Total cost of £100 stock = £86¾ + £⅛ = £86½.

∴   ,,   £1,500 stock = £86½ × 15 = £1,297 10s.

EXERCISE 113.

(1) Find the cost of £650 stock at 92.

(2) How much stock at 85 can be bought for £867 ?

(3) Find the annual income from £950 stock at 4 per cent.

(4) Find the *half-yearly* yield from £750 stock at 5 per cent.

(5) Find the half-yearly income obtained by investing £676 in 5½ per cent. stock at 104.

(6) What sum must be invested in 5 per cent. stock at 95 to produce an income of £52 10s. annually ?

(7) Find the cost of 60 £5 shares in a company at £4 15s. per share, and find the annual income at 4½ per cent. (£4½ for 20 shares. ∵ £5 × 20 = £100.)

(8) Find the half-yearly income from 100 £5 shares at 4 per cent.

(9) If a man pays £394 10s. to his broker for the purchase of 5 per cent. stock at 98½, the brokerage being ⅛, find how much stock he gets and his annual income from it.

(10) A man who holds £850 stock sells it through a broker. If the selling price is 102¾, and the brokerage ¼, what is the net cash he receives ?

(11) If a man buys 4 per cent. Victory Loan at 85, what rate of interest is he receiving on his money ?

(12) If a man gets an income of £375 from £7,500 stock, what is the rate of interest ?

(13) If a man gets an income of £240 by investing £4,800 in a certain stock at 90, what is the rate of interest of the stock ?

(14) How much must a man pay to get an income of £70 from 3½ per cent. stock at 84¾ with ¼ for brokerage ?

(15) What net amount must a man invest in 5 per cent. stock at 90 to get an income of £33 15s. *half-yearly*, ⅛ being charged for brokerage ?

(16) A man received £890 7s. 6d. by the sale of £850 stock. If the broker deducted ¼ as his charge, at what price was the stock sold ?

Additional Examples—

(17) Which is the more profitable investment, 4 per cent. stock at 95, or $3\frac{1}{2}$ per cent. stock at 84 ? What difference would there be per annum on an investment of £1,900 ?

(18) At what rate per cent. does a person receive interest, who invests his money in $5\frac{2}{3}$ per cent. stock at £102 ?

(19) A man invested £2,800 in 4 per cent. stock at $87\frac{3}{8}$. When the price rose to $92\frac{7}{8}$, he sold out. How much did he gain, if the brokerage was $\frac{1}{8}$ per cent. in each case ?

(20) An income of £63 is obtained by investing £1,254 in stock at $5\frac{1}{4}$ per cent. Find the price of the stock.

(21) What should be the price of $3\frac{1}{2}$ per cent. stock so that it may pay at the same rate as $3\frac{3}{4}$ per cent. stock at 105 ?

(22) An income of £48 is obtained by investing £1,332 in stock at $92\frac{1}{2}$. At what rate per cent. is the stock quoted ?

(23) £3,750 stock at $3\frac{3}{4}$ per cent. was sold out at $97\frac{5}{8}$, and the proceeds were invested in $4\frac{2}{3}$ per cent. stock at $103\frac{7}{8}$, brokerage being $\frac{1}{8}$ in each case. By how much was the income increased ?

(24) How much $5\frac{1}{2}$ per cent. stock does a man hold, if by selling out at 108, and investing the proceeds in $4\frac{3}{4}$ per cent. stock at 90, he increases his income by £3 4s. ?

CHAPTER XX.

AREAS OTHER THAN RECTANGULAR.

I.—PARALLELOGRAMS.

THE area of a parallelogram is equal to the area of a rectangle on the same base and having the same altitude.

Parallelogram ABCD = rectangle ABEF.

∴ **Area of parallelogram = base × altitude.**

Example.—One side of a parallelogram is 2 ft. 8 ins. long, and its distance from the opposite side is 1 ft. 9 ins. Find its area.

$$\text{Area} = 32 \times 21 \text{ sq. ins.}$$
$$= 672 \text{ sq. ins.} = 4 \text{ sq. ft. } 96 \text{ sq. ins.}$$

or $\quad$ area $= 2\frac{2}{3} \times 1\frac{3}{4}$ sq. ft.

$$= \frac{8}{3} \times \frac{7}{4} \text{ sq. ft.} = \frac{14}{3} \text{ sq. ft.}$$
$$= 4\frac{2}{3} \text{ sq. ft.} = 4 \text{ sq. ft. } 96 \text{ sq. ins.}$$

EXERCISE (*a*).

Find the areas of the following parallelograms :—

(**1**) One side = 11 ins. $\quad$ Distance from opp. side = 6 ins.
(**2**) $\quad$,, $\quad$ = 2 ft. 7 ins. $\quad$,, $\quad$,, $\quad$ = 1 ft. 4 ins.
(**3**) $\quad$,, $\quad$ = 1 yd. 2 ft. 8 ins. ,, $\quad$,, $\quad$ = 2 ft. 6 ins.
(**4**) $\quad$,, $\quad$ = 13·75 cm. $\quad$,, $\quad$,, $\quad$ = 8·5 cm.
(**5**) $\quad$,, $\quad$ = 3 metres. $\quad$,, $\quad$,, $\quad$ = 1·8 metres.
(**6**) $\quad$,, $\quad$ = 3 m. 8 dm. $\quad$,, $\quad$,, $\quad$ = 2 m. 3 dm.
(**7**) A field in the shape of a parallelogram has a side 45 chains long and its distance from the opposite side is 25 chains. Find its area.

(8) The length of one side of a field shaped like a parallelogram is 20 chains 25 links, and the distance between it and the opposite side is 15 chains 10 links. Find its area.

(9) If iron sheeting weighs 22 lbs. to the square foot, find the weight of a piece cut from it in the shape of a parallelogram if one of its sides is 2 ft. 6 ins. long and the distance between it and the opposite side is 1 ft. 9 ins. long.

If the area of a parallelogram is known, and also the length of a side, then the distance between this side and the opposite side is got by dividing the area by the side. Similarly, the length of a side is equal to the area divided by the distance between it and the opposite side.

Example.—Find the area of a parallelogram if the distance between two opposite sides is 1 ft. 3 ins. and each of these sides is 2 ft. 4 ins. Hence find the distance between the two remaining sides if each is 1 ft. 8 ins. long.

(1) Area $= 15 \times 28$ sq. ins.
$= 420$ sq. ins. $= 2$ sq. ft. 132 sq. ins.

(2) Reqd. distance $= 420 \div 20$ ins.
$= 21$ ins. $= 1$ ft. 9 ins.

EXERCISE (b).

(1) The area of a parallelogram is 345 sq. ins., and one side is 1 ft. 11 ins., find the distance between it and the opposite side.

(2) If the distance between two opposite sides of parallelogram is 1 ft. 10 ins., and its area is 3 sq. ft. 96 sq. ins., find the length of each of these sides.

(3) One side of a parallelogram is 1 ft. 9 ins. long, and its distance from the opposite side is 10 ins. Find its area. If the length of each of the others is 1 ft. 3 ins., find the distance between them.

(4) Two opposite sides of a parallelogram are each 5·5 cms. long, and the distance between them is 2·1 cms. long. Find the distance between the two remaining sides if each of them is 3·5 cms. in length.

(5) If lead sheeting weighs 5 lbs. to the square foot, and a piece in the shape of a parallelogram weighs 40 lbs., find the distance between two opposite sides which are 3·2 ft. long.

(6) A plot of ground in the shape of a parallelogram has two opposite sides, each 91 yds. long, and the distance between them is 55 yds. If the distance between the other two sides is 65 yds., find the length of the perimeter (or boundary) of the field.

II.—TRIANGLES.

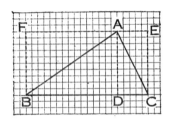

Area of △ ABC = ½ area of rect. BCEF.
= ½ base × altitude.

and $\text{base} = \dfrac{2 \text{ area}}{\text{altitude}}$, and $\text{altitude} = \dfrac{2 \text{ area}}{\text{base}}$.

The base may be any side, and the altitude is the distance of the base from the opposite vertex.

Example 1.—If the base of a triangular piece of steel plate is 3 ft. 6 ins., and its altitude is 4 ft. 3 ins., find its weight, being given that every square foot weighs 4 lbs.

$$\text{Area} = \frac{3\frac{1}{2} \times 4\frac{1}{4}}{2} \text{ sq. ft.}$$

$$= 7\tfrac{7}{16} \text{ sq. ft.}$$

∴ $\text{Weight} = 7\tfrac{7}{16} \times 4 \text{ lbs.} = 29\tfrac{3}{4} \text{ lbs.}$

Example 2.—If one side of a triangular field is 13 chains 50 links, and its area is $10\frac{4}{5}$ acres, find the distance of this side from the opposite angular point of the field.

Area $= 10\frac{4}{5}$ acres $= 10\cdot8$ acres $= 108$ sq. chains.

Now $\qquad$ reqd. distance $= \dfrac{2\text{ area}}{\text{side}}$

$$= \frac{108 \times 2}{13\cdot5} \text{ chains}$$

$$= \frac{2,160}{135} \text{ chains} = 16 \text{ chains.}$$

EXERCISE (c).

Find the areas of the following triangles :—

(1) Base $= 1$ ft. 5 ins. $\qquad$ Altitude $= 8$ ins.
(2) ,, $= 2$ ft. 9 ins. $\qquad$,, $= 2$ ft.
(3) ,, $= 2$ ft. 5 ins. $\qquad$,, $= 2$ ft. 8 ins.
(4) ,, $= 9\cdot6$ cm. $\qquad$,, $= 11\cdot9$ cm.
(5) ,, $= 1$ m. 6 dm. $\qquad$,, $= 1$ m. 5 dm.
(6) ,, $= 50$ ch. 40 links. $\qquad$,, $= 56$ ch. 4 links.
(7) If the area of a triangle is 4 sq. ft., and its base is 2 ft. 8 ins., find its altitude.
(8) The area of a triangle is 4 sq. ft. 104 sq. ins., and its altitude is 3 ft. 4 ins., find its base.
(9) A field in the shape of a triangle contains 8 acres 3,780 sq. yds., and one side is 250 yds. long. Find the distance of this side from the opposite angular point.
(10) A triangle is equal in area to a rectangle whose length is 1 ft. 9 ins. and breadth 1 ft. 8 ins. If the base of the triangle is 2 ft. 6 ins., find its altitude.
(11) A triangle has a base of 1 ft. 8 ins. and an altitude of 1 ft. 9 ins., and is equal in area to a rectangle whose breadth is 1 ft. 2 ins. Find the length of the rectangle.
(12) If a rectangular piece of sheet iron measuring 1 ft. 1 in. by 11 ins. weighs 4 lbs., find the weight of a triangular piece of the same sheet whose base is 7 ft. 7 ins. and altitude 9 ft. 2 ins.
(13) A rectangle measures $3\cdot9$ metres by $3\cdot5$ metres. Find the base of a triangle of equal area whose altitude is $6\cdot5$ metres.

(14) The gable of a house is 25 ft. wide, and the height to the eaves is 20 ft., and to the ridge 30 ft. Find its area.

(15) The gable of a house is 30 ft. wide, and the height of the eaves above the ground is 25 ft. If the total area of the gable is 930 sq. ft., find the height of the ridge from the ground.

(16) A right-angled triangle has the sides containing the right angle equal to 3 ft. 4 ins. and 2 ft. 8 ins. respectively. Find its area. (*If one of the sides containing the right angle is taken as the base, the other is the altitude*).

In a right-angled triangle, the side opposite the right angle is called the hypotenuse, either of the other two sides is called the base, and the remaining side is called the perpendicular.

The square on the hypotenuse = the sum of the squares on the other two sides.

Area of a right-angled triangle = $\frac{1}{2}$ product of the two sides containing the right angle.

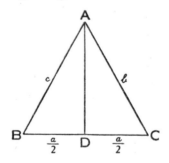

When the three sides of a triangle are equal, the triangle is equilateral.

$$AD = \frac{a \cdot \sqrt{3}}{2} \quad (a = \text{length of side}).$$

Area of equilateral triangle = $\frac{1}{2} a \times \dfrac{a \sqrt{3}}{2}$

$$= \frac{a^2 \sqrt{3}}{4} = a^2 \times {\cdot}433.$$

EXERCISE (c)—*Continued*.

Example 1.—The hypotenuse of a right-angled triangle is 2 ft. 2 ins. and the base is 10 ins. Find the length of the perpendicular and the area of the triangle.

Square on perpendicular = square on hypotenuse — square on base
$$= (26^2 - 10^2) \text{ sq. ins.}$$
$$= 576 \text{ sq. ins.}$$

∴   length of perpendicular = $\sqrt{576}$ ins. = 24 ins. = 2 ft.
Area of triangle = $\frac{1}{2}$ base × perpendicular.
$$= \frac{1}{2} \times 10 \times 24 \text{ sq. ins.}$$
$$= 120 \text{ sq. ins.}$$

Example 2.—Find the area of an equilateral triangle whose side is 2 ft. 6 ins. long.

Area of equilateral triangle $= a^2 \times \cdot 433$
$$= 30^2 \times \cdot 433 \text{ sq. ins.}$$
$$= 389 \cdot 7 \text{ sq. ins.}$$
$$= 2 \text{ sq. ft. } 101 \cdot 7 \text{ sq. ins.}$$

(17) The hypotenuse of a right-angled triangle is 3 ft. 5 ins. and the base is 9 ins. Find the length of the perpendicular and the area of the triangle.

(18) The base of a right-angled triangle is 2 ft. 11 ins. and the perpendicular is 7 ft. Find the hypotenuse and the area of the triangle.

(19) One side of a rectangle is 1 ft. 3 ins. long, and the other is 3 ft. Find the length of the diagonal.

(20) The diagonal of a rectangular field is 205 yards long, and one of the sides is 45 yards long. Find the length of the other side and the area of the field.

(21) Find correct to one decimal place the length of the diagonal of a square whose side is 15 ins. long.

(22) A ladder 17 ft. 4 ins. long rests against a wall. If the foot of the ladder is 6 ft. 8 ins. from the wall, to what height does the ladder reach ?

(23) A sheet of iron is in the shape of a right-angled triangle. The longest side measures 65 cm., and one of the other sides is 39 cm. If the iron weighs 7·5 g. per sq. cm., find the weight of the sheet in Kg.

EXERCISE (c)—*Continued.*

(24) A garden plot is in the form of a right-angled triangle. The longest side is 13 yards and one of the other sides is 12 yards. Find the area of the plot.

(25) A field is in the form of a right-angled triangle. The sides containing the right angle are 392 yards and 231 yards respectively. Find the cost of fencing the field at 1s. 6d. per yard.

(26) A field in the form of a right-angled triangle contains 3 acres 2,760 sq. yards, and one of the sides containing the right angle is 120 yards long. What is the length of the longest side ?

(27) Find the area of an equilateral triangle whose side measures 110 yards.

(28) The side of an equilateral triangle is 4 ft. 2 ins. Find its area.

(29) An equilateral triangle has an area of 3 acres 2,800 sq. yards. Find the length of its side.

(30) Find, to the nearest yard, the length of the side of a square field equal in area to a field in the shape of an equilateral triangle whose side is 80 yards long.

(31) The length of the side of a square field is 120 yards. Find, to the nearest yard, the length of the side of a field in the shape of an equilateral triangle having the same area.

The area of a triangle may also be calculated by means of a formula in which the lengths of three sides are used.

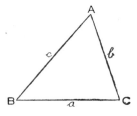

If a, b, c denotes the sides,
and if $s = \frac{1}{2}(a + b + c)$,

the area of the triangle $= \sqrt{s\,(s - a)\,(s - b)\,(s - c)}$.

Example 1.—Find the area of a triangle whose sides are 34 ins., 50 ins., and 52 ins.

$$a = 34$$
$$b = 50$$
$$c = 52$$
$$\therefore \quad 2s = 136$$
$$\therefore \quad s = 68$$
$$s - a = 34$$
$$s - b = 18$$
$$s - c = 16$$

$$\text{Area} = \sqrt{s\,(s - a)\,(s - b)\,(s - c)}$$
$$= \sqrt{68 \times 34 \times 18 \times 16} \quad \text{sq. ins.}$$
$$= \sqrt{2 \times 34 \times 34 \times 18 \times 16} \quad \text{,,}$$
$$= \sqrt{34^2 \times 6^2 \times 4^2} \quad \text{,,}$$
$$= 34 \times 6 \times 4 \quad \text{,,}$$
$$= 816 \text{ sq. ins.}$$

If the number under the radical is a complete square, its square root is best found by factors as in the above example. If it is not a complete square, the square root may be extracted by the method on p. 128 to one or more decimal places, as may be desired.

EXERCISE (*d*).

Find the areas of the triangles whose sides are—

(**1**) 5 ins., 5 ins., and 6 ins.
(**2**) 13 ins., 14 ins., and 15 ins.
(**3**) 13 ins., 20 ins., and 21 ins.
(**4**) 17 cms., 25 cms., and 26 cms.
(**5**) 25 ft., 39 ft., and 40 ft.
(**6**) 6·5 ins., 10 ins., and 10·5 ins.
(**7**) 2 ft. 2 ins., 3 ft. 4 ins., and 3 ft. 6 ins.
(**8**) 4 ft. 4 ins., 4 ft. 8 ins., and 5 ft.
(**9**) 6 ft. 8 ins., 6 ft. 8 ins., and 8 ft.
(**10**) 3·9 dms., 4·2 dms., and 4·5 dms.
(**11**) 32·5 cms., 35 cms., and 37·5 cms.
(**12**) 9·75 m., 15 m., and 15·75 m.

Find correct to the nearest one decimal place approximation the areas of the triangles whose sides are—

(**13**) 11 ft., 14 ft., and 15 ft.
(**14**) 16 ins., 18 ins., and 26 ins.
(**15**) 17 cms., 19 cms., and 24 cms.

16

III.—TRAPEZIUMS AND OTHER QUADRILATERALS.

A trapezium is a quadrilateral or four-sided figure with two of its sides parallel.

The area of any quadrilateral may be found by dividing it into

two triangles by drawing a diagonal and then finding the areas of the triangles. In the case of a trapezium, if the parallel sides are taken as the bases of the triangles, each triangle has the same altitude—viz., the distance between the parallel sides.

Let ABCD be a trapezium with AB parallel to DC.

Draw diagonal AC, and draw AP perp. to CD.

Area of trap. ABCD = Area of $\triangle$ ACD + Area of $\triangle$ ABC

$$= \tfrac{1}{2} CD . AP + \tfrac{1}{2} AB . AP$$
$$= \tfrac{1}{2} AP (CD + AB).$$

∴ **The area of a trapezium = $\tfrac{1}{2}$ sum of parallel sides × altitude.**

Example.—Find the area of a field in the shape of a trapezium whose parallel sides are 23 chains 20 links and 12 chains 60 links, and the distance between them 5 chains 40 links.

Area = $\tfrac{1}{2}$ (23·2 + 12·6) × 5·4 sq. chains
= 17·9 × 5·4 sq. chains = 96·66 sq. chains.
= 9 ac. 2 ro. 26·56 po.

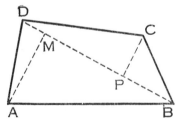

In the case of a quadrilateral of irregular shape it is convenient to take the diagonal as the base of each of the triangles into which it divides the quadrilateral, the altitudes (or **offsets**) being the distances of the opposite vertices from the diagonal.

Let ABCD be any quadrilateral. Draw a diag. BD. From C and A draw perps. CP and AM on BD.

Area of quadrilateral ABCD = Area of $\triangle$ ABD + Area of $\triangle$ BCD

$$= \tfrac{1}{2} BD . AM + \tfrac{1}{2} BD . CP$$
$$= \tfrac{1}{2} BD (AM + CP).$$

∴ **Area of any quadrilateral = $\tfrac{1}{2}$ diagonal × sum of offsets.**

Example.—The length of one of the diagonals of a quadrilateral is 9 metres, and the lengths of the perpendiculars drawn to it from the opposite vertices are 8·6 metres and 4·8 metres. Find the area of the quadrilateral.

$$\text{Area} = \tfrac{1}{2} \times 9 \times (8 \cdot 6 + 4 \cdot 8) \text{ sq. metres}$$
$$= \frac{9}{2} \times 13 \cdot 4 = 9 \times 6 \cdot 7 \text{ sq. metres}$$
$$= 60 \cdot 3 \text{ sq. metres.}$$

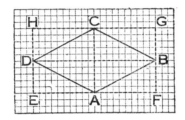

A Rhombus is a parallelogram whose sides are all equal.

The diagonals of a rhombus bisect each other at right angles.

In the figure, ABCD is a rhombus, and EFGH is the rectangle formed by its diagonals.

Rhombus ABCD = $\tfrac{1}{2}$ rectangle EFGH.

Area of rhombus = $\tfrac{1}{2}$ product of its diagonals.

$$\textbf{Side of rhombus} = \sqrt{\left(\frac{\textbf{1st diagonal}}{\textbf{2}}\right)^2 + \left(\frac{\textbf{2nd diagonal}}{\textbf{2}}\right)^2}.$$

Example.—The diagonals of a rhombus are 8 ins. and 6 ins. respectively. Find the area and the length of a side of the rhombus.

$$\text{Area of rhombus} = \tfrac{1}{2} \text{ product of diagonals}$$
$$= \tfrac{1}{2} \times 8 \times 6 \text{ sq. ins.} = 24 \text{ sq. ins.}$$

$$\text{Side of rhombus} = \sqrt{\left(\frac{\text{1st diagonal}}{2}\right)^2 + \left(\frac{\text{2nd diagonal}}{2}\right)^2}$$
$$= \sqrt{4^2 + 3^2} \text{ ins.} = \sqrt{25} \text{ ins.}$$
$$= 5 \text{ ins.}$$

EXERCISE (e).

Find the areas of the following trapeziums:—

(1) Parallel sides—2 ft. 7 ins. and 3 ft. 5ins. ; altitude, 1 ft. 8 ins.
(2) Parallel sides—1 ft. 8 ins. and 1 ft. 10 ins. ; altitude, 2 ft.
(3) Parallel sides—1 m. 4 dm. and 2 m. 6 dm. ; altitude, 1 m. 8 dm.
(4) Parallel sides—350 yds. and 260 yds. ; altitude, 300 yds.
(5) Parallel sides—21 ch. 40 lk. and 16 ch. 12 lk. ; altitude, 18 ch. 5 lk.

Find the areas of the following quadrilaterals:—

(6) Diagonal—2 ft. 6 ins. ; offsets, 1 ft. 7 ins and 1 ft. 4 ins.
(7) ,, —3 ft. 8 ins. ; offsets, 2 ft. 8 ins. and 1 ft. 10 ins.
(8) ,, —19·5 cms. ; offsets, 12·3 cms. and 11·7 cms.
(9) ,, —25 ch. ; offsets, 10 ch. 26 lk. and 14 ch. 24 lk.
(10) A field in the shape of a trapezium has its parallel sides equal to 326 ft. and 474 ft. and the distance between them is 256 ft. Find the area of the field.
(11) A piece of ground in the shape of a quadrilateral has two parallel sides, measuring 684 links and 796 links, and the distance between them is 945 links. Find the acreage of the piece of ground.
(12) Find the area of a quadrilateral-shaped field, one of its diagonals measuring 150 ft., and the perpendiculars on it from the opposite angular points 78 ft. and 92 ft.
(13) The hipped roof of a house is 20 ft. 6 ins. long at the ridge and 56 ft. long in the eaves from hip to hip. If the distance between the ridge and the eaves be 25 ft., find the number of sq. yds. of slating in the roof.
(14) A field in the shape of a trapezium has an area of 90,000 sq. yds. ; if the parallel sides are 320 yds. and 400 yds. in length, find the distance between them.
(15) A field in the shape of a trapezium has an area of 15 acres. One of the parallel sides is 15 chains in length, and the distance between them is 12 chains. Find the length of the other parallel side.
(16) The diagonals of a rhombus are 8 ft. 8 ins. and 6 ft. 6 ins. respectively. Find its area and the length of its side.
(17) The diagonals of a rhombus are 42 ft. and 56 ft. respectively. Find its area and the length of its side.

(18) The area of a rhombus is 20 sq. ft. 120 sq. ins., and one of its diagonals is 10 ft. long. Find the length of its side.

(19) The area of a field in the form of a rhombus is 1 acre 1,040 sq. yards, and one of the diagonals is 70 yards. Find the length of its side.

IV.—RECTILINEAL FIGURES WITH MORE THAN FOUR
SIDES.

To find the area of rectilineal figures with more than four sides, a diagonal is drawn by joining two vertices, and then perpendiculars are drawn to this diagonal from the opposite vertices. The figure is thus divided into triangles and trapeziums whose areas can be found.

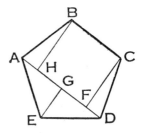

For example, let ABCDE be a recti- lineal figure. Draw the diagonal AD, and BH, CF, EG perpendicular to AD. Then

$$ABCDE = \triangle\, ABH + \text{trap. } BCFH + \triangle\, CFD + \triangle\, ADE.$$
$$= \tfrac{1}{2}\, BH \times AH + \tfrac{1}{2}\, (BH + CF) \times HF + \tfrac{1}{2}\, CF \times FD$$
$$+ \tfrac{1}{2}\, AD \times GE.$$

If the above figure represented a field, then, for the purposes of calculation, AD, HD, GD, FD, BH, CF, and GE are measured. Thus if AD = 50 yds., HD = 40 yds. GD = 28 yds., FD = 16 yds., BH = 15 yds., CF = 17 yds., and GE = 16 yds.

Then

$$
\begin{aligned}
\triangle\, ABH &= \tfrac{1}{2} \times 15 \times (50 - 40) &&= 15 \times\ 5 =\ 75 \text{ sq. yds.}\\
BCFH &= \tfrac{1}{2}(15 + 17) \times (40 - 16) &&= 16 \times 24 = 384 \quad\text{,,}\\
\triangle\, CFD &= \tfrac{1}{2} \times 17 \times 16 &&= 17 \times\ 8 = 136 \quad\text{,,}\\
\triangle\, ADE &= \tfrac{1}{2} \times 50 \times 16 &&= 50 \times\ 8 = 400 \quad\text{,,}
\end{aligned}
$$

$$\therefore\ \text{Area of } ABCDE = \overline{995} \text{ sq. yds.}$$

The measurements of the last example would be entered in a surveyor's field-book thus :—

	Yards.	
	To A	
	50	
	40	15 to B.
To E, 16	28	
	16	17 to C.
	from D	

A plan of the field would be drawn to scale.

EXERCISE (f).

Find the areas of the fields represented by the following field-book entries :—

(1) Yards.

	140	
55	110	
	70	60
45	50	

(2) Yards.

	155	
	115	60
50	90	
	70	80

(3) Links.

	350	
	280	100
180	200	
	150	80
60	100	

(4) Chains.

	20	
9	14	
	12	6
4	8	
	5	8
10	3	

(5) Metres.

	200	
	130	140
125	90	
	60	40

(6) Metres.

	210	
70	170	
	120	60
20	90	
	60	30
50	40	

(7)	Chains.		(8)	Chains.	
	Go North			Go West	
	To B			To B	
	30			12	
	20	9·5 to G.		8	4 to G.
To F, 11	15		To F, 5	7	
To E, 9	10			6·5	5 to E.
	6	7·5 to D.	To D, 4	5	
To C, 8	From A			2·5	3 to C.
				From A	

V.—THE CIRCLE.

(a) The Circumference.

The ratio which the circumference of a circle bears to its diameter is a fixed quantity, but cannot be expressed exactly in numbers, and is, therefore, represented by a symbol—viz., the Greek letter π (pi).

If the radius is represented by r, then the diameter $= 2r$.

Thus, $$\frac{\text{Circumference}}{2r} = \pi$$

or $$\text{Circumference} = 2\pi r.$$

Approximately π is equal to $\frac{22}{7}$ or 3·1416.

Example 1.—Find the circumference of a circle whose radius is 2 ft. 8 ins.

$$\text{Circumference} = 2\pi r$$
$$= 2 \times 3\cdot1416 \times 32 \text{ ins.}$$
$$= 201\cdot06 \text{ ins. approximately.}$$

Example 2.—The circumference of a circle is 132 ins. Find its radius (taking $\pi = \frac{22}{7}$).

$$2\,\pi\,r = 132 \text{ ins.}$$
$$r = \frac{132}{2\pi} \text{ ins.} = 66 \times \frac{7}{22} \text{ ins.}$$
$$= 21 \text{ ins.}$$

EXERCISE (*g*).   Take $\pi = \frac{22}{7}$ unless otherwise stated.

(1) Find the circumferences of the following circles (take π = 3·1416) :—

     (1) Radius = 5 ins.   (2) Radius = 2·5 cm.

     (3)   ,,   = 2 ft. 4 ins.   (4)   ,,   = 1 yd. 1 ft.

     (5) Diameter = 8 ins.   (6) Diameter = 3 ft. 6 ins.

(2) Find radii of the circles whose circumferences are as follows :—   (1) 396 inches.   (2) 8 yds. 1 ft. 8 ins.

                     (3) 1 yd. 1 ft. 8 ins.   (4) 11 ins.

(3) A bicycle wheel is 35 ins. in diameter. How many revolutions does it make in going 11 miles ?

(4) If the driving wheel of a bicycle makes 120 revolutions per minute, what is the speed, the diameter of wheel being 3 ft. ?

(5) If the driving wheel of a bicycle makes 1,120 revolutions in going 2 miles, find its diameter.

(6) A locomotive is travelling at the rate of 30 miles per hour. If the diameter of the driving wheel be 6 ft., how many revolutions does it make per minute ?

(7) When a locomotive is travelling at the rate of $37\frac{1}{2}$ miles per hour its driving wheel makes 150 revolutions per minute. Find the diameter of the wheel.

(*b*) The Area of a Circle.

To find the area of a circle, we square radius and multiply by π. Thus, **Area of a circle** $= \pi r^2$.

Example 1.—Find the area of a circle whose diameter is 10 ft. 6 ins. ($\pi = \frac{22}{7}$).

Here $r = \dfrac{10 \text{ ft. } 6 \text{ ins.}}{2} = 5 \text{ ft. } 3 \text{ ins.} = 5\frac{1}{4} \text{ ft.}$

$$\text{Area} = \pi r^2 = \frac{22}{7} \times (5\tfrac{1}{4})^2 \text{ sq. ft.}$$

$$= \frac{\overset{11}{\cancel{22}}}{\cancel{7}} \times \frac{\overset{3}{\cancel{21}}}{\cancel{4}} \times \frac{21}{\underset{2}{\cancel{4}}} \text{ sq. ft.}$$

$$= \frac{693}{8} \text{ sq. ft.} = 86\tfrac{5}{8} \text{ sq. ft.}$$

$$= 86 \text{ sq. ft. } 90 \text{ sq. ins.}$$

Example 2.—The area of a circle is 4 sq. ft. $131\frac{1}{7}$ sq. ins. **Find** its radius.

$$\text{Area} = \pi\, r^2$$

∴ $\qquad \pi\, r^2 = 4 \text{ sq. ft. } 131\frac{1}{7} \text{ sq. ins.}$

i.e., $\qquad \dfrac{22}{7} \times r^2 = 707\frac{1}{7} \text{ sq. ins.}$

∴ $\qquad r^2 = 707\frac{1}{7} \times \dfrac{7}{22} \text{ sq. ins.}$

$$= \frac{4,950}{7} \times \frac{7}{22} = 225 \text{ sq. ins.}$$

∴ $\qquad r = \sqrt{225} \text{ ins.} = 15 \text{ ins.} = 1 \text{ ft. } 3 \text{ ins.}$

Thus, if the area is given, to find the radius we divide by π (or $\frac{22}{7}$), and then extract the square root.

Example 3.—Find the area of a plane circular ring whose internal radii are 6 ins. and 5 ins. respectively.

The area of ring = difference between areas of the two circles, where radii are 6 ins. and 5 ins.

∴ $\qquad \text{Area} = \pi \times 6^2 - \pi \times 5^2$
$$= \pi\,(6^2 - 5^2)$$
$$= \frac{22}{7} \times 11 = 34\frac{4}{7} \text{ sq. ins.}$$

Example 4.—The circumference of a circle is 7 ft. 4 ins. **Find** its area ($\pi = \frac{22}{7}$).

$\qquad 2\,\pi\, r = 7 \text{ ft. } 4 \text{ ins.} = 88 \text{ ins.}$

∴ $\qquad \pi\, r = 44 \text{ ins.}$

∴ $\qquad r = 44 \div \pi = 44 \times \dfrac{7}{22} = 14 \text{ ins.}$

∴ $\qquad \pi\, r^2 = \pi\, r \times r = 44 \times 14 \text{ sq. ins.} = 616 \text{ sq. ins.}$

EXERCISE (*h*).

Take $\pi = \frac{22}{7}$ unless otherwise stated.

(1) Find the areas of the circle whose radii are—

    (1) 14 ins.   (2) 1 ft. 9 ins.
    (3) 3 ft. 6 ins.   (4) 2 yds. 1 ft.
    (5) 3·2 cm.   (6) 4 chains 20 links.

(2) Find the area of a circle whose diameter is 5 ft. (taking π to be 3·14).

(3) Find the weight of a circular steel plate whose radius is $3\frac{1}{2}$ ft., if the weight of a square foot be 30 lbs.

(4) Find the radii of the circles whose areas are ($\pi = 3\cdot1416$)—
    (1) 3·1416 sq. ins.   (2) 28·2744 sq. ins.

(5) Find the diameters of the circles whose areas are—
    (1) 154 sq. ins.   (2) $78\frac{4}{7}$ sq. ins.

(6) Find the circumferences of the circles whose areas are—
    (1) 1,386 sq. ins.   (2) 13 sq. ft. $92\frac{2}{7}$ sq. ins.

(7) Find the areas of the circles whose circumferences are—
    (1) 88 ins.   (2) 22 ft.

(8) Find the area of a circle whose circumference is 37·68 cm. ($\pi = 3\cdot14$).

(9) Find the area of a plane circular ring whose internal and external radii are 4 ins. and 6 ins. respectively.

(10) Find the area of a plane circular ring if the diameters of the circles bounding it be 3 ft. 2 ins. and 2 ft.

(11) Find the weight of a metal ring bounded by circles whose diameters are 3 ft. 8 ins. and 2 ft. 6 ins. at 24 lbs. per square foot.

(12) If the internal radius of a plane circular ring be 1 ft. 3 ins., and if the width of the ring be 6 ins., find the circumference of the outer circle.

(13) If a circular lawn whose diameter is 200 yds. be surrounded by a path 14 ft. wide, find the area of the path.

(14) If a circular piece $3\frac{1}{2}$ ft. in radius be cut from a sheet of lead 8 ft. square, find the weight of the remaining piece at 5 lbs. per sq. ft.

(15) If two circular discs of metal of 3 ins. and 4 ins. radii be melted and made into one disc of the same thickness as the other two, find the radius of new disc.

VI.—THE CURVED SURFACES OF CYLINDER, CONE, AND SPHERE.

The curved surface of a cylinder $= 2\pi rh$.

Where $r =$ radius of circular end, and $h =$ height or length of the cylinder—*i.e., the area = circumference of the end multiplied by the height.*

The curved surface of a cone $= \pi rs$.

Where $r =$ radius of circular base and $s =$ the length of slant side or slope of cone from apex to the base—*i.e., area $= \frac{1}{2}$ circumference of the end multiplied by the slant side.*

The surface of a sphere $= 4\pi r^2$, where r is its radius.

EXERCISE (*i*).   Take π to be 3·14.

(1) Find the areas of the curved surfaces of cylinders :—
　　(1) Height $= 9$ ins. ; radius of base $= 5$ ins.
　　(2)　　,,　　$= 2$ ft. 4 ins. ; radius of base $= 1$ ft. 6 ins.
　　(3)　　,,　　$= 65$ cms. ; radius of base $= 20$ cms.
(2) A hollow metal tube is 3 ft. long. Its internal diameter is 3 ins. ; find the area of its inner surface.
(3) If the metal of the tube in the last example is $\frac{1}{8}$ of an inch thick, find the area of the outer surface.
(4) Find the areas of the curved surfaces of the following cones:—
　　(1) Slant side $= 10$ ins. ; radius of base $= 4$ ins.
　　(2)　　,,　　$= 3$ ft. 4 ins. ; radius of base $= 1$ ft. 2 ins.
　　(3)　　,,　　$= 2·5$ m. ; radius of base $= ·8$ m.
(5) A conical canvas tent is 10 ft. in diameter at the base and the slant side is 14 ft. long ; find the area of the canvas.
(6) Find the areas of the surfaces of the following spheres :—
　　(1) Radius $= 3$ ins.　　　　(2) Radius $= 8·5$ cms.
　　(3) Diameter $= 4$ ft.　　　　(4) Diameter $= 5$ m.
(7) Find area of earth's surface, taking radius as 4,000 miles.
(8) Find the total surface of a hemisphere whose radius is 4 ft.
(9) Find the total surface of a cone, if the diameter of its base is 8 ft. and the slant side is 12 ft.
(10) A cylindrical boiler has one end flat and the other hemispherical in shape. Find the total external surface, if the length of cylindrical part is 15 ft. and external diameter 5 ft.

CHAPTER XXI.

VOLUMES OF SOLIDS OTHER THAN RECTANGULAR.

PRISM, CYLINDER, PYRAMID, CONE, SPHERE.

The volume of a   prism $=$ base $\times$ height.

   ,,   ,,   cylinder $=$ base $\times$ height.

   ,,   ,,   pyramid $= \dfrac{1}{3}$ base $\times$ height.

   ,,   ,,   cone $= \dfrac{1}{3}$ base $\times$ height.

   ,,   ,,   sphere $= \dfrac{4}{3}\,\pi\,r^3$ (where $r =$ radius).

Example 1.—Find volume of a cylinder whose height is 3 ft., and whose base has a radius of 8 ins.

$$\text{Area of base } (\pi r^2) = 3 \cdot 14 \times \left(\frac{2}{3}\right)^2 \text{ sq. ft.}$$

$$\therefore \qquad \text{Volume } (\pi\,r^2\,h) = 3 \cdot 14 \times \frac{4}{9} \times 3 \text{ cubic ft.}$$

$$= 4 \cdot 18\dot{6} \text{ cubic ft.}$$

Example 2.—Find the volume of a cone whose height is 1 ft. 3 ins., and the diameter of whose base is 10 ins.

$$\text{Volume of cone } \left(\frac{1}{3}\pi r^2 h\right) = \frac{1}{3} \text{ base } \times \text{ height}$$

$$= \frac{1}{3} \times 3 \cdot 14 \times 5^2 \times 15 \text{ cubic ins.}$$

$$= 3 \cdot 14 \times 5^2 \times 5 \text{ cubic ins.}$$

$$= 392 \cdot 5 \text{ cubic ins.}$$

Example 3.—Find the volume of a sphere whose radius is 1 ft. 6 ins.

$$\text{Volume} = \frac{4}{3}\,\pi\,r^3$$

$$= \frac{4}{3} \times 3\cdot14 \times \left(\frac{3}{2}\right)^3 \text{ cubic ft.}$$

$$= \frac{4}{3} \times 3\cdot14 \times \frac{27}{8} = 1\cdot57 \times 9 \text{ cubic ft.}$$

$$= 14\cdot13 \text{ cubic ft.}$$

When the slant height is given, it is necessary first to find the perpendicular height.

Example 4.—The base of a square pyramid is 10 ins. long, and the distance from the vertex to the middle point of the side of the base is 1 ft. 1 in. Find the volume of the pyramid.

Slant height = 13 ins., base = 10 ins.

$\therefore$ Perpendicular height $= \sqrt{s^2 - \left(\dfrac{b}{2}\right)^2}$

$$= \sqrt{13^2 - 5^2} \text{ ins.} = 12 \text{ ins.}$$

Volume of pyramid $= \frac{1}{3}$ base $\times$ height.

$$= \tfrac{1}{3} \times 100 \times 12 \text{ cub. ins.}$$

$$= 400 \text{ cub. ins.}$$

Example 5.—The diameter of the base of a cone is 1 ft. 8 ins., and its slant height is 2 ft. 2 ins. Find its volume.

Slant height = 26 ins., diameter = 20 ins.

$\therefore$ Perpendicular height $= \sqrt{s^2 - \left(\dfrac{b}{2}\right)^2}$

$$= \sqrt{26^2 - 10^2} \text{ ins.} = 24 \text{ ins.}$$

Volume of cone $= \frac{1}{3}$ base $\times$ height $(\frac{1}{3}\,\pi\,r^2 h)$

$$= \tfrac{1}{3} \times 3\cdot14 \times 10 \times 10 \times 24 \text{ cub. ins.}$$

$$= 1 \text{ cub. ft. } 784 \text{ cub. ins.}$$

EXERCISE (j).

(Take $\pi = 3\cdot14$.)

(1) A cylinder is 2 ft. high, and the radius of its base is 6 ins. Find its volume.

(2) Find the volume of a prism 14 ins. in height and whose base is a triangle with its sides equal to 3, 4, and 5 inches respectively.

(3) A prism has a triangular base with sides equal to 13 ins., 14 ins., and 15 ins. The height of the prism is 20 ins. Find its volume.

(4) A pyramid is 2 ft. in height and stands on a triangular base. If the sides of the triangle are 13 ins., 20 ins., and 21 ins. respectively, find the volume of the pyramid.

(5) A cone is 18 ins. high, and the radius of its base 5 ins. Find its volume.

(6) Find the volume of a sphere of 3 ft. radius.

(7) If the radius of a spherical ball is $5\cdot4$ cms., find its volume.

(8) How many spherical balls, each 3 ins. in diameter, can be made out of a cubic foot of rubber ? How much rubber is left over ?

(9) A circular cone has a base 2 ft. in diameter. If its volume contains $3\cdot14$ (π) cubic feet, find its height.

(10) A conical tent has a base 12 ft. in diameter, and stands 15 ft. high. If it is occupied by four persons, how much air space is allowed for each person ?

(11) If a solid cylinder is 3 ft. high, and if the base is 3 ft. in diameter, find the volume of the largest sphere that could be cut out of it.

(12) A hollow metal cylindrical pipe is 9 ft. long. The external diameter of its end is 2 ft. 6 ins., and the metal is an inch thick. Find the volume of the metal.

(13) The base of a pyramid is an equilateral triangle whose side is 10 ins. If the pyramid is 1 ft. 8 ins. high, find its volume to the nearest cubic inch.

(14) The side of the base of a square pyramid is 12 ft. and its slant height is 10 ft. Find the volume of the pyramid.

(15) A stone pyramid stands on a square base 30 ft. long. If its slant height measures 25 ft., and the stone weighs 175 lbs. per cub. ft., what weight of stone is in the pyramid. ?

(16) The base of a triangular prism is right-angled, and the sides containing this angle are each 12 cms. If the height of the prism is 15 cms., find its volume.

(17) The curved surface of a cylinder has an area of 17 sq. ft. 64 sq. ins., and the diameter of its base is 1 ft. 4 ins. Find its volume.

(18) A cylindrical boiler is 12 ft. long and 6 ft. in diameter. It is closed at each end by a hemisphere. How many cubic feet of water will it contain ?

(19) The base of a pyramid is a regular hexagon whose edge is 9 ft. Each slant edge is 15 ft. long. Find the volume of the pyramid.

(A regular hexagon contains 6 equal equilateral triangles.)

(20) The height of a cone is equal to the circumference of its base, and the radius of its base is 2 ft. 1 ins. Find its volume in cub. ft. and cub. ins., correct to 1 decimal place.

(21) The volume of a cone is 2411·52 cub. ft., and the diameter of its base is 24 ft. Find the area of its curved surface.

(22) A spire in the shape of a cone is built of stone, which weighs 175 lbs. per cub. ft. The diameter of the cone is 10 ft. and its height is 18 ft. What weight of stone is in the spire ?

REVISION EXERCISES.

All the examples in these Exercises are from Leaving Certificate Examination Papers (published by permission of the Controller of H.M. Stationery Office).

EXERCISE I.

(1) Reduce £4,126 17s. 11½d. to farthings, and 156,482 ounces, avoirdupois, to tons, cwts., etc.

(2) I collected £123 1s. 11d. to be distributed equally to a number of persons. The cost of advertising was £3 15s. 6d., that of stationery and stamps £2 13s. 10d., and each person received £5 1s. 5d. To how many persons was the money distributed ?

(3) What sum will amount to £1,513 6s. 8d. in 3 years at 4½ per cent. simple interest ?

(4) Find (1) the cost of 27,938 things at £4 12s. 9¾d. each ; and (2) the rent of 47 acres 3 roods 8 poles at £5 6s. 3d. an acre, by practice.

(5) Add together $\dfrac{3}{10}$, $\dfrac{5}{14}$, $\dfrac{8}{21}$, and $\dfrac{17}{35}$; and divide $\left(\dfrac{2}{5} \text{ of } \dfrac{3}{7}\right)$ by $\left(\dfrac{3}{5} - \dfrac{2}{7}\right)$.

(6) If 124 horses are fed for 7 weeks at a cost of £651, how many horses can be fed for 11 weeks at a cost of £288 15s. ?

(7) Find the square root of 733,922,281.

(8) Divide 4·3046721 by ·0729, and find the value of 3·16875 of £1.

(9) Express 5 cwts. 2 qrs. 21 lbs. as a decimal fraction of a ton correctly to 6 places.

(10) A tea-dealer blends 100 lbs. of tea at 1s. 5d. a lb. with 40 lbs. at 1s. 8½d. At what price must he sell the mixture so as to gain 25 per cent. ?

(11) A gallon of water weighs 10 lbs. and a cubic foot of water weighs 1,000 ounces. If a rectangular cistern be 6 ft. long and 4 ft. broad, and contains 200 gallons, what will be the depth of the water in the cistern ?

EXERCISE II.

(1) Reduce 571,536 farthings to guineas ; and 3 weeks 2 days 14 hours 25 minutes 41 seconds to seconds.

(2) Find the greatest common measure of 29,256 and 21,413 ; and the least common multiple of 294, 315, 350, and 360.

(3) Simplify—   (1) $4\frac{3}{4} + 5\frac{1}{20} + 3\frac{1}{9} - 11\frac{2}{5}$.

$$(2) \ \frac{\dfrac{3}{11} \text{ of } 3\dfrac{15}{17}}{\dfrac{20}{23} \text{ of } 2\dfrac{1}{34}}.$$

(4) Find the value of $\dfrac{252}{485}$ of $2\dfrac{97}{114}$ of £15 7s. 2d. ; and reduce £3 15s. 7½d. to the decimal of 2s.

(5) A room is 17 feet long, and 13 feet 6 inches broad ; find (1) how many yards or carpet, 2 ft. 3 ins. wide, will be required to cover the floor ; (2) the price of the carpet at 5s. 4d. a yard.

(6) The gold reserve of a bank weighs 27 tons 10 cwts. 3 qrs. 3 lbs. If there be 7,000 grains in 1 lb. avoirdupois, and a sovereign weighs 123·374 grains, find the value of the reserve.

(7) £135 accumulating at simple interest becomes £189 in 12 years ; find the rate per cent. per annum.

(8) An egg merchant buys eggs at 9d. per dozen, and sells them at 15 for 1s. ; how much per cent. on his outlay does he gain or lose ?

(9) A runs a mile race with B, and receives 75 yards start, but loses one foot every seven yards he runs. By how much will A gain or lose the race ?

(10) Turf is taken from a field 2 furlongs 36 poles 3 yds. 2 ft. long and 2 furlongs 14 poles 2 yds. 2 ft. 3 ins. broad, and is found to be exactly sufficient to cover a square garden. Find the length of one side of the garden.

EXERCISE III.

(1) How often is £410 3s. 4d. contained in £7,793 3s. 4d. ?

(2) Simplify—
     (1) $\dfrac{7}{12} - \dfrac{13}{84} + \dfrac{20}{63} - \dfrac{5}{7}$;

     (2) $\dfrac{13}{63} \times 1\dfrac{7}{20} \times 2\dfrac{3}{11} \div 8\dfrac{1}{8}$.

(3) (1) Express $\dfrac{2}{27}$ of a foot as a vulgar fraction of an inch.

     (2) Express 17s. 4d. as a vulgar fraction of two guineas.

(4) Find the square root of 47·706649.

(5) A cistern is 13 feet 4 inches long, 11 feet 3 inches wide, and 4 feet 2 inches deep. How many cubic feet of water will it contain ?

(6) Find the value of—
     (1) ·875 of £3 7s. 6d.
     (2) 2·25 of $3\frac{1}{2}$ acres.
     (3) 4·90 of 4 days 3 hours (take 24 hours in a day).

(7) Four bells begin to toll simultaneously, and toll at intervals of 16, 18, 20, and 25 seconds respectively. After what time will they again toll simultaneously ?

(8) In what time will £120 amount to £138 18s. at 4 per cent. simple interest ? (Express your answer in years and fraction of a year.)

(9) A owes B £505, B owes C £495, C owes D £490, and D owes A £500. Show that they can settle accounts by two payments, and determine the payments.

(10) There are 156 boys in the junior and 162 in the senior department of a school. If the boys constitute 65 per cent. of the scholars in the junior department and 45 per cent. of those in the senior department, what percentage are they of the whole school ?

EXERCISE IV.

(1) Add together £48 16s. 4d., £93 12s. 11d., £87 16s. 5d., £38 14s. 9d., £75 9s. 8d., £95 19s. 10d., £78 18s. 7d., £49 17s. 9d., £83 13s. 8d., and £97 8s. 10d.

(2) From 5 tons 10 cwts. 2 qrs. 18 lbs. 9 ozs., take 2 tons 19 cwts. 1 qr. 25 lbs. 15 ozs.

EXERCISE IV.—*Continued.*

(3) The length of a man's step is 3 feet 1½ inches, how many steps will he take in a journey of 14 miles 3 furlongs 25 poles ?

(4) Find, by two different methods, the cost of 1,440 articles at £3 6s. 4½d. each.

(5) A gardener was given a load of gravel. He used $\frac{4}{7}$ of it for the flower garden, $\frac{5}{9}$ of the rest for the shrubbery, and $\frac{9}{16}$ of what then remained for the kitchen garden. What fraction of the load then remained unused ?

(6) Simplify—

$$\frac{\left(\dfrac{5}{12} + \dfrac{9}{20}\right) \div \dfrac{2}{15}}{\left(\dfrac{5}{12} \text{ of } \dfrac{9}{20}\right) - \dfrac{2}{15}} \div \frac{\dfrac{5}{12} + \dfrac{9}{20} + \dfrac{2}{15}}{\dfrac{5}{12} \text{ of } \dfrac{9}{20} \text{ of } \dfrac{2}{15}}$$

(7) Find the value of £7·134225 + 8·903 shillings + 10·2 pence.

(8) Resolve 7,315 and 8,415 into their prime factors, and find their greatest common factor.

(9) Find the simple interest on £128 19s. 2d. in 5 years at 4½%.

(10) Express as vulgar fractions in their lowest terms—·8, ·0625, ·14̇, ·003̇7̇.
    Express the sum of the last two as a circulating decimal, and as a vulgar fraction in its lowest terms.

(11) A square field contains 59 acres 2 roods 12 poles 26 square yards. Find the length of one side in yards, and reduce the result to furlongs, poles, etc.

EXERCISE V.

(1) Find the price of 3,175 articles at £4 6s. 10¼d. each.

(2) How many parcels, each weighing 5 lbs. 7 ozs., can be made up from goods weighing 6 cwts. 2 qrs. 27 lbs. 13 ozs. ?

(3) The area of Scotland is 29,785 square miles, and the average number of inhabitants in each square mile is 139. Find the whole population.

(4) Resolve 1,560, 2,574, and 2,925 into their prime factors, and hence write down their highest common factor.

(5) Simplify—   (1) $\dfrac{18}{27} + \dfrac{24}{32} - \dfrac{55}{60}$.

(2) $\dfrac{4\frac{1}{3} + 3\frac{1}{4}}{4\frac{1}{3} - 3\frac{1}{4}} \div \dfrac{4\frac{1}{3} \times 3\frac{1}{4}}{4\frac{1}{3} \div 3\frac{1}{4}}$.

EXERCISE V.—*Continued.*

(6) Simplify—

(1) $\dfrac{14 \cdot 44 \times \cdot 0133}{\cdot 0057 \times 1 \cdot 805}$.

(2) ·325 of £1 3s. 4d. — ·0013 of 2s. 6d. — ·031 of 2s. 7d.

(7) Express 41 yards 9 inches as (1) a vulgar, (2) a decimal fraction of a furlong.

(8) One bookseller allows his customers 2d. in the shilling discount, and, in addition, 5 per cent. on the remaining price ; another simply allows 20 per cent. on the published price of the books. Find which terms are the best for the customer by considering the case when the published price of the books is £6.

(9) A man bought 23 baskets of fruit at 4s. 6d. each. Five baskets proved to be bad and were thrown away. Find at what price per basket he must sell the others so as to get back his original outlay and also make a profit of one guinea on the whole transaction.

(10) A debtor who owes £15,040 pays £7,238. How much in the pound does he pay ?

(11) Find the sum which, along with simple interest at four per cent. per annum, will amount to £92 16s. in four years.

(12) A path, $4\frac{1}{2}$ feet wide, is made round a lawn 12 yards long and 5 yards wide. How many square yards are there in the surface covered by the path ?

EXERCISE VI.

(1) What sum will remain out of 25 guineas, after paying 8s. 6d. for bread, £2 15s. $3\frac{1}{2}$d. for meat, 19s. 6d. for fish, 8s. $10\frac{1}{2}$d. for vegetables, £1 16s. 8d. for groceries, £1 4s. $6\frac{1}{2}$d. for milk, 14s. 8d. for washing, £3 14s. 6d. for dress, £4 13s. 6d. for wages, and £5 8s. 4d. for rent ?

(2) A steam engine, working steadily day and night, consumes a hundredweight of coal in $7\frac{1}{2}$ hours. How many tons will be used in 100 days ?

(3) An army of 145,600 men loses $12\frac{1}{2}$ per cent. of its number through disease, and 15 per cent. of the remainder in battle ; how many men are left ?

EXERCISE VI.—*Continued.*

(4) (1) Show that the numbers 111 and 11,111 are prime to each other.

(2) Find the least common multiple of the even numbers from 2 to 20, inclusive.

(5) A grain of gold if beaten into gold leaf will cover $67\frac{1}{2}$ square inches. Find, in yards, the length of the side of a square than can be covered by an ounce Troy of gold leaf. (1 oz. Troy = 480 grains.)

(6) Simplify— (1) $\frac{17}{20} + \frac{18}{24} + \frac{10}{25} + \frac{12}{40}$;

(2) $\dfrac{6\frac{1}{2} - 3\frac{1}{4}}{7\frac{1}{3} + 1\frac{4}{7}} \div \dfrac{4\frac{1}{3} \text{ of } 1\frac{1}{4}}{2\frac{3}{7} \text{ of } 3\frac{2}{3}}$.

(7) Express (1) 5 yds. 2 ft. 4 ins. as a vulgar fraction of a mile ;
(2) £2 17s. 4d. as a decimal fraction of £13 8s. 9d.

(8) (1) Multiply ·02475 by ·64, and divide the result by ·000125 ;

(2) Reduce to a single vulgar fraction $\dfrac{\cdot 6\dot{8}\dot{1} \times \cdot 6\dot{1}}{1 \cdot 1\dot{8} \div \cdot 3\dot{6}}$.

(9) Find the total rental of a town if a tax of 9d. in the pound on rents brings in £2,163 14s. 3d.

(10) A rectangular tank is 18 feet long, 14 feet broad, and 10 feet deep. Find the cost of painting the sides and bottom of the inside at 1s. $1\frac{1}{2}$d. the square yard.

(11) At what rate must simple interest be charged in order that £2,375 may increase to £2,826 5s. in four years ?

EXERCISE VII.

(1) Find, by practice, the dividend on £7,126 10s. at 9s. 6d. in the pound.

(2) A bronze medal is composed of copper, tin, and zinc. If $\frac{15}{19}$ of the medal be copper and $\frac{1}{9}$ be tin, what fraction of it is zinc ?

(3) A square paddock contains 16 square poles, and is enclosed by hurdles $2\frac{3}{4}$ yards long. How many hurdles are required ?

(4) How many yards of paper, 27 inches broad, will be required to cover a wall $3\frac{1}{2}$ yards high and $5\frac{1}{4}$ yards broad ?

(5) Find the greatest common factor and the least common multiple of 336, 468, and 792.

EXERCISE VII.—*Continued.*

(**6**) Simplify—(*a*) $\dfrac{\dfrac{2}{2\frac{1}{4}} - \dfrac{1\frac{3}{4}}{2}}{\dfrac{2}{2\frac{1}{4}} \text{ of } \dfrac{1\frac{3}{4}}{2}} \div \left(\dfrac{2}{2\frac{1}{4}} + \dfrac{1\frac{3}{4}}{2}\right).$ (*b*) $\dfrac{\dfrac{39}{713}}{\dfrac{55}{56} \times \dfrac{91}{115} \times \dfrac{24}{341}}.$

(**7**) A picture, 18 inches broad and $10\frac{1}{2}$ inches deep, is to be photographed on a reduced scale, so that the breadth of the photograph may be $7\frac{1}{2}$ inches. Find the depth of the photograph.

(**8**) Simplify—
(*a*) $(8\cdot47 + \cdot016 - \cdot0028) \times (\cdot75 + \cdot075 - \cdot8125)$.
(*b*) $3\cdot4\dot{3}9\dot{9} \div \cdot4\dot{3}\dot{5}$.

(**9**) (*a*) Express $\cdot0390625$ of a day (24 hours) in minutes and seconds.
(*b*) If 8 metres are equal to 315 inches, express one metre as a decimal fraction of a yard.

(**10**) In a school of 1,200 the number presented for an examination was 20 per cent. of the whole, while the numbers passing in the first and second classes were respectively $12\frac{1}{2}$ and $32\frac{1}{2}$ per cent. of those presented. Find the number presented and the number passing in each class.

(**11**) A customer deposits £100 in a bank on 31st January, £150 on 30th April, and £125 on 31st July. What interest is due to him on 31st December, the rate being $2\frac{1}{2}$ per cent. per annum, and one-twelfth of a year's interest being allowed for each calendar month ?

EXERCISE VIII.

(**1**) Resolve into prime factors 3,234,000 and 151,200, and find their least common multiple as a product of prime factors.

(**2**) If a bicyclist ride a mile in 2 minutes 12 seconds, how long will he take to ride a kilometre, assuming that a metre is $3\cdot29$ feet ?

(**3**) A room 27 feet long requires 52 square yards of carpet to cover the floor. Find the breadth of the room.

(**4**) If 3 per cent. be gained by selling an article for £1 14s. 4d., at what price must it be sold to gain $5\frac{3}{4}$ per cent. ?

(**5**) Extract the square root of $37\frac{36}{49}$.

EXERCISE VIII.—*Continued.*

(6) Simplify—(1) $\dfrac{\left(\dfrac{1}{12} + \dfrac{1}{16}\right) \text{ of } \dfrac{5}{14}}{\left(\dfrac{1}{12} - \dfrac{1}{16}\right) \text{ of } \dfrac{4}{21}} \div \dfrac{\dfrac{3}{8} + \left(\dfrac{3}{5} \text{ of } \dfrac{1}{4}\right)}{\dfrac{3}{8} - \left(\dfrac{3}{5} \text{ of } \dfrac{1}{4}\right)}.$

$\quad$ (2) $\dfrac{4}{7} \text{ of } \dfrac{5}{8} \text{ of } \dfrac{3}{\dfrac{4}{7} + \dfrac{5}{8}} - \dfrac{1}{1 + \dfrac{1}{4 - \dfrac{3}{14}}}.$

(7) Express as vulgar fractions in their lowest terms—

$\quad$ (1) $\dfrac{(\cdot 36 \times \cdot 25) + 4 \cdot 05}{4 \cdot 2 \times \cdot 024 \div \cdot 02},$

$\quad$ (2) $\cdot 375 \times \cdot \dot{8} \times \cdot \dot{3}\dot{6} \times \cdot 7\dot{7}\dot{2}.$

(8) A takes 10 days to do a piece of work which B can do in 8 days. If A work at it for $3\frac{1}{2}$ days, and is then joined by B, how long will they take to finish it ?

(9) A gallon of water weighs 10 lbs. avoirdupois, and a cubic foot of water 997 ounces ; find how many gallons are contained in a cistern 12 feet long, 10 feet broad, and 6 feet deep.

(10) What sum will amount to £411 17s. 9d. in 7 years at $3\frac{1}{2}$ per cent. simple interest ?

EXERCISE IX.

(1) Resolve 1,800, 1,225, and 945 into their prime factors, and find their least common multiple.

(2) A railway covers ground to the breadth of 22 yards ; how many acres will be covered by a mile of the railway ?

(3) Simplify $\quad$ (1) $\dfrac{4}{7} + \dfrac{13}{15} - \dfrac{27}{35} ;$

$\quad$ (2) $\dfrac{561}{935} - \dfrac{524}{917}.$

(4) I read $\frac{3}{8}$ of a book on one day and $\frac{4}{5}$ of the remainder on another day. If there were now 30 pages unread, how many pages did the book contain ?

EXERCISE IX.—*Continued.*

(5) Express $\frac{7}{8}$, $\frac{14}{125}$, $\frac{4}{9}$, $\frac{6}{13}$ as decimal fractions, and ·625, ·312, ·3̇, ·03̇7̇ as vulgar fractions in their lowest terms.

(6) Simplify—   (1) $\dfrac{\frac{4}{7} \text{ of } 1\frac{5}{9}}{\frac{2}{13} \text{ of } 8\frac{1}{2}} \div \dfrac{1\frac{1}{3} - \frac{8}{9}}{10\frac{3}{4} - 6\frac{1}{2}}$;

            (2) $\dfrac{2\cdot34 - \cdot0025}{74\cdot8 \times \cdot025}$.

(7) Express (1) £2 1s. 3d. as a vulgar fraction of £2 11s. 4d.
             (2) 5 cwts. 2 qrs. 7 lbs. as a decimal fraction of a ton.

(8) A man mixes 1 cwt. of tea at 1s. 7d. per lb. with 2 cwts. 14 lbs. at 2s. per lb. What is the value of 5 lbs. of the mixture ?

(9) If a metre be 39·37 inches, express an inch in millimetres correct to four significant figures.

(10) The bank rate of interest is raised from $3\frac{1}{4}$ to $3\frac{1}{2}$ per cent., and a depositor finds that his interest is increased by 1s. $5\frac{1}{2}$d. per month ; find the amount of his deposit.

EXERCISE X.

(1) When a certain number is divided by 967 the quotient is 475 and the remainder is 288 ; find the number.

(2) A man's annual income is £483 17s. and his average daily expenditure during the year 1900 is £1 2s. 4d. ; how much will he save in that year ?

(3) Find the value of 8 tons 13 cwts. 24 lbs. at £16 16s. the ton.

(4) A bankrupt's property, after all expenses are paid, amounts to £849, while his debts are £4,075. Find to the nearest penny how much a creditor, to whom he owes £500, will receive.

(5) Find the simple interest on £1,804 3s. 4d. for 73 days at $4\frac{1}{2}$ per cent. per annum.

(6) The circumferences of the two wheels of a bicycle are 84 and 88 inches ; before starting a mark is made at the lowest point of each ; how far will the bicycle travel before the marks reach the ground simultaneously ?

EXERCISE X.—*Continued.*

(7) (1) Explain the meaning of $\frac{2}{5}$ and $\frac{6}{15}$, and show that they are equal to each other.

(2) Simplify the fractions $\frac{42030}{116750}$, $\frac{45769}{87727}$.

(8) (1) Multiply $\dfrac{6}{\frac{3}{5} + \frac{5}{6} + \frac{7}{10}}$ by $\frac{4}{5} + \frac{7}{9} + \frac{13}{15}$.

(2) Divide 253·53549 by ·0507.

(9) Express in kilograms the weight of a kilometre of uniform wire, 25 centimetres of which weigh 41 decagrams.

(10) A room is 20 feet long and 16 feet 6 inches broad, and it is required to cover all of it, except a margin of 18 inches, with carpet ; the roll of carpet is 2 feet 3 inches broad, and costs 4s. 6d. a yard ; find the cost of the carpet required.

EXERCISE XI.

(1) A man owes his creditors £2,656, but can only pay them 8s. 7½d. in the pound ; how much money has he ?

(2) Divide £100 between A, B, and C, so that A may have 20 more than B, and £30 more than C.

(3) Find H.C.F. and L.C.M. of 3,150, 3,525, and 825 by resolution into prime factors.

(4) In a school $\frac{3}{5}$ of the scholars are girls and the rest boys. If $\frac{2}{9}$ of the girls and $\frac{1}{4}$ of the boys be absent, what fraction of the whole number of scholars is present ?

(5) (1) Reduce £9·21875 to pounds, shillings and pence.

(2) Simplify $\dfrac{4\cdot403 + \cdot0165 - \cdot000556}{1,580 \times \cdot0064}$.

(6) A man borrowed £280 and repaid it 9 months later ; find the simple interest due at 4¾ per cent. per annum.

(7) A grocer bought a box of tea containing 3 cwts. 2 qrs. 22 lbs. for £36, and sold the tea at 2s. the pound ; find (1) the amount of his profit, (2) the gain per cent. on his outlay.

(8) An oblong piece of land is 165 yards long and 143 yards broad ; find (1) its area in acres, roods, and poles, (2) its rent at £3 6s. per acre.

(**9**) Find the value of 52·5 kilometres of copper wire at ·15 centimes per centimetre, taking £1 as equivalent to 25 francs 20 centimes.

EXERCISE XII.

(**1**) Amongst how many persons can £249 be divided, if each receive £3 13s. $2\frac{1}{2}$d., and how much will remain over ?

(**2**) A piece of material weighing 50 kilograms costs £8 6s. 8d. ; what is the value of a portion which weighs 6 kilograms 350 grams ?

(**3**) If a dollar be worth 4s. 2d., and a rupee 1s. $3\frac{1}{2}$d., how many rupees are 186 dollars worth ?

(**4**) Simplify—

(1) $\dfrac{\dfrac{3}{4} + \dfrac{7}{12} + \left(\dfrac{7}{15} \text{ of } 1\dfrac{1}{7}\right)}{\dfrac{5}{5} + \dfrac{9}{10} - \left(\dfrac{2}{3} \text{ of } \dfrac{13}{20}\right)}$

(2) $\dfrac{1521531}{4148925}.$

(**5**) In the following piece of work, state what is done in each step, showing the reason for it :—

$$\frac{7}{10} + \frac{4}{15} + \frac{5}{6} = \frac{21}{30} + \frac{8}{30} + \frac{25}{30} = \frac{54}{30} = \frac{9}{5} = 1\frac{4}{5}.$$

(**6**) If ·087 of a ton cost £4·71, find the value of 3·4 cwts., expressing the answer in pounds, shillings, and pence to the nearest penny.

(**7**) A debtor owes his three creditors £1,200, £900, and £300 respectively ; if his assets be £850, what should each creditor receive ?

(**8**) If a cistern measures 3·75 metres in length, 2·6 metres in breadth, ·92 metre in height, find how many litres it will hold, a litre being a cubic decimetre.

(**9**) Five per cent. of an army are killed in battle, and fifteen per cent. of the survivors die of wounds and disease, leaving 18,088 men alive ; what was the original number of men in the army ?

EXERCISE XIII.

(1) If a yard of wire cost a penny, find the value of a kilometre of the same wire, taking a yard as equal to $9\frac{1}{7}$ decimetres.

-(2) A man bought a gross of pencils at $6\frac{1}{2}$d. per dozen, a hundred at 1s. 4d., per score, and 44 at $1\frac{1}{4}$d. each. If he then sold them all at $9\frac{1}{2}$d. per dozen, how much did he gain or lose ?

(3) The average number of persons admitted to an exhibition during the first five days was 416, the average number during the first six days was 551 ; how many were admitted on the sixth day ?

(4) Show that $\frac{3}{5} = \frac{12}{20}$, illustrating your answer by a figure.

(5) (1) Explain how the difference between two fractions can be found.

(2) One box contains $\frac{3}{7}$ of a hundredweight of flour, another contains $\frac{7}{16}$ of a hundredweight. Find which contains most flour, and how many pounds it contains more than the other.

(6) (1) State and prove the rule for multiplying two decimal numbers, taking as an example the product $\cdot072 \times 13\cdot55$.

(2) Simplify £4·375 + 5·25s. + 4·5d.

(7) Find the simple interest on £3,516 13s. 4d. for 3 years at $4\frac{1}{2}$ per cent. per annum.

EXERCISE XIV.

(1) Find which of the following numbers are prime, and express the others as products of prime numbers :—

143, 151, 287, 307, 323, 525.

(2) A firm fails and pays 13s. 4d. in the pound on debts amounting to £17,420 10s. 6d. If the expenses of liquidation amounted to £185 14s. 4d., find the value of the assets.

(3) Simplify—

(1) $\dfrac{\dfrac{3}{4} + \dfrac{2}{3} - \dfrac{5}{14}}{\left(\dfrac{1}{2} - \dfrac{1}{3}\right) \text{ of } \left(\dfrac{3}{4} - \dfrac{5}{7}\right)}$

(2) $\dfrac{3}{7}$ of a ton + $\dfrac{5}{8}$ of a cwt. − $\dfrac{3}{4}$ of a quarter avoirdupois.

EXERCISE XIV.—*Continued.*

(**4**) I bought a sack of potatoes, but found that $\frac{3}{7}$ were bad and had to be thrown away ; I set aside $\frac{3}{4}$ of the remainder for planting ; find what fraction of the sackful remained for other purposes.

(**5**) State and prove the rule for the multiplication of two decimal numbers.

Simplify—   (1) $4\cdot93 \times 3\cdot571 \times 1,000$.

(2) $(\cdot0005)^2 \div (\cdot002)^3$.

(**6**) If, during the year 1904, a man were to receive 25s. per week for 50 weeks' work, and were to spend, during the whole year, average sums of 1s. 1½d. per day for food, 8s. 9d. per week for lodgings, and 29s. per month for other expenses ; how much would he save ?

(**7**) If 20 square inches be taken as equal to 129 square centimetres, express a square yard as a decimal fraction of a square metre correct to the nearest digit in the third significant figure.

EXERCISE XV.

(**1**) Find the prime factors of 193545 and 417384.

Hence write down their greatest common factor as a product of prime numbers, and find its value.

(**2**) Simplify—

(1) $\left(\frac{3}{7} + \frac{11}{15} - \frac{22}{35}\right) \div \left(\frac{26}{45} - \frac{34}{63}\right)$.

(2) $\dfrac{\cdot4 - \cdot004}{1 - \cdot99375} \div \dfrac{52\cdot8}{5\cdot375}$, expressing the answer as a decimal.

(**3**) A room is 15 metres long and 9·8 metres broad, and its floor is to be made of planks 2·5 metres long and 20 centimetres broad. How many planks will be required ?

(**4**) A fortification contains 16,800 men and is provisioned for seven months. After three months' siege, 5,600 men break through the enemy's ranks ; for how much longer than the seven months will the provisions last ?

(**5**) If 5 per cent. be gained by selling an aritcle for 18s. 4½d., at what price should it have been sold in order to have gained 10 per cent. ?

EXERCISE XV.—*Continued.*

(6) The area of a page of foolscap paper is ·733 of a square foot. If the breadth of the page be 8·168 inches, find the length in inches correct to three decimal places, without unnecessary calculation.

EXERCISE XVI.

(1) Find to the nearest penny the sum required to pay interest at $2\frac{3}{4}$ per cent. on £768,443,386.

(2) A metre of wire weighs 43 grams ; find to the nearest millimetre the lengths of portions of the same wire which weigh

(1) 15 grams,

(2) 1 kilogram.

(3) A piece of platinum 17 cubic inches in volume weighs 12 pounds avoirdupois, while a piece of gold 77 cubic inches in volume weighs 54 lbs. ; find to the nearest ounce the difference between the weight of a cubical block of platinum measuring 5 inches each way and the weight of an equally large block of gold.

(4) A town contains 75,614 inhabitants, of whom 51 per cent. are females. Of the females 23 per cent. are married. Find the number of unmarried females in the town without unnecessary calculation.

(5) There are 12 stations on a railway line. Single and return tickets have to be printed from each station to each of the others for first, second, and third-class passengers ; find the cost of printing 500 of each kind at 9d. per hundred tickets.

(6) It has been proposed to divide £1 into 1,000 equal parts called mils.

(1) Express the difference between a farthing and a mil as a decimal fraction of 1d.

(2) Express 4,496 mils in pounds, shillings, and pence correct to the nearest farthing.

EXERCISE XVII.

(1) Find the simple interest on £417 10s. for 7 years and 4 months at $4\frac{1}{4}$ per cent. per annum.

(2) (1) Write out a list of the numbers between 100 and 120 which are prime numbers.

(2) Find the greatest common factor of 1,155, 2,145, 3,003.

(3) Express—(1) $1\frac{4}{7} + 2\frac{1}{6} - 3\frac{3}{8}$ as a single vulgar fraction, and

(2) $\dfrac{7\cdot565 + 4\cdot165}{7\cdot565 - 4\cdot165}$ as a single decimal.

(4) A man left one-third of his property to his wife, one-fourth to his son, one-fifth to his daughter, and £386 15s. remained for other purposes. Find the amount of the property.

(5) (1) An acre contains 10 square chains, and a chain is 22 yards in length ; find the number of square yards in an acre.

(2) The chain is divided into 100 equal links. If a field measures 15 chains 25 links in length and 13 chains 46 links in breadth, find its area in square chains.

(3) Write down the number of acres in the field correct to the nearest acre.

(6) (1) The length of a cistern is 5·4 metres, its breadth 4·7 metres, and its depth 3·8 metres, find the number of cubic metres of water it will contain.

(2) If a cubic centimetre of water weighs a gram, find in kilograms the weight of the water contained by the cistern.

EXERCISE XVIII.

(1) Among how many people can £1,000 be divided, so that each shall receive £4 10s. 6d., and how much money will remain over ?

(2) A man left one-half of his property to his wife. Of the remainder, three-fifths were divided equally between his four sons ; and the rest was divided equally between his three daughters. What fraction of the whole did (1) each son, (2) each daughter receive ?

(3) Simplify—(1) $\dfrac{11}{12}\left(\dfrac{4}{5}-\dfrac{1}{4}\right)-\dfrac{12}{13}\left(\dfrac{7}{10}-\dfrac{5}{9}\right)-\dfrac{14}{15}\left(\dfrac{5}{8}-\dfrac{3}{7}\right)$.

(2) $\dfrac{(10^5\times 3\cdot5691)-(10^4\times 31\cdot8253)}{10^3\times\cdot899}$.

(4) A coffee merchant mixed 80 lbs. of coffee at £9 6s. 8d. per cwt. with 12 lbs. of chicory at £2 2s. per cwt., and sold the mixture at 1s. 10d. per lb. Find how much money he gained.

(5) Having given that a metre = 39·37 inches, express in square inches the amount by which a square metre exceeds a square yard.

(6) An ocean liner, sailing day and night, covered 2,780 nautical miles in 4 days 20 hours ; find its average rate per hour in nautical miles, correct to two decimal places.

EXERCISE XIX.

(1) Three new pennies weigh one ounce avoirdupois. Find in hundredweights, quarters, pounds, and ounces the weight of 12,549 new pennies.

(2) Find the simple interest due on a loan of £724 10s. for $4\frac{1}{2}$ years, the yearly rate of interest being $3\frac{3}{4}$ per cent.

(3) Express 7,875 and 9,450 as products of prime factors, and hence express their greatest common factor and their least common multiple as products of prime factors.

(4) A cubic centimetre of water weighs a gram. Express in kilograms the weight of the water contained in a cistern 1 metre long, 81 centimetres broad, and 28 centimetres deep.

(5) A dealer buys 750 sheep at £1 7s. 6d. each, and sells them at £1 10s. 4d. each. Find the amount of his profit on the transaction. Express this profit as a percentage of his outlay.

EXERCISE XX.

(1) Find the smallest number which must be added to 17,589, in order that the number thus formed may be divisible without remainder by 276.

(2) Simplify—
$$\frac{\frac{5}{8} + \frac{7}{16}}{3\frac{7}{8} - 2\frac{1}{4}} \times \frac{1\frac{4}{9}}{\frac{2}{3} \div \frac{3}{5}}.$$

and find the product $3 \cdot 14159 \times 62 \cdot 4817$ correct to 3 decimal places without unnecessary calculation.

(3) Find, correct to the nearest penny, the interest on £482 for 80 days at $3\frac{1}{2}$ per cent. per annum.

(4) A solid block, 18 metres long, 12 metres broad, and 6 metres high, is built of bricks each of which is $22 \cdot 5$ centimetres long, $12 \cdot 5$ centimetres broad, and $7 \cdot 5$ centimetres thick. Find the number of bricks in the block.

(5) A man pays income tax at the rate of 9d. in the pound. After his income tax is deducted he has £688 3s. 9d. left. Find the amount deducted.

EXERCISE XXI.

(1) A workman earned 40s. a week and found that after paying all necessary expenses he could save 5s. per week. He then emigrated to a country where he earns 30 per cent. more, but where his expenses are 35 per cent. higher. Find how much he can now save in a week.

(2) A man received a legacy of £2,000. He invested £1,250 at $4\frac{1}{2}$ per cent. and the rest at $3\frac{1}{2}$ per cent. Find his annual income from the legacy after paying income tax on the whole of the interest at 1s. 2d. in the pound.

(3) Express the following fractions as decimals correct to two places and arrange them in ascending order of magnitude :—
$$\frac{3}{4}, \frac{5}{6}, \frac{5}{7}, \frac{6}{7}, \frac{7}{9}, \frac{7}{10}, \frac{8}{11}.$$

(4) A contractor undertakes to do a certain piece of work in 175 days, and employs 72 men for the purpose. After 130 days one-third of the work has still to be done. How many additional men will he require to employ during the remaining days in order to carry out his contract ?

EXERCISE XXII.

(1) Passengers by a certain line of steamers are allowed 20 cubic feet of luggage. A passenger wishes to take two boxes, each 3 feet long and $2\frac{1}{2}$ broad, and of the same height; what is the greatest height he can have them made so as not to exceed the limit allowed?

(2) A father leaves £5,600 to be divided between his sons, aged 30, 34, and 41, so that their shares may be in the same ratio as their ages. Find the share of each.

(3) A tank is 2·45 metres long, 1·46 metres broad, and ·56 metres deep. Find its volume in cubic metres, and also how many litres it contains, a litre being equal in volume to a cubic decimetre.

(4) From January to July of 1911 a Scottish Railway Company sold 821,670 first-class tickets and 18,150,737 third-class tickets, receiving £60,966 0s. 8d. for the first-class and £614,933 6s. for the third-class. Find the average costs of a first-class and a third-class ticket, correct to the nearest farthing.

(6) A building is insured for an annual premium equal to $\frac{9}{80}$ per cent. of the value of the building. If this premium is £5 2s. $4\frac{1}{2}$d., find the value of the building.

EXERCISE XXIII.

(1) Find the simple interest on £325 16s. 8d. lent for 3 years and 5 months at $4\frac{1}{2}$ per cent. simple interest.

(2) Express 3,861, 18,876, 40,425 as products of prime factors; and find their greatest common measure, and their least common multiple.

(3) Taking a metre as 1·094 yards, express 8 kilometres as a decimal fraction of 5 miles, correct to 3 places.

(4) Simplify—(1) $\dfrac{\dfrac{4}{7}\left(\dfrac{3}{5}-\dfrac{5}{11}\right)-\dfrac{5}{11}\left(\dfrac{3}{5}-\dfrac{4}{7}\right)}{\dfrac{3}{5}\left(\dfrac{4}{7}-\dfrac{5}{11}\right)-\dfrac{3}{11}\left(\dfrac{4}{5}-\dfrac{5}{7}\right)}$;

(2) 1·145 × 3·897 ÷ 4·216, correct to three places.

18

(5) A plot of ground covers 940 square yards, and is divided into 17 rectangular strips, each 7 feet broad ; find the length of the strips, expressing it in yards, feet, and inches correct to the nearest inch.

(6) A grocer, by selling tea at 1s. 6d. per pound, loses 4 per cent. of the buying price. How much per cent. would he gain if he sold the tea at 1s. 8d. per pound ?

EXERCISE XXIV.

(1) Express $\dfrac{86625}{1794375}$

    (1) as a vulgar fraction in its lowest terms,

    (2) as a decimal fraction correct to four decimal places.

How many " significant " figures are there in your answer to (2) ?

(2) A man's house rent is $\frac{1}{8}$ of his income, and his taxes are $\frac{1}{4}$ of his house rent ; find the fraction of his income which remains after rent and taxes are paid ; and illustrate it by a diagram on the square-ruled paper, representing his income by a square, each side of which measures 2·4 inches.

(3) On an earned income, income tax is charged at the rate of 9d. in the pound ; on an unearned income it is 1s. 2d. in the pound. On all incomes between £500 and £600, the tax is paid on the sum found by deducting £120 from the income ; from all incomes between £600 and £700 a similar deduction of £70 is made before the payment is calculated. A's income is £560, all unearned, and B's is £680, all earned. Find which will have to pay the greater tax, and by how much it will be greater.

(4) Find the value of $\dfrac{31{\cdot}6245 \times 147{\cdot}81967}{25{\cdot}7423}$ correct to two decimal places, preferably without unnecessary calculation.

(5) In a school 48 per cent. of the boys are over 7 years of age, and the number under 7 is 130 ; find how many boys there are in the school. But there are also girls in attendance, the number of the boys being $55\frac{5}{9}$ per cent. of the whole number of scholars ; find how many girls there are in the school.

(6) A cubic decimetre of water is poured into a cylindrical vessel, the area of whose base is 6,250 square millimetres.

    (1) Express in square decimetres the area of the base of the vessel.

    (2) Express as a decimal fraction of a cubic metre the volume of the water.

    (3) Express in centimetres the height at which the water stands in the vessel.

What name is given to the liquid measure which contains the volume of a cubic decimetre ?

EXERCISE XXV.

(1) Express the following sums as decimal fractions of £1, correct to three places :—

    14s. 6d., 17s. 11d., 5s. 8¼d., 12s. 10½d., 3s. 1¾d.

If you have written these down by mental calculation, state the rule by which you do so ; if otherwise, give the full working.

(2) A dealer bought 17 lbs. 8 ozs. of cheese at 1d. per oz., 3 qrs. 10 lbs. at 1s. 2d. per lb., 13 cwts. 1 qr. at £1 8s. 6d. per qr., and 1 ton 6 cwts. at £4 17s. per cwt. ; find the total weight of cheese and the total cost.

(3) If I buy 160 articles for £5, and sell 66 of them for £2, find, in pence and farthings, the smallest price I must charge per article for the rest, so that my profit on the whole transaction may not fall short of 8 per cent.

(4) Multiply 34·621 by 0·8725 and divide the product by 438·9, obtaining the quotient correct to four significant figures.

(5) A carpet is 4·5 metres long and 3·4 metres broad. Find how many square metres it covers, expressing any fraction of a metre in square decimetres.

(6) A man borrowed £456 10s. on the 31st December, 1914, and promised to repay one-third of the principal at the end of each of the three following years, and at the same time to pay interest at 5 per cent. on the sum owed during the year. Find the total amount he will have to pay on each occasion.

(7) A wall, 2 feet thick and 6 feet high, encloses a square plot, each side of which is 14 feet. Draw on the squared paper a plan of the ground on the scale of 4 feet to the inch, roughly shading the part on which the wall stands.

Find the number of square feet in the ground covered by the wall.

Find the number of cubic feet in the wall.

Express this last number in cubic yards.

EXERCISE XXVI.

(1) A tea merchant buys 3 hundredweight of India tea at £9 10s. per hundredweight, and 2 hundredweight of China tea at £7 10s. per hundredweight. He mixes them and sells the blend at 1s. 10d per lb. Find his gross profit.

If the expense of selling amounts to $2\frac{1}{2}$ per cent. of his receipts, find his net profit.

(2) If £84 15s. is invested, £80 at $4\frac{1}{2}$ per cent. and the remainder at 5 per cent., find the simple interest due in 6 years 5 months.

(3) If a metre be taken as 39·371 inches, express in square inches correct to 3 decimal places the difference between a square decimetre and $15\frac{1}{2}$ square inches.

(4) A, B, and C hire a pasture for £68. A puts in 15 horses for 4 months, B puts in 7 horses for 9 months, and C 3 horses for 10 months. Find what part of the rent each should pay.

(5) Reduce each of the following expressions to a single *vulgar* fraction in its lowest terms :—

$$(1)\ \frac{4}{9}\left\{\frac{15}{16}-\frac{3}{5}\left(\frac{7}{8}-\frac{5}{12}\right)\right\},$$

$$(2)\ \frac{12\cdot1\times1\cdot26}{14\cdot4\times1\cdot331}.$$

(6) If a cubic foot of gold weighs 1,200 lbs., and is beaten so thin that the gold leaf from 1 lb. covers 16,200 square inches, find to the nearest inch the side of a square which can be just covered by the gold leaf from a cubic inch of gold.

EXERCISE XXVII.

(1) (*a*) Find the prime factors of 8,316 and 18,304.

    (*b*) Write down in *prime factors* the least number that is divisible by each of these numbers without a remainder; and the greatest number that is contained in them an exact number of times.

(2) (*a*) Find, with as little working as you can, the exact cost of 750 articles at £3 19s. 11d. each.

    (*b*) Express 19s. 11d. as the decimal of a pound, correct to the nearest thousandth, and find the approximate cost of the 750 articles in this way.

(3) For every 15s. 6d. invested in War Savings Certificates now, £1 will be returned five years hence. If the interest allowed be regarded as simple interest, what is the rate per cent. per annum ?

(4) A man's income is £750. If he pays income-tax at the rate of 2s. 3d. in the pound on three-fourths of his income, and at the rate of 3s. 6d. in the pound on the remainder,

    (*a*) What is his whole income-tax ?

    (*b*) What is the *average* rate of his income-tax per pound of income ?

(5) A cubic *foot* of water weighs 1,000 ounces, and mercury is 13·6 times as heavy as water,

    (*a*) What is the weight of a cubic *inch* of mercury (correct to the nearest hundredth of an ounce) ?

    (*b*) What is the weight of a column of mercury 30 inches high and 1 square inch in section (correct to the nearest ounce) ?

EXERCISE XXVIII.

(1) One inch = 2·54 centimetres. Find, correct to the second decimal place,

    (*a*) The number of square centimetres in a square inch ;

    (*b*) The number of cubic centimetres in a cubic inch.

(2) Make the following calculations with as little working as you can :—

    (*a*) 72,050 articles at 7s. 6d. per thousand.

    (*b*) 729 tons 15 cwts. 2 qrs. at £7 15s. per ton.

EXERCISE XXVIII.—*Continued.*

(3) A piece of silk, 725 metres long, was bought in France for 3,190 francs. Taking a metre as equal to 1·1 yards and a franc as equal to £·04, find the cost of the silk per yard in British money, to the nearest penny.

(4) I have £500 to invest. With half of this sum I buy National War Bonds yielding 5 per cent. per annum, subject to deduction of income tax, and with the other half I buy National War Bonds yielding 4 per cent., free of income tax. Find my net yearly income (that is, after deduction of income tax) when the tax is at 3s. 9d. per £1.

(5) The total area of the six faces of a cube is 30 square feet 54 square inches. Find the weight in ounces of the cube if a cubic foot of it weighs 2,000 ozs.

EXERCISE XXIX.

(1) If a litre of water weighs 2·205 lbs., and pint of water weighs 1·250 lbs., express
　　(i.) a pint as a decimal fraction of a litre.
　　(ii.) 32·5 litres in pints,
giving the result in each case to three places of decimals.

(2) Make the following calculations with as little working as you can :—
　　(*a*) the cost of 4,041 tons of coal at £1 19s. 6d. per ton ;
　　(*b*) the price of 1 ton if 8 tons 2 cwts. 2 qrs. cost £14 12s. 6d.

(3) A swimmer who takes 30 strokes per minute can swim a mile in 38 minutes 20 seconds. What is the average length in yards of each stroke ?

(4) A merchant had marked a certain article at £8 12s. 6d., a price that would have given him a profit of 15 per cent. If he resolved to double his profit, at what price should he mark the article ?

(5) The inside measurements of a cistern are :—Length, 4 ft. 8 ins. ; breadth, 3 ft. 7 ins. ; depth, 2 ft. 9 ins.
　　(*a*) How many cubic feet of water can the cistern hold ?
　　(*b*) If the cistern is empty and 20 cubic feet of water are run in, find to the nearest inch how far the surface of the water will be from the top of the cistern.

ANSWERS.

ANSWERS.

EXERCISE 1.

(**1**) £69 19s. 11d.

(**2**) £51 3s. 4d.

(**3**) £50 19s. 3d.

(**4**) £42 12s. 3d.

(**5**) £174 15s. 4d.

(**6**) £204 8s. 10d.

(**7**) £271 7s. 9d.

(**8**) £371 5s.

(**9**) £373 8s. 6$\frac{3}{4}$d.

(**10**) £390 6s. 3$\frac{3}{4}$d.

(**11**) £335 8s. 5$\frac{3}{4}$d.

(**12**) £340 9s. 7$\frac{3}{4}$d.

(**13**) £1,999 17s. 8d.

(**14**) £2,443 16s. 5d.

(**15**) £3,567 17s. 0$\frac{1}{2}$d.

(**16**) £1,875 18s. 4$\frac{1}{2}$d.

(**17**) £838 1s. 4$\frac{1}{2}$d.

(**18**) £806 2s. 3$\frac{1}{2}$d.

(**19**) £8,353 8s. 3$\frac{1}{2}$d.

(**20**) £5,559 14s. 1d.

(**21**) £4,611 13s. 10$\frac{1}{4}$d.

EXERCISE 2.

(**1**) 4s. 2d.

(**2**) 1s. 9d.

(**3**) 2s. 9d.

(**4**) £2 11s. 9d.

(**5**) £1 2s. 11d.

(**6**) £3 0s. 3d.

(**7**) £5 7s. 11d.

(**8**) £22 10s. 6d.

(**9**) £1 10s. 9$\frac{1}{4}$d.

(**10**) £1 1s. 4d.

(**11**) £2 1s. 10$\frac{3}{4}$d.

(**12**) £3 13s. 8$\frac{3}{4}$d.

(**13**) £20 1s. 4$\frac{1}{2}$d.

(**14**) £800 3s. 10$\frac{1}{4}$d.

(**15**) £58 16s. 11$\frac{1}{4}$d.

(**16**) £70 4s. 9d.

(**17**) £314 2s. 7d.

(**18**) £76 3s. 4$\frac{1}{4}$d.

(**19**) £3 6s. 6d.

(**20**) £21 4s. 2$\frac{1}{4}$d.

(**21**) £14 3s. 9$\frac{1}{2}$d.

(**22**) £9,149 3s. 3$\frac{3}{4}$d.

(**23**) £235 8s. 9$\frac{1}{2}$d.

(**24**) £74 6s. 7$\frac{1}{4}$d.

EXERCISE 3.

(**1**) 147,831 pence ; 345,117 halfpence.

(**2**) (*a*) 245,081 halfpence ; (*b*) 1,650,741 farthings.

(**3**) (*a*) 6,867 crowns ; (*b*) 650 crowns ; (*c*) 645 crowns.

(**4**) (*a*) 1,452 half-crowns ; (*b*) 205 half-crowns ; (*c*) 1,502 half-crowns ; (*d*) 5,531 half-crowns ; (*e*) 703 half-crowns ; (*f*) 553 half-crowns ; (*g*) 610 half-crowns.

(**5**) (*a*) 972 florins ; (*b*) 1,875 florins ; (*c*) 961 florins ; (*d*) 873 florins ; (*e*) 1,986 florins ; (*f*) 799 florins ; (*g*) 567 florins ; (*h*) 754 florins ; (*k*) 5,768 florins.

(**6**) 5,262 ; 14,315 ; 5,241 ; 3,412.

(**7**) 13,871.

(**8**) £9 19s. 3$\frac{3}{4}$d. ; £17 16s. 9d. ; £35 13s. 11d.

(**9**) £535 5s. 6d.

(**10**) £14 5s. 5$\frac{1}{2}$d.

(**11**) 17,784.

(**12**) 500.

(**13**) £108 16s.

(**14**) £62 3s. 8$\frac{3}{4}$d.

19

(15) 14,655.   (16) £26 17s. 8¼d.   (17) 891.
(18) £40 10s. 6½d.   (19) 2,959 lbs.   (20) £106 16s. 2½d.
(21) £306,789 11s. 8d.

EXERCISE 4.

(1) £23 14s. 8¼d.   (2) £1,127 2s. 6d.   (3) £1 4s. 10¾d.
(4) £28, 12s. 3d.   (5) £2,303 14s. 8d. (6) £1 18s. 6½d.
(7) 12 ; £1 18s. 6d.   (8) £158,644 1s.   (9) 5.
(10) £9 18s. 11¾d.   (11) 34.   (12) 21.
(13) £173 15s. 0¼d.   (14) 380 ; 18s. 1½d. (15) 95 ; 12s. 8½d.
(16) £4,863 11s. 7d.   (17) 8s. 6d.   (18) £20 18s.
(19) £2 13s. 8d.   (20) £17 1s.

EXERCISE 5.

(1) 2 tons 13 cwts. 1 qr. 4 lbs. 1 oz.
(2) 50 tons 1 qr. 14 lbs. 15 ozs. 3 drs.
(3) 62 tons 2 cwts. 3 qrs. 5 lbs. 9 ozs. 6 drs.
(4) 56 miles 1 fur. 1 pole 5 yards.
(5) 78 miles 144 yards 2 ft. 4 ins.
(6) 61 miles 29 poles 1½ yards 2 ft. 5 ins.
(7) 74 miles 5 fur. 2 chains 18 yards 1 ft.
(8) 72 days 5 hours 7 mins. 48 seconds.
(9) 108 days 15 hours 52 mins. 50 secs.
(10) 44 ozs. 11 dwts. 20 grains.
(11) 39 lbs. 10 ozs. 11 dwts. 11 grains.
(12) 46 ac. 1 ro. 12 sq. poles 6¼ sq. yds.
(13) 29 ac. 1 ro. 2¼ sq. yards.
(14) 47 sq. yds. 4 sq. ft. 88 sq. ins.
(15) 22 qrs. 7 bushels 1 peck.
(16) 20 gallons 1 quart.
(17) 3 tons 7 cwts. 1 qr. 26 lbs.
(18) 5 tons 2 qrs. 11 lbs. 13 ozs.
(19) 3 miles 6 fur. 8 poles 2½ yds.
(20) 6 fur. 32 poles 1½ yds. 2 ft. 3 ins = 6 fur. 32 poles 2 yds. 9 ins.
(21) 7 days 5 hours 42 mins. 10 secs.
(22) 8 ac. 2 ro. 35 sq. poles 29¼ sq. yds.
(23) 13 lbs. 10 ozs. 18 dwts. 20 grs.
(24) 30 bush. 1 peck 1 gallon.
(25) 2 years 351 days 3 hours 30 mins.

EXERCISE 6.

(1) 203,573.

(2) 290 tons 14 cwts. 1 qr.

(3) 4,103,680.

(4) 3,736.

(5) 20.

(6) 1 ton 6 cwts. 2 qrs. 21 lbs. 8 ozs. 12 drs.

(7) 120 ; 1 qr. 15 lbs.

(8) £19 6s. $2\frac{1}{2}$d.

(9) 1,186.

(10) 16,041,984 drs.

(11) 560.

(12) 200.

(13) 60.

(14) 106 tons 15 cwts. 2 qrs. 21 lbs. 8 ozs. 7 drs.

(15) 7 tons 11 cwts. 3 qrs. 8 lbs.

(16) $103\frac{73}{80}$ lbs.

(17) 27 tons 18 cwts. 4 lbs.

(18) 491 yds. 4 ins.

(19) 5 fur. 137 yds. 1 ft. 6 ins.

(20) 315,360,000.

(21) 15 miles 6 fur. 10 poles 2 yds. 2 ft. 4 ins.

(22) 134,190.

(23) 64.

(24) 3 miles 1,585 yds. 1 ft.

(25) 570 ac. 2 ro. 20 sq. poles.

(26) 1,210.

(27) 470,154.

(28) 13 miles 6 fur. 26 poles 5 yds. 1 ft.

(29) 140.

(30) 640.

(31) 14,640.

(32) $1,485\frac{5}{7}$.

(33) 11.

(34) 259,200.

(35) 1s. 5d.

(36) 22 yards.

(37) $3\frac{1}{4}$d. per lb.

(38) 121 yards.

(39) £4 13s. 4d.

(40) £2.

(41) £1 2s. 5d.

(42) 35 cwts.

(43) 88 drills ; $7\frac{1}{2}$ miles.

(44) 4 hours.

(45) 12 stones.

(46) 8,400 miles.

(47) 18 plots.

(48) 6 hours.

EXERCISE 7.

(1) c.

(2) p.

(3) p.

(4) c.

(5) p.

(6) c.

(7) p.

(8) p.

(9) c.

(10) c.

(11) p.

(12) p.

(13) c.

(14) p.

(15) c.

(16) p.

(17) c.

(18) p.

(19) p.

(20) c.

(21) c.

(22) p.

(23) c.

(24) p.

(25) c.

(26) 101, 103, 107, 109, 113.

(27) 181, 191, 193, 197, 199.

EXERCISE 8.

(1) $2 \times 5 \times 7$.

(2) $3 \times 5 \times 7$.

(3) $2 \times 7 \times 11$.

(4) $5 \times 7 \times 13$.

(5) $2^2 \times 5 \times 11$.

(6) $3^2 \times 5 \times 7$.

(7) $2^2 \times 3^2 \times 7$.

(8) $3 \times 5^2 \times 7$.

(9) $3^2 \times 5^2 \times 7$.

(10) $2^3 \times 3^3 \times 7$.

(11) $3^4 \times 5 \times 7$.

(12) $2^2 \times 5 \times 11^2$.

(13) $3^2 \times 5 \times 7 \times 11$.   **(14)** $5 \times 7 \times 13 \times 17$.
(15) $3^2 \times 5 \times 7 \times 23$.   **(16)** $11 \times 13 \times 17$.
(17) $3 \times 5^2 \times 7 \times 11$.   **(18)** $2^2 \times 3^2 \times 5 \times 7 \times 13$.
(19) $2 \times 5 \times 11^3$.   **(20)** $2^3 \times 3^3 \times 7 \times 11$.

EXERCISE 9.

(1) 6.   **(2)** 15.   **(3)** 24.   **(4)** 30.
(5) 46.   **(6)** 40.   **(7)** 21.   **(8)** 20.
(9) 15.   **(10)** 63.   **(11)** 63.   **(12)** 39.
(13) 70.   **(14)** 12.   **(15)** 660.   **(16)** 168.
(17) 33.   **(18)** 105.   **(19)** 77.   **(20)** 39.
(21) 44.   **(22)** 51.   **(23)** 57.   **(24)** 11.
(25) 24.   **(26)** 1.   **(27)** 81.

EXERCISE 10.

(1) 24.   **(2)** 144.   **(3)** 336.   **(4)** 420.
(5) 144.   **(6)** 630.   **(7)** 2,268.   **(8)** 11,550.
(9) 11,700.   **(10)** 3,456.   **(11)** 9,576.   **(12)** 2,520.
(13) 1,080.   **(14)** 2,100.   **(15)** 12,600.   **(16)** 9,240.
(17) 11,520.   **(18)** 2,520.   **(19)** 25,410.   **(20)** 6,552.
(21) 19,404.   **(22)** 756.

EXERCISE 11.

(1) 23.   **(2)** 13.   **(3)** 36.   **(4)** 37.
(5) 57.   **(6)** 311.   **(7)** 81.   **(8)** 91.
(9) 27.   **(10)** 101.   **(11)** 31.   **(12)** 47.
(13) 273.   **(14)** 97.   **(15)** 65.   **(16)** 7.
(17) 11.   **(18)** 103.   **(19)** 91.   **(20)** 41.
(21) 14.   **(22)** 753.

EXERCISE 12.

(1) 9, 9,765.   **(2)** 39, 6,435.   **(3)** 29, 5,423.
(4) 13, 4,199.   **(5)** 63, 145,530.   **(6)** 5, 2,316,195.
(7) 41, 36,859.   **(8)** 105, 185,115.   **(9)** 211, 268,181.
(10) 212, 428,452.   **(11)** 201, 500,691.   **(12)** 221, 795,379.
(13) $2 \times 3 \times 7$; $2^2 \times 3 \times 7^2 \times 11 \times 13$.
(14) $2^3 \times 3$; $2^3 \times 3^2 \times 5 \times 7$.
(15) $2 \times 3 \times 5 \times 7$; $2^4 \times 3^3 \times 5 \times 7 \times 11$.
(16) 2^4; $2^7 \times 3^2$.   **(17)** 17; $5 \times 7 \times 11 \times 17$.
(18) 5×7; $2 \times 3 \times 5 \times 7^2 \times 11 \times 13$.

EXERCISE 13.

(1) 27.
(2) 721.
(3) 330.
(4) 213.
(5) 6.
(6) 10s.
(7) £10 10s.
(8) £22 10s.
(9) 3 dollars.
(10) 2 dollars.
(11) 1,500 ins.
(12) 60 ft.
(13) 3 mm.
(14) 2,520.
(15) 2 mins. 24 secs.
(16) 2 mins.
(17) 1 hour.
(18) 12 mins.
(19) 240 ins., 8, 5.
(20) 10 ins.
(21) 504.
(22) 5 ins. square.

EXERCISE 14.

(1) $\frac{3}{5}$.
(2) $\frac{1}{2}$.
(3) $\frac{2}{3}$.
(4) $\frac{1}{12}$.
(5) $\frac{12}{13}$.
(6) $\frac{10}{11}$.
(7) $\frac{11}{13}$.
(8) $\frac{5}{7}$.
(9) $\frac{13}{17}$.
(10) $\frac{7}{11}$.
(11) $\frac{7}{8}$.
(12) $\frac{3}{16}$.
(13) $\frac{7}{9}$.
(14) $\frac{11}{13}$.
(15) $\frac{17}{19}$.
(16) $\frac{214}{219}$.
(17) $\frac{7}{9}$.
(18) $\frac{111}{121}$.
(19) $\frac{212}{313}$.
(20) $\frac{234}{313}$.

EXERCISE 15.

(1) $1\frac{3}{4}$.
(2) $2\frac{1}{8}$.
(3) $4\frac{1}{6}$.
(4) $7\frac{9}{13}$.
(5) $23\frac{12}{37}$.
(6) $24\frac{29}{41}$.
(7) $\frac{13}{4}$.
(8) $\frac{38}{7}$.
(9) $\frac{251}{14}$.
(10) $\frac{362}{17}$.
(11) $\frac{258}{11}$.
(12) $\frac{281}{16}$.
(13) $\frac{131}{15}$.
(14) $\frac{257}{20}$.
(15) $\frac{899}{28}$.
(16) $\frac{334}{35}$.
(17) $\frac{511}{27}$.
(18) $\frac{1447}{48}$.

EXERCISE 16.

(1) $\frac{16}{21}, \frac{4}{21}, \frac{9}{21}$.
(2) $\frac{45}{105}, \frac{84}{105}, \frac{40}{105}$.
(3) $\frac{105}{21}, \frac{56}{21}, \frac{27}{21}$.
(4) $\frac{45}{120}, \frac{50}{120}, \frac{56}{120}$.
(5) $\frac{40}{74}, \frac{28}{72}, \frac{21}{72}$.
(6) $\frac{105}{385}, \frac{220}{385}, \frac{154}{385}$.
(7) $\frac{5}{12}, \frac{7}{18}, \frac{11}{30}$.
(8) $\frac{3}{5}, \frac{6}{11}, \frac{17}{33}, \frac{7}{15}$.
(9) $\frac{9}{16}, \frac{5}{9}, \frac{13}{24}$.
(10) $\frac{7}{16}, \frac{5}{12}, \frac{9}{26}$.
(11) $\frac{9}{28}, \frac{11}{36}, \frac{7}{24}$.
(12) $\frac{34}{69}, \frac{11}{23}, \frac{7}{16}$.
(13) $\frac{40}{5}, \frac{60}{5}, \frac{155}{5}$.
(14) $\frac{132}{11}, \frac{143}{11}, \frac{187}{11}$.
(15) $\frac{39}{13}, \frac{91}{13}, \frac{247}{13}$.

EXERCISE 17.

(1) $1\frac{1}{2}$.
(2) $1\frac{7}{9}$.
(3) $\frac{5}{6}$.
(4) $\frac{7}{12}$.
(5) $1\frac{5}{12}$.
(6) $1\frac{5}{12}$.
(7) $1\frac{17}{18}$.
(8) $\frac{29}{36}$.
(9) $1\frac{47}{144}$.
(10) $1\frac{59}{60}$.
(11) $3\frac{1}{48}$.
(12) $1\frac{49}{120}$.
(13) $1\frac{31}{33}$.
(14) $2\frac{191}{240}$.
(15) $1\frac{13}{42}$.
(16) $1\frac{11}{18}$.
(17) $1\frac{14}{15}$.
(18) $2\frac{93}{176}$.
(19) $3\frac{29}{240}$.
(20) $2\frac{85}{112}$.
(21) $3\frac{3}{44}$.
(22) $3\frac{61}{240}$.
(23) $2\frac{185}{264}$.

EXERCISE 18.

(1) $4\frac{7}{60}$. (2) $7\frac{5}{34}$. (3) $4\frac{33}{55}$. (4) $4\frac{1}{6}$.

(5) $9\frac{57}{92}$. (6) $3\frac{2105}{2431}$. (7) $15\frac{11}{12}$. (8) $15\frac{17}{18}$.

(9) 16. (10) $18\frac{17}{60}$. (11) $11\frac{7}{8}$. (12) $10\frac{1}{4}$.

(13) $19\frac{5}{24}$. (14) $14\frac{1}{14}$. (15) $14\frac{55}{63}$. (16) $11\frac{34}{75}$.

(17) $26\frac{11}{180}$. (18) $56\frac{469}{1584}$. (19) $158\frac{101}{480}$. (20) $89\frac{239}{1008}$.

(21) $40\frac{3911}{5544}$. (22) $44\frac{319}{560}$. (23) $39\frac{383}{2520}$.

EXERCISE 19.

(1) $\frac{5}{9}$. (2) $\frac{5}{12}$. (3) $\frac{7}{20}$. (4) $\frac{25}{42}$.

(5) $\frac{2}{323}$. (6) $\frac{1}{90}$. (7) $\frac{83}{156}$. (8) $\frac{43}{132}$.

(9) $\frac{13}{48}$. (10) $\frac{1}{48}$. (11) $\frac{41}{150}$. (12) $5\frac{2}{15}$.

(13) $3\frac{5}{14}$. (14) $5\frac{17}{36}$. (15) $6\frac{1}{4}$. (16) $6\frac{67}{156}$.

(17) $4\frac{1}{5}$. (18) $6\frac{1}{12}$. (19) $5\frac{1}{3}$. (20) $2\frac{11}{24}$.

(21) $10\frac{9}{110}$. (22) $3\frac{91}{288}$. (23) $12\frac{1}{15}$.

EXERCISE 20.

(1) $3\frac{3}{4}$. (2) $1\frac{13}{15}$. (3) $4\frac{51}{77}$. (4) $4\frac{349}{642}$.

(5) $11\frac{3}{16}$. (6) $1\frac{130}{231}$. (7) $1\frac{23}{28}$. (8) $2\frac{5}{12}$.

(9) $2\frac{55}{96}$. (10) $2\frac{17}{60}$. (11) $\frac{1}{4}$. (12) $2\frac{1}{60}$.

(13) $1\frac{17}{24}$. (14) $\frac{43}{60}$. (15) $\frac{1}{6}$. (16) $4\frac{17}{60}$.

(17) $3\frac{5}{8}$. (18) $3\frac{1}{12}$. (19) $1\frac{7}{15}$. (20) $6\frac{35}{48}$.

(21) $9\frac{1}{8}$. (22) 6. (23) $7\frac{23}{30}$. (24) $4\frac{7}{10}$.

(25) $7\frac{1}{72}$. (26) $10\frac{1}{6}$. (27) $9\frac{1}{52}$. (28) $1\frac{53}{60}$.

(29) $\frac{2}{7}$. (30) $5\frac{31}{60}$. (31) $\frac{1}{56}$. (32) $2\frac{4}{15}$.

(33) $1\frac{23}{24}$. (34) $\frac{89}{160}$. (35) $1\frac{81}{112}$. (36) $3\frac{33}{35}$.

EXERCISE 21.

(1) $1\frac{2}{3}$. (2) $4\frac{1}{2}$. (3) 22. (4) $13\frac{1}{7}$.

(5) $\frac{1}{8}$. (6) $\frac{10}{21}$. (7) $\frac{5}{24}$. (8) $\frac{4}{9}$.

(9) $2\frac{1}{2}$. (10) $9\frac{1}{2}$. (11) $\frac{2}{5}$. (12) $\frac{1}{2}$.

(13) $9\frac{3}{5}$. (14) $6\frac{10}{17}$. (15) $26\frac{5}{18}$. (16) $12\frac{3}{32}$.

(17) 62. (18) 24. (19) $80\frac{1}{2}$. (20) 8.

(21) $93\frac{19}{21}$. (22) $12\frac{3}{16}$.

EXERCISE 22.

(1) $\frac{2}{15}$. (2) $\frac{7}{12}$. (3) $17\frac{1}{2}$. (4) $\frac{9}{16}$.
(5) $\frac{5}{6}$. (6) $1\frac{31}{32}$. (7) $1\frac{9}{25}$. (8) $2\frac{2}{7}$.
(9) $\frac{8}{65}$. (10) $\frac{3}{4}$. (11) $2\frac{5}{39}$. (12) $\frac{19}{25}$.
(13) $1\frac{25}{37}$. (14) $1\frac{10}{11}$. (15) $2\frac{2}{13}$. (16) $1\frac{1}{15}$.
(17) $\frac{11}{81}$. (18) $2\frac{1}{2}$. (19) $\frac{33}{119}$. (20) $\frac{5}{14}$.

EXERCISE 23.

(1) 1. (2) $\frac{1}{12}$. (3) $\frac{1}{6}$. (4) $\frac{1}{2}$.
(5) $11\frac{1}{4}$. (6) $1\frac{2}{3}$. (7) $3\frac{5}{13}$. (8) $3\frac{7}{39}$.
(9) $3\frac{7}{56}$. (10) $\frac{1101}{1400}$. (11) $1\frac{1}{5}$. (12) $1\frac{557}{640}$.
(13) $\frac{19}{21}$. (14) $1\frac{61}{70}$. (15) $2\frac{13}{25}$. (16) $\frac{1}{7}$.
(17) $3\frac{3}{10}$. (18) $\frac{15}{52}$. (19) $3\frac{29}{32}$. (20) $3\frac{13}{20}$.
(21) $3\frac{2}{7}$. (22) $2\frac{121}{140}$. (23) $2\frac{37}{100}$. (24) 38.
(25) 28. (26) $2\frac{2}{7}$. (27) $\frac{29}{160}$. (28) $\frac{2}{5}$.
(29) $\frac{37}{160}$. (30) $\frac{79}{160}$. (31) $1\frac{9}{10}$. (32) $\frac{39}{160}$.
(33) $3\frac{9}{10}$. (34) $1\frac{131}{136}$. (35) $\frac{151}{505}$. (36) $7\frac{2}{23}$.
(37) $\frac{136}{189}$. (38) $\frac{33}{35}$. (39) $11\frac{1}{2}$. (40) $36\frac{1}{5}$.
(41) 35. (42) $26\frac{2}{3}$. (43) $16\frac{9}{20}$. (44) $94\frac{2}{3}$.

EXERCISE 24.

(1) $\frac{9}{10}$. (2) $\frac{9}{14}$. (3) $16\frac{1}{5}$. (4) $\frac{5}{7}$.
(5) $2\frac{7}{8}$. (6) $5\frac{92}{103}$. (7) $\frac{26}{207}$. (8) $1\frac{131}{203}$.
(9) $1\frac{19}{45}$. (10) $4\frac{13}{23}$. (11) $\frac{45}{343}$. (12) $\frac{5}{91}$.
(13) 1. (14) $\frac{8}{13}$. (15) $10\frac{5}{12}$. (16) $\frac{79}{435}$.
(17) $1\frac{77}{340}$. (18) $2\frac{23}{39}$. (19) 15. (20) $\frac{699}{889}$.
(21) $16\frac{4}{5}$. (22) $\frac{61}{492}$. (23) $\frac{5}{11}$. (24) 1.
(25) $\frac{13}{102}$. (26) $109\frac{3}{8}$. (27) $\frac{2}{75}$. (28) $\frac{11}{54}$.
(29) $\frac{975}{54208}$. (30) 4. (31) $\frac{29}{30}$. (32) $\frac{128}{693}$.
(33) $1\frac{25}{26}$. (34) $1\frac{16}{49}$. (35) $1\frac{11}{13}$. (36) $\frac{49}{3000}$.
(37) $2\frac{385}{496}$. (38) $\frac{13}{30}$. (39) $2\frac{1}{68}$. (40) $\frac{29}{76}$.
(41) $2\frac{8}{45}$. (42) $\frac{9}{11}$. (43) $\frac{3}{5}$. (44) $\frac{7}{9}$.
(45) $1\frac{44}{175}$. (46) $\frac{81}{112}$. (47) $2\frac{95}{144}$. (48) $9\frac{5}{6}$.
(49) $3\frac{2}{5}$. (50) 1.

EXERCISE 25.

(1) 3s. 6d.

(2) 7s.

(3) 1 ft. 5 ins.

(4) £3 6s. 1d.

(5) 17s. 9¾d.

(6) 4 lbs. 6 ozs.

(7) 17s. 10d.

(8) 320 yards.

(9) 1s. 1d.

(10) 3 miles 1 fur.

(11) 3s. $1\frac{2}{7}$d.

(12) £5 5s. 7½d.

(13) 16s. 4d.

(14) 3 tons 9 cwts.

(15) £1 19s. 4½d.

(16) £16 5s. 1½d.

(17) £4 11s.

(18) 8 cwts. 1 qr.

(19) 1 ro. 6 sq. poles 4 sq. yds.

(20) £6 18s. 6d.

(21) £3 2s. 2½d.

(22) 18s. 3½d.

(23) 5s. 7½d.

(24) 10s. 5d.

(25) £7 7s. 2½d.

(26) £2 16s. 1¾d.

(27) 14s. 5d.

(28) £1 2s. 9d.

(29) 13s. 0½d.

(30) £8 8s. 2¾d.

(31) 19s. 6d.

(32) 3 lbs. 11 ozs.

(33) 13 miles 4 fur.

(34) 15 cwts. 3 qrs. 16⅔ lbs.

(35) 17 tons 5 cwts.

(36) 2 sq. yds. 7 sq. ft. 56 sq. ins.

(37) 9 yds. 2 ft. 2 ins.

EXERCISE 26.

(1) $\frac{107}{400}$.

(2) $\frac{1}{2}$.

(3) $3\frac{1}{45}$.

(4) $\frac{1}{4}$.

(5) $\frac{2}{3}$.

(6) $\frac{2}{7}$.

(7) $\frac{139}{466}$.

(8) $\frac{1}{5}$.

(9) $\frac{3}{4}$.

(10) $\frac{6}{11}$.

(11) $\frac{7}{8}$.

(12) $\frac{515}{723}$.

(13) $\frac{7}{9}$.

(14) $\frac{3}{5}$.

(15) $\frac{2}{3}$.

(16) $\frac{3}{110}$.

(17) $\frac{7}{10}$.

(18) $\frac{5}{11}$.

(19) $\frac{4}{13}$.

(20) $\frac{2}{7}$.

(21) $\frac{1}{216}$.

(22) $\frac{5}{9}$.

(23) $3\frac{1}{32}$.

(24) $\frac{151}{660}$.

(25) $\frac{1}{9}$.

(26) $\frac{37}{220}$.

(27) $\frac{7}{24}$.

(28) $\frac{4}{21}$.

(29) $\frac{77}{90}$.

(30) $\frac{1}{3}$.

EXERCISE 27.

(1) $\frac{11}{24}$.

(2) £600.

(3) $\frac{7}{60}$.

(4) 18s. 6d.

(5) £2 10s.

(6) 2,100.

(7) $\frac{3}{100}$.

(8) $11\frac{1}{5}$.

(9) 93½ ft., 34, 33.

(10) £8 5s.

(11) £7,700.

(12) 180.

(13) 30 ft.

(14) 26 ; 4 ins. over.

(15) 20 ; ⅔ qt.

(16) £1,500.

(17) First ; 3 lbs.

(18) £1,050.

(19) $\frac{24}{35}$.

(20) 20,000.

EXERCISE 28.

(1) $\frac{3}{10}$, $\frac{3}{100}$, $\frac{3}{1000}$, $\frac{3}{10} + \frac{3}{100}$, $3\frac{3}{10}$.

(2) $\frac{3}{10} + \frac{7}{100} + \frac{5}{1000} = \frac{375}{1000}$.

(3) $\frac{3}{4}$, $\frac{1}{8}$, $\frac{1}{4}$, $\frac{5}{8}$, $\frac{7}{8}$, $\frac{1}{80}$, $\frac{3}{80}$, $\frac{1}{16}$, $\frac{1}{200}$, $\frac{7}{2000}$, $\frac{1}{5000}$ $\frac{9}{20000}$.

(4) $6\frac{7}{80}$, $4\frac{1}{400}$, $5\frac{1}{2000}$, $7\frac{1}{20}$, $16\frac{13}{40}$, $4\frac{1}{100}$, $5\frac{3}{1000}$.

EXERCISE 29.

(1) 10·11956. (2) 30·30648. (3) 12·80484.
(4) 22·066659. (5) 43·12532. (6) 728·517709.
(7) 1·052855. (8) 51·1644. (9) 10·1882.
(10) 21·4984. (11) 21·08775. (12) 29·8162.

EXERCISE 30.

(1) ·425. (2) 2·9125. (3) 2·9325.
(4) 2·7735. (5) ·6625. (6) 14·3375.
(7) 8·34255. (8) 2·504. (9) 4·555.
(10) 22·2025. (11) 1·7125. (12) 4·6175.
(13) 4·88. (14) ·0288.

EXERCISE 31.

(1) 19·29, 64·3, 643, 112·525. (2) ·0625, ·3125, 3·125.
(3) 25·476, 2·5476, ·25476, ·025476. (4) ·125, ·0125, ·00125.
(5) ·03. (6) ·003. (7) ·0003.
(8) ·02415. (9) ·00315. (10) ·01575.
(11) ·039483. (12) 2·36081. (13) 13·1127.
(14) 13·1127. (15) ·0132392. (16) ·0001491.
(17) ·01491. (18) 149·1. (19) 14·91.
(20) ·3782. (21) ·000027. (22) ·015625.
(23) ·02928. (24) ·000002744.

EXERCISE 32.

(1) 30·21. (2) 40·16. (3) 2·45.
(4) 2,016. (5) ·1 and 1. (6) 1 and 10.
(7) 10 and 100. (8) 1,100.

EXERCISE 33.

(1) 79·56, 39·78, 26·52, 19·89, 10·608, 3·1824.
(2) 3·125, ·625.   (3) ·0316, ·0079, ·01896.
(4) ·0024, ·00216.   (5) ·08245, ·0206125.
(6) 2·552.   (7) ·0123.
(8) ·5023.   (9) ·035.
(10) ·0146.

EXERCISE 34.

(1) 6·131, 61·31.   (2) 1·687, 168·7.   (3) ·0708.
(4) ·3002.   (5) ·0061.   (6) ·5023.
(7) ·7.   (8) 146, 1·46, ·146. (9) ·146.
(10) ·0085, ·85, 85. (11) ·425.   (12) 1·0625.
(13) 106·25.   (14) ·010625.   (15) ·47.
(16) 1·3734.   (17) ·1328.   (18) ·0635.
(19) 2·6714.   (20) 2·0390.   (21) ·0058.
(22) 1·5789.   (23) 4·3478.   (24) ·0142.
(25) 59·1216.   (26) 1·3110.   (27) 586·6013.
(28) 68·7543.   (29) 2·1905.   (30) 4·0162. . .
(31) 15·02475.   (32) 4·0656. . . .   (33) 2·91101. . . .
(34) 42.   (35) 2·2.   (36) ·00506.
(37) 1.

EXERCISE 35.

(1) ·5, ·25, ·2, ·125.   (2) ·75, ·4, ·375.   (3) 1·25, 1·4, 1·875.
(4) ·4375, 1·1875, 2·0625.   (5) ·46875, ·64, ·072.
(6) 5·3125, 7·40625.   (7) 1·9, ·019.   (8) 30·17.
(9) ·05078125.   (10) ·9504.

EXERCISE 36.

(1) £1 17s. 6d.   (2) £3 12s. 6d.   (3) 9d.
(4) 3 cwts. 3 qrs.   (5) 6 cwts. 1 qr.   (6) 13 ozs.
(7) 15 ozs.   (8) 2 ro. 10 sq. poles.
(9) 10 sq. poles.   (10) 2 qrs.   (11) 12 cwts.
(12) 14 cwts. 2 qrs. (13) 8 cwts.   (14) 1 oz. 12 drs.
(15) 2 ro. 10 sq. poles.   (16) 1 ro. 15 sq. poles.
(17) 1s. 1½d.   (18) 9s. 3d.   (19) £3 2s. 6d.

(20) 7s. 8½d. (21) 5s. 11¼d. (22) £45 17s. 6d.
(23) £16 0s. 11¾d. (24) £15 6s. 0½d. (25) 13s. 10½d.
(26) 5s. 4d. (27) 7s. 8¾d. (28) 14s. 3¾d.
(29) 8 cwts. 3 qrs. 19 lbs. (30) 1s. 3¾d.
(31) 7s. 6d. (32) 303·66 lbs.

EXERCISE 37.

(1) ·775. (2) ·3125. (3) ·25.
(4) ·5. (5) ·125. (6) ·2.
(7) ·625. (8) ·8834. (9) ·25.
(10) ·375. (11) ·0478. (12) ·1931.
(13) ·0625. (14) ·03125. (15) ·1875.
(16) ·1875. (17) ·6176 . . . . . (18) ·2̇85714̇.
(19) ·0̇9̇. (20) ·3̇84615̇. (21) ·675.
(22) 3·64. (23) ·963.

EXERCISE 37(a).

(1) ·975. (2) ·9375. (3) 2·525.
(4) 1·5375. (5) 2·63125. (6) 4·78̇3̇.
(7) 3·74375. (8) 7·81875. (9) 9·928125.
(10) 11·596875. (11) 2·665625. (12) 5·359375.
(13) 4·471875. (14) 5·584375. (15) 7·9̇10416̇.
(16) ·691875. (17) ·756875. (18) ·7671875.
(19) ·724375. (20) ·465625. (21) ·418̇75̇.
(22) ·96875. (23) ·7. (24) ·875.
(25) ·65625.

EXERCISE 38.

(1) ·6̇, ·5̇, ·7̇. (2) ·0̇9̇, ·4̇5̇, ·6̇3̇.
(3) ·3̇84615̇, ·5̇38461̇, ·7̇69230̇.
(4) ·1̇42857̇, ·2̇85714̇, ·4̇28571̇, ·5̇71428̇.
(5) ·2̇2̇7̇, ·2̇692307̇. (6) ·36̇53846̇1̇. (7) ·1̇85̇.
(8) 1·5̇4̇. (9) 2·7̇14285̇. (10) ·1̇142857̇.
(11) ·5̇92̇. (12) ·1̇076923̇.

EXERCISE 39.

(1) $\frac{2}{9}, \frac{2}{3}$. (2) $\frac{1}{9}, \frac{1}{99}, \frac{1}{999}$. (3) $\frac{2}{11}, \frac{3}{11}$. (4) $\frac{41}{111}$.

(5) $\frac{8}{333}$. (6) $\frac{9}{1111}$. (7) $\frac{679}{1111}$. (8) $\frac{2}{7}$.

(9) $\frac{15}{37}$. (10) $\frac{8}{13}$. (11) $\frac{31}{39}$. (12) $\frac{65}{81}$.

EXERCISE 40.

(1) $\frac{7}{30}$. (2) $\frac{137}{330}$. (3) $\frac{12}{55}$. (4) $\frac{91}{550}$.

(5) $\frac{121}{555}$. (6) $\frac{2}{55}$. (7) $\frac{4}{275}$. (8) $\frac{32131}{99900}$.

(9) $\frac{47}{350}$. (10) $\frac{7}{36}$. (11) $\frac{29}{88}$. (12) $\frac{67}{144}$.

(13) $\frac{57}{104}$. (14) $\frac{81}{148}$.

EXERCISE 41.

(1) $11 \cdot \dot{3}\dot{6}$. (2) $12 \cdot 6\dot{7}\dot{2}$. (3) $1 \cdot \dot{1}6643\dot{9}$.

(4) $6 \cdot 075866\dot{7}$. (5) $\cdot 2\dot{6}$. (6) $1 \cdot 76\dot{2}\dot{1}$.

(7) $4 \cdot 31\dot{8}$. (8) $2 \cdot 10492\dot{3}$.

EXERCISE 42.

(1) $\frac{7}{15}$. (2) $\frac{2}{165}$. (3) $1\frac{39}{44}$.

(4) $1\frac{1}{12}$. (5) $1\frac{4}{9}$. (6) $\frac{341}{450}$.

(7) $\cdot 59\dot{2}$. (8) $5 \cdot 0875$. (9) $\cdot 0952$.

(10) $23 \cdot \dot{3}$. (11) $\cdot 5477$. (12) $2 \cdot 2944$.

EXERCISE 43.

(1) 6,270. (2) $58 \cdot 4\dot{7}\dot{2}$ lbs. (3) 540.

(4) 17 ; 2·35 ins. (5) L.C.M. of $\frac{105}{10}, \frac{96}{10} = 336$ ft.

(6) £1 10s. 2½d. (7) £6,000. (8) $\frac{18}{43}$.

(9) £2,850. (10) ·0755. (11) $\frac{2}{5}$.

(12) £4,000. (13) 2·4. (14) 168·26.

(15) 7·854. (16) £23 7s. 6d. (17) ·57.

EXERCISE 44.

(1) 3·71, 3·7125. (2) 15·44, 15·4390. (3) ·45, ·4536.

(4) 22 51. (5) 6·80. (6) 25·60.

(7) ·071. (8) ·008. (9) 9·205.

(10) 8 368 (11) 12·74.

EXERCISE 45.

(**1**) 695·64. (**2**) 95·04. (**3**) 27·98.
(**4**) 176·91. (**5**) 223·87. (**6**) 227·34.
(**7**) 189·301. (**8**) 29·991. (**9**) 13·410.
(**10**) 21·745. (**11**) ·900. (**12**) ·209.
(**13**) 3·7493. (**14**) ·0075. (**15**) ·0053.
(**16**) ·0022. (**17**) 4·0062. (**18**) 2·8870.
(**19**) 78·8654. (**20**) 1·3910. (**21**) ·00023.
(**22**) ·00098. (**23**) ·00002. (**24**) ·00170.
(**25**) ·00014. (**26**) ·00016. (**27**) 1·063.
(**28**) ·002. (**29**) ·011. (**30**) 2.
(**31**) 3. (**32**) 5.

EXERCISE 46.

(**1**) ·2053. (**2**) ·8358. (**3**) ·1015.
(**4**) 4·2197. (**5**) ·2630. (**6**) ·2010.
(**7**) ·06453. (**8**) ·11073. (**9**) ·01423.
(**10**) ·45485. (**11**) ·00758. (**12**) ·00645.
(**13**) ·012755. (**14**) ·007190. (**15**) ·001077.
(**16**) ·002714. (**17**) 8·4566. (**18**) 8·141.
(**19**) 6·8546. (**20**) 13·119.

EXERCISE 47.

(**1**) 1·508. (**2**) 2·625. (**3**) 5·421.
(**4**) 7·754. (**5**) 13·858, (**6**) 14·460.
(**7**) 2·275. (**8**) 15·516. (**9**) 17·569.
(**10**) 1·992. (**11**) 2·841. (**12**) 4·395.
(**13**) 3·075. (**14**) 5·082. (**15**) 25·099.
(**16**) 2·034. (**17**) 1·089. (**18**) 2·668.

EXERCISE 48.

(**1**) 10s. 6d. (**2**) 12s. $4\frac{1}{4}$d. (**3**) £1 8s. $8\frac{3}{4}$d.
(**4**) £3 10s. $11\frac{3}{4}$d. (**5**) £6 2s. 2d. (**6**) £4 13s. 2d.
(**7**) 15s. $3\frac{1}{2}$d. (**8**) £15 5s. 5d. (**9**) £2 17s. $8\frac{1}{4}$d.
(**10**) £3 14s. $4\frac{1}{4}$d. (**11**) £16 1s. 7d. (**12**) £15 1s. $1\frac{1}{4}$d.
(**13**) £1 0s. 2d. (**14**) 1s. 6d. (**15**) £3 0s. $3\frac{1}{4}$d.
(**16**) 1s. $7\frac{1}{4}$d.

EXERCISE 49.

(1) £51 15s.
(4) £20 18s. 9d.
(7) £84 12s.
(10) £57 7s. 3d.
(13) £41 11s.
(16) £43 17s. 11¾d.
(18) £1,171 17s. 6d.
(20) £3,508 13s. 11½d.
(22) £3,088 15s. 9½d.
(24) £4,762 1s. 6d.
(26) £2,648 1s. 11d.
(28) £3,051 8s. 0¼d.
(30) £2,712 18s. 9d.
(32) £8,067 19s. 2d.
(34) £5,302 4s. 10d.
(36) £2,800 17s.
(38) £2,709 9s. 4d.
(40) £1,160 5s. 2d.

(2) £45.
(5) £63.
(8) £32 11s.
(11) £20 17s. 11d.
(14) £59 17s. 9½d.

(3) £38 13s. 4d.
(6) £53 12s.
(9) £35 6s. 4d.
(12) £11 16s. 7d.
(15) £48 11s. 10½d.
(17) £13 11s. 3d.
(19) £2,073 14s.
(21) £1,897 2s. 2¼d.
(23) £4,652 15s. 2½d.
(25) £2,714 18s. 7d.
(27) £4,305 5s. 3d.
(29) £2,406 0s. 3¾d.
(31) £3,121 16s. 5¾d.
(33) £2,092 12s. 7½d.
(35) £9,718 11s. 7¼d.
(37) £5,776 19s. 11¼d.
(39) £1,396 6s. 0½d.

EXERCISE 50.

(1) £75 10s.
(4) £75 14s. 11d.
(7) £17 12s. 6d.
(10) £195 12s. 6¾d.
(13) £24 15s. 4½d.
(16) £74 2s. 6½d.
(19) £62 14s. 4½d.
(22) £43 11s. 2¼d.
(25) £14 1s.
(28) £46 14s. 9d.
(31) £63 15s. 8d.
(34) £39 4s. 8d.
(37) £100 4s. 7d.
(40) £212 19s. 6d.
(43) £38 1s. 11d.

(2) £61 8s.
(5) £13 16s. 3d.
(8) £34 0s. 2d.
(11) £16 11s. 6¾d.
(14) £78 2s. 1d.
(17) £205 6s. 0½d.
(20) £9 9s.
(23) £62 18s. 10¼d.
(26) £13 3s. 7d.
(29) £100 8s. 6d.
(32) £33 1s. 2d.
(35) £44 14s. 2d.
(38) £236 11s. 3d.
(41) £580 12s. 6d.

(3) £70 10s.
(6) £12 15s. 6¾d.
(9) £67 3s. 1½d.
(12) £16 14s. 10½d.
(15) £79 11s. 1½d.
(18) £36 19s. 0¾d.
(21) £37.
(24) £46 2s. 8½d.
(27) £36 6s. 5d.
(30) £26 8s. 7d.
(33) £52 6s. 7d.
(36) £104 3s.
(39) £599 13s. 11d.
(42) £19 11s. 2d.

EXERCISE 51.

(1) £2 3s. 6½d.   **(2)** £2 17s. 9½d.   **(3)** £31 5s. 9½d.
(4) £16 17s. 3d.   **(5)** £3 6s. 11d.   **(6)** £15 18s. 4¾d.
(7) £3 9s. 7d.   **(8)** £6 4s.   **(9)** £2 18s. 5½d.
(10) £5 5s. 5d.   **(11)** £24 8s. 4d.   **(12)** £21 6s. 10d.
(13) £4 2s. 8¾d.   **(14)** £23 5s. 10d.   **(15)** £30 19s. 4¾d.
(16) £23 2s. 2d.

EXERCISE 52.

(1) 17s. 6d.   **(2)** £1 19s. 6d.   **(3)** £1 1s.
(4) £2.   **(5)** £1 7s. 1d.   **(6)** £1 10s.
(7) £2 2s. 6d.   **(8)** 15s. 9d.   **(9)** £9 10s.
(10) £15.   **(11)** £53.   **(12)** £6.
(13) £12 6s. 8d.   **(14)** £4 10s.   **(15)** £3 15s.
(16) £2 1s. 8d.   **(17)** £2 1s. 3d.   **(18)** £152.
(19) £124.   **(20)** £32.   **(21)** £72 10s.
(22) £141.   **(23)** £158.   **(24)** 9s. 4d.
(25) £2 16s.   **(26)** £2 14s. 10d.   **(27)** £10.
(28) £26 8s.   **(29)** £28.   **(30)** £33 14s. 6d.
(31) £2 10s.   **(32)** £123.   **(33)** £14.
(34) £72 10s.   **(35)** £19 10s.   **(36)** £22.

EXERCISE 53.

(1) 6,700 mm.   **(2)** 8,970 mm.   **(3)** 5·464 m.
(4) 74·3 dm.   **(5)** 1,157·6 cm.   **(6)** 3,000 m.
(7) 550,000 cm.   **(8)** 740,000 mm.   **(9)** 5,754,000 mm.
(10) 435·6 cm., 4·356 m.   **(11)** 4·763 Km.
(12) 5 Km. 3 Hm. 2 Dm. 4 m. 6 dm. 3 cm. 8 mm.
(13) 7,412·036 m. 741·2036 Dm. 74·12036 Hm. 7·412036 Km.
(14) 7·456315 Km. 7,456,315 mm.   **(15)** ·056 Km.
(16) 41·36 m.   **(17)** 3·632·1 mm.
(18) 5 yds. 1 ft. 4·85 ins.   **(19)** 50·8 cm.
(20) 1,066·8 mm.   **(21)** 3,282 yds.
(22) 4 miles 1,712 yds., or nearly 5 miles.

EXERCISE 54.

(**1**) 6,152,300 sq. m.   (**2**) 43,045 sq. m.
(**3**) 506 sq. m.   (**4**) 560 sq. m.
(**5**) 45,080,900 sq. m.   (**6**) 5·36 sq. m.
(**7**) 7·8516 sq. m.   (**8**) 8·604305 sq. m.
(**9**) 9·5367 sq. Km.   (**10**) 5·036210 sq. Km.
(**11**) 5·465 sq. Km.   (**12**) 10·0605 sq. Km.
(**13**) 4 sq. Km. 53 sq. Hm. 1 sq. Dm. 64 sq. m.
(**14**) 6 sq. Km. 13 sq. Hm. 4 sq. Dm. 30 sq. m. 47 sq. dm.
(**15**) 1,500 sq. m.   (**16**) 7·56 ares.   (**17**) 43 a. 56 ca.
(**18**) 74,563 sq. m.   (**19**) 123·55 acres.   (**20**) 2·0235 Ha.
(**21**) 7·75 sq. ins.   (**22**) 64·52 sq. cms.

EXERCISE 55.

(**1**) 3,000 g.   (**2**) 20 g.   (**3**) 4,530 g.
(**4**) 63 g.   (**5**) 6·43 g.   (**6**) ·036 g.
(**7**) 6·324 g.   (**8**) 6,000,000 mg.   (**9**) 6,000 mg.
(**10**) 5,630 mg.   (**11**) 60 mg.   (**12**) 45 mg.
(**13**) 6·435 Kg.   (**14**) ·004326 Kg.   (**15**) 84·045 g.
(**16**) 3,489·62 g.   (**17**) 7,036·17 litres. (**18**) £6,520.
(**19**) 181·08 Kg.   (**20**) 10·8 Kl.   (**21**) 14·25 Kg.
(**22**) 1,250 grams.   (**23**) 440 gallons.
(**24**) 1·4336 g. ; 22·077 grains.   (**25**) 1,293 grams.
(**26**) 1·4336 g.   (**27**) 14·85 lbs.   (**28**) 11,250 grams.
(**29**) 93·3 grains.   (**30**) 28·8 grams.   (**31**) 981·456.
(**32**) 981·456 cm. per sec.   (**33**) 1·88125 grams.
(**34**) 38·65 m.   (**35**) 933·75 Kg.   (**36**) 8·2 g.

EXERCISE 56.

(**1**) $1\frac{1}{2}$ sq. ft.   (**2**) 7 sq. ft. 18 sq. ins.
(**3**) 3 sq. yds.   (**4**) 10 sq. ft.
(**5**) 3 acres 894 sq. yds. (**6**) 29 acres 440 sq. yds.
(**7**) $7\frac{9}{16}$ sq. ft.   (**8**) 182·25 sq. cm.
(**9**) 28 sq. yds. 4 sq. ft. (**10**) 10 ac. 16·04 sq. poles.
(**11**) 303·208 acres.   (**12**) 179 ac. 3 ro. 33·72 sq. poles.
(**13**) 16 acres 2 ro. 13·2 sq. poles.
(**14**) $1,100\frac{3}{4}$ lbs.   (**15**) £6.   (**16**) 2s. 11d.
(**17**) £8 15s.   (**18**) £120.   (**19**) 7s. 6d.
(**20**) 4s.

EXERCISE 57.

(1) 9 ft.

(2) 2 ft. 8 ins.

(3) 1 ft. 8 ins.

(4) 2 ft. 6 ins.

(5) 2 ft. 7 ins.

(6) 125 yards.

(7) 367 yards.

(8) 10 chains 60 links.

(9) 11·4 chains.

(10) 4 yards.

EXERCISE 58.

(1) 62 sq. ft.

(2) 264 sq. yds.

(3) 436 sq. ft., 18s. 2d.

(4) 291 sq. yds. 6 sq. ft.

(5) 3 sq. ft. 48 sq. ins.

(6) 48 sq. ins.

(7) 180 sq. ins.

(8) $25\frac{3}{8}$ sq. ft. ; $6\frac{15}{32}$ sq. ft.

(9) 390 sq. ft. ; 10s. 10d.

(10) 56 sq. yds. ; £2 6s. 8d.

EXERCISE 59.

(1) 5 strips.

(2) 112 ft. ; £10 5s. 4d.

(3) 32 yds. ; £9 12s.

(4) (a) 90 ft. ; $7\frac{1}{2}$ ft. ; (b) 88 ft. ; $5\frac{1}{2}$ ft. ; (c) $82\frac{1}{2}$ ft.

(5) 100 yds. ; £17 10s.

(6) £14 8s.

(7) 2 ft. 3 ins.

(8) £8.

(9) 12 ft.

(10) 20 ft.

(11) £10 16s.

(12) 57 yds. ; £17 2s. ; $2\frac{5}{7}$ yds. of roll = $14\frac{1}{4}$ sq. ft.

(13) 1st and 2nd ; least waste in 3rd. ; $4\frac{2}{9}$ ft. of roll = $9\frac{1}{2}$ sq. ft.

EXERCISE 60.

(1) 270 sq. ft. ; $193\frac{3}{4}$ sq. ft. ; $76\frac{1}{4}$ sq. ft.

(2) £4 14s. $1\frac{1}{3}$d.

(3) 150 sq. ft. ; £4 3s. 4d.

(4) $1\frac{1}{2}$ ft. ; 3s. 4d.

(5) £4.

(6) 16 sq. yds. ; 2 ft.

EXERCISE 61.

(1) 726 sq. ft.

(2) 720 sq. ft.

(3) 864 sq. ft.

(4) 840 sq. ft.

(5) 680 sq. ft.

(6) 924.

(7) £1 13s. 1d.

(8) 19s. $7\frac{1}{2}$d.

(9) £5 2s. 8d.

(10) 11 ft.

(11) 12 ft.

EXERCISE 62.

(1) £1 13s. 4d.   (2) £1 6s. 8d.   (3) £2.
(4) 13s. 4d.   (5) 20s.   (6) £2 12s. 6d.
(7) 19s. 3d.   (8) £1 19s.   (9) £1 10s.
(10) £2 9s.   (11) £1 2s. 6d.   (12) £1 4s. 9d.

EXERCISE 63.

(1) 8 ft.   (2) 32 lbs.   (3) 108.
(4) 3,000.   (5) 13,440.   (6) 46 yds.
(7) £24.   (8) £1 5s.   (9) 47 sq. ft.
(10) £5 2s. 1d.   (11) 3s. 4d.   (12) £3 7s. $9\frac{3}{4}$d.
(13) £6 3s.   (14) 2d.   (15) £1 18s.
(16) £4.   (17) 18s. 2d.   (18) £1 5s. 4d.
(19) 64 yds.   (20) 6 ins. by 6 ins.
(21) $77\frac{1}{2}$ sq. ft. ; 6s. $5\frac{1}{2}$d.   (22) £91.
(23) 1s. 9d.   (24) 250 sq. yds.   (25) 13 ft.
(26) 23·8 sq. m.   (27) 345 ares.   (28) 1,500 ares.
(29) 240 m.   (30) 25,600.   (31) 666.
(32) 200 m. ; 11 mins.   (33) 5·7.
(34) 3·94 sq. in. ; 19 fr. 70 c.

EXERCISE 64.

(1) 90 cub. ins.   (2) 224 cub. ins.   (3) 540 cub. ins.
(4) 750 cub. ins.   (5) 169 cub. ft.   (6) 30 cub. ft.
(7) $104\frac{1}{2}$ cub. ft.   (8) $393\frac{1}{4}$ cub. ft.
(9) 10 cub. ft. 120 cub. ins.
(10) 600 cub. ft. 75 cub. ins.   (11) $7\frac{1}{2}$ cub. ft.
(12) 2 cub. ft. 1,044 cub ns.
(13) 155 cub. yds. 15 cub. ft.   (14) $409\frac{1}{2}$ cub. ft.
(15) 2 tons 1,707 lbs. 8 ozs.   (16) £11 13s. 4d.
(17) 120 cub. ft. ; 11s. $1\frac{1}{3}$d.   (18) £3 8s.
(19) 34 tons 10 cwts. 7 lbs. 8 ozs.   (20) 914 lbs. 1 oz.
(21) 69 cub. yds. 12 cub. ft.
(22) 450 cub. ft. ; 12 tons 9 cwts. 12 lbs.
(23) 60.   (24) 1,620 gallons.   (25) $833\frac{1}{3}$ lbs.
(26) 116·8 gallons.   (27) 777,600.   (28) 216.
(29) 82,944.
(30) 1 cub. ft. 1,198 cub. ins. ; 1,442 cub. ins.
(31) £165 2s. 6d.

EXERCISE 65.

(1) 4 ft.
(2) $2\frac{1}{2}$ ft.
(3) 28 sq. ft.
(4) 15 ft.
(5) 18 sq. ins.
(6) $11\frac{1}{4}$ ins.
(7) 554·5.
(8) $2\frac{3}{80}$ sq. ins.
(9) 10 ft. 5 ins. per min.
(10) £4.
(11) $2\frac{1}{2}$ ft.
(12) 1 ft. 3 ins.
(13) 18 ft.
(14) 36 ft.
(15) 2 ft. 6 ins.
(16) 4 ins.
(17) $6\frac{2}{3}$ ins.
(18) ·1188 cm.
(19) 88,400 c.c. ; 47·736 Kg.
(20) 6·475 ; 6,475.
(21) 12,250.
(22) 64,800.
(23) 76,800.
(24) 1,008.
(25) 2·4 m.
(26) ·9 m.
(27) 2·8 m.
(28) 51·2 Kg.
(29) 126 Kg.

EXERCISE 66.

(1) 169.
(2) 196.
(3) 225.
(4) 256.
(5) 625.
(6) 10,000.
(7) 4.
(8) 8.
(9) 11.
(10) 50.
(11) 90.
(12) 100.
(13) 14.
(14) 16.
(15) 160.

EXERCISE 67.

(1) 18.
(2) 24.
(3) 15.
(4) 42.
(5) 28.
(6) 35.
(7) 105.
(8) 210.
(9) 77.
(10) 231.
(11) 385.
(12) 1,008.

EXERCISE 68.

(1) 37.
(2) 54.
(3) 36.
(4) 98.
(5) 89.
(6) 213.
(7) 432.
(8) 531.
(9) 504.
(10) 706.
(11) 1,412.
(12) 639.
(13) 1,062.
(14) 1,008.
(15) 1,593.
(16) 3,186.
(17) 6,372.
(18) 12,744.
(19) 38,232.
(20) 76,464.

EXERCISE 69.

(1) 1·78.
(2) 17·8.
(3) 1·08.
(4) ·108.
(5) ·196.
(6) ·074.
(7) ·072.
(8) ·426.
(9) ·2124.
(10) ·01412.
(11) ·01278.
(12) 20·16.

ANSWERS.

EXERCISE 70.

  (1) 2·327 (2·3265).   **(2)** 1·772.   **(3)** 11·549.
  (4) 1·871 (1·8708).   **(5)** 5·916.   **(6)** 2·646 (2·6459).
  (7) ·837 (·8366).   **(8)** 1·732.   **(9)** 1·414.
(10) 3·317 (3·3166). **(11)** 1·049 (1·0488). **(12)** 2·828.
(13) 3·873 (3·8729). **(14)** ·707.   **(15)** 1·803 (1·8027).

EXERCISE 71.

  (1) $\frac{5}{2}$.   **(2)** $\frac{8}{5}$.   **(3)** $\frac{14}{3}$.
  (4) $\frac{16}{5}$.   **(5)** $\frac{14}{5}$.   **(6)** $\frac{15}{4}$.
  (7) $\frac{12}{5}$.   **(8)** 2·261 (2·2607). **(9)** 2·693 (2·6925).
(10) 1·464 (1·4637). **(11)** 1·789 (1·7888). **(12)** ·913.
(13) ·447.   **(14)** 1·225 (1·2247). **(15)** 1·808 (1·8077).
(16) 5·871.

EXERCISE 72.

  (1) 225 yds.   **(2)** 235 yds.   **(3)** 1 ft. 9 ins.
  (4) £102 10s.   **(5)** 2 ft. 6 ins.   **(6)** 12 ft. 6 ins.
  (7) 440 yds.   **(8)** 8 chains 50 links.
  (9) 110 yds. ; 330 yds. ; £110.
(11) 165 yds. ; £61 17s. 6d.   **(10)** £12 16s. 8d.
(13) 16 ins.   **(14)** 4 ft. 9 ins.   **(12)** 5 yds.
(16) 5 ft. 10 ins.   **(17)** 15 mins.   **(15)** 840 yds.
(19) 864 sq. yds.   **(20)** 80.   **(18)** $42\frac{6}{7}$ mins.
(22) 210.   **(23)** 56.   **(21)** 105 ; 7.

EXERCISE 73.

  (1) 5s. 6d.   **(2)** 8s. 4d.   **(3)** 4 hrs.
  (4) £13.   **(5)** $7\frac{1}{2}$.   **(6)** 6s. 3d.
  (7) £3 9s.   **(8)** 2 tons 5 cwts. **(9)** 44 days.
(10) £220.   **(11)** 3s. 3d.   **(12)** 3 months.

EXERCISE 74.

  (1) 15 days.   **(2)** 20.   **(3)** 4 days.
  (4) 10.   **(5)** 42.   **(6)** 84 days.
  (7) 10 months. **(8)** 500 men.   **(9)** 84.
(10) 40 miles.   **(11)** 30 mins.   **(12)** 50 miles.
(13) 8 men.   **(14)** 20 men.

EXERCISE 75.

(**1**) £8 8s. (**2**) 9 hrs. (**3**) £2 2s.
(**4**) £25. (**5**) 5s. per yd. (**6**) 40 miles.
(**7**) $2\frac{1}{2}$ hrs. (**8**) 135 cub. ins. (**9**) 140 lbs.
(**10**) 80 days. (**11**) 6 horses. (**12**) £4 13s. 4d.
(**13**) £131 5s. (**14**) £1,800. (**15**) 70 miles.
(**16**) $7\frac{1}{2}$. (**17**) 6 days. (**18**) $3\frac{5}{7}$ tons.
(**19**) £746 13s. 4d. (**20**) 35. (**21**) £10.
(**22**) 7 men. (**23**) 15 lbs. (**24**) 3 hrs. 20 mins.
(**25**) 39 gallons. (**26**) $4\frac{1}{2}$ months. (**27**) £29 8s.

EXERCISE 76.

(**1**) £2 10s. (**2**) 10d. (**3**) 13s. 6d.
(**4**) 10 days. (**5**) 32. (**6**) 28 acres.
(**7**) £5 8s. (**8**) 8 days. (**9**) £4 10s.
(**10**) 28. (**11**) $26\frac{2}{3}$. (**12**) £105.
(**13**) £2 16s. 3d. (**14**) £115 4s. (**15**) 1 ton 4 cwts.
(**16**) 36 days. (**17**) 40 days. (**18**) 54 days.
(**19**) 28 days. (**20**) 15 days.

EXERCISE 77.

(**1**) $\frac{3}{4}$. (**2**) $\frac{26}{29}$. (**3**) $\frac{1}{10}$.
(**4**) $\frac{1}{2}$. (**5**) $\frac{9}{16}$. (**6**) $\frac{130}{73}$.
(**7**) $\frac{15}{17}$. (**8**) $\frac{19}{14}$. (**9**) $\frac{2}{3}$.
(**10**) $\frac{1839}{2660}$. (**11**) 9. (**12**) $\frac{57}{250}$.
(**13**) $\frac{11}{13}$. (**14**) $\frac{6}{7}$. (**15**) $\frac{9}{7}$.
(**16**) $\frac{7}{5}$. (**19**) $2\frac{1}{3}$. (**20**) 12s. 6d.
(**21**) 13s. (**22**) 2 yds. 2 ft. 9 ins.
(**23**) £1 5s. $4\frac{1}{2}$d. (**24**) 9s. $7\frac{1}{2}$d. (**25**) $\frac{106}{231}$.
(**26**) 66 ins. (**27**) 35 ins.
(**28**) 4 sq. ft. 40 sq. ins. (**29**) 312.
(**30**) £274.

EXERCISE 78.

(**1**) 25s. (**2**) £6 10s. (**3**) £12 10s.
(**4**) £1,050. (**5**) $1\frac{1}{4}$ hrs. (**6**) 80 miles.
(**7**) $13\frac{1}{2}$ lbs. (**8**) 6s. 6d. (**9**) 66 days.

302 ANSWERS.

(10) 3 yds. 1 ft. (11) £4 12s. 3d. (12) £330.
(13) 50 yds. (14) 37·68 ins. (15) 8 ft.
(16) 115 ft.

EXERCISE 79.

(1) 32 days. (2) 4 days. (3) 20 men.
(4) 8 men. (5) 6 months. (6) 24 days 8 hrs.
(7) 10 mins. (8) 16 miles per hour.
(9) 12. (10) 30 days. (11) 16 days.
(12) 111. (13) 30. (14) 12 months.
(15) 16⅔ months. (16) 20 yds. (17) 2 yds.

EXERCISE 80.

(1) £13 2s. 6d. (2) £1 17s. 6d. (3) 56 mins.
(4) 3⅓. (5) 5 tons 4 cwts. (6) £1 7s.
(7) £3. (8) 300 yds. (9) 52.
(10) 6 tons. (11) £1 3s. 10d. (12) 5 hrs.
(13) 12·5664 sq. ins. (14) 16·1 ft. (15) 12 days.
(16) 135. (17) 132. (18) £1,050.
(19) 100 days. (20) 480 men. (21) 3·14 ft.
(22) 714. (23) 80 yds. (24) 156 acres.
(25) 9 yds. (26) 3 days. (27) 10 secs.
(28) 4 litres. (29) 2s. 6d. (30) 15s.

EXERCISE 81.

(1) 12 days. (2) 7½ hours. (3) 54 men.
(4) 20. (5) 12 months. (6) 143.
(7) 100 days. (8) 80. (9) 250 yds.
(10) £105. (11) 3s. (12) 30 miles.
(13) £50 8s. (14) 100. (15) 10,000.
(16) 120 reams. (17) 5 days. (18) 7 days.
(19) 28 days. (20) 10 tons. (21) 6¼ ozs.
(22) 4,050 tons. (23) 50 days. (24) 21.
(25) 16. (25) £187 10s. (27) 28 days.
(28) 500 pages. (29) 100 mins. (30) 3 pumps.
(31) £40 10s. (32) 2·4 cm. (33) 27 men.
(34) 32 miles. (35) 10 hours.

EXERCISE 82.

(1) £4 10s.
(2) £56.
(3) £1,600.
(4) £4,205.
(5) £3 9s. 9d.
(6) £18.
(7) £3 10s.
(8) £11 5s.
(9) 3s. 3d.
(10) £30,000.
(11) £5,833 6s. 8d.
(12) 8s.
(13) £360.
(14) £226 16s. 8d.
(15) £45.
(16) £144, £168, £252.
(17) £572 14s.
(18) £848 19s. 10d.
(19) £10,213 16s. 8d.
(20) £214 7s. 6d.
(21) £5,290 13s. 3d.
(22) £115.
(23) £12 15s.
(24) £43 10s.
(25) £262 10s.
(26) £22 15s.
(27) $\frac{1}{3}$.
(28) £66 13s. 4d. ; £2,600.
(29) £6,000.
(30) £2 per £100.
(31) £50 2s. 1d.
(32) 350.
(33) £104 10s. 4d.
(34) £150.
(35) 3,576.
(36) 2,958.
(37) 16s.
(38) £2 11s. 3½d.
(39) £13 2s. 6d.
(40) £68 15s.
(41) £342 1s.
(42) £180 10s. ; £245 8s. 4d. ; £113 4s. 2d.
(43) £113 3s. 11½d.
(44) £4,000.
(45) 450 dollars.
(46) 14s. 5d. gain.

EXERCISE 83.

(1) 24, 32.
(2) 26 ; 39.
(3) 63, 105, 147.
(4) £8 8s. 4d. ; £16 16s. 8d. ; £25 5s.
(5) £4 1s. ; £6 1s. 6d. ; £10 2s. 6d.
(6) £6 6s. ; £10 10s. ; £12 12s.
(7) £34 17s. 2d. ; £52 5s. 9d. ; £69 14s. 4d.
(8) £7 0s. 6d. ; £14 1s. ; £28 2s.
(9) £2 3s. ; £6 9s. ; £10 15s. ; £15 1s.
(10) £6 9s. ; £4 6s.
(11) £18 12s. ; £12 8s. ; £9 6s.
(12) 6 cwts. ; 8 cwts. ; 12 cwts.
(13) 15s. ; 20s. ; 18s.
(14) 15s. ; 22s. 6d. ; 24s.
(15) £75 ; £100 ; £127 10s.
(16) £19 5s. ; £35 ; £61 12s. ; £80 10s.
(17) £45 10s. ; £36 8s.
(18) £20 10s. ; £10 5s. ; £8 4s.
(19) £30 6s. 9d. ; £40 9s.
(20) £150 7s. 6d. ; £120 6s. ; £90 4s. 6d.
(21) £7 10s. ; £5.
(22) 1,000 ; 1,375 ; 1,125.
(23) 13s. 4d. ; 16s. 8d. ; 20s. ; 25s.
(24) £1,400 ; £1,750 ; £2,100.
(25) £4 4s. ; £6 6s. ; £8 8s. ; £10 10s.

EXERCISE 84.

(1) 6s. 8d. ; 8s. 4d.   **(2)** 15s. ; 15s.   **(3)** £360 ; £510.
(4) £700 ; £420 ; £420.
(5) £14 17s. 6d. ; £10 4s. ; £6 7s. 6d.
(6) £1 16s. 3d.   **(7)** 8s. ; 6s.
(8) 9s. 3d. woman ; 6s. 2d. boy ; 3s. 1d. girl.
(9) 40 ; 24 ; 42.   **(10)** £3 10s. ; £5.   **(11)** 18s. ; 9s. ; 3s.
(12) 9s. ; 3s. ; 1s. 6d.   **(13)** £32 10s. ; £48 15s. ; £39.
(14) £3,750 ; £3,000 ; £1,800.   **(15)** £30 ; £22 10s. ; £18.
(16) 10 ; 15 ; 30.   **(17)** 6s. 8d. ; 7s. 6d. ; 9s.
(18) £18 18s. ; £12 12s. ; £21 ; £15 15s.
(19) 9s. ; 18s. ; 24s. ; 60s. ;   **(20)** £2,325 ; £750.

EXERCISE 85.

(1) $\frac{1}{5}$.   **(2)** $\frac{3}{5}$.   **(3)** $\frac{1}{4}$.
(4) $\frac{1}{3}$.   **(5)** $\frac{1}{6}$.   **(6)** $\frac{9}{40}$.
(7) $\frac{11}{80}$.   **(8)** $\frac{8}{25}$.   **(9)** $\frac{17}{20}$.
(10) $\frac{9}{25}$.   **(11)** $\frac{21}{400}$.   **(12)** $\frac{3}{40}$.
(13) $\frac{13}{150}$.   **(14)** $\frac{1}{14}$.   **(15)** $\frac{1}{44}$.
(16) $\frac{4}{65}$.   **(17)** 5 ; 65.   **(18)** 4 ; 445.
(19) 45 ; 825.   **(20)** 256.   **(21)** 17.
(22) 572.   **(23)** 99·2.   **(24)** 20.
(25) 48.   **(26)** 4s.   **(27)** 3s. 9d.
(28) 30$\frac{3}{4}$ cwts.   **(29)** 13s.   **(30)** 6 ins.
(31) 8s. 2d.   **(32)** £1,204.   **(33)** £151 4s.
(34) £943 0s. 4·8d.   **(35)** £1 2s.   **(36)** 4s. 10d.
(37) £1 12s. 6$\frac{1}{2}$d.   **(38)** 4 tons 18·7 cwts.
(39) 13 yds. 2 ft. 11$\frac{1}{4}$ ins.   **(40)** 3 cwts. 3 lbs.
(41) 10 lbs. 7 ozs. 10 drams.   **(42)** 1 qr. 14 lbs.

EXERCISE 86.

(1) 50.   **(2)** 33$\frac{1}{3}$.   **(3)** 25.   **(4)** 20.
(5) 16$\frac{2}{3}$.   **(6)** 12$\frac{1}{2}$.   **(7)** 66$\frac{2}{3}$.   **(8)** 60.
(9) 83$\frac{1}{3}$.   **(10)** 87$\frac{1}{2}$.   **(11)** 52$\frac{1}{2}$.   **(12)** 150.
(13) 46.   **(14)** 116$\frac{2}{3}$.   **(15)** 28$\frac{4}{7}$.   **(16)** 80.
(17) 94$\frac{2}{7}$.   **(18)** 48$\frac{11}{18}$.   **(19)** 14$\frac{2}{3}$.   **(20)** 32$\frac{1}{2}$.
(21) 46$\frac{7}{8}$.   **(22)** 35.   **(23)** 42$\frac{1}{2}$.   **(24)** 25$\frac{5}{11}$.
(25) 31$\frac{1}{4}$.   **(26)** 72$\frac{2}{9}$.

EXERCISE 87.

(1) 90.   (2) 66⅔.   (3) 33⅓.   (4) 66⅔.
(5) 33⅓.   (6) 33⅓.   (7) 12½.   (8) 10.
(9) 2½.   (10) 6¼.   (11) 133⅓.   (12) 31¼.
(13) 18 2/11.   (14) 19 17/57.   (15) 23 1/18.   (16) 12·5.
(17) 19·9.   (18) 26·4.   (19) 378 18/19.   (20) 32 1/32.
(21) 19 4/9.   (22) 25.   (23) 16⅔.   (24) 33⅓.
(25) 38·67.

EXERCISE 88.

(1) 75.   (2) 64.   (3) 36.
(4) 51.   (5) 88.   (6) 180.
(7) 75.   (8) 400.   (9) 30.
(10) 55.   (11) 40.   (12) 6s. 3d.
(13) £1 19s. 7d.   (14) £205.   (15) £7 3s. 8d.
(16) £27 3s. 4d.   (17) £24.   (18) £16 13s. 4d.
(19) £12 18s. 4d.   (20) £1 17s. 1d.   (21) £8 17s.
(22) 33⅓ cwts.   (23) 25 cwts.   (24) 12 lbs. 8 ozs.
(25) 13 yds. 2 ft. 8 ins.   (26) 37 bush, 2 pecks.
(27) 50 mins.   (28) 25 mins.   (29) 16 ft. 8 ins.
(30) 12 gallons 2 quarts.   (31) 17 sq. yds. 7 sq. ft.

EXERCISE 89.

(1) 25°/₀.   (2) 20°/₀.   (3) 20,000.
(4) 15,000.   (5) 20,000.   (6) 12,100.
(7) 51.   (8) 20°/₀.   (9) 160.
(10) £277 17s. 6d.   (11) £6 18s. 9d.   (12) 2,500.
(13) 5,625.   (14) £1,200.   (15) £93 15s.
(16) £37 12s. 6d.   (17) 65,000.   (18) 171.
(19) 25.   (20) 30.   (21) 1,996,500.
(22) 25.   (23) 465.   (24) £960 13s. 4d.
(25) £29 15s. 1d.   (26) 182.

EXERCISE 90.

(1) £2 10s.   (2) £24.   (3) £60.
(4) £12.   (5) 2s.   (6) 1s. 6d. loss.
(7) 17s. 2d.   (8) 2s.   (9) £3 15s.
(10) £16 10s.

EXERCISE 91.

(1) 25 %.
(2) 20 %.
(3) 20 %.
(4) $16\frac{2}{3}$ %.
(5) $33\frac{1}{3}$ %.
(6) 25 %.
(7) 25 %.
(8) 20 %.
(9) $14\frac{2}{7}$ %.
(10) $18\frac{2}{11}$ %.
(11) 40 %.
(12) 10 %.
(13) 75 %.
(14) $37\frac{1}{2}$ %.
(15) 27 %.
(16) $14\frac{2}{7}$ %.
(17) $8\frac{16}{83}$ %.
(18) $9\frac{1}{11}$ %.

EXERCISE 92.

(1) 50 % gain.
(2) 50 % gain.
(3) 25 % gain.
(4) 20 % loss.
(5) 26 % gain.
(6) 10 % loss.
(7) $16\frac{2}{3}$ % loss.
(8) $12\frac{1}{2}$ % loss.
(9) 40 %.
(10) £30 ; 25 %.
(11) 5 %.
(12) 25 %.
(13) $16\frac{2}{3}$.
(14) $22\frac{2}{9}$.
(15) $56\frac{1}{4}$.
(16) 36.
(17) 50.
(18) 20.
(19) 25.
(20) $81\frac{9}{11}$.

EXERCISE 93.

(1) 2s. 6d.
(2) 4s. 8d.
(3) $2\frac{1}{4}$d.
(4) 7s. 6d.
(5) 2s. 4d.
(6) 1s. 9d.
(7) 1s. 3d.
(8) £20.
(9) $3\frac{3}{4}$d.
(10) 3s.
(11) 12s.
(12) $3\frac{3}{4}$d.
(13) £950.
(14) 3d.
(15) £6 13s. $2\frac{1}{2}$d.

EXERCISE 94.

(1) 4s.
(2) £5.
(3) 3d.
(4) £4.
(5) £20.
(6) 2s. 6d.
(7) 2s. 6d.
(8) 10d.
(9) 1s. 3d.
(10) £40.
(11) £200.
(12) 2s.
(13) £11 4s.
(14) £10.
(15) £1 6s. 8d.
(16) 1s. 3d.
(17) £6 13s. 4d.

EXERCISE 95.

(1) $66\frac{2}{3}$ %.
(2) 20 %.
(3) 60 %.
(4) 10s.
(5) 10s. 6d.
(6) 40 %.
(7) 8 %.
(8) $33\frac{1}{3}$ %.
(9) £15 10s.

(10) 37 °/$_{\circ}$.   **(11)** 3d.   **(12)** £1.
(13) 19s. 6d.   **(14)** £7 10s.   **(15)** 8s.
(16) £3.   **(17)** £2 10s.   **(18)** £1 10s.
(19) $18\frac{3}{4}$ °/$_{\circ}$.

EXERCISE 96.

(1) £12 13s.   **(2)** £20.   **(3)** £1 8s.
(4) £5 1s. 3d.   **(5)** £2 10s.   **(6)** £42 8s. 3d.
(7) 1s. 9d.   **(8)** 5s. 10d.

EXERCISE 97.

(1) $4\frac{16}{21}$ °/$_{\circ}$ gain.   **(2)** 10s. ; $58\frac{14}{17}$ %.   **(3)** 2s. 6d.
(4) 50 °/$_{\circ}$.   **(5)** 20 °/$_{\circ}$.   **(6)** $16\frac{2}{3}$ °/$_{\circ}$.
(7) $66\frac{2}{3}$ °/$_{\circ}$.   **(8)** 90 °/$_{\circ}$.   **(9)** $127\frac{3}{11}$ °/$_{\circ}$.
(10) £12 7s. ; $23\frac{1}{2}$ °/$_{\circ}$.   **(11)** £15 ; £19 4s. ; 28 °/$_{\circ}$.
(12) 20 °/$_{\circ}$.   **(13)** £3 5s. ; £2 10s. ; $23\frac{1}{2}$ %.
(14) $8\frac{1}{3}$ °/$_{\circ}$; $26\frac{1}{24}$ °/$_{\circ}$.   **(15)** 25 °/$_{\circ}$.
(16) $9\frac{1}{2}$d.   **(17)** $9\frac{13}{18}$ °/$_{\circ}$ gain.

EXERCISE 98.

(1) £40.   **(2)** £90 4s.   **(3)** £14.
(4) £1 11s. 6d.   **(5)** £2 14s. ; 15 %.   **(6)** 524 lbs.
(7) £1 4s.   **(8)** $14\frac{2}{7}$.   **(9)** 3s. 3d. ; $14\frac{54}{89}$ %.
(10) £1 17s. 4d.   **(11)** £56.   **(12)** 25 %.
(13) $38\frac{8}{9}$ %.   **(14)** £38 12s. 6d. ; $42\frac{11}{12}$ %.
(15) £3 3s.   **(16)** £8 10s.   **(17)** £1 2s. 6d.
(18) 112 lbs.   **(19)** £2 18s. 6d.   **(20)** $33\frac{1}{3}$ %.
(21) $5\frac{1}{2}$d. ; $36\frac{4}{11}$ %.   **(22)** $33\frac{1}{3}$ %.
(23) $3\frac{1}{2}$d.   **(24)** £2 2s. 4d.   **(25)** 2s. 6d.
(26) 2s. 10d.   **(27)** £27.   **(28)** 20 %.
(29) $18\frac{8}{19}$ %.   **(30)** 12 st.
(31) £2 10s. ; £2 ; $21\frac{7}{8}$ %.   **(32)** 4 % ; 25s.
(33) 20 %.   **(34)** $33\frac{1}{3}$ %.   **(35)** $39\frac{23}{43}$ %.
(36) £6 13s.   **(37)** $6\frac{2}{3}$ % gain : $6\frac{2}{3}$ % loss.
(38) 3s. 6d.   **(39)** £50.   **(40)** £40 ; £80.
(41) 2 pints.   **(42)** 10d.   **(43)** $1\frac{1}{2}$d.

EXERCISE 99.

(**1**) £126.   (**2**) £36.   (**3**) £165.
(**4**) £281 5s.   (**5**) £1,606 10s.   (**6**) £30 16s.
(**7**) £80.   (**8**) £46 1s. 6½d.   (**9**) £1,537 4s.
(**10**) £25 0s. 6d.   (**11**) £920 11s. 6d.   (**12**) £1,113 19s. 7½d.

EXERCISE 100.

(**1**) £1 15s.   (**2**) £13 12s.   (**3**) £3.
(**4**) £18 15s.   (**5**) £4 18s.   (**6**) £1 8s. 6d.
(**7**) 4s.   (**8**) 7s.   (**9**) £1 4s. 5d.
(**10**) £1 16s.   (**11**) £1 9s. 4½d.   (**12**) £51 10s.
(**13**) £61 12s. 11d.   (**14**) £1 7s. 3d.

EXERCISE 101.

(**1**) £450.   (**2**) £640.   (**3**) £1,125.
(**4**) £840.   (**5**) £563 6s. 8d.   (**6**) £31.
(**7**) 5.   (**8**) 8.   (**9**) 2½.
(**10**) 2¾.   (**11**) 4⅖.   (**12**) 4.
(**13**) 11 yrs.   (**14**) 10 yrs.   (**15**) 11 yrs.
(**16**) 11 yrs.   (**17**) 6 yrs.   (**18**) 6½ yrs.
(**19**) £840.   (**20**) 2⅔ %.   (**21**) 7½ yrs.
(**22**) 15 yrs.   (**23**) 3½ %.   (**24**) £70.
(**25**) 10 yrs.   (**26**) 5 %.   (**27**) £90.
(**28**) 5 %.   (**29**) £365.   (**30**) 10 %.
(**31**) 73 days.   (**32**) 14th Aug.   (**33**) 2½ %.
(**34**) £36 10s.

EXERCISE 102.

(**1**) £70.   (**2**) £150.   (**3**) £226 5s.
(**4**) £280.   (**5**) £750.   (**6**) £90.
(**7**) £18 4s.   (**8**) £46 10s.   (**9**) £420.
(**10**) £1,125.   (**11**) £350.   (**12**) £50.
(**13**) £75.   (**14**) £840.   (**15**) £155.
(**16**) £4 10s.   (**17**) £187 10s.

EXERCISE 103.

(**1**) £46 4s.   (**2**) £45 0s. 6¾d.   (**3**) £46 1s. 6½d.
(**4**) £281 5s.   (**5**) 4 %.   (**6**) 5 %,
(**7**) 3 years.   (**8**) 4 years.   (**9**) £78 15s.
(**10**) £1,260.   (**11**) 11 years.   (**12**) £131 12s.
(**13**) 12 years.   (**14**) £1,034.   (**15**) £6 15s.
(**16**) 5 %.   (**17**) £2,555.   (**18**) 73 days.
(**19**) £1 10s.   (**20**) £2 5s.   (**21**) 4 %.
(**22**) £182 10s.   (**23**) 17th Jan., 1917.   (**24**) 4 %.
(**25**) 26th Sept., 1918.   (**26**) £195.
(**27**) £292 10s.   (**28**) 4th March, 1918.
(**29**) 18th Sept., 1915.   (**30**) £4 16s. 10d.
(**31**) £25.   (**32**) £51 2s.   (**33**) £91 5s.
(**34**) £300.   (**35**) £184 16s.   (**36**) £240.
(**37**) £160.

EXERCISE 104.

(**1**) £865 5s. 7d.   (**2**) £1,061 4s. 2d.   (**3**) £1,311 5s. 5d.
(**4**) £661 18s. 9d.   (**5**) £983 19s. 7d.   (**6**) £998 5s. 3d.
(**7**) £926 2s. 6d.   (**8**) £819 11s. 4d.   (**9**) £873 18s. 8d.
(**10**) £1,001 1s.   (**11**) £88 7s. 9d.   (**12**) £93 14s.
(**13**) £273 19s. 11d.   (**14**) £142 5s. 10d.   (**15**) £105 12s. 6d.
(**16**) £20 5s. 6d.   (**17**) £25 0s. 3d.   (**18**) £56 16s. 3d.
(**19**) £50 14s. 3d.   (**20**) £22 6s. 1d.

EXERCISE 105.

(**1**) 19.   (**2**) 11.   (**3**) 11 stones.
(**4**) 5 mins. 20 secs. ; 11¼ miles per hour.   (**5**) 1·0154.
(**6**) 12·425.   (**7**) 12¾ stones.   (**8**) 40.
(**9**) 24.   (**10**) 870.   (**11**) 24.
(**12**) 19.

EXERCISE 106.

(**1**) 2⅔ hrs.   (**2**) 7½ days.   (**3**) 4 hours.
(**4**) 24 hours.   (**5**) 1 day.   (**6**) 2 days.
(**7**) 1 hour.   (**8**) 12 mins.   (**9**) 8 mins.
(**10**) 1½ mins.   (**11**) 13s. 4d. ; 10s. ; 8s.
(**12**) A 12 hrs. ; B 16 hrs.

EXERCISE 107.

(1) 80 mins.   (2) 4 o'clock ; 40 miles.
(3) 40 mins. ; $13\frac{1}{3}$ and $14\frac{2}{3}$ miles from stations.
(4) 176 yds.   (5) 94 yds.   (6) 86 yds.
(7) $12\frac{3}{11}$ secs.   (8) 45 miles an hour.
(9) $10\frac{10}{11}$ mins. past 2.   (10) $21\frac{9}{11}$ and $54\frac{6}{11}$ mins. past 1.
(11) $43\frac{7}{11}$ mins. past 2.   (12) $16\frac{4}{11}$ mins. and $49\frac{1}{11}$ mins. past 6.
(13) 4 miles per hour.   (14) $6\frac{1}{2}$ miles per hour.

EXERCISE 108.

(1) 348 yds.   (2) 130 yds.   (3) $25\frac{2}{3}$ yds.
(4) $9\frac{11}{21}$ yds.   (5) 24 yds.   (6) 79 yds.
(7) 144.   (8) 40.   (10) 306.
(11) 15.

EXERCISE 109.

(1) 16s. 8d.   (2) 4s.   (3) £8.
(4) 18s.   (5) 8s.   (6) 7d.
(7) £4 13s. 9d.   (8) 5 mins.   (9) 42 hours.
(10) 2·18 Kg.

EXERCISE 110.

(1) 1 to 2.   (2) 7 to 3.   (3) 2 to 3.
(4) 3, 3, 5.   (5) 2, 1, 1.
(6) 4 of 18s. to 1 of 28s.
(7) 5 of 4s. 6d. to 6 of 10s.
(8) 3 at 16s. to 5 at 12s.   (9) 14 tons.
(10) 8 gallons.   (11) 28 lbs.

EXERCISE 111.

(1) £30 8s.   (2) £3 15s., £246 5s.   (3) 11s.
(4) £3 15s.   (5) 6s. 6d.   (6) £4 8s.
(7) £3 12s.   (8) 16s. 10d.   (9) £11 4s.
(10) £868 17s. 6d.   (11) £288 16s.   (12) £271 15s,
(13) 4 per cent.   (14) 3rd Sept.

EXERCISE 112.

(**1**) £450.   (**2**) £1 1s. 8d.   (**3**) £3 6s. 8d.
(**4**) £7 13s.   (**5**) £2 12s. 6d.   (**6**) £6 16s. 6d.
(**7**) T.D. = £9, B.D. = £9 3s. $4\frac{1}{2}$d.   (**8**) 5d.
(**9**) 6 months.   (**10**) 4 months.   (**11**) 4 per cent.
(**12**) £1,510 ; £10 1s. 4d.
(**13**) £1,220 ; 5 per cent.   (**14**) £1,540.
(**15**) 6s.

EXERCISE 113.

(**1**) £598.   (**2**) £1,020.   (**3**) £38.
(**4**) £18 15s.   (**5**) £17 17s. 6d.   (**6**) £997 10s.
(**7**) £285, £13 10s.   (**8**) £10.   (**9**) £400, £20.
(**10**) £871 5s.   (**11**) $4\frac{12}{17}$ per cent.   (**12**) 5 per cent.
(**13**) $4\frac{1}{2}$ per cent.   (**14**) £1,700.   (**15**) £1,216 13s. 9d.
(**16**) £105.   (**17**) 4 per cent. ; 16s. 8d.
(**18**) $5\frac{5}{9}$ per cent.   (**19**) £168.   (**20**) $104\frac{1}{2}$.
(**21**) 98.   (**22**) $3\frac{1}{3}$ per cent.   (**23**) £23 8s. 9d.
(**24**) £1,600.

EXERCISE (a).

(**1**) 66 sq. ins.   (**2**) 3 sq. ft. 64 sq. ins.
(**3**) 1 sq. yd. 5 sq. ft. 24 sq. ins.   (**4**) 116·875 sq. cm.
(**5**) 5·4 sq. m.   (**6**) 8·74 sq. m.
(**7**) 112·5 acres.   (**8**) 30 ac. 2 ro. 12·4 poles.
(**9**) $96\frac{1}{4}$ lbs.

EXERCISE (b).

(**1**) 1 ft. 3 ins.   (**2**) 2 ft.   (**3**) 1 ft. 2 ins.
(**4**) 3·3 cms.   (**5**) 2 ft. 6 ins.   (**6**) 336 yds.

EXERCISE (c).

(**1**) 68 sq. ins.   (**2**) $2\frac{3}{4}$ sq. ft.   (**3**) 3 sq. ft. 32 sq. ins.
(**4**) 57·12 sq. cm.   (**5**) 1·2 sq. m.   (**6**) 141·2208 acres.
(**7**) 3 ft.   (**8**) 2 ft. 10 ins.   (**9**) 340 yds.
(**10**) 2 ft. 4 ins.   (**11**) 1 ft. 3 ins.   (**12**) 140 lbs.

(13) 4·2 m.   (14) 625 sq. ft.   (15) 37 ft.
(16) 4 sq. ft. 64 sq. ins.
(17) 3 ft. 4 ins. ; 1 sq. ft. 36 sq. ins.
(18) 7 ft. 7 ins. ; 10 sq. ft. 30 sq. ins.   (19) 3 ft. 3 ins.
(20) 200 yards ; 1 acre 4,160 sq. yds.   (21) 21·2 ins.
(22) 16 ft.   (23) 7·605 Kg.   (24) 30 sq yds.
(25) £80 17s.   (26) 312 yards.   (27) 5239·3 sq. yds.
(28) 7 sq. ft. 74·5 sq. ins.   (29) 200 yards.
(30) 53 yards.   (31) 182 yards.

EXERCISE (d).

(1) 12 sq. ins.   (2) 84 sq. ins.   (3) 126 sq. ins.
(4) 204 sq. cm.   (5) 468 sq. ft.   (6) 31·5 sq. ins.
(7) 3 sq. ft. 72 sq. ins.
(8) 9 sq. ft. 48 sq. ins.
(9) 21 sq. ft. 48 sq. ins.
(10) 7·56 sq. dm.   (11) 525 sq. cm.   (12) 70·875 sq. m.
(13) 73·5 sq. ft.   (14) 142·0 sq. ins. (15) 160·4 sq. cm.

EXERCISE (e).

(1) 5 sq. ft.   (2) 3½ sq. ft.   (3) 3·6 sq. m.
(4) 91,500 sq. yds. (5) 33·8618 acres.   (6) 3 sq. ft. 93 sq. ins.
(7) 8 sq. ft. 36 sq. ins.   (8) 234 sq. cm.
(9) 30 ac. 2 ro. 20 poles.   (10) 11,377$\frac{7}{9}$ sq. yds.
(11) 6·993 ac.   (12) 1,416 sq. yds. 6 sq. ft.
(13) 106¼ sq. yds.   (14) 250 yds.   (15) 10 chains.
(16) 28 sq. ft. 24 sq. ins. ; 5 ft. 5 ins.
(17) 1,176 sq. ft. ; 35 ft.   (18) 5 ft. 5 ins.
(19) 91 yards.

EXERCISE (f).

(1) 9,150 sq. yds.   (2) 11,025 sq. yds.
(3) 4·97 sq. chains.   (4) 209 sq. chains.
(5) 24,900 sq. m.   (6) 14,050 sq. m.
(7) 35 acres 24 sq. poles.   (8) 6 acres 2 roods 16 sq. poles.

EXERCISE (*g*).

(1) (1) 31·416 ins., (2) 15·708 cm., (3) 175·93 ins. nearly,
(4) 25·1328 ft., (5) 25·1328 ins., (6) 11 ft. nearly.
(2) (1) 5 ft. 3 ins., (2) 4 ft. 1 in., (3) $8\frac{10}{11}$ ins., (4) $1\frac{3}{4}$ in.
(3) 6,336.　　　　　　　**(4)** $12\frac{6}{7}$ miles per hr. (or 12·852).
(5) 3 ft.　　　　**(6)** 140.　　　　**(7)** 7 ft.

EXERCISE (*h*).

(1) (1) 616 sq. ins., (2) 9 sq. ft. 90 sq. ins., (3) $38\frac{1}{2}$ sq. ft.,
(4) 17 sq. yds. 1 sq. ft., (5) 32·18 sq. cm., (6) 55·44 sq. chains
(2) $19\frac{5}{8}$ sq. ft.　　**(3)** 1,155 lbs.　　**(4)** (1) 1 in., (2) 3 ins.
(5) (1) 14 ins., (2) 10 ins.
(6) (1) 132 ins., (2) $157\frac{1}{7}$ ins.
(7) (1) 616 sq. ins., (2) $38\frac{1}{2}$ sq. ft.　　**(8)** 113·04 sq. cm.
(9) $62\frac{6}{7}$ sq. ins.　**(10)** 4 sq. ft. 106 sq. ins.
(11) $135\frac{2}{3}$ lbs.　**(12)** 132 ins.
(13) 3,001 sq. yds. 7 sq. ft.　　**(14)** $127\frac{1}{2}$ lbs.
(15) 5 ins.

EXERCISE (*i*).

(1) (1) 282·6 sq. ins., (2) 21·98 sq. ft., (3) 8,164 sq. cm.
(2) 339·12 sq. ins.　　　　**(3)** 367·38 sq. ins.
(4) (1) 125·6 sq. ins., (2) 1,758·4 sq. ins., (3) 6·28 sq. m.
(5) 219·8 sq. ft.
(6) (1) 113·04 sq. ins., (2) 907·46 sq. cm., (3) 50·24 sq. ft.,
(4) 78·5 sq. m.
(7) 200,960,000 sq. miles.　　**(8)** 150·72 sq. ft.
(9) 200·96 sq. ft.　　　　**(10)** 294·375 sq. ft.

EXERCISE (*j*).

(1) 1·57 c. ft.　　**(2)** 84 c. ins.　　**(3)** 1,680 c. ins.
(4) 1,008 c. ins.　**(5)** 471 c. ins.　**(6)** 113·04 c. ft.
(7) 659·24928 c. cms.
(8) 122 balls and 4·14 c. ins. over.　**(9)** 3 ft.
(10) 141·3 c. ft.　**(11)** 14·13 c. ft.
(12) 5 c. ft. 1,194·48 c. ins.　　**(13)** 289 cub. ins.
(14) 384 cub. ft.　**(15)** $468\frac{3}{4}$ tons.　**(16)** 1,080 c.c.

(**17**) 5 cub. ft. 1,408 cub. ins.   (**18**) 452·16 cub. ft.

(**19**) 841·752 cub. ft.

(**20**) 59 cub. ft. 752·2 cub. ins.   (**21**) 753·6 cub. ft.

(**22**) 36 tons 15 cwts. 105 lbs.

ANSWERS TO THE REVISION EXERCISES.

EXERCISE I.

(**1**) 3,961,822 ; 4 tons 7 cwts. 1 qr. 8 lbs. 2 ozs.

(**2**) 23.   (**3**) £1,333 6s. 8d.

(**4**) (1) £129,649 15s. 7½d. ; (2) £253 18s. 9d.

(**5**) $1\frac{11}{21}$; $\frac{6}{11}$. (**6**) 35.   (**7**) 27,091.

(**8**) 59·049 ; £3 3s. 4½d.   (**9**) ·284375.

(**10**) 1s. 10½d. (**11**) 1 ft. 4 ins.

EXERCISE II.

(**1**) 567 ; 2,039,141.   (**2**) 23 ; 88,200.

(**3**) (1) $1\frac{23}{45}$; (2) $\frac{3}{5}$.   (**4**) £22 15s. ; 37·8125.

(**5**) (1) 34 yds. ; (2) £9 1s. 4d.

(**6**) £3,500,000.   (**7**) $3\frac{1}{3}$ %.

(**8**) Gains $6\frac{2}{3}$ %.   (**9**) A loses by 5 yds.

(**10**) 2 fur. 25 poles, or $577\frac{1}{2}$ yds.

EXERCISE III.

(**1**) 19.   (**2**) (1) $\frac{2}{63}$; (2) $\frac{6}{77}$. (**3**) (1) $\frac{8}{9}$; (2) $\frac{26}{63}$.

(**4**) 6·907.   (**5**) 625.

(**6**) (1) £2 19s. 0¾d. ; (2) 7 ac. 3 ro. 20 pls. ; (3) 20 days 6 hours.

(**7**) 1 hour. (**8**) $3\frac{15}{16}$ years.

(**9**) A pays £5 to C, D pays £10 to B. (**10**) 53 %.

EXERCISE IV.

(**1**) £750 8s. 9d. (**2**) 2 tons 11 cwts. 20 lbs. 10 ozs.

(**3**) 24,420.   (**4**) £4,779.   (**5**) $\frac{1}{12}$.

(**6**) 3.   (**7**) £7 12s. 5¼d.

(**8**) $5 \times 7 \times 11 \times 19$; $3^2 \times 5 \times 11 \times 17$; 55.

(**9**) £29 0s. 3¾d. (**10**) $\frac{4}{5}$, $\frac{1}{16}$, $\frac{13}{90}$, $\frac{1}{270}$; ·148 ; $\frac{4}{27}$.

(**11**) 537 yds. = 2 fur. 17 pls. 3 yds. 1 ft. 6 ins.

EXERCISE V.

(1) £13,788 1s. 11¾d.   (2) 139.

(3) 4,140,115.

(4) $2^3 \times 3 \times 5 \times 13$; $2 \times 3^2 \times 11 \times 13$; $3^2 \times 5^2 \times 13$; 39.

(5) (1) $\frac{1}{2}$; (2) $\frac{112}{169}$.

(6) (1) 18·6̇ ; (2) 7s. 6d.

(7) (1) $\frac{3}{16}$; (2) ·1875.

(8) The first is the better by 1s. in the £6.

(9) 6s. 11d.   (10) 9s. 7½d.   (11) £80.

(12) 60 sq. yds.

EXERCISE VI.

(1) £4 0s. 7½d.   (2) 16 tons.   (3) 108,290 men.

(4) (1) Divide 11,111 by 111, etc., H.C.F. = 1 ; (2) 5,040.

(5) 5 yds.   (6) (1) $2\frac{3}{10}$; (2) $\frac{3}{5}$.   (7) (1) $\frac{13}{3960}$; (2) ·213.

(8) (1) 126·72 ; (2) $\frac{5}{39}$.   (9) £57,699.

(10) £5 11s. 6d.   (11) $4\frac{3}{4}$ %.

EXERCISE VII.

(1) £3,385 1s. 9d.   (2) $\frac{17}{171}$.   (3) 32.

(4) $24\frac{1}{2}$.   (5) 12 ; 144,144.   (6) (a) $\frac{9}{889}$; (b) 1.

(7) $4\frac{3}{8}$ inches.   (8) (a) ·10604 ; (b) 7·9.

(9) (a) 56 mins. 15 secs. ; (b) 1·09375.   (10) 240 ; 30 ; 78.

(11) £6 1s. 10½d.

EXERCISE VIII.

(1) $2^4 \times 3 \times 5^3 \times 7^2 \times 11$; $2^5 \times 3^3 \times 5^2 \times 7$; L.C.M. = $2^5 \times 3^3 \times 5^3 \times 7^2 \times 11$.

(2) 1 min. 22¼ secs.   (3) 5 yds. 2 ft. 4 ins.

(4) £1 15s. 3d.   (5) $6\frac{1}{7}$.

(6) (1) $5\frac{5}{8}$; (2) $\frac{7}{67}$.   (7) (1) $\frac{23}{28}$; (2) $\frac{17}{180}$.

(8) $2\frac{8}{9}$ days.   (9) $4,486\frac{1}{2}$.

(10) £330 16s. 8d,

EXERCISE IX.

(1) $2^3 \times 3^2 \times 5^2$, $5^2 \times 7^2$, $3^3 \times 5 \times 7$; 264,600.
(2) 8 acres.   (3) (1) $\frac{2}{3}$; (2) $\frac{1}{35}$.   (4) 240.
(5) ·875, ·112, ·$\dot{4}$, ·46153$\dot{8}$; $\frac{5}{8}$, $\frac{39}{125}$, $\frac{1}{3}$, $\frac{1}{27}$.
(6) $6\frac{1}{2}$; 1·25.   (7) (1) $\frac{45}{56}$; (2) ·278125.
(8) 9s. 4d.   (9) 25·40005.   (10) £350.

EXERCISE X.

(1) 459,613.   (2) £76 5s. 4d.   (3) £145 10s.
(4) £104 3s. 5d.   (5) £16 4s. 9d.   (6) 154 ft.
(7) (2) $\frac{9}{25}$; $\frac{1237}{2371}$.   (8) (1) $6\frac{7}{8}$; (2) 5000·7.
(9) 1,640.   (10) £7 13s.

EXERCISE XI.

(1) £1,145 8s.   (2) A has £50, B £30, C £20.
(3) 75 ; 1,628,550.   (4) $\frac{23}{30}$.
(5) (1) £9 4s. $4\frac{1}{2}$d. ; (2) ·437.   (6) £9 19s. 6d.
(7) £5 8s. ; 15 %.
(8) 4 ac. 3 ro. 20 po. ; £16 1s. 9d.
(9) 7,875 fr., or £312 10s.

EXERCISE XII.

(1) 68 ; 1s. 10d.   (2) £1 1s. 2d.   (3) 600 rupees.
(4) (1) $1\frac{17}{39}$; (2) $\frac{981}{5267}$.   (6) £9 4s. 1d.
(7) £425 ; £318 15s. ; £106 5s.   (8) 8,970 litres.
(9) 22,400.

EXERCISE XIII.

(1) £4 11s. $1\frac{3}{4}$d.   (2) Gained 1s. 3d.   (3) 1,226.
(5) (2) The second ; 1 lb.
(6) (1) ·97560 ; (2) £4 13s. $1\frac{1}{2}$d.   (7) £474 15s,

EXERCISE XIV.

(1) Prime numbers :—151, 307. 143 = 11 × 13 ; 287 = 7 × 41 ; 323 = 17 × 19 ; 525 = 3 × 5 × 5 × 7

(2) £11,799 8s. (3) (1) 178 ; (2) 9 cwts. 1 lb.

(4) $\frac{1}{7}$. (5) (1) 17,605·03 ; (2) 31·25.

(6) £1 12s. 9d. (7) ·836.

EXERCISE XV.

(1) $3^2 \times 5 \times 11 \times 17 \times 23$; $2^3 \times 3^2 \times 11 \times 17 \times 31$; $3^2 \times 11 \times 17 = 1,683$.

(2) (1) 14 ; (2) 6·45. (3) 294.

(4) 2 months. (5) 19s. 3d. (6) 12·923 ins.

EXERCISE XVI.

(1) £21,132,193 2s. 4d.

(2) (1) 3 dm. 4 cm. 9 mm. ; (2) 23 m. 2 dm. 5 cm. 6 mm.

(3) 9 ozs. (4) 29,694. (5) £148 10s.

(6) (1) ·01d. ; (2) £4 9s. 11d.

EXERCISE XVII.

(1) £130 2s. 5d.

(2) (1) 101, 103, 107, 109, 113 ; (2) 33.

(3) (1) $\frac{61}{168}$; (2) 3·45. (4) £1,785.

(5) (1) 4,840 ; (2) 205·265 sq. chains ; (3) 21.

(6) (1) 96·444 c.m. ; (2) 96,444 Kg.

EXERCISE XVIII.

(1) 220 persons ; £4 10s. over. (2) (1) $\frac{3}{40}$; (2) $\frac{1}{15}$.

(3) (1) $\frac{3}{16}$; (2) 43. (4) £1 10s. 10d.

(5) 253·9969 sq. ins. (6) 23·97 miles.

EXERCISE XIX.

(1) 2 cwts. 1 qr. 9 lbs. 7 ozs. (2) £122 5s. 2¼d.

(3) $3^2 \times 5^3 \times 7, 2 \times 3^3 \times 5^2 \times 7$; $3^2 \times 5^2 \times 7, 2 \times 3^3 \times 5^3 \times 7$.

(4) 226·8 Kg. (5) £106 5s. ; $10\frac{10}{33}$ per cent.

EXERCISE XX.

(1) 75.   **(2)** $\frac{17}{20}$, 196·292.   **(3)** £3 13s. 11d.
(4) 614,400.   **(5)** £26 16s. 3d.

EXERCISE XXI.

(1) 4s. 9d.   **(2)** £77 13s. 9d.
(3) ·70, ·71, ·73, ·75, ·78, ·83, ·86.   **(4)** 32.

EXERCISE XXII.

(1) 1 ft. 4 ins.   **(2)** £1,600 ; £1,813$\frac{1}{3}$; £2,186$\frac{2}{3}$.
(3) 2·00312 c. m. ; 2,003·12 litres.   **(4)** 1s. 5$\frac{3}{4}$d. ; 8$\frac{1}{4}$d.
(5) £4,550.

EXERCISE XXIII.

(1) £50 1s. 11$\frac{1}{4}$d.
(2) $3^3 \times 11 \times 13$; $2^2 \times 3 \times 11^2 \times 13$; $3 \times 5^2 \times 7^2 \times 11$.
     G.C.M. = 33 ; L.C.M. = 208,107,900.
(3) ·995.   **(4)** (1) 1$\frac{1}{2}$; (2) 1·058.
(5) 23 yds. 2 ft. 1 in.   **(6)** 6$\frac{2}{3}$.

EXERCISE XXIV.

(1) (1) $\frac{7}{145}$; (2) ·0483 ; three significant figures.
(2) $\frac{27}{32}$.
(3) A pays £2 15s. 10d. more than B.   **(4)** 181·59.
(5) 250 boys ; 200 girls.
(6) (1) ·625 ; (2) ·001 ; (3) 16 ; a litre.

EXERCISE XXV.

(1) ·725, ·896, ·284, ·644, ·157.
(2) 2 tons 27 lbs. 8 ozs. ; £208 5s. 6d.   **(3)** 8$\frac{3}{4}$d.
(4) ·06882.   **(5)** 15 sq. m. 30 sq. dm.
(6) £174 19s. 10d. ; £167 7s. 8d. ; £159 15s. 6d.
(7) 128 sq. ft. ; 768 cub. ft. ; 28$\frac{4}{9}$ cub. yds.

EXERCISE XXVI.

(1) £7 16s. 8d. ; £6 11s. (2) £24 12s. 5¾d.
(3) ·001 sq. in. ; ·0007. (4) £26⅔ ; £28 ; £13⅓.
(5) (1) $\frac{53}{180}$; (2) $\frac{35}{44}$. (6) 106 ins.

EXERCISE XXVII.

(1) (a) $2^2 \times 3^3 \times 7 \times 11$; $2^7 \times 11 \times 13$; (b) $2^7 \times 3^3 \times 7 \times 11 \times 13$; $2^2 \times 11$.
(2) (a) £2,996 17s. 6d. ; (b) ·996 ; £2,997. (3) $5\frac{25}{31}$.
(4) (a) £96 1s. 10½d. ; (b) 2s. 6¾d.
(5) (a) 7·87 ozs. ; (b) 236 ozs., or 14 lbs. 12 ozs.

EXERCISE XXVIII.

(1) (a) 6·45 sq. cm. ; (b) 16·39 c.c.
(2) (a) £27 0s. 4½d. ; (b) £5,655 15s. 1½d. (3) 3s. 2d.
(4) £20 3s. 1½d. (5) 22,781¼ ozs.

EXERCISE XXIX.

(1) (i) ·567 litre ; (ii) 57·330 pints.
(2) (a) £7,980 19s. 6d. ; (b) £1 16s. (3) $1\frac{61}{115}$ yards.
(4) £9 15s. (5) (a) $45\frac{71}{72}$ cub. ft. ; (b) 19 ins.

Train travels 30 miles an hour & passes
a platform 90 yds long in 12 secs
Find length of train

Train goes 30 miles in 1 hour

Train goes 1+90 yds in 12 sec

Train goes $\dfrac{30 \times 1760}{\underset{2}{60} \times 60} \times \dfrac{12}{1}$

176 yds in 12 secs

∴ Length of train = 86 yds

$$P = \frac{100 \times A}{100 + (N \times R)}$$

$$= \frac{100 \times 180}{100 + (10 \times 2)}$$

$$= \frac{18000}{100 + 20}$$

$$= \frac{18000}{120}$$

$$= £150$$

<u>Mon.</u> Arithmetic.

<u>Tue.</u> English.

~~L.C.P.~~
<u>Wed.</u> Maths, ~~English~~, ~~Gym~~, ~~History~~, <u>Science</u> L.C.P.
      ~~Commercial~~, ~~Miss Jaffrey~~, Miss Johns L.C.P.

          L.C.P.   L. CP   L.C.P.
<u>Thu</u>. Maths, Gym, Maths, Latin, ~~English~~
      L.C.P.
   French.

<u>Fri</u>.   <u>History</u>   Sc B,   Sc B

            L.C.P.   L.C.P
<u>Tue</u> ~~Maths~~ Latin ~~Art~~ ~~Comm~~ Latin
      ~~French~~

212

SHAKESPEARE
CRITICISM
A SELECTION
1623–1840

Oxford University Press, Amen House, London E.C.4

GLASGOW NEW YORK TORONTO MELBOURNE WELLINGTON
BOMBAY CALCUTTA MADRAS KARACHI KUALA LUMPUR
CAPE TOWN IBADAN NAIROBI ACCRA

SHAKESPEARE
CRITICISM

A SELECTION
1623-1840

With an Introduction
by
D. NICHOL SMITH

LONDON
OXFORD UNIVERSITY PRESS

This volume of Shakespeare Criticism *was first published in* The World's Classics *in* 1916 *and reprinted in* 1923, 1926, 1930, 1934, 1936, 1939, 1942, *and* 1944. *Reset in* 1946, *reprinted in* 1949, 1953, 1954, *and* 1958.

INTRODUCTION

THERE have been many collections of criticisms on Shakespeare. They begin with the verses which were contributed by friends, seven years after his death, to the first complete volume of his plays, the 'First Folio' of 1623; and they vary in character with the times in which they were published. At the end of the century Sir Thomas Pope Blount attempted to represent contemporary opinion on Shakespeare in his *De Re Poetica, or Remarks upon Poetry* (1694). In the eighteenth century, when the text of the plays came to be examined and explained, the prefaces or introductory essays of the different editors were sometimes printed in a body, as in the edition of Samuel Johnson; and the first critical anthology was produced by David Garrick under the title 'Testimonies to the Genius and Merits of Shakespeare'—a short selection of notable statements which was added to his Ode for the Stratford celebration in 1769. In the nineteenth century the continued growth of scholarly and methodical study gave us in such a book as Ingleby's *Shakespeare's Centurie of Prayse* the kind of compilation that aims at being an exhaustive record of allusions.

This little volume has thus many predecessors. It does not, however, as far as the editor is aware, follow directly in the tracks of any of them. While it claims to give the greatest pieces of Shakespeare criticism from his death till the middle of the nineteenth century, it also tries to represent the general movement in critical opinion and method. Occasionally an extract has been included mainly because the views it expresses were novel or important at the time of publication, or because it helps to place the work of subsequent critics in truer perspective.

No good writer, as Landor says, was ever long neglected; no great man overlooked by men equally great.
There is abundant proof of the esteem in which Shakespeare was held in his own day. He was recognized as the
greatest of them all. His writings were confessed to be

such

As neither *Man*, nor *Muse*, can praise too much;

and this was 'all men's suffrage'. His contemporaries
had never any doubt of his greatness. But, as contemporaries always do, they knew wherein he faulted. He
was not always a careful writer; sometimes his unap-
proachable facility carried him into error, or gave too
free play to his wit. Ben Jonson, who lacked this facility,
spoke of it with something of the consolation that comes
from superior scholarship; just as the sense of contrast
with Shakespeare also made him pride himself on the
originality and construction of his plots. But no nobler
tribute will ever be paid to a friend than the verses of
this warm-hearted burly rival 'to the memory of my
beloved, the Author, Mr. William Shakespeare, and
what he hath left us'. Shakespeare is admitted to have
surpassed the Greek and Latin dramatists, Jonson's own
masters; he was not of an age, but for all time; and he
had excelled not merely because he was the poet of
nature, but by reason of his art. In private conversation
Jonson is known to have said that Shakespeare 'wanted
art', meaning thereby that he did not always take sufficient care; and Jonson has some responsibility for the
statement to be found again and again, in varied words,
in later critics, that there was more art in his work and
more nature in Shakespeare's. It is therefore important
to note that in his most deliberate testimony to the
genius of Shakespeare he acknowledged him to have
been master of an art which no one else could reach.

With all his faults Shakespeare was to Jonson the greatest
of dramatists. This was the contemporary view, and it
was never seriously challenged throughout the seventeenth century.[1] Though the claims of Jonson were
occasionally urged by his 'sons', though after the Restoration Fletcher was for some time more frequently
acted, and though the vagaries of theatrical taste, then
as now, called for alterations or adaptations, Shakespeare
did not lose his hold on the national pride and affection.

The extracts in this volume from the seventeenth century may appear to occupy comparatively little space.
But the mere bulk of criticism on any author is never
to be taken as the measure of his fame. It is one thing
to admire an author; it is quite another thing to publish
the reasons of that admiration. In the seventeenth century

---

[1] In a poem prefixed to the edition of Shakespeare's Poems
published in 1640, Leonard Digges bore remarkable testimony
to the popularity of Shakespeare's plays, especially in comparison with the plays of Jonson:

> So have I seene, when Cesar would appeare,
> And on the Stage at halfe-sword parley were
> *Brutus* and *Cassius*: oh how the Audience
> Were ravish'd, with what wonder they went thence,
> When some new day they would not brooke a line
> Of tedious (though well laboured) *Catiline*;
> *Sejanus* too was irkesome, they priz'de more
> Honest *Iago*, or the jealous Moore.
> And though the Fox and subtill Alchimist,
> Long intermitted, could not quite be mist,
> Though these have sham'd all the Ancients, and might raise
> Their Authours merit with a crowne of Bayes,
> Yet these sometimes, even at a friends desire
> Acted, have scarce defrai'd the Seacoale fire
> And doore-keepers: when let but *Falstaffe* come,
> *Hall*, *Poines*, the rest, you scarce shall have a roome,
> All is so pester'd: let but *Beatrice*
> And *Benedicke* be seene, loe in a trice
> The Cockpit, Galleries, Boxes, all are full
> To heare *Malvoglio*, that crosse garter'd Gull.

criticism had not yet become an organized industry. There were no editions to be furnished with critical prefaces; the periodicals did not print literary essays; and many years had to pass before the public discovered a taste for lectures.

The criticism of Shakespeare which deliberately discusses principles and determines merits begins with Dryden. A dramatist himself, with a happy faculty of meeting and guiding the public taste, he was compelled to review the many problems of dramatic art that had been forced into prominence since Shakespeare's death. The Elizabethans, by the mere lapse of half a century, had come to appear somewhat antiquated; and pride in the great national tradition could not conceal its exhaustion. The old life had gone from it at the very time when the French drama, following other methods, was attaining its highest perfection. There were scholars who, like Milton in *Samson Agonistes,* favoured neither English nor French methods, but held that Aeschylus, Sophocles, and Euripides were 'the best rule to all who endeavour to write tragedy'. Yet other methods were found in the Spanish plays, which were well known and even occasionally acted. The very stage had altered, with the introduction of movable scenery and the substitution of women for the Elizabethan boy actors. The whole theory of the drama demanded scrutiny by dramatist and critic alike; and Shakespeare had to be tested by what had been achieved under different conditions elsewhere. If in other countries plays were written on principles which theoretically appeared more reasonable, were the English to persist in sheltering their extravagances under Shakespeare's name? Or, while continuing to boast of him as a great irregular genius, should they adopt the simpler and severer style of the classical and the French drama? It was not a new problem, and it was not a question of submitting to foreign fashion: Ben Jonson had championed stricter methods, and was he not a safer guide than a genius who had triumphed in spite of his irregularities?

In general Shakespeare was considered to have reached his goal by dangerous routes which he need not have taken. But the construction of his plays was not the only point at issue. The language of the Elizabethans was old-fashioned, and the men of the Restoration were too ready to discover in it impropriety or meanness of expression. They also made the common mistake of assuming that the changes in the modes of wit were refinements. 'The wit of the last age', said Dryden, 'was yet more incorrect than their language.' Of Shakespeare, who had not neglected the taste of his audience and was always a rapid writer, he had to say that 'he is many times flat, insipid; his comic wit degenerating into clenches, his serious swelling into bombast'.

Censures such as these must be viewed in relation to Dryden's enthusiastic praise of Shakespeare's genius. Nor is it to be thought that a critic like Thomas Rymer represented a large body of opinion. The whole spirit of his attack on Shakespeare shows that he was leading a forlorn hope. All his life he was entirely out of sympathy with the modern drama, in France as well as in England. His *Short View of Tragedy* (1693) repeated with emphasis the views which he had expressed in *The Tragedies of the last Age Consider'd and Examin'd by the Practice of the Ancients, and by the Common sense of all Ages* (1678). He held that the English should have built on the same foundation as Sophocles and Euripides, or after their model, and that the chorus is the most necessary part of tragedy. He was a learned man, clever, and boisterously witty, but when he attacked *Othello* with ridicule he knew that it was his last weapon. He called it the 'Tragedy of the Handkerchief', he found in it the moral that wives should look well to their linen, and he summed up his censures thus: 'There is in this Play, some burlesk, some humour, and ramble of Comical Wit, some shew, and some Mimickry to divert the spectators: but the tragical part is plainly none other than a Bloody Farce, without salt or savour.' This is not the language of a man who thought he could win his cause. His own tragedy, *Edgar*, had shown that to be a successful dramatist it was not sufficient to be a learned critic. Dryden expressed the general verdict when he said in the Prologue to *Love Triumphant* that

> To Shakespear's Critic he bequeaths the Curse,
> To find his faults, and yet himself make worse;
> A precious Reader in Poetic Schools,
> Who by his own Examples damns his Rules.

There was much talk about the 'rules' at this time, and for many years to come; but the importance attached to them can easily be overstated. The greater critics never laid stress on the rules: neglect of text-book methods can always be justified by success. 'Better a mechanic rule were stretched or broken than a great beauty were omitted,' said Dryden. 'There is more beauty', said Addison, 'in the works of a great genius who is ignorant of the rules of art, than in those of a little genius who knows and observes them.' Pope said much the same in his *Essay on Criticism*, and said it at length in the Preface to his edition of Shakespeare.

Dryden was so fully representative of his age that the public debate on the methods of the drama is adequately reflected in the debate in his own mind. At times he conformed to 'the exactest rules by which a play is wrought'; at others, he ignored them. His apparent inconsistencies are only proof of a live intelligence open to new impressions, and ready for new ventures. Amid all his doubts, he was guided and controlled by tastes and sympathies that were proudly English. Some of his statements, if taken out of their setting, may suggest scant respect for the Elizabethans. In self-defence he enlarged on the failings of the 'last age'; and he never hesitated to speak of Shakespeare's faults. But he also said that Shakespeare's critics

> in the attempt are lost,
> When most they rail, know then they envy most.

His belief in the unmatched greatness of Shakespeare was stated deliberately, once and for all, in the glowing tribute in the early *Essay of Dramatic Poesy*.

This 'model of encomiastic criticism', this 'epitome of excellence', as Samuel Johnson called it, introduced the clearly marked type of appreciation which prevailed till the third quarter of the eighteenth century and is excellently represented by the Preface of Pope. Progress of far-reaching importance was made in other directions. This period gave us, in the Introduction to Rowe's edition, the first biography of Shakespeare; it discussed the extent of his learning and the sources of his plots, notably in Whalley's *Enquiry into the Learning of Shakespeare* (1748), Farmer's *Essay on the Learning of Shakespeare* (1767), and Charlotte Lennox's *Shakespear Illustrated* (1753); above all, it began the examination of the texts of the plays and the explanation of their difficulties. But in the more general criticism that deals with merits and characteristics—the kind of criticism that is the matter of this volume—there is one prevailing manner during the hundred years from Dryden's Essay (1668) to Johnson's Preface (1765).

Johnson set himself to review the common topics of Shakespeare criticism, and to give his judgement on the points at issue. There is little new matter in his Preface, except where he deals with his work as an editor. Its importance lies mainly in its being a conclusive summing up, by a strong, wise, and impartial mind, of a prolonged discussion. The question of Shakespeare's irregularities, though it had been losing interest, still required to be settled. They were felt to be right, and argued to be wrong. Learned opinion was as a whole against them, and it had an ally in timidity. Johnson's own *Irene* was regular to dullness, but in *The Rambler* he showed that he recognized the weight of the arguments on either side. He now set himself to reason out the whole question, and settled it for good. Henceforth no writer of any standing expressed his doubts on Shakespeare's irregularities, or had any doubts to express; and when a change of fashion in criticism had turned these very irregularities into a stock theme of praise, the arguments which Johnson had advanced were used by a generation which did him too little justice. It misunderstood the impartiality with which he spoke of Shakespeare's faults. 'We must confess the faults of our favourite', he explained in a letter to Charles Burney, 'to gain credit to our praise of his excellencies.' The passage on the carelessnesses and inequalities, the quibbles and idle conceits, is remarkably searching, and may here and there be too strongly worded. Perhaps it errs through the fear of betraying what he called 'superstitious veneration'. It gives the impression that Johnson, in his scrupulous regard for truth, had tried to say the very worst that a judicious admirer could ever be forced to admit. No one who understands it, however unwelcome he may find it, will allow it to cast doubt on Johnson's admiration. Such faults, says Johnson, were 'sufficient to obscure and overwhelm any other merit'. But they did not affect the real greatness of Shakespeare.

The same reasoned impartiality which led him to describe the faults also compelled him to pronounce as high a eulogy as has ever been written on this side idolatry: 'This therefore is the praise of Shakespeare, that his drama is the mirror of life; that he who has mazed his imagination, in following the phantoms which other writers raise up before him, may here be cured of his delirious ecstasies by reading human sentiments in human language; by scenes from which a hermit may estimate the transactions of the world, and a confessor predict the progress of the passions.' Or again: 'The stream of time, which is continually washing the dissoluble fabrics of other poets, passes without injury by the adamant of Shakespeare.'

Johnson is the last great representative of what may be called the judicial manner. He is the true successor of Dryden, who looked upon Shakespeare as a brother dramatist, certainly of surpassing genius, but not therefore beyond the pale of censure. Johnson never ran any risk of forgetting that Shakespeare was an author who had to write for his living. We may apply to him a sentence which he himself wrote about Shakespeare: 'Among his other excellencies it ought to be remarked that his *Heroes are Men.*' To Johnson, Shakespeare was always a man among men. The later critics sometimes seem to treat him as if he belonged to a different order of beings.

Nothing could have been better than Johnson's Preface as a balanced estimate. The new triumphs were to be won in other ways. There had been many signs of the coming change. Joseph Warton had contributed to *The Adventurer* in 1753-4 five papers on *The Tempest* and *King Lear*, in one of which he had said that 'general criticism is on all subjects useless and unentertaining, but is more than commonly absurd with respect to

Shakespeare, who must be accompanied step by step, and scene by scene, in his gradual developments of characters and passions, and whose finer features must be singly pointed out, if we would do complete justice to his genuine beauties'; and he carried these views into practice in his analysis of the two plays, not with remarkable ability, it must be admitted, but with sufficient competence to make his work historically important. Attention came to be centred more and more on the characters. Henry Home (better known as Lord Kames) pointed out in his *Elements of Criticism* that Shakespeare's method was not descriptive, as was Corneille's and the later dramatists', but directly imitative or representative, the sentiments being 'the legitimate offspring of passion, and therefore in themselves expressive of personality'. Lyttelton, in his *Dialogues of the Dead*, said that Shakespeare's knowledge of the passions, the humours, and the sentiments of mankind was so perfect, and so perfectly expressed, that 'if human nature were destroyed, and no monument were left of it except his works, other beings might know what man was from those writings'. The periodical essays show that a public which was more familiar than we are now with Shakespeare's characters as seen on the stage was also interested in discussing them. The change which becomes marked after Johnson's Preface was far from being a revolution. It was in fact only a natural and even an unavoidable sequel. The older criticism had accepted Shakespeare as the 'mirror of life', and the newer criticism now proceeded to supply the exposition. Johnson himself had heralded it in the notes to the various plays, where he introduced descriptive comments on the characters, such as those on Falstaff and Polonius. Pope had said that Shakespeare's characters are 'so much nature herself that 'tis a sort of injury to call them by so distant a name as copies of her'. The time had come when a couplet in his *Essay on Criticism* that has often been quoted against him could be applied with literal truth to the student of Shakespeare:

> But when t' examine every part he came,
> Nature and *Shakespeare* were, he found, the same.

Henceforth to study the one was to study the other.

It is further proof of the steady and full preparation for the new criticism that three writers should have been engaged independently about the same time on essays which, taken together, mark its real beginning. Thomas Whately, an active politician, William Richardson, a young Professor of Latin in the University of Glasgow, and Maurice Morgann, a government official with a special knowledge of American affairs, all wrote on Shakespeare by way of relaxation from their main duties, and all could claim for their work the credit of novelty. Whately expressly stated that 'the distinction and preservation of *character*' was 'a subject for criticism more worthy of attention than the common topics of discussion', and produced the first elaborate analysis of two of Shakespeare's characters in his comparison of Macbeth and Richard III. He intended to have dealt with others in the same manner, but his scheme was cut short by his death in 1772. What he left had been written before 1770, but was not published till 1785, under the title *Remarks on some of the Characters of Shakespeare*. Richardson was the first of the three writers to get into print, his *Philosophical Analysis and Illustration of some of Shakespeare's Remarkable Characters* appearing in 1774. His work had an ethical aim; he had indulged in what he described as an exercise no less adapted to improve the heart, than to inform the understanding. 'My intention', he says, 'is to make poetry subservient to philosophy, and to employ it in tracing the principles of human conduct.' The main interest of this work is that it took Shakespeare's characters as examples for moral disquisitions.[1] Morgann's much greater *Essay on the Dramatic Character of Sir John Falstaff* was written about the same time, though it was not published till 1777. He knew neither Richardson nor Whately, and believed that in considering Shakespeare in detail he was undertaking 'a task hitherto unattempted'. The book grew under his hands till it became more than its title promised—not merely a vindication of Falstaff's courage, but an enthusiastic exposition of the genius of Shakespeare as revealed in the minute examination of a single character. No title could have been more misleading in its modesty. 'Falstaff is the word only, Shakespeare is the theme.' The passage where he breaks away exultantly from his main subject to write in sheer delight of Shakespeare's essential difference from all other writers and his imperishable gifts, is one of the great things in the whole range of English criticism. There is nothing greater—perhaps nothing so great—in Coleridge or Hazlitt. Forty years were to pass before they gave us the new criticism in all its strength, and they, to their loss, did not know Morgann. In the interval the best work on Shakespeare was done by the scholars, such as Steevens and Malone, who contributed to the elucidation of the text so great a wealth of linguistic, antiquarian, and bibliographical knowledge that later

[1] A substantial volume entitled *The Morality of Shakespeare's Drama Illustrated* was brought out by Elizabeth Griffith in 1775 (the dedication is dated November 1, 1774). It must have been in preparation at the same time as Richardson's *Philosophical Analysis*, of which it is wholly independent, though its purpose is similar. It expounds Johnson's statement (*infra*, p. 88) that from Shakespeare's writings 'a system of social duty may be selected'.

research has done little more than supplement it; too frequently it has been used without due acknowledgement.

When Hazlitt published his *Characters of Shakespear's Plays* in 1817 he spoke of it in his Preface as if it were a new venture in criticism, and the novelty of its manner was remarked on by Jeffrey in an article in *The Edinburgh Review*. It was the first *book* in which the criticism of the nineteenth century spoke clearly and confidently. But Coleridge had already been lecturing on Shakespeare for several years; and Lamb had written his magazine article 'On the Tragedies of Shakespeare'. When Hazlitt brought out his book the new criticism was thus in all its vigour. Unfortunately little is preserved of Coleridge's early lectures. His most important course was not delivered till 1818.[1]

---

[1] See the footnote on p. 226. Coleridge regarded himself as the leader of the new critics, and resented the suggestion that he was in any way indebted to the Germans. Wordsworth had said in 1815 ('Essay Supplementary to Preface') that 'the Germans only, of foreign nations, are approaching towards a knowledge and feeling of what he (Shakespeare) is. In some respects they have acquired a superiority over the fellow countrymen of the Poet. . . . How long may it be before . . . it becomes universally acknowledged that the judgment of Shakespeare in the selection of his materials, and in the manner in which he has made them, heterogeneous as they often are, constitute a unity of their own, and contribute all to one great end, is not less admirable than his imagination, his invention, and his intuitive knowledge of human nature?' Hazlitt also had neglected Coleridge's lectures when he said in 1817 that 'some little jealousy of the character of the national understanding was not without its share in producing' his *Characters of Shakespear's Plays*, 'for we were piqued that it should be reserved for a foreign critic to give reasons for the faith which we English have in Shakespear'. Coleridge was moved to make an indignant protest. In a private letter written in 1819 he pointed out that, in a course of lectures which he assigned to 1802, he had argued 'that Shakespeare's judgment was, if possible, still more

These critics were possessed with all the joy of a discovery. They thought that they understood Shakespeare as he had never been understood before. They liked to show how they differed from the older critics; in their pride in their new power they did not feel their relationship. Like Coriolanus, they would 'stand as if a man were author of himself and knew no other kin'.

The differences are obvious at a glance. There is the greater freedom of movement, the clearer signs of real pleasure in writing or speaking about Shakespeare. Enthusiasm is not checked by the desire to strike a just balance; there is no longer any fear of being misled by 'superstitious veneration'. These critics did not hold with Johnson that it was necessary to confess faults in order to gain credit to their praise of excellences. Their purpose was to explain these excellences. They did not pass judgement; they gave an interpretation. They held, in Hazlitt's words, that 'a genuine criticism should reflect the colours, the light and shade, the soul and body of a work'. The great question they set themselves to

wonderful than his genius, or rather, that the contradistinction itself between judgment and genius rested on an utterly false theory'; and he also expressed the regret that the idea should have been produced by other English writers [e.g. Wordsworth] as if it were their own, or that the merit of it should be given to 'a foreign writer [i.e. A. W. Schlegel] whose lectures were not given orally till two years after mine'. He believed that there was not 'one single principle in Schlegel's work (which is not an admitted drawback from its merits), that was not established and applied in detail by me'. This letter was first printed in *The Canterbury Magazine* for September 1834, pp. 125–6; cf. *Biographia Epistolaris*, ed. A. Turnbull, vol. ii, pp. 168–9. The priority of Coleridge or Schlegel is a matter of little importance. The main fact is that no German influence is necessary to account for the character of English criticism on Shakespeare at the beginning of the nineteenth century. The criticism of Coleridge and Hazlitt is a natural and direct development from earlier English criticism.

answer was not how far has Shakespeare succeeded, but
how is Shakespeare to be understood. The plays are
regarded as embodiments of real life; the characters are
treated as fellow beings of whom the plays preserve our
only record. There is none of the aloofness which must
accompany the judicial attitude of watching the craftsman at his work and noting the varying results. Johnson's main interest was in Shakespeare the man; the
business of nineteenth-century critics was with the world
of his creation. When they studied the ordered development of his art and demonstrated its unity, their attitude
was the philosopher's in describing the phases of a great
phenomenon in nature. 'The Englishman', said Coleridge, 'who without reverence, a proud and affectionate
reverence, can utter the name of William Shakespeare,
stands disqualified for the office of critic.' 'It may be
said of Shakespeare', said Hazlitt, 'that "those who are
not for him are against him". An overstrained enthusiasm is more pardonable with respect to Shakespeare
than the want of it.'

Taken as a whole the criticism of Shakespeare in the
first half of the nineteenth century is our greatest, alike
in range and insight and in stimulus. As an aid to the
appreciation of the plays, it has no equal. It opens new
vistas and communicates a sense of exaltation and wonder. It is nothing if not reverential and intuitively sympathetic. But the imaginative freedom which it derives
from contact with Shakespeare's mind sometimes renders it an unsafe guide. A critic who sets out to give an
interpretation of a work of art is always beset by the
danger of reading himself into it, and the danger is the
greater if he is himself an artist—a poet or a brilliant
essayist. He may begin to create a new work on the
basis of the original. The impression derived from a
passage may be expounded out of proportion to the

impression derived from the play as a whole. A wealth of subtle meaning may be extracted from what cooler judgements will not regard as specially significant, sometimes even from a rhyming tag. Or if the critic have an ethical bias, he may regard the play as a statement of a moral doctrine, and find in it the illustration of his own prepossessions. Those who aim at giving an interpretation intend to subject themselves to their author; but the results show that there is no kind of criticism in which the personality of the critic is allowed freer scope.

It was Maurice Morgann who first said that Shakespeare's characters may be considered 'rather as historic than dramatic beings'. We are more familiar with some of them than with most of our everyday acquaintances, and it is the easiest illusion to think of them as having an existence in real life. The criticism of the nineteenth century as a whole owes some of its finest qualities to its habit of forgetting that they are the creatures of art. But it has also been led by the same cause into much needless discussion. Shakespeare expects us to think of his characters as they are shown within the limits of the plays. We gain nothing by asking what was Hamlet's history before we first meet him; and when we trouble ourselves with the problem of his exact age we forget that, if the matter were of any importance, we should not have been left in doubt. Such inquiries are irrelevant to the impression derived from the drama, and in the drama, as Morgann said, 'the impression is the fact'. It is a supreme testimony to Shakespeare that the life which he gave to his characters should be treated as if it carried them beyond the dramatic conditions in which alone they have their existence. But it is a testimony which may not give due recognition to the genius of the craftsman. In his own eyes Shakespeare was a craftsman; and so he was to his contemporaries and the earlier critics.

Carlyle's paean is a fitting climax to the passages in this volume. Subsequent criticism to the end of the century shows no conspicuous change in attitude and purpose. The three books which stand out prominently are Edward Dowden's *Shakspere, His Mind and Art* (1874); Swinburne's *Study of Shakespeare* (1880); and A. C. Bradley's *Shakespearean Tragedy*. Though not published till 1904, Mr. Bradley's penetrative analysis of the four chief tragedies is the last great representative of nineteenth-century criticism, and nothing better in its kind need be expected. It continues the traditions inaugurated by Whately and Morgann, and established by Coleridge and Hazlitt. A clear break with these traditions is to be found already in the criticism of the twentieth century.

1916

CONTENTS

CONTENTS

JOHN HEMINGE AND HENRY CONDELL

PREFACE TO THE FIRST COLLECTION OF SHAKESPEARE'S PLAYS

To the great Variety of Readers

FROM the most able, to him that can but spell: There you are number'd. We had rather you were weighd. Especially, when the fate of all Bookes depends vpon your capacities: and not of your heads alone, but of your purses. Well! It is now publique, & you wil stand for your priuiledges wee know: to read, and censure. Do so, but buy it first. That doth best commend a Booke, the Stationer saies. Then, how odde soeuer your braines be, or your wisedomes, make your licence the same, and spare not. Iudge your sixe-pen'orth, your shillings worth, your fiue shillings worth at a time, or higher, so you rise to the iust rates, and welcome. But, what euer you do, Buy. Censure will not driue a Trade, or make the Iacke go. And though you be a Magistrate of wit, and sit on the Stage at *Black-Friers*, or the *Cock-pit*, to arraigne Playes dailie, know, these Playes haue had their triall alreadie, and stood out all Appeales; and do now come forth quitted rather by a Decree of Court, then any purchas'd Letters of commendation.

It had bene a thing, we confesse, worthie to haue bene wished, that the Author himselfe had liu'd to haue set forth, and ouerseen his owne writings; But since it hath bin ordain'd otherwise, and he by death departed from that right, we pray you do not envie his Friends, the office of their care, and paine, to haue collected & publish'd them; and so to haue publish'd them, as where

B

(before) you were abus'd with diuerse stolne, and sur-
reptitious copies, maimed, and deformed by the frauds
and stealthes of iniurious impostors, that expos'd them:
euen those, are now offer'd to your view cur'd, and perfect of their limbes; and all the rest, absolute in their
numbers, as he conceiued them. Who, as he was a happie
imitator of Nature, was a most gentle expresser of it.
His mind and hand went together: And what he
thought, he vttered with that easinesse, that wee haue
scarse receiued from him a blot in his papers. But it is
not our prouince, who onely gather his works, and giue
them you, to praise him. It is yours that reade him. And
there we hope, to your diuers capacities, you will finde
enough, both to draw, and hold you: for his wit can no
more lie hid, then it could be lost. Reade him, therefore;
and againe, and againe: And if then you doe not like
him, surely you are in some manifest danger, not to
vnderstand him. And so we leaue you to other of his
Friends, whom if you need, can bee your guides: if you
neede them not, you can leade your selues, and others.
And such Readers we wish him.

Iohn Heminge
Henrie Condell

Prefixed to the First Folio, 1623.

BEN JONSON

To the memory of my beloued,
The AVTHOR
Mr. William Shakespeare:
And
what he hath left vs.

To draw no enuy (*Shakespeare*) on thy name,
  Am I thus ample to thy Booke, and Fame:
While I confesse thy writings to be such,
  As neither *Man*, nor *Muse*, can praise too much.
'Tis true, and all mens suffrage. But these wayes
  Were not the paths I meant vnto thy praise:
For seeliest Ignorance on these may light,
  Which, when it sounds at best, but eccho's right;
Or blinde Affection, which doth ne're aduance
  The truth, but gropes, and vrgeth all by chance;
Or crafty Malice, might pretend this praise,
  And thinke to ruine, where it seem'd to raise.
These are, as some infamous Baud, or Whore,
  Should praise a Matron. What could hurt her more?
But thou art proofe against them, and indeed
  Aboue th' ill fortune of them, or the need.
I, therefore will begin. Soule of the Age!
  The applause! delight! the wonder of our Stage!
My *Shakespeare*, rise; I will not lodge thee by
  Chaucer, or *Spenser*, or bid *Beaumont* lye
A little further, to make thee a roome:
  Thou art a Moniment, without a tombe.
And art aliue still, while thy Booke doth liue,
  And we haue wits to read, and praise to giue.
That I not mixe thee so, my braine excuses;
  I meane with great, but disproportion'd *Muses*:

For, if I thought my iudgement were of yeeres,
   I should commit thee surely with thy peeres,
And tell, how farre thou didst our *Lily* out-shine,
   Or sporting *Kid*, or *Marlowes* mighty line.
And though thou hadst small *Latine*, and less
      Greeke,
   From thence to honour thee, I would not seeke
For names; but call forth thund'ring *Æschilus*,
   Euripides, and *Sophocles* to vs,
Paccuuius, *Accius*, him of *Cordoua* dead,
   To life againe, to heare thy Buskin tread,
And shake a Stage: Or, when thy Sockes were on,
   Leaue thee alone, for the comparison
Of all, that insolent *Greece*, or haughtie *Rome*
   Sent forth, or since did from their ashes come.
Triúmph, my *Britaine*, thou hast one to showe,
   To whom all Scenes of *Europe* homage owe.
He was not of an age, but for all time!
   And all the *Muses* still were in their prime,
When like *Apollo* he came forth to warme
   Our eares, or like a *Mercury* to charme!
Nature her selfe was proud of his designes,
   And ioy'd to weare the dressing of his lines!
Which were so richly spun, and wouen so fit,
   As, since, she will vouchsafe no other Wit.
The merry *Greeke*, tart *Aristophanes*,
   Neat *Terence*, witty *Plautus*, now not please;
But antiquated, and deserted lye
   As they were not of Natures family.
Yet must I not giue Nature all: Thy Art,
   My gentle *Shakespeare*, must enioy a part.
For though the *Poets* matter, Nature be,
   His Art doth giue the fashion. And, that he,
Who casts to write a liuing line, must sweat,
   (Such as thine are) and strike the second heat

Vpon the *Muses* anuile: turne the same,
 (And himselfe with it) that he thinkes to frame;
Or for the lawrell, he may gaine a scorne,
 For a good *Poet's* made, as well as borne.
And such wert thou. Looke how the fathers face
 Liues in his issue, euen so, the race
Of *Shakespeares* minde, and manners brightly shines
 In his well torned, and true-filed lines:
In each of which, he seemes to shake a Lance,
 As brandish't at the eyes of Ignorance.
Sweet Swan of *Auon!* what a sight it were
 To see thee in our waters yet appeare,
And make those flights vpon the bankes of *Thames*,
 That so did take *Eliza*, and our *Iames!*
But stay, I see thee in the *Hemisphere*
 Aduanc'd, and made a Constellation there!
Shine forth, thou Starre of *Poets*, and with rage,
 Or influence, chide, or cheere the drooping Stage;
Which, since thy flight from hence, hath mourn'd like
 night,
 And despaires day, but for thy Volumes light.

BEN: IONSON

Prefixed to the First Folio, 1623.

De Shakespeare nostrati

I remember, the Players have often mentioned it as an honour to *Shakespeare*, that in his writing, (whatsoever he penn'd) hee never blotted out line. My answer hath beene, would he had blotted a thousand. Which they thought a malevolent speech. I had not told posterity this, but for their ignorance, who choose that circumstance to commend their friend by, wherein he most faulted. And to justifie mine owne candor, (for I lov'd the man, and doe honour his memory (on this side Idolatry)

as much as any.) Hee was (indeed) honest, and of an
open, and free nature: had an excellent *Phantsie*; brave
notions, and gentle expressions: wherein hee flow'd with
that facility, that sometime it was necessary he should be
stop'd: *Sufflaminandus erat*; as *Augustus* said of *Haterius*.
His wit was in his owne power; would the rule of it had
beene so too. Many times hee fell into those things,
could not escape laughter: As when hee said in the person of *Cæsar*, one speaking to him; *Cæsar thou dost me
wrong*. Hee replyed: *Cæsar did never wrong, but with just
cause:* and such like; which were ridiculous. But hee re-
deemed his vices, with his vertues. There was ever more
in him to be praysed, then to be pardoned.

From *Timber: or, Discoveries; Made upon Men and Matter,*
published 1641, pp. 97, 98.
    The passage in *Julius Cæsar* to which Jonson refers (III. i. 47,
48) stands thus in the First Folio:

        Know, *Cæsar* doth not wrong, nor without cause
        Will he be satisfied.

JOHN MILTON

On *Shakespear*. 1630

WHAT needs my *Shakespear* for his honour'd Bones,
The labour of an age in piled Stones,
Or that his hallow'd reliques should be hid
Under a Star-ypointing *Pyramid?*
Dear son of memory, great heir of Fame,
What need'st thou such weak witnes of thy name?
Thou in our wonder and astonishment
Hast built thy self a live-long Monument.
For whilst to th' shame of slow-endeavouring art,
Thy easie numbers flow, and that each heart,
Hath from the leaves of thy unvalu'd Book,
Those Delphick lines with deep impression took,
Then thou our fancy of it self bereaving,
Dost make us Marble with too much conceaving;
And so Sepulcher'd in such pomp dost lie,
That Kings for such a Tomb would wish to die.

This, the first of Milton's poems to be published, appeared
originally at the beginning of the Second Folio of Shakespeare's
plays, 1632. It there had the title 'An Epitaph on the admirable
Dramaticke Poet, W. Shakespeare', and was anonymous.
Milton acknowledged his authorship by including it in the
collected edition of his poems published by Humphrey Moseley
in 1645,—*Poems of Mr. John Milton, . . . Printed by his true Copies*;
and he also stated, in the new and shorter title, that it had been
written as early as 1630. The poem is here reprinted from the
text of 1645. There are a few variant readings in the text of 1632,
and several differences in spelling.

I. M. S.

On Worthy Master Shakespeare and his Poems

A MIND reflecting ages past, whose cleere
And equall surface can make things appeare
Distant a Thousand yeares, and represent
Them in their lively colours just extent.
To out run hasty time, retrive the fates,
Rowle backe the heavens, blow ope the iron gates
Of death and Lethe, where (confused) lye
Great heapes of ruinous mortalitie.
In that deepe duskie dungeon to discerne
A royall Ghost from Churles; By art to learne
The Physiognomie of shades, and give
Them suddaine birth, wondring how oft they live.
What story coldly tells, what *Poets* faine
At second hand, and picture without braine
Senselesse and soulelesse showes. To give a Stage
(Ample and true with life) voyce, action, age,
As *Plato's* yeare and new Scene of the world
Them unto us, or us to them had hurld.
To raise our auncient Soveraignes from their herse
Make Kings his subjects, by exchanging verse
Enlive their pale trunkes, that the present age
Ioyes in their joy, and trembles at their rage:
Yet so to temper passion, that our eares
Take pleasure in their paine; And eyes in teares
Both weepe and smile; fearefull at plots so sad,
Then laughing at our feare; abus'd, and glad
To be abus'd, affected with that truth
Which we perceive is false; pleas'd in that ruth
At which we start; and by elaborate play
Tortur'd and tickled; by a crablike way

Time past made pastime, and in ugly sort
Disgorging up his ravaine for our sport——
——While the *Plebeian* Impe from lofty throne,
Creates and rules a world, and workes upon
Mankind by secret engines; Now to move
A chilling pitty, then a rigorous love:
To strike up and stroake downe, both joy and ire;
To steere th' affections; and by heavenly fire
Mould us anew. Stolne from our selves——
    This and much more which cannot bee exprest,
But by himselfe, his tongue and his owne brest,
Was *Shakespeares* freehold, which his cunning braine
Improv'd by favour of the nine fold traine.
The buskind Muse, the Commicke Queene, the graund
And lowder tone of *Clio*; nimble hand,
And nimbler foote of the melodious paire,
The Silver voyced Lady; the most faire
Calliope, whose speaking silence daunts:
And she whose prayse the heavenly body chants.
    These joyntly woo'd him, envying one another
(Obey'd by all as Spouse, but lov'd as brother)
And wrought a curious robe of sable grave
Fresh greene, and pleasant yellow, red most brave,
And constant blew, rich purple, guiltlesse white,
The lowly Russet, and the Scarlet bright;
Branch't and embroydred like the painted Spring
Each leafe match't with a flower, and each string
Of golden wire, each line of silke; there run
Italian workes whose thred the Sisters spun;
And there did sing, or seeme to sing, the choyce
Birdes of a forraine note and various voyce.
Here hangs a mossey rocke; there playes a faire
But chiding fountaine purled: Not the ayre
Nor cloudes nor thunder, but were living drawne
Not out of common Tiffany or Lawne.

But fine materialls, which the Muses know
And onely know the countries where they grow.
    Now when they could no longer him enjoy
In mortall garments pent; death may destroy
They say his body, but his verse shall live
And more then nature takes, our hands shall give.
In a lesse volumne, but more strongly bound
Shakespeare shall breath and speake, with Laurell crown'd
Which never fades. Fed with Ambrosian meate
In a well-lyned vesture rich and neate
    So with this robe they cloath him, bid him weare it
    For time shall never staine, nor envy teare it.

The friendly admirer of his

Endowments.

I. M. S.

Prefixed to the Second Folio, 1632.

There is no satisfactory explanation of 'I.M.S.' Malone suggested 'Jasper Mayne, Student' (Mayne was elected a 'student' of Christ Church, Oxford, in 1627), and Coleridge made the strange statement that internal evidence was decisive for 'John Milton, Student'. C. M. Ingleby was inclined, with little reason, to favour 'In Memoriam Scriptoris'. The position of the letters makes it probable that they are a signature; but in a seventeenth-century signature of this kind only two letters are to be taken as the initials of the writer's name.

THOMAS FULLER

WILLIAM SHAKESPEARE was born at *Stratford* on *Avon* in this County, in whom three eminent Poets may seem in some sort to be compounded, 1. *Martial* in the *Warlike* sound of his Sur-name, (whence some may conjecture him of a *Military extraction,*) *Hasti-vibrans* or *Shake-speare.* 2. *Ovid,* the most *naturall* and *witty* of all Poets, and hence it was that Queen *Elizabeth* coming into a Grammar-School made this extemporary verse,

> Persius *a Crab-staffe,* Bawdy Martial, Ovid *a fine Wag.*

3. *Plautus,* who was an exact Comœdian, yet never any Scholar, as our *Shake-speare* (if alive) would confess himself. Adde to all these, that though his Genius generally was *jocular,* and inclining him to *festivity,* yet he could (when so disposed) be *solemn* and *serious,* as appears by his Tragedies, so that *Heraclitus* himself (I mean if secret and unseen) might afford to smile at his Comedies, they were so *merry,* and *Democritus* scarce forbear to sigh at his Tragedies they were so *mournfull.*

He was an eminent instance of the truth of that Rule, *Poeta non fit, sed nascitur,* one is not *made* but *born* a Poet. Indeed his Learning was very little, so that as *Cornish diamonds* are not polished by any Lapidary, but are pointed and smoothed even as they are taken out of the Earth, so *nature* it self was all the *art* which was used upon him.

Many were the *wit-combates* betwixt him and *Ben Johnson,* which two I behold like a *Spanish great Gallion,* and an *English man of War;* Master *Johnson* (like the former) was built far higher in Learning; *Solid,* but *Slow* in his performances. *Shake-spear* with the *English-man of War,* lesser in *bulk,* but lighter in *sailing,* could turn with all tides, tack about and take advantage of all winds, by the quickness of his Wit and Invention. He died *Anno Domini* 16. . and was buried at *Stratford* upon *Avon*, the Town of his Nativity.

> *From* The History of the Worthies of England,
> 1662,—*Warwickshire*, p. 126.

The *Worthies of England* appeared posthumously, Fuller having died in 1661. He had long been engaged on it, and the above passage should be dated considerably earlier than the year of publication.

MARGARET CAVENDISH,

Marchioness (afterwards Duchess) of Newcastle

Madam,

I Wonder how that Person you mention in your Letter, could either have the Conscience, or Confidence to Dispraise *Shakespear*'s Playes, as to say they were made up onely with Clowns, Fools, Watchmen, and the like; But to Answer that Person, though *Shakespear*'s Wit will Answer for himself, I say, that it seems by his Judging, or Censuring, he Understands not Playes, or Wit; for to Express Properly, Rightly, Usually, and Naturally, a Clown's, or Fool's Humour, Expressions, Phrases, Garbs, Manners, Actions, Words, and Course of Life, is as Witty, Wise, Judicious, Ingenious, and Observing, as to Write and Express the Expressions, Phrases, Garbs, Manners, Actions, Words, and Course of Life, of Kings and Princes; and to Express Naturally, to the Life, a Mean Country Wench, as a Great Lady, a Courtesan, as a Chast Woman, a Mad man, as a Man in his right Reason and Senses, a Drunkard, as a Sober man, a Knave, as an Honest man, and so a Clown, as a Well-bred man, and a Fool, as a Wise man; nay, it Expresses and Declares a Greater Wit, to Express, and Deliver to Posterity, the Extravagancies of Madness, the Subtilty of Knaves, the Ignorance of Clowns, and the Simplicity of Naturals, or the Craft of Feigned Fools, than to Express Regularities, Plain Honesty, Courtly Garbs, or Sensible Discourses, for 'tis harder to Express Nonsense than Sense, and Ordinary Conversations, than that which is Unusual; and 'tis Harder, and Requires more Wit to Express a Jester, than a Grave Statesman; yet *Shakespear* did not want Wit, to Express to the Life all Sorts of Persons, of what Quality, Profession, Degree, Breeding, or Birth soever; nor did he want Wit to Express the Divers, and Different Humours, or Natures, or Several Passions in Mankind; and so Well he hath Express'd in his Playes all Sorts of Persons, as one would think he had been Transformed into every one of those Persons he hath Described; and as sometimes one would think he was Really himself the Clown or Jester he Feigns, so one would think, he was also the King, and Privy Coun-sellor; also as one would think he were Really the Co-ward he Feigns, so one would think he were the most Valiant, and Experienced Souldier; Who would not think he had been such a man as his Sir *John Falstaff*? and who would not think he had been *Harry* the Fifth? & certainly *Julius Cæsar, Augustus Cæsar,* and *Antonius,* did never Really Act their parts Better, if so Well, as he hath Described them, and I believe that *Antonius* and *Brutus* did not Speak Better to the People, than he hath Feign'd them; nay, one would think that he had been Metamorphosed from a Man to a Woman, for who could Describe *Cleopatra* Better than he hath done, and many other Females of his own Creating, as *Nan Page,* Mrs. *Page,* Mrs. *Ford,* the Doctors Maid, *Bettrice,* Mrs. *Quickly, Doll Tearsheet,* and others, too many to Relate? and in his Tragick Vein, he Presents Passions so Naturally, and Misfortunes so Probably, as he Peirces the Souls of his Readers with such a True Sense and Feeling thereof, that it Forces Tears through their Eyes, and almost Per-swades them, they are Really Actors, or at least Present at those Tragedies. Who would not Swear he had been a Noble Lover, that could Woo so well? and there is not any person he hath Described in his Book, but his Readers might think they were Well acquainted with them; indeed *Shakespear* had a Clear Judgment, a Quick Wit,

a Spreading Fancy, a Subtil Observation, a Deep Apprehension, and a most Eloquent Elocution; truly, he was
a Natural Orator, as well as a Natural Poet, and he was
not an Orator to Speak Well only on some Subjects, as
Lawyers, who can make Eloquent Orations at the Bar,
and Plead Subtilly and Wittily in Law-Cases, or Divines,
that can Preach Eloquent Sermons, or Dispute Subtilly
and Wittily in Theology, but take them from that, and
put them to other Subjects, and they will be to seek; but
Shakespear's Wit and Eloquence was General, for, and
upon all Subjects, he rather wanted Subjects for his Wit
and Eloquence to Work on, for which he was Forced to
take some of his Plots out of History, where he only
took the Bare Designs, the Wit and Language being all
his Own; and so much he had above others, that those,
who Writ after him, were Forced to Borrow of him, or
rather to Steal from him; I could mention Divers Places,
that others of our Famous Poets have Borrow'd, or
Stoln, but lest I should Discover the Persons, I will not
Mention the Places, or Parts, but leave it to those that
Read his Playes, and others, to find them out. I should
not have needed to Write this to you, for his Works
would have Declared the same Truth: But I believe,
those that Dispraised his Playes, Dispraised them more
out of Envy, than Simplicity or Ignorance. . . . But
leaving *Shakespear*'s Works to their own Defence, and
his Detractors to their Envy, and you to your better
Imployments, than Reading my Letter, I rest,
      Madam,

                    Your faithful Friend
                    and humble Servant.

CCXI. Sociable Letters, written by the Thrice
    Noble, Illustrious, and Excellent Princess, The
    Lady Marchioness of Newcastle. 1664.—
    Letter CXXIII, pp. 244-248.

JOHN DRYDEN

To begin then with *Shakespeare*; he was the man who of all Modern, and perhaps Ancient Poets, had the largest and most comprehensive soul. All the Images of Nature were still present to him, and he drew them not laboriously, but luckily: when he describes any thing, you more than see it, you feel it too. Those who accuse him to have wanted learning, give him the greater commendation: he was naturally learn'd; he needed not the spectacles of Books to read Nature; he look'd inwards, and found her there. I cannot say he is every where alike; were he so, I should do him injury to compare him with the greatest of Mankind. He is many times flat, insipid; his Comick wit degenerating into clenches, his serious swelling into Bombast. But he is always great, when some great occasion is presented to him: no man can say he ever had a fit subject for his wit, and did **not** then raise himself as high above the rest of Poets,

Quantum lenta solent inter viburna cupressi.

The consideration of this made Mr. *Hales* of *Eaton* say, That there was no subject of which any Poet ever writ, but he would produce it much better treated of in *Shakespeare*; and however others are now generally prefer'd before him, yet the Age wherein he liv'd, which had contemporaries with him *Fletcher* and *Johnson*, never equall'd them to him in their esteem: And in the last Kings Court, when *Ben's* reputation was at its highest, Sir *John Suckling*, and with him the greater part of the Courtiers, set our *Shakespeare* far above him.[1]

. . . . .

[1] Other accounts of the conversation in which Hales made his famous statement are found in Charles Gildon's *Reflections*

Shakespeare was the *Homer*, or Father of our Dramatick Poets; *Johnson* was the *Virgil*, the pattern of elaborate writing; I admire him, but I love *Shakespeare*.

From Of Dramatick Poesie, An Essay, 1668.

IN my Stile I have profess'd to imitate the Divine *Shakespeare*; which that I might perform more freely, I have dis-incumber'd my self from Rhyme. Not that I condemn my former way, but that this is more proper to my present purpose. I hope I need not to explain my self, that I have not Copy'd my Author servilely: Words and Phrases must of necessity receive a change in succeeding Ages: but 'tis almost a Miracle that much of his Language remains so pure; and that he who began Dramatique Poetry amongst us, untaught by any, and, as *Ben Johnson* tells us, without Learning, should by the force of his own Genius perform so much, that in a manner he has left no praise for any who come after him. The occasion is fair, and the subject would be pleasant to handle the difference of Stiles betwixt him and *Fletcher*, and wherein, and how far they are both to be imitated. But since I must not be over-confident of my own performance after him, it will be prudence in me to be silent. Yet I hope I may affirm, and without vanity, that by imitating him, I have excell'd my self throughout the Play.

From the Preface to All for Love: or, The World well Lost, 1678.

on Mr. *Rymer's Short View of Tragedy*, 1694, and in Nicholas Rowe's *Account of the Life &c. of Mr. William Shakespear*, 1709. The conversation appears to have taken place between 1633 and 1637. Dryden probably derived his knowledge of it from Sir William Davenant, who is said by Rowe to have been one of the company.

If *Shakespear* be allow'd, as I think he must, to have
made his Characters distinct, it will easily be infer'd that
he understood the nature of the Passions: because it has
been prov'd already, that confus'd passions make undis-
tinguishable Characters: yet I cannot deny that he has
his failings; but they are not so much in the passions
themselves, as in his manner of expression: he often
obscures his meaning by his words, and sometimes
makes it unintelligible. I will not say of so great a Poet,
that he distinguish'd not the blown puffy stile, from true
sublimity; but I may venture to maintain that the fury
of his fancy often transported him, beyond the bounds
of Judgment, either in coyning of new words and
phrases, or racking words which were in use, into the
violence of a Catachresis: 'Tis not that I would explode
the use of Metaphors from passions, for *Longinus* thinks
'em necessary to raise it: but to use 'em at every word,
to say nothing without a Metaphor, a Simile, an Image,
or description, is I doubt to smell a little too strongly of
the Buskin. I must be forc'd to give an example of expressing passion figuratively; but that I may do it with
respect to *Shakespear*, it shall not be taken from any
thing of his: 'tis an exclamation against Fortune, quoted
in his *Hamlet*, but written by some other Poet.

> *Out, out, thou strumpet fortune; all you Gods,*
> *In general Synod, take away her Power,*
> *Break all the spokes and fallyes from her Wheel,*
> *And bowl the round Nave down the hill of Heav'n*
> *As low as to the Fiends.*

And immediately after, speaking of *Hecuba*, when *Priam*
was kill'd before her eyes:

The mobbled Queen ran up and down,
Threatning the flame with bisson rheum: a clout about that
*   head,*
Where late the Diadem stood; and for a Robe

About her lank and all o're-teemed loyns,
A blanket in th' alarm of fear caught up.
Who this had seen, with tongue in venom steep'd
'Gainst Fortune's state would Treason have pronounc'd;
But if the Gods themselves did see her then,
When she saw Pyrrhus make malicious sport
In mincing with his sword her Husband's Limbs,
The instant burst of clamor that she made
(Unless things mortal meant them not at all)
Would have made milch the burning eyes of Heav'n,
And passion in the Gods.

What a pudder is here kept in raising the expression of trifling thoughts. Would not a man have thought that the Poet had been bound Prentice to a Wheelwright, for his first Rant? and had follow'd a Ragman, for the clout and blanket, in the second? Fortune is painted on a wheel; and therefore the writer in a rage, will have Poetical Justice done upon every member of that Engin: after this execution, he bowls the Nave downhill, from Heaven, to the Fiends: (an unreasonable long mark a man would think;) 'tis well there are no solid Orbs to stop it in the way, or no Element of fire to consume it: but when it came to the earth, it must be monstrous heavy, to break ground as low as the Center. His making milch the burning eyes of Heaven, was a pretty tollerable flight too; and I think no man ever drew milk out of eyes before him: yet to make the wonder greater, these eyes were burning. Such a sight indeed were enough to have rais'd passion in the Gods, but to excuse the effects of it, he tells you perhaps they did not see it. Wise men would be glad to find a little sence couch'd under all those pompous words; for Bombast is commonly the delight of that Audience, which loves Poetry, but understands it not: and as commonly has been the practice of those Writers, who not being able to infuse

a natural passion into the mind, have made it their
business to ply the ears, and to stun their Judges by the
noise. But *Shakespear* does not often thus; for the passions in his Scene between *Brutus* and *Cassius* are extreamly natural, the thoughts are such as arise from the
matter, and the expression of 'em not viciously figura-
tive. I cannot leave this Subject before I do justice to
that Divine Poet, by giving you one of his passionate
descriptions: 'tis of *Richard* the Second when he was de-
pos'd, and led in Triumph through the Streets of *London*
by *Henry* of *Bullingbrook*: the painting of it is so lively,
and the words so moving, that I have scarce read any
thing comparable to it, in any other language. Suppose
you have seen already the fortunate Usurper passing
through the croud, and follow'd by the shouts and
acclamations of the people; and now behold King
Richard entring upon the Scene: consider the wretchedness of his condition, and his carriage in it; and refrain
from pitty if you can.

> *As in a Theatre, the eyes of men*
> *After a well-grac'd Actor leaves the Stage,*
> *Are idly bent on him that enters next,*
> *Thinking his prattle to be tedious:*
> *Even so, or with much more contempt, mens eyes*
> *Did scowl on* Richard: *no man cry'd God save him:*
> *No joyful tongue gave him his welcom home,*
> *But dust was thrown upon his Sacred head,*
> *Which with such gentle sorrow he shook off,*
> *His face still combating with tears and smiles*
> *(The badges of his grief and patience)*
> *That had not God (for some strong purpose) steel'd*
> *The hearts of men, they must perforce have melted,*
> *And Barbarism it self have pity'd him.*

To speak justly of this whole matter; 'tis neither
height of thought that is discommended, nor pathetic

vehemence, nor any nobleness of expression in its proper place; but 'tis a false measure of all these, something which is like 'em, and is not them: 'tis the *Bristol-stone*, which appears like a Diamond; 'tis an extravagant thought, instead of a sublime one; 'tis roaring madness instead of vehemence; and a sound of words, instead of sence. If *Shakespear* were stript of all the Bombast in his passions, and dress'd in the most vulgar words, we should find the beauties of his thoughts remaining; if his embroideries were burnt down, there would still be silver at the bottom of the melting-pot: but I fear (at least, let me fear it for my self) that we who Ape his sounding words, have nothing of his thought, but are all out-side; there is not so much as a dwarf within our Giants cloaths. Therefore, let not *Shakespear* suffer for our sakes; 'tis our fault, who succeed him in an Age which is more refin'd, if we imitate him so ill, that we coppy his failings only, and make a virtue of that in our Writings, which in his was an imperfection.

For what remains, the excellency of that Poet was, as I have said, in the more manly passions; *Fletcher's* in the softer: *Shakespear* writ better betwixt man and man; *Fletcher*, betwixt man and woman: consequently, the one describ'd friendship better; the other love: yet *Shakespear* taught *Fletcher* to write love; and *Juliet*, and *Desdemona*, are Originals. 'Tis true, the Scholar had the softer soul; but the Master had the kinder. Friendship is both a virtue, and a Passion essentially; love is a passion only in its nature, and is not a virtue but by Accident: good nature makes Friendship; but effeminacy Love. *Shakespear* had an Universal mind, which comprehended all Characters and Passions; *Fletcher* a more confin'd, and limited: for though he treated love in perfection, yet Honour, Ambition, Revenge, and generally all the

stronger Passions, he either touch'd not, or not Masterly.
To conclude all; he was a Limb of *Shakespear*.

*From the Preface, 'Containing the Grounds
of Criticism in Tragedy,'* to Troilus and
Cressida, 1679.

As when a Tree's cut down the secret root
Lives under ground, and thence new Branches shoot,
So, from old *Shakespear*'s honour'd dust, this day
Springs up and buds a new reviving Play.
Shakespear, who (taught by none) did first impart
To *Fletcher* Wit, to labouring *Johnson* Art;
He Monarch-like gave those his subjects law,
And is that Nature which they paint and draw.
Fletcher reach'd that which on his heights did grow,
Whilst *Johnson* crept and gather'd all below.
This did his Love, and this his Mirth digest:
One imitates him most, the other best.
If they have since out-writ all other men,
'Tis with the drops which fell from *Shakespear*'s Pen.
The Storm which vanish'd on the Neighb'ring shore,
Was taught by *Shakespear*'s Tempest first to roar.
That innocence and beauty, which did smile
In *Fletcher*, grew on this *Enchanted Isle*.
But *Shakespear*'s Magick could not copy'd be;
Within that Circle none durst walk but he.
I must confess 'twas bold, nor would you now
That liberty to vulgar Wits allow,
Which works by Magick supernatural things:
But *Shakespear*'s pow'r is sacred as a King's.

From the Prologue to The Tempest, *or* The
Enchanted Island, 1667, *published* 1670.

PROLOGUES

Our Author by experience finds it true,
'Tis much more hard to please himself than you:
And out of no feign'd modesty, this day,
Damns his laborious Trifle of a Play:
Not that its worse than what before he writ,
But he has now another taste of Wit;
And to confess a truth, (though out of Time)
Grows weary of his long-lov'd Mistris, Rhyme.
Passion's too fierce to be in Fetters bound,
And Nature flies him like Enchanted Ground.
What Verse can do, he has perform'd in this,
Which he presumes the most correct of his:
But spite of all his pride, a secret shame
Invades his breast at *Shakespear*'s sacred name:
Aw'd when he hears his Godlike *Romans* rage,
He, in a just despair, would quit the Stage,
And to an Age less polish'd, more unskill'd,
Does with disdain the foremost Honours yield.

From the Prologue to Aureng-Zebe, 1675,
published 1676.

See, my lov'd *Britons*, see your *Shakespeare* rise,
An awfull ghost confess'd to human eyes!
Unnam'd, methinks, distinguish'd I had been
From other shades, by this eternal green,
About whose wreaths the vulgar Poets strive,
And with a touch, their wither'd Bays revive.
Untaught, unpractis'd, in a barbarous Age,
I found not, but created first the Stage.
And, if I drain'd no *Greek* or *Latin* store,
'Twas, that my own abundance gave me more.

*From the Prologue, 'Spoken by Mr. Betterton,
representing the Ghost of* Shakespear,' *to*
Troilus and Cressida, 1679.

IN Country Beauties as we often see
Something that takes in their simplicity,
Yet while they charm, they know not they are fair,
And take without their spreading of the snare;
Such Artless beauty lies in *Shakespears* wit,
'Twas well in spight of him what ere he writ.
His Excellencies came and were not sought,
His words like casual Atoms made a thought:
Drew up themselves in Rank and File, and writ,
He wondring how the Devil it were such wit.
Thus like the drunken Tinker, in his Play,
He grew a Prince, and never knew which way.
He did not know what trope or Figure meant,
But to perswade is to be eloquent.
So in this Cæsar which this day you see,
Tully ne'r spoke as he makes *Anthony.*
Those then that tax his Learning are to blame,
He knew the thing, but did not know the Name:
Great *Iohnson* did that Ignorance adore,
And though he envi'd much, admir'd him more.
The faultless *Iohnson* equally writ well,
Shakespear made faults; but then did more excel.
One close at Guard like some old Fencer lay,
Tother more open, but he shew'd more play.
In Imitation *Iohnsons* wit was shown,
Heaven made his men but *Shakespear* made his own.
Wise *Iohnson's* talent in observing lay,
But others follies still made up his play
He drew the like in each elaborate line,
But *Shakespear* like a Master did design.
Iohnson with skill dissected humane kind,
And show'd their faults that they their faults might find,
But then as all Anatomists must do,
He to the meanest of mankind did go,
And took from Gibbets such as he would show

Both are so great that he must boldly dare,
Who both of 'em does judge and both compare.
If amongst Poets one more bold there be,
The man that dare attempt in either way, is he.

Prologue to Shakespear's Julius Cæsar, *printed
without the name of the writer in* Covent
Garden Drolery, 1672, pp. 9, 10.

The only evidence for Dryden's authorship of this anonymous prologue is the style. It was attributed to Dryden by
Bolton Corney, *Notes and Queries*, 1854, 1st Series, ix, pp. 95, 96.
Though portions are clearly in Dryden's manner, the evidence
for attributing the whole prologue to him is far from conclusive.

EDWARD PHILLIPS

William Shakespear, the Glory of the English Stage; whose nativity at *Stratford* upon *Avon*, is the highest honour that Town can boast of: from an Actor of Tragedies and Comedies, he became a *Maker*; and such a Maker, that though some others may perhaps pretend to a more exact *Decorum* and *œconomie*, especially in Tragedy, never any express't a more lofty and Tragic heighth; never any represented nature more purely to the life, and where the polishments of Art are most wanting, as probably his Learning was not extraordinary, he pleaseth with a certain wild and native Elegance; and in all his Writings hath an unvulgar style, as well in his *Venus and Adonis*, his *Rape of Lucrece* and other various Poems, as in his Dramatics.[1]

> *From* Theatrum Poetarum, Or A Compleat Collection of the Poets . . . By Edward Phillips. M.DC.LXXV.

[1] This is the first account of Shakespeare in a dictionary of authors. In the preface it is said that '*Shakespear*, in spight of all his unfiled expressions, his rambling and indigested Fancys, the laughter of the *Critical*, yet must be confess't a *Poet* above many that go beyond him in Literature some degrees.' Edward Phillips was Milton's nephew.

The account in William Winstanley's *Lives Of the most Famous English Poets* (1687) is based on what had been said by Fuller and Phillips. The longer and more valuable account in Gerard Langbaine's *Account of the English Dramatick Poets* (1691) is mainly a descriptive catalogue of the plays.

NICHOLAS ROWE

HIS Plays are properly to be distinguish'd only into Comedies and Tragedies. Those which are called Histories, and even some of his Comedies, are really Tragedies, with a run or mixture of Comedy amongst 'em. That way of Trage-Comedy was the common Mistake of that Age, and is indeed become so agreeable to the *English* Tast, that tho' the severer Critiques among us cannot bear it, yet the generality of our Audiences seem to be better pleas'd with it than with an exact Tragedy. *The Merry Wives of* Windsor, *The Comedy of Errors*, and *The Taming of the Shrew*, are all pure Comedy; the rest, however they are call'd, have something of both Kinds. 'Tis not very easie to determine which way of Writing he was most Excellent in. There is certainly a great deal of Entertainment in his Comical Humours; and tho' they did not then strike at all Ranks of People, as the Satyr of the present Age has taken the Liberty to do, yet there is a pleasing and a well-distinguish'd Variety in those Characters which he thought fit to meddle with. *Falstaff* is allow'd by every body to be a Master-piece; the Character is always well-sustain'd, tho' drawn out into the length of three Plays; and even the Account of his Death, given by his Old Landlady Mrs. *Quickly*, in the first Act of *Henry* V, tho' it be extremely Natural, is yet as diverting as any Part of his Life. If there be any Fault in the Draught he has made of this lewd old Fellow, it is, that tho' he has made him a Thief, Lying, Cowardly, Vainglorious, and in short every way Vicious, yet he has given him so much Wit as to make him almost too agreeable; and I don't know whether some People have not, in remembrance of the Diversion he had formerly afforded 'em, been sorry to see his Friend *Hal* use him so scurvily, when he comes to the Crown in the End of the Second Part of *Henry* the Fourth. Amongst other Extravagances, in *The Merry Wives of* Windsor, he has made him a Dear-stealer, that he might at the same time remember his *Warwickshire* Prosecutor, under the Name of Justice *Shallow*; he has given him very near the same Coat of Arms which *Dugdale*, in his Antiquities of that County, describes for a Family there, and makes the *Welsh* Parson descant very pleasantly upon 'em. That whole Play is admirable; the Humours are various and well oppos'd; the main Design, which is to cure *Ford* of his unreasonable Jealousie, is extremely well conducted. *Falstaff's* Billet-doux, and Master *Slender's*

Ah! Sweet Ann Page!

are very good Expressions of Love in their Way. In *Twelfth-Night* there is something singularly Ridiculous and Pleasant in the fantastical Steward *Malvolio*. The Parasite and the Vain-glorious in *Parolles*, in *All's Well that ends Well*, is as good as any thing of that Kind in *Plautus* or *Terence*. *Petruchio*, in *The Taming of the Shrew*, is an uncommon Piece of Humour. The Conversation of *Benedick* and *Beatrice*, in *Much ado about Nothing*, and of *Rosalind* in *As you like it*, have much Wit and Sprightliness all along. His Clowns, without which Character there was hardly any Play writ in that Time, are all very entertaining: And, I believe, *Thersites* in *Troilus and Cressida*, and *Apemantus* in *Timon*, will be allow'd to be Master-Pieces of ill Nature, and satyrical Snarling. To these I might add, that incomparable Character of *Shylock* the Jew, in *The Merchant of* Venice; but tho' we have seen that Play Receiv'd and Acted as a Comedy, and the Part of the *Jew* perform'd by an Excellent Comedian, yet I cannot but think it was design'd Tragically by the Author. There appears in it such a deadly Spirit of

Revenge, such a savage Fierceness and Fellness, and such
a bloody designation of Cruelty and Mischief, as cannot
agree either with the Stile or Characters of Comedy.
The Play it self, take it all together, seems to me to be
one of the most finish'd of any of *Shakespear's*. The
Tale indeed, in that Part relating to the Caskets, and the
extravagant and unusual kind of Bond given by *Antonio*,
is a little too much remov'd from the Rules of Probability: But taking the Fact for granted, we must allow it
to be very beautifully written. There is something in
the Friendship of *Antonio* to *Bassanio* very Great, Generous and Tender. The whole fourth Act, supposing, as I
said, the Fact to be probable, is extremely Fine. But
there are two Passages that deserve a particular Notice.
The first is, what *Portia* says in praise of Mercy, [Act. IV];
and the other on the Power of Musick, [Act. V]. The
Melancholy of *Jaques*, in *As you like it*, is as singular and
odd as it is diverting. And if what *Horace* says

Difficile est proprie communia Dicere,

'Twill be a hard Task for any one to go beyond him in
the Description of the several Degrees and Ages of Man's
Life, tho' the Thought be old, and common enough.

> ——*All the World's a Stage,*
> *And all the Men and Women meerly Players;*
> *They have their Exits and their Entrances,*
> *And one Man in his time plays many Parts,*
> *His Acts being seven Ages. At first the Infant*
> *Mewling and puking in the Nurse's Arms:*
> *And then, the whining School-boy with his Satchel,*
> *And shining Morning-face, creeping like Snail*
> *Vnwillingly to School. And then the Lover*
> *Sighing like Furnace, with a woful Ballad*
> *Made to his Mistress' Eye-brow. Then a Soldier*
> *Full of strange Oaths, and bearded like the Pard,*
> *Jealous in Honour, sudden and quick in Quarrel,*

Seeking the bubble Reputation
Ev'n in the Cannon's Mouth. And then the Justice
In fair round Belly, with good Capon lin'd,
With Eyes severe, and Beard of formal Cut,
Full of wise Saws and modern Instances;
And so he plays his Part. The sixth Age shifts
Into the lean and slipper'd Pantaloon,
With Spectacles on Nose, and Pouch on Side;
His youthful Hose, well sav'd, a world too wide
For his shrunk Shank; and his big manly Voice
Turning again tow'rd childish treble Pipes,
And Whistles in his Sound. Last Scene of all,
That ends this strange eventful History,
Is second Childishness and meer Oblivion,
Sans Teeth, sans Eyes, sans Tast, sans ev'ry thing.

[Act II, Sc. vii.]

His Images are indeed ev'ry where so lively, that the
Thing he would represent stands full before you, and
you possess ev'ry Part of it. I will venture to point out
one more, which is, I think, as strong and as uncommon
as any thing I ever saw; 'tis an Image of Patience. Speaking of a Maid in Love, he says,

——*She never told her Love,*
But let Concealment, like a Worm i'th' Bud
Feed on her Damask Cheek: She pin'd in Thought,
And sate like Patience *on a Monument,*
Smiling at Grief.

What an Image is here given! and what a Task would it
have been for the greatest Masters of *Greece* and *Rome*
to have express'd the Passions design'd by this Sketch of
Statuary? The Stile of his Comedy is, in general, Natural
to the Characters, and easie in it self; and the Wit most
commonly sprightly and pleasing, except in those places
where he runs into Dogrel Rhymes, as in *The Comedy
of Errors*, and a Passage or two in some other Plays. As
for his Jingling sometimes, and playing upon Words, it

was the common Vice of the Age he liv'd in: And if we
find it in the Pulpit, made use of as an Ornament to the
Sermons of some of the Gravest Divines of those Times;
perhaps it may not be thought too light for the Stage.

But certainly the greatness of this Author's Genius do's
no where so much appear, as where he gives his Imagination an entire Loose, and raises his Fancy to a flight
above Mankind and the Limits of the visible World.
Such are his Attempts in *The Tempest, Midsummer-
Night's Dream, Macbeth* and *Hamlet*. Of these, *The
Tempest*, however it comes to be plac'd the first by the
former Publishers of his Works, can never have been
the first written by him: It seems to me as perfect in its
Kind, as almost any thing we have of his. One may
observe, that the Unities are kept here with an Exactness
uncommon to the Liberties of his Writing: Tho' that
was what, I suppose, he valu'd himself least upon, since
his Excellencies were all of another Kind. I am very
sensible that he do's, in this Play, depart too much from
that likeness to Truth which ought to be observ'd in
these sort of Writings; yet he do's it so very finely, that
one is easily drawn in to have more Faith for his sake,
than Reason does well allow of. His Magick has something in it very Solemn and very Poetical: And that extravagant Character of *Caliban* is mighty well sustain'd,
shews a wonderful Invention in the Author, who could
strike out such a particular wild Image, and is certainly
one of the finest and most uncommon Grotesques that
was ever seen. The Observation, which I have been inform'd[1] three very great Men concurr'd in making upon
this Part, was extremely just. *That* Shakespear *had not
only found out a new Character in his* Caliban, *but had also
devis'd and adapted a new manner of Language for that
Character.* Among the particular Beauties of this Piece,

[1] *Ld.* Falkland, *Ld. C. J.* Vaughan, *and Mr.* Selden.

I think one may be allow'd to point out the Tale of
Prospero in the First Act; his Speech to *Ferdinand* in the
Fourth, upon the breaking up the Masque of *Juno* and
Ceres; and that in the Fifth, where he dissolves his
Charms, and resolves to break his Magick Rod. . . .

It is the same Magick that raises the Fairies in *Midsummer Night's Dream*, the Witches in *Macbeth*, and the
Ghost in *Hamlet*, with Thoughts and Language so proper
to the Parts they sustain, and so peculiar to the Talent of
this Writer. But of the two last of these Plays I shall
have occasion to take notice, among the Tragedies of
Mr. *Shakespear*. If one undertook to examine the greatest
part of these by those Rules which are establish'd by
Aristotle, and taken from the Model of the *Grecian* Stage,
it would be no very hard Task to find a great many
Faults: But as *Shakespear* liv'd under a kind of mere
Light of Nature, and had never been made acquainted
with the Regularity of those written Precepts, so it
would be hard to judge him by a Law he knew nothing
of. We are to consider him as a Man that liv'd in a State
of almost universal License and Ignorance: There was
no establish'd Judge, but every one took the liberty to
Write according to the Dictates of his own Fancy. When
one considers, that there is not one Play before him of
a Reputation good enough to entitle it to an Appearance
on the present Stage, it cannot but be a Matter of great
Wonder that he should advance Dramatick Poetry so
far as he did. The Fable is what is generally plac'd the
first, among those that are reckon'd the constituent
Parts of a Tragick or Heroick Poem; not, perhaps, as it
is the most Difficult or Beautiful, but as it is the first
properly to be thought of in the Contrivance and Course
of the whole; and with the Fable ought to be consider'd,
the fit Disposition, Order and Conduct of its several
Parts. As it is not in this Province of the *Drama* that the

Strength and Mastery of *Shakespear* lay, so I shall not undertake the tedious and ill-natur'd Trouble to point out the several Faults he was guilty of in it. His Tales were seldom invented, but rather taken either from true History, or Novels and Romances: And he commonly made use of 'em in that Order, with those Incidents, and that extent of Time in which he found 'em in the Authors from whence he borrow'd them. So *The Winter's Tale*, which is taken from an old Book, call'd, *The Delectable History* of *Dorastus and Faunia*, contains the space of sixteen or seventeen Years, and the Scene is sometimes laid in *Bohemia*, and sometimes in *Sicily*, according to the original Order of the Story. Almost all his Historical Plays comprehend a great length of Time, and very different and distinct Places: And in his *Antony and Cleopatra*, the Scene travels over the greatest Part of the *Roman* Empire. But in Recompence for his Carelessness in this Point, when he comes to another Part of the *Drama, The Manners of his Characters, in Acting or Speaking what is proper for them, and fit to be shown by the Poet*, he may be generally justify'd, and in very many places greatly commended. For those Plays which he has taken from the *English* or *Roman* History, let any Man compare 'em, and he will find the Character as exact in the Poet as the Historian. He seems indeed so far from proposing to himself any one Action for a Subject, that the Title very often tells you, 'tis *The Life of King* John, *King* Richard, *&c.* What can be more agreeable to the Idea our Historians give of *Henry* the Sixth, than the Picture *Shakespear* has drawn of him! His Manners are every where exactly the same with the Story; one finds him still describ'd with Simplicity, passive Sanctity, want of Courage, weakness of Mind, and easie Submission to the Governance of an imperious Wife, or prevailing Faction: Tho' at the same time the Poet do's

Justice to his good Qualities, and moves the Pity of his
Audience for him, by showing him Pious, Disinterested,
a Contemner of the Things of this World, and wholly
resign'd to the severest Dispensations of God's Provi-
dence. There is a short Scene in the Second Part of
Henry VI. [Act III, Sc. iii.] which I cannot but think
admirable in its Kind. Cardinal *Beaufort*, who had murder'd the Duke of *Gloucester*, is shewn in the last Agonies
on his Death-Bed, with the good King praying over
him. There is so much Terror in one, so much Tenderness and moving Piety in the other, as must touch any
one who is capable either of Fear or Pity. In his *Henry*
VIII. that Prince is drawn with that Greatness of Mind,
and all those good Qualities which are attributed to him
in any Account of his Reign. If his Faults are not shewn
in an equal degree, and the Shades in this Picture do not
bear a just Proportion to the Lights, it is not that the
Artist wanted either Colours or Skill in the Disposition
of 'em; but the truth, I believe, might be, that he forbore
doing it out of regard to Queen *Elizabeth*, since it could
have been no very great Respect to the Memory of his
Mistress, to have expos'd some certain Parts of her
Father's Life upon the Stage. He has dealt much more
freely with the Minister of that Great King, and certainly nothing was ever more justly written, than the
Character of Cardinal *Wolsey*. He has shewn him Tyrannical, Cruel, and Insolent in his Prosperity; and yet,
by a wonderful Address, he makes his Fall and Ruin the
Subject of general Compassion. The whole Man, with
his Vices and Virtues, is finely and exactly describ'd in
the second Scene of the fourth Act. The Distresses likewise of Queen *Katherine*, in this Play, are very movingly
touch'd; and tho' the Art of the Poet has skreen'd King
Henry from any gross Imputation of Injustice, yet one is
inclin'd to wish, the Queen had met with a Fortune

more worthy of her Birth and Virtue. Nor are the Manners, proper to the Persons represented, less justly observ'd, in those Characters taken from the *Roman* History; and of this, the Fierceness and Impatience of *Coriolanus*, his Courage and Disdain of the common People, the Virtue and Philosophical Temper of *Brutus*, and the irregular Greatness of Mind in *M. Antony*, are beautiful Proofs. For the two last especially, you find 'em exactly as they are describ'd by *Plutarch*, from whom certainly *Shakespear* copy'd 'em. He has indeed follow'd his Original pretty close, and taken in several little Incidents that might have been spar'd in a Play. But, as I hinted before, his Design seems most commonly rather to describe those great Men in the several Fortunes and Accidents of their Lives, than to take any single great Action, and form his Work simply upon that. However, there are some of his Pieces, where the Fable is founded upon one Action only. Such are more especially, *Romeo* and *Juliet*, *Hamlet*, and *Othello*. The Design in *Romeo* and *Juliet*, is plainly the Punishment of their two Families, for the unreasonable Feuds and Animosities that had been so long kept up between 'em, and occasion'd the Effusion of so much Blood. In the management of this Story, he has shewn something wonderfully Tender and Passionate in the Love-part, and very Pitiful in the Distress. *Hamlet* is founded on much the same Tale with the *Electra* of *Sophocles*. In each of 'em a young Prince is engag'd to Revenge the Death of his Father, their Mothers are equally Guilty, are both concern'd in the Murder of their Husbands, and are afterwards married to the Murderers. There is in the first Part of the *Greek* Trajedy, something very moving in the Grief of *Electra*; but as Mr. *D'Acier* has observ'd, there is something very unnatural and shocking in the Manners he has given that Princess and *Orestes* in the

latter Part. *Orestes* embrues his Hands in the Blood of
his own Mother; and that barbarous Action is perform'd,
tho' not immediately upon the Stage, yet so near, that
the Audience hear *Clytemnestra* crying out to *Ægysthus*
for Help, and to her Son for Mercy: While *Electra*, her
Daughter, and a Princess, both of them Characters that
ought to have appear'd with more Decency, stands upon
the Stage and encourages her Brother in the Parricide.
What Horror does this not raise! *Clytemnestra* was a
wicked Woman, and had deserv'd to Die; nay, in the
truth of the Story, she was kill'd by her own Son; but
to represent an Action of this Kind on the Stage, is certainly an Offence against those Rules of Manners proper
to the Persons that ought to be observ'd there. On the
contrary, let us only look a little on the Conduct of
Shakespear. *Hamlet* is represented with the same Piety
towards his Father, and Resolution to Revenge his Death,
as *Orestes*; he has the same Abhorrence for his Mother's
Guilt, which, to provoke him the more, is heighten'd
by Incest: But 'tis with wonderful Art and Justness of
Judgment, that the Poet restrains him from doing Violence to his Mother. To prevent any thing of that Kind,
he makes his Father's Ghost forbid that part of his Vengeance.

> *But howsoever thou pursu'st this Act,*
> *Taint not thy Mind; nor let thy Soul contrive*
> *Against thy Mother ought; leave her to Heav'n,*
> *And to those Thorns that in her Bosom lodge,*
> *To prick and sting her.*
>
>   [Act I, Sc. v.]

This is to distinguish rightly between *Horror* and *Terror*.
The latter is a proper Passion of Tragedy, but the former
ought always to be carefully avoided. And certainly no
Dramatick Writer ever succeeded better in raising *Terror*
in the Minds of an Audience than *Shakespear* has done.

The whole Tragedy of *Macbeth*, but more especially the Scene where the King is murder'd, in the second Act, as well as this Play, is a noble Proof of that manly Spirit with which he writ; and both shew how powerful he was, in giving the strongest Motions to our Souls that they are capable of. I cannot leave *Hamlet*, without taking notice of the Advantage with which we have seen this Master-piece of *Shakespear* distinguish it self upon the Stage, by Mr. *Betterton*'s fine Performance of that Part. A Man, who tho' he had no other good Qualities, as he has a great many, must have made his way into the Esteem of all Men of Letters, by this only Excellency. No Man is better acquainted with *Shakespear*'s manner of Expression, and indeed he has study'd him so well, and is so much a Master of him, that whatever Part of his he performs, he does it as if it had been written on purpose for him, and that the Author had exactly conceiv'd it as he plays it.

From 'Some Account of the Life, &c. of Mr. William Shakespear,' prefixed to Rowe's edition of The Works of Mr. William Shakespear, *1709.*

THE SPECTATOR

THE Age in which *the Punn* chiefly flourished, was the Reign of King *James* the First. . . . The greatest Authors, in their most serious Works, made frequent use of Punns. The Sermons of Bishop *Andrews*, and the Tragedies of *Shakespear*, are full of them. The Sinner was punned into Repentance by the former, as in the latter nothing is more usual than to see a Hero weeping and quibbling for a dozen Lines together.

No. 61—May 10, 1711—*by Addison.*

THE Gentleman who writ this Play [Shadwell's *Lanca-shire Witches*], and has drawn some Characters in it very justly, appears to have been mis-led in his Witchcraft by an unwary following the inimitable *Shakespear*. The Incantations in *Mackbeth* have a Solemnity admirably adapted to the Occasion of that Tragedy, and fill the Mind with a suitable Horror; besides, that the Witches are a part of the Story itself, as we find it very particularly related in *Hector Boetius*, from whom he seems to have taken it. This therefore is a proper Machine where the Business is dark, horrid and bloody; but is extreamly foreign from the Affair of Comedy. Subjects of this kind, which are in themselves disagreeable, can at no time become entertaining, but by passing thro' an Imagination like *Shakespear*'s to form them; for which Reason Mr. *Dryden* wou'd not allow even *Beaumont* and *Fletcher* capable of imitating him.

> *But Shakespear's Magick cou'd not copy'd be,*
> *Within that Circle none durst Walk but He.*

No. 141—August 11, 1711—*by Steele.*

AMONG great Genius's, those few draw the Admiration

of all the World upon them, and stand up as the Prodigies of Mankind, who by the meer Strength of natural Parts, and without any Assistance of Art or Learning, have produced Works that were the Delight of their own Times and the Wonder of Posterity. There appears something nobly wild and extravagant in these great natural Genius's, that is infinitely more beautiful than all the Turn and Polishing of what the *French* call a *Bel Esprit*, by which they would express a Genius refined by Conversation, Reflection, and the Reading of the most polite Authors. The greatest Genius which runs through the Arts and Sciences, takes a kind of Tincture from them, and falls unavoidably into Imitation.

Many of these great natural Genius's that were never disciplined and broken by Rules of Art, are to be found among the Ancients, and in particular among those of the more Eastern Parts of the World. *Homer* has innumerable Flights that *Virgil* was not able to reach, and in the Old Testament we find several Passages more elevated and sublime than any in *Homer*. At the same Time that we allow a greater and more daring Genius to the Ancients, we must own that the greatest of them very much failed in, or, if you will, that they were much above the Nicety and Correctness of the Moderns. . . . Our Countryman *Shakespear* was a remarkable Instance of this first kind of great Genius's.

No. 160—September 3, 1711—by Addison.

It shews a greater Genius in *Shakespear* to have drawn his *Calyban*, than his *Hotspur* or *Julius Cæsar*: The one was to be supplied out of his own Imagination, whereas the other might have been formed upon Tradition, History and Observation.

No. 279—January 19, 1712—by Addison.

THERE is a kind of Writing, wherein the Poet quite loses sight of Nature, and entertains his Reader's Imagination with the Characters and Actions of such Persons as have many of them no Existence, but what he bestows on them. Such are Fairies, Witches, Magicians, Demons, and departed Spirits. This Mr. *Dryden* calls *the Fairy way of Writing*, which is, indeed, more difficult than any other that depends on the Poet's Fancy, because he has no Pattern to follow in it, and must work altogether out of his own Invention.

There is a very odd turn of Thought required for this sort of Writing, and it is impossible for a Poet to succeed in it, who has not a particular Cast of Fancy, and an Imagination naturally fruitful and superstitious. . . .

Among the *English*, *Shakespear* has incomparably excelled all others. That noble Extravagance of Fancy, which he had in so great Perfection, throughly qualified him to touch this weak superstitious Part of his Reader's Imagination; and made him capable of succeeding, where he had nothing to support him besides the Strength of his own Genius. There is something so wild and yet so solemn in the Speeches of his Ghosts, Fairies, Witches and the like Imaginary Persons, that we cannot forbear thinking them natural, tho' we have no Rule by which to judge of them, and must confess, if there are such Beings in the World, it looks highly probable they should talk and act as he has represented them.

No. 419—July 1, 1712—*by Addison.*

OUR Criticks do not seem sensible that there is more Beauty in the Works of a great Genius who is ignorant of the Rules of Art, than in those of a little Genius who knows and observes them. It is of these Men of Genius that *Terence* speaks, in opposition to the little artificial Cavillers of his Time;

> *Quorum æmulari exoptat negligentiam*
> *Potiùs, quàm istorum obscuram diligentiam.*

A Critick may have the same Consolation in the ill Success of his Play, as Dr. *South* tells us a Physician has at the Death of a Patient, That he was killed *secundum artem*. Our inimitable *Shakespear* is a Stumbling-block to the whole Tribe of these rigid Criticks. Who would not rather read one of his Plays, where there is not a single Rule of the Stage observed, than any Production of a modern Critick, where there is not one of them violated? *Shakespear* was indeed born with all the Seeds of Poetry, and may be compared to the Stone in *Pyrrhus*'s Ring, which, as *Pliny* tells us, had the Figure of *Apollo* and the Nine Muses in the Veins of it, produced by the spontaneous Hand of Nature, without any Help from Art.[1]

No. 592—September 10, 1714—*by Addison*.

[1] The views expressed by Addison in this passage had been frequently expressed by Dryden. For example, in the 'Dedication of the Æneis,' 1697, he said 'better a Mechanick Rule were stretch'd or broken, than a great Beauty were omitted'; and in the Prologue to *Love Triumphant*, 1694, he referred thus to Thomas Rymer, who had attacked Shakespeare's art in *A Short View of Tragedy*, 1693, and had himself written a tragedy entitled *Edgar*:—

> To *Shakespear*'s Critique he bequeaths the Curse,
> To find his faults; and yet himself make worse;
> A precious Reader in Poetique Schools,
> Who by his own Examples damns his Rules.

ALEXANDER POPE

It is not my design to enter into a Criticism upon this Author; tho' to do it effectually and not superficially, would be the best occasion that any just Writer could take, to form the judgment and taste of our nation. For of all *English* Poets *Shakespear* must be confessed to be the fairest and fullest subject for Criticism, and to afford the most numerous, as well as most conspicuous instances, both of Beauties and Faults of all sorts. But this far exceeds the bounds of a Preface, the business of which is only to give an account of the fate of his Works, and the disadvantages under which they have been transmitted to us. We shall hereby extenuate many faults which are his, and clear him from the imputation of many which are not: A design, which tho' it can be no guide to future Criticks to do him justice in one way, will at least be sufficient to prevent their doing him an injustice in the other.

I cannot however but mention some of his principal and characteristic Excellencies, for which (notwithstanding his defects) he is justly and universally elevated above all other Dramatic Writers. Not that this is the proper place of praising him, but because I would not omit any occasion of doing it.

If ever any Author deserved the name of an *Original*, it was *Shakespear*. *Homer* himself drew not his art so immediately from the fountains of Nature, it proceeded thro' *Ægyptian* strainers and channels, and came to him not without some tincture of the learning, or some cast of the models, of those before him. The Poetry of *Shakespear* was Inspiration indeed: he is not so much an Imitator, as an Instrument, of Nature; and 'tis not so just to say that he speaks from her, as that she speaks thro' him.

His *Characters* are so much Nature her self, that 'tis a sort of injury to call them by so distant a name as Copies of her. Those of other Poets have a constant resemblance, which shews that they receiv'd them from one another, and were but multiplyers of the same image: each picture like a mock-rainbow is but the reflection of a reflection. But every single character in *Shakespear* is as much an Individual, as those in Life itself; it is as impossible to find any two alike; and such as from their relation or affinity in any respect appear most to be Twins, will upon comparison be found remarkably distinct. To this life and variety of Character, we must add the wonderful Preservation of it; which is such throughout his plays, that had all the Speeches been printed without the very names of the Persons, I believe one might have apply'd them with certainty to every speaker.

The *Power* over our *Passions* was never possess'd in a more eminent degree, or display'd in so different instances. Yet all along, there is seen no labour, no pains to raise them; no preparation to guide our guess to the effect, or be perceiv'd to lead toward it: But the heart swells, and the tears burst out, just at the proper places. We are surpriz'd, the moment we weep; and yet upon reflection find the passion so just, that we shou'd be surpriz'd if we had not wept, and wept at that very moment.

How astonishing is it again, that the passions directly opposite to these, Laughter and Spleen, are no less at his command! that he is not more a master of the *Great*, than of the *Ridiculous* in human nature; of our noblest tendernesses, than of our vainest foibles; of our strongest emotions, than of our idlest sensations!

Nor does he only excell in the Passions: In the coolness of Reflection and Reasoning he is full as admirable.

His *Sentiments* are not only in general the most pertinent
and judicious upon every subject; but by a talent very
peculiar, something between Penetration and Felicity,
he hits upon that particular point on which the bent of
each argument turns, or the force of each motive depends. This is perfectly amazing, from a man of no
education or experience in those great and publick scenes
of life which are usually the subject of his thoughts: So
that he seems to have known the world by Intuition, to
have look'd thro' humane nature at one glance, and to
be the only Author that gives ground for a very new
opinion, That the Philosopher and even the Man of the
world, may be *Born*, as well as the Poet.

It must be own'd that with all these great excellencies,
he has almost as great defects; and that as he has certainly
written better, so he has perhaps written worse, than
any other. But I think I can in some measure account
for these defects, from several causes and accidents;
without which it is hard to imagine that so large and
so enlighten'd a mind could ever have been susceptible
of them. That all these Contingencies should unite to his
disadvantage seems to me almost as singularly unlucky,
as that so many various (nay contrary) Talents should
meet in one man, was happy and extraordinary.

It must be allowed that Stage-Poetry of all other, is
more particularly levell'd to please the *Populace*, and its
success more immediately depending upon the *Common
Suffrage*. One cannot therefore wonder, if *Shakespear*
having at his first appearance no other aim in his writings
than to procure a subsistence, directed his endeavours
solely to hit the taste and humour that then prevailed.
The Audience was generally composed of the meaner
sort of people; and therefore the Images of Life were to
be drawn from those of their own rank: accordingly we
find, that not our Author's only but almost all the old

Comedies have their Scene among *Tradesmen* and *Mechanicks*: And even their Historical Plays strictly follow the common *Old Stories* or *Vulgar Traditions* of that kind of people. In Tragedy, nothing was so sure to *Surprize* and cause *Admiration*, as the most strange, un-expected, and consequently most unnatural, Events and Incidents; the most exaggerated Thoughts; the most verbose and bombast Expression; the most pompous Rhymes, and thundering Versification. In Comedy, nothing was so sure to *please*, as mean buffoonry, vile ribaldry, and unmannerly jests of fools and clowns. Yet even in these, our Author's Wit buoys up, and is born above his subject: his Genius in those low parts is like some Prince of a Romance in the disguise of a Shepherd or Peasant; a certain Greatness and Spirit now and then break out, which manifest his higher extraction and qualities.

It may be added, that not only the common Audience had no notion of the rules of writing, but few even of the better sort piqu'd themselves upon any great degree of knowledge or nicety that way; till *Ben Johnson* getting possession of the Stage, brought critical learning into vogue: And that this was not done without difficulty, may appear from those frequent lessons (and indeed almost Declamations) which he was forced to prefix to his first plays, and put into the mouth of his Actors, the *Grex, Chorus*, &c. to remove the prejudices, and inform the judgment of his hearers. Till then, our Authors had no thoughts of writing on the model of the Ancients: their Tragedies were only Histories in Dialogue; and their Comedies follow'd the thread of any Novel as they found it, no less implicitly than if it had been true History.

To judge therefore of *Shakespear* by *Aristotle's* rules, is like trying a man by the Laws of one Country, who acted under those of another. He writ to the *People*; and writ at first without patronage from the better sort, and therefore without aims of pleasing them: without assistance or advice from the Learned, as without the advantage of education or acquaintance among them: without that knowledge of the best models, the Ancients, to inspire him with an emulation of them; in a word, without any views of Reputation, and of what Poets are pleas'd to call Immortality: Some or all of which have encourag'd the vanity, or animated the ambition, of other writers.

Yet it must be observ'd, that when his performances had merited the protection of his Prince, and when the encouragement of the Court had succeeded to that of the Town; the works of his riper years are manifestly raised above those of his former. The Dates of his plays sufficiently evidence that his productions improved, in proportion to the respect he had for his auditors. And I make no doubt this observation would be found true in every instance, were but Editions extant from which we might learn the exact time when every piece was composed, and whether writ for the Town, or the Court.

Another Cause (and no less strong than the former) may be deduced from our Author's being a *Player*, and forming himself first upon the judgments of that body of men whereof he was a member. They have ever had a Standard to themselves, upon other principles than those of *Aristotle*. As they live by the Majority, they know no rule but that of pleasing the present humour, and complying with the wit in fashion; a consideration which brings all their judgment to a short point. Players are just such judges of what is *right*, as Taylors are of what is *graceful*. And in this view it will be but fair to allow, that most of our Author's faults are less to be ascribed to his wrong judgment as a Poet, than to his right judgment as a Player.

By these men it was thought a praise to *Shakespear*, that he scarce ever *blotted a line*. This they industriously propagated, as appears from what we are told by *Ben Johnson* in his *Discoveries*, and from the preface of *Heminges* and *Condell* to the first folio Edition. But in reality (however it has prevailed) there never was a more groundless report, or to the contrary of which there are more undeniable evidences. As, the Comedy of the *Merry Wives of Windsor*, which he entirely new writ; the *History of* Henry *the 6th*, which was first published under the Title of the *Contention of* York *and* Lancaster; and that of *Henry the 5th*, extreamly improved; that of *Hamlet* enlarged to almost as much again as at first, and many others. I believe the common opinion of his want of Learning proceeded from no better ground. This too might be thought a Praise by some; and to this his Errors have as injudiciously been ascribed by others. For 'tis certain, were it true, it could concern but a small part of them; the most are such as are not properly Defects, but Superfœtations: and arise not from want of learning or reading, but from want of thinking or judging: or rather (to be more just to our Author) from a compliance to those wants in others. As to a wrong choice of the subject, a wrong conduct of the incidents, false thoughts, forc'd expressions, &c. if these are not to be ascrib'd to the foresaid accidental reasons, they must be charg'd upon the Poet himself, and there is no help for it. But I think the two Disadvantages which I have mentioned (to be obliged to please the lowest of people, and to keep the worst of company) if the consideration be extended as far as it reasonably may, will appear sufficient to mislead and depress the greatest Genius upon earth. Nay the more modesty with which such a one is endued, the more he is in danger of submitting and conforming to others, against his own better judgment.

But as to his *Want of Learning*, it may be necessary to say something more: There is certainly a vast difference between *Learning* and *Languages*. How far he was ignorant of the latter, I cannot determine; but 'tis plain he had much Reading at least, if they will not call it Learning. Nor is it any great matter, if a man has Knowledge, whether he has it from one language or from another. Nothing is more evident than that he had a taste of natural Philosophy, Mechanicks, ancient and modern History, Poetical learning and Mythology: We find him very knowing in the customs, rites, and manners of Antiquity. In *Coriolanus* and *Julius Cæsar*, not only the Spirit, but Manners, of the *Romans* are exactly drawn; and still a nicer distinction is shown, between the manners of the *Romans* in the time of the former, and of the latter. His reading in the ancient Historians is no less conspicuous, in many references to particular passages: and the speeches copy'd from *Plutarch* in *Coriolanus* may, I think, as well be made an instance of his learning, as those copy'd from *Cicero* in *Catiline*, of *Ben Johnson's*. The manners of other nations in general, the *Egyptians*, *Venetians*, *French*, &c. are drawn with equal propriety. Whatever object of nature, or branch of science, he either speaks of or describes; it is always with competent, if not extensive knowledge: his descriptions are still exact; all his metaphors appropriated, and remarkably drawn from the true nature and inherent qualities of each subject. When he treats of Ethic or Politic, we may constantly observe a wonderful justness of distinction, as well as extent of comprehension. No one is more a master of the Poetical story, or has more frequent allusions to the various parts of it: Mr. *Waller* (who has been celebrated for this last particular) has not shown more learning this way than *Shakespear*. We have Translations from *Ovid* published in his name,

among those Poems which pass for his, and for some of
which we have undoubted authority, (being published
by himself, and dedicated to his noble Patron the Earl
of *Southampton*:) He appears also to have been conversant in *Plautus*, from whom he has taken the plot of one
of his plays: he follows the *Greek* Authors, and particularly *Dares Phrygius*, in another: (altho' I will not pretend
to say in what language he read them.) The modern
Italian writers of Novels he was manifestly acquainted
with; and we may conclude him to be no less conversant
with the Ancients of his own country, from the use he
has made of *Chaucer* in *Troilus* and *Cressida*, and in the
Two Noble Kinsmen, if that Play be his, as there goes a
Tradition it was, (and indeed it has little resemblance of
Fletcher, and more of our Author than some of those
which have been received as genuine.)

I am inclined to think, this opinion proceeded originally from the zeal of the Partizans of our Author and
Ben Johnson; as they endeavoured to exalt the one at the
expence of the other. It is ever the nature of Parties to
be in extremes; and nothing is so probable, as that because *Ben Johnson* had much the most learning, it was said
on the one hand that *Shakespear* had none at all; and
because *Shakespear* had much the most wit and fancy, it
was retorted on the other, that *Johnson* wanted both.
Because *Shakespear* borrowed nothing, it was said that
Ben Johnson borrowed every thing. Because *Johnson* did
not write extempore, he was reproached with being a
year about every piece; and because *Shakespear* wrote
with ease and rapidity, they cryed, he never once made
a blot. Nay the spirit of opposition ran so high, that
whatever those of the one side objected to the other, was
taken at the rebound, and turned into Praises; as injudiciously, as their antagonists before had made them
Objections. . . .

I will conclude by saying of *Shakespear*, that with all his faults, and with all the irregularity of his *Drama*, one may look upon his works, in comparison of those that are more finish'd and regular, as upon an ancient majestick piece of *Gothick* Architecture, compar'd with a neat Modern building: The latter is more elegant and glaring, but the former is more strong and more solemn. It must be allow'd, that in one of these there are materials enough to make many of the other. It has much the greater variety, and much the nobler apartments; tho' we are often conducted to them by dark, odd, and uncouth passages. Nor does the Whole fail to strike us with greater reverence, tho' many of the Parts are childish, ill-plac'd, and unequal to its grandeur.

From the Preface to Pope's edition of The Works
of Shakespear, 1725.

SHAKESPEAR, (whom you and ev'ry Play-house bill
Style the divine, the matchless, what you will)
For gain, not glory, wing'd his roving flight
And grew Immortal in his own despight.

. . . . .

Late, very late, correctness grew our care
When the tir'd nation breath'd from civil war.
Exact Racine, and Corneille's noble fire
Show'd us that France had something to admire.
Not but the Tragic spirit was our own,
And full in Shakespear, fair in Otway shone:
But Otway fail'd to polish or refine,
And fluent Shakespear scarce effac'd a line.
Ev'n copious Dryden wanted, or forgot,
The last and greatest Art, the Art to blot.

From the Epistle 'To Augustus,' 1737, ll. 69-72,
272-281.

THOMAS GRAY

In truth, Shakespear's language is one of his principal
beauties; and he has no less advantage over your Addi-
sons and Rowes in this, than in those other great excellencies you mention. Every word in him is a picture.
Pray put me the following lines into the tongue of our
modern Dramatics:

> But I, that am not shaped for sportive tricks,
> Nor made to court an amorous looking-glass:
> I, that am rudely stampt, and want love's majesty
> To strut before a wanton ambling nymph:
> I, that am curtail'd of this fair proportion,
> Cheated of feature by dissembling nature,
> Deform'd, unfinish'd, sent before my time
> Into this breathing world, scarce half made up—

And what follows. To me they appear untranslatable; and
if this be the case, our language is greatly degenerated.

> *From a Letter to Richard West, April 1742 (first*
> *published in Mason's 'Memoirs of Gray,' 1775).*

> Far from the sun and summer-gale,
> In thy[1] green lap was Nature's Darling laid,
> What time, where lucid Avon stray'd,
> To Him the mighty Mother did unveil
> Her aweful face: The dauntless Child
> Stretch'd forth his little arms, and smiled.
> This pencil take (she said) whose colours clear
> Richly paint the vernal year:
> Thine too these golden keys, immortal Boy!
> This can unlock the gates of Joy;
> Of Horrour that, and thrilling Fears,
> Or ope the sacred source of sympathetic Tears.

> *From The Progress of Poesy, 1757.*

[1] Albion's.

JOSEPH WARTON

The Tempest[1]

WRITERS of a mixed character, that abound in trans-
cendent beauties and in gross imperfections, are the most
proper and most pregnant subjects for criticism. The
regularity and correctness of a Virgil or Horace, almost
confine their commentators to perpetual panegyric, and
afford them few opportunities of diversifying their remarks by the detection of latent blemishes. For this
reason, I am inclined to think, that a few observations
on the writings of Shakespeare, will not be deemed useless or unentertaining, because he exhibits more numerous examples of excellencies and faults, of every kind,
than are, perhaps, to be discovered in any other author.
I shall, therefore, from time to time, examine his merit
as a poet, without blind admiration, or wanton invective.

As Shakespeare is sometimes blameable for the conduct of his fables, which have no unity; and sometimes
for his diction, which is obscure and turgid; so his
characteristical excellencies may possibly be reduced to
these three general heads: 'his lively creative imagination; his strokes of nature and passion; and his preservation of the consistency of his characters.' These excellencies, particularly the last, are of so much importance

[1] Warton's five papers in *The Adventurer* on *The Tempest* and
King Lear have the historical interest of being the first pieces of
Shakespeare criticism to form a series in a periodical. In this
respect they correspond to Addison's papers on Milton in *The
Spectator*.

In 1715 Lewis Theobald had contributed to *The Censor* two
papers (Nos. 7 and 10) on *King Lear*. The first of them gives 'an
abstract of the real story.' and only the second is critical.

in the drama, that they amply compensate for his trans-
gressions against the rules of Time and Place, which
being of a more mechanical nature, are often strictly
observed by a genius of the lowest order; but to portraye
characters naturally, and to preserve them uniformly,
requires such an intimate knowledge of the heart of
man, and is so rare a portion of felicity, as to have been
enjoyed, perhaps, only by two writers, Homer and
Shakespeare.

Of all the plays of Shakespeare, the *Tempest* is the
most striking instance of his creative power. He has
there given the reins to his boundless imagination, and
has carried the romantic, the wonderful, and the wild,
to the most pleasing extravagance. The scene is a
desolate island; and the characters the most new and
singular that can well be conceived; a prince who practises magic, an attendant spirit, a monster the son of a
witch, and a young lady who had been brought to this
solitude in her infancy, and had never beheld a man
except her father.

As I have affirmed that Shakespeare's chief excellence
is the consistency of his characters, I will exemplify the
truth of this remark, by pointing out some master-
strokes of this nature in the drama before us. . . .

From The Adventurer, No. 93. September 25,
1753.

'WHOEVER ventures,' says Horace, 'to form a character
totally original, let him endeavour to preserve it with
uniformity and consistency; but the formation of an
original character is a work of great difficulty and hazard.' In this arduous and uncommon task, however,
Shakespeare has wonderfully succeeded in his *Tempest*:

the monster Calyban is the creature of his own imagination, in the formation of which he could derive no assistance from observation or experience.

Calyban is the son of a witch begotten by a demon: the sorceries of his mother were so terrible, that her countrymen banished her into this desart island as unfit for human society: in conformity, therefore, to this diabolical propagation, he is represented as a prodigy of cruelty, malice, pride, ignorance, idleness, gluttony, and lust. He is introduced with great propriety, cursing Prospero and Miranda whom he had endeavoured to defile; and his execrations are artfully contrived to have reference to the occupations of his mother:

> As wicked dew, as e'er my mother brush'd
> With raven's feather from unwholesome fen,
> Drop on you both!————————
> ————————All the charms
> Of Sycorax, toads, beetles, bats, light on you!

His kindness is, afterwards, expressed as much in character, as his hatred, by an enumeration of offices, that could be of value only in a desolate island, and in the estimation of a savage:

> I pr'ythee, let me bring thee where crabs grow;
> And I with my long nails will dig thee pig-nuts;
> Shew thee a jay's nest; and instruct thee how
> To snare the nimble marmazet. I'll bring thee
> To clust'ring filberds; and sometimes I'll get thee
> Young sea-malls from the rock————
> I'll shew thee the best springs; I'll pluck thee berries;
> I'll fish for thee, and get thee wood enough.

Which last is, indeed, a circumstance of great use in a place, where to be defended from the cold was neither easy nor usual; and it has a farther peculiar beauty, because the gathering wood was the occupation to which

Calyban was subjècted by Prospero, who, therefore,
deemed it a service of high importance.

The gross ignorance of this monster is represented
with delicate judgment: he knew not the names of the
sun and moon, which he calls the bigger light and
the less; and he believes that Stephano was the man in the
moon, whom his mistress had often shewn him: and
when Prospero reminds him that he first taught him to
pronounce articulately, his answer is full of malevolence
and rage:

> You taught me language; and my profit on't
> Is, I know how to curse:————

the properest return for such a fiend to make for such a
favour. The spirits whom he supposes to be employed
by Prospero perpetually to torment him, and the many
forms and different methods they take for this purpose, are
described with the utmost liveliness and force of fancy:

> Sometimes like apes, that moe and chatter at me,
> And after bite me; then like hedge-hogs, which
> Lie tumbling in my bare-foot way, and mount
> Their pricks at my foot-fall: sometimes am I
> All wound with adders, who with cloven tongues
> Do hiss me into madness.

It is scarcely possible for any speech to be more expressive of the manners and sentiments, than that in which
our poet has painted the brutal barbarity and unfeeling
savageness of this son of Sycorax, by making him enu-
merate, with a kind of horrible delight, the various ways
in which it was possible for the drunken sailors to surprize and kill his master:

> ————There thou may'st brain him,
> Having first seiz'd his books; or with a log
> Batter his skull; or paunch him with a stake;
> Or cut his wezand with thy knife————

He adds, in allusion to his own abominable attempt, 'above all be sure to secure the daughter; whose beauty, he tells them, is incomparable.' The charms of Miranda could not be more exalted, than by extorting this testimony from so insensible a monster.

Shakespeare seems to be the only poet who possesses the power of uniting poetry with propriety of character; of which I know not an instance more striking, than the image Calyban makes use of to express silence, which is at once highly poetical and exactly suited to the wildness of the speaker:

Pray you tread softly, that the blind mole may not
Hear a foot-fall.————

I always lament that our author has not preserved this fierce and implacable spirit in Calyban, to the end of the play; instead of which, he has, I think, injudiciously put into his mouth, words that imply repentance and understanding:

————I'll be wise hereafter
And seek for grace. What a thrice double ass
Was I, to take this drunkard for a God,
And worship this dull fool!

It must not be forgotten, that Shakespeare has artfully taken occasion from this extraordinary character, which is finely contrasted to the mildness and obedience of Ariel, obliquely to satirize the prevailing passion for new and wonderful sights, which has rendered the English so ridiculous. 'Were I in England now,' says Trinculo, on first discovering Calyban, 'and had but this fish painted, not an holiday fool there but would give a piece of silver.—When they will not give a doit to relieve a lame beggar, they will lay out ten to see a dead Indian.'

Such is the inexhaustible plenty of our poet's invention, that he has exhibited another character in this play, entirely his own; that of the lovely and innocent Miranda.

When Prospero first gives her a sight of Prince Ferdinand, she eagerly exclaims,

> ————What is't? a spirit?
> Lord, how it looks about! Believe me, Sir,
> It carries a brave form. But 'tis a spirit.

Her imagining that as he was so beautiful he must necessarily be one of her father's aërial agents, is a stroke of nature worthy admiration: as are likewise her entreaties to her father not to use him harshly, by the power of his art;

> Why speaks my father so ungently? This
> Is the third man that e'er I saw; the first
> That e'er I sigh'd for!————

Here we perceive the beginning of that passion, which Prospero was desirous she should feel for the prince; and which she afterwards more fully expresses upon an occasion which displays at once the tenderness, the innocence, and the simplicity of her character. She discovers her lover employed in the laborious task of carrying wood, which Prospero had enjoined him to perform. 'Would,' says she, 'the lightning had burnt up those logs that you are enjoined to pile!'

> ————If you'll sit down
> I'll bear your logs the while. Pray give me that,
> I'll carry't to the pile.————
> ————You look wearily.

It is by selecting such little and almost imperceptible circumstances, that Shakespeare has more truly painted the passions than any other writer: affection is more powerfully expressed by this simple wish and offer of assistance, than by the unnatural eloquence and witticisms of Dryden, or the amorous declamations of Rowe.

The resentment of Prospero for the matchless cruelty
and wicked usurpation of his brother; his parental affection and solicitude for the welfare of his daughter, the
heiress of his dukedom; and the awful solemnity of his
character, as a skilful magician; are all along preserved
with equal consistency, dignity, and decorum. One
part of his behaviour deserves to be particularly pointed
out: during the exhibition of a mask with which he had
ordered Ariel to entertain Ferdinand and Miranda, he
starts suddenly from the recollection of the conspiracy
of Calyban and his confederates against his life, and dismisses his attendant spirits, who instantly vanish to a
hollow and confused noise. He appears to be greatly
moved; and suitably to this agitation of mind, which
his danger has excited, he takes occasion, from the sudden disappearance of the visionary scene, to moralize
on the dissolution of all things:

> ———These our actors,
> As I foretold you, were all spirits; and
> Are melted into air, into thin air.
> And, like the baseless fabric of this vision,
> The cloud-capt towers, the gorgeous palaces,
> The solemn temples, the great globe itself,
> Yea, all which it inherit, shall dissolve;
> And, like this unsubstantial pageant faded,
> Leave not a rack behind———

To these noble images he adds a short but comprehensive observation on human life, not excelled by any
passage of the moral and sententious Euripides:

> ———We are such stuff
> As dreams are made on; and our little life
> Is rounded with a sleep!———

Thus admirably is an uniformity of character, that
leading beauty in dramatic poesy, preserved throughout the *Tempest*. And it may be farther remarked, that

the unities of action, of place, and of time, are in this play, though almost constantly violated by Shakespeare, exactly observed. The action is one, great, and entire, the restoration of Prospero to his dukedom; this business is transacted in the compass of a small island, and in or near the cave of Prospero; though, indeed, it had been more artful and regular to have confined it to this single spot; and the time which the action takes up, is only equal to that of the representation; an excellence which ought always to be aimed at in every well-conducted fable, and for the want of which a variety of the most entertaining incidents can scarcely atone.

The Adventurer, No. 97. October 9, 1753.

King Lear

ONE of the most remarkable differences betwixt ancient and modern tragedy, arises from the prevailing custom of describing only those distresses that are occasioned by the passion of love; a passion which, from the universality of its dominion, may doubtless justly claim a large share in representations of human life; but which, by totally engrossing the theatre, hath contributed to degrade that noble school of virtue into an academy of effeminacy.

When Racine persuaded the celebrated Arnauld to read his *Phædra*, 'Why,' said that severe critic to his friend, 'have you falsified the manners of Hippolitus, and represented him in love?'—'Alas!' replied the poet, 'without that circumstance, how would the ladies and the beaux have received my piece?' And it may well be imagined, that to gratify so considerable and important a part of his audience, was the powerful motive that induced Corneille to enervate even the matchless and affecting story of Œdipus, by the frigid and impertinent episode of Theseus's passion for Dirce.

Shakespeare has shewn us, by his *Hamlet*, *Macbeth*, and *Cæsar*, and above all by his *Lear*, that very interesting tragedies may be written, that are not founded on gallantry and love; and that Boileau was mistaken, when he affirmed,

> ———*de l'amour la sensible peinture,*
> *Est pour aller au cœur la route la plus sûre.*

> Those tender scenes that pictur'd love impart,
> Insure success and best engage the heart.

The distresses in this tragedy are of a very uncommon nature, and are not touched upon by any other dramatic author. They are occasioned by a rash resolution of an aged monarch of strong passions and quick sensibility, to resign his crown and to divide his kingdom amongst his three daughters; the youngest of whom, who was his favourite, not answering his sanguine expectations in expressions of affection to him, he for ever banishes, and endows her sisters with her allotted share. Their unnatural ingratitude, the intolerable affronts, indignities and cruelties he suffers from them, and the remorse he feels from his imprudent resignation of his power, at first inflame him with the most violent rage, and by degrees drive him to madness and death. This is the outline of the fable.

I shall confine myself at present to consider singly the judgment and art of the poet, in describing the origin and progress of the distraction of Lear; in which, I think, he has succeeded better than any other writer; even than Euripides himself, whom Longinus so highly commends for his representation of the madness of Orestes.

It is well contrived, that the first affront that is offered Lear, should be a proposal from Gonerill, his eldest daughter, to lessen the number of his knights, which must needs affect and irritate a person so jealous of his rank and the respect due to it. He is at first astonished at the complicated impudence and ingratitude of this design; but quickly kindles into rage, and resolves to depart instantly:

>——Darkness and devils!——
> Saddle my horses, call my train together—
> Degen'rate bastard, I'll not trouble thee.——

This is followed by a severe reflection upon his own folly for resigning his crown; and a solemn invocation to Nature, to heap the most horrible curses on the head of Gonerill, that her own offspring may prove equally cruel and unnatural;

>——That she may feel,
> How sharper than a serpent's tooth it is,
> To have a thankless child!——

When Albany demands the cause of this passion, Lear answers, 'I'll tell thee!' but immediately cries out to Gonerill,

>——Life and death! I am asham'd,
> That thou hast power to shake my manhood thus.
> ——Blasts and fogs upon thee!
> Th' untented woundings of a father's curse
> Pierce every sense about thee!

He stops a little and reflects:

>   Ha! is it come to this?
> Let it be so! I have another daughter,
> Who, I am sure, is kind and comfortable.
> When she shall hear this of thee, with her nails
> She'll flea thy wolfish visage——

He was, however, mistaken; for the first object he encounters in the castle of the Earl of Gloucester, whither he fled to meet his other daughter, was his servant in the stocks; from whence he may easily conjecture what reception he is to meet with:

> ————Death on my state! Wherefore
> Should he sit here?

He adds immediately afterwards,

> O me, my heart! my rising heart!—but down.

By which single line, the inexpressible anguish of his mind, and the dreadful conflict of opposite passions with which it is agitated, are more forcibly expressed, than by the long and laboured speech, enumerating the causes of his anguish, that Rowe and other modern tragic writers would certainly have put into his mouth. But Nature, Sophocles, and Shakespeare, represent the feelings of the heart in a different manner; by a broken hint, a short exclamation, a word, or a look:

> They mingle not, 'mid deep-felt sighs and groans,
> Descriptions gay, or quaint comparisons.
> No flowery far-fetch'd thoughts their scenes admit;
> Ill suits conceit with passion, woe with wit.
> Here passion prompts each short, expressive speech;
> Or silence paints what words can never reach.   J. W.

When Jocasta, in Sophocles, has discovered that Œdipus was the murderer of her husband, she immediately leaves the stage; but in Corneille and Dryden, she continues on it during a whole scene, to bewail her destiny in set speeches. I should be guilty of insensibility and injustice, if I did not take this occasion to acknowledge, that I have been more moved and delighted, by hearing this single line spoken by the only actor of the age who understands and relishes these little touches of nature, and therefore the only one qualified to personate this most difficult character of Lear, than by the most pom-

pous declaimer of the most pompous speeches in *Cato
Tamerlane*. . . .

From The Adventurer, No. 113. December 4, 1753.

THUNDER and a ghost have been frequently introduced
into tragedy by barren and mechanical play-wrights, as
proper objects to impress terror and astonishment, where
the distress has not been important enough to render it
probable that nature would interpose for the sake of the
sufferers, and where these objects themselves have not been
supported by suitable sentiments. Thunder has, however,
been made use of with great judgment and good effect by
Shakespeare, to heighten and impress the distresses of Lear.

The venerable and wretched old king is driven out
by both his daughters, without necessaries and without
attendants, not only in the night, but in the midst of a
most dreadful storm, and on a bleak and barren heath.
On his first appearance in this situation, he draws an
artful and pathetic comparison betwixt the severity of
the tempest and of his daughters:

> Rumble thy belly full! spit, fire! spout, rain!
> Nor rain, wind, thunder, fire, are my daughters.
> I tax not you, you elements, with unkindness;
> I never gave you kingdom, called you children;
> You owe me no subscription. Then let fall
> Your horrible pleasure. Here I stand your slave;
> A poor, infirm, weak, and despis'd old man!

The storm continuing with equal violence, he drops
for a moment the consideration of his own miseries, and
takes occasion to moralize on the terrors which such
commotions of nature should raise in the breast of secret
and unpunished villainy:

> ————————Tremble thou wretch,
> That hast within thee undivulged crimes
> Unwhipt of justice! Hide thee, thou bloody hand;
> Thou perjur'd, and thou simular of virtue

>   That art incestuous!—
>   —Close pent-up guilts
>   Rive your concealing continents, and cry
>   These dreadful summoners grace!—

He adds, with reference to his own case,

>   ————I am a man
>   More sinn'd against, than sinning.

Kent most earnestly entreats him to enter a hovel which
he had discovered on the heath; and on pressing him
again and again to take shelter there, Lear exclaims,

>   Wilt break my heart?————

Much is contained in these four words; as if he had said,
'the kindness and the gratitude of this servant exceeds
that of my own children. Tho' I have given them a
kingdom, yet have they basely discarded me, and suffered a head so old and white as mine to be exposed to
this terrible tempest, while this fellow pities and would
protect me from its rage. I cannot bear this kindness from
a perfect stranger; it breaks my heart.' All this seems
to be included in that short exclamation, which another
writer, less acquainted with nature, would have displayed
at large: such a suppression of sentiments plainly implied,
is judicious and affecting. The reflections that follow are
drawn likewise from an intimate knowledge of man:

>   When the mind's free,
>   The body's delicate: the tempest in my mind
>   Doth from my senses take all feeling else,
>   Save what beats there.————

Here the remembrance of his daughters behaviour rushes
upon him, and he exclaims, full of the idea of its unparalleled cruelty,

>   ————Filial ingratitude!
>   Is it not, as this mouth should tear this hand
>   For lifting food to it!—

He then changes his stile, and vows with impotent menaces, as if still in possession of the power he had resigned, to revenge himself on his oppressors, and to steel his breast with fortitude:

> ———But I'll punish home.
> No, I will weep no more!—

But the sense of his sufferings returns again, and he forgets the resolution he had formed the moment before:

> In such a night,
> To shut me out?—Pour on, I will endure—
> In such a night as this?———

At which, with a beautiful apostrophe, he suddenly addresses himself to his absent daughters, tenderly reminding them of the favours he had so lately and so liberally conferred upon them:

> ———O Regan, Gonerill,
> Your old kind father; whose frank heart gave all!—
> O that way madness lies; let me shun that;
> No more of that!—

The turns of passion in these few lines are so quick and so various, that I thought they merited to be minutely pointed out by a kind of perpetual commentary.

The mind is never so sensibly disposed to pity the misfortunes of others, as when it is itself subdued and softened by calamity. Adversity diffuses a kind of sacred calm over the breast, that is the parent of thoughtfulness and meditation. The following reflections of Lear in his next speech, when his passion has subsided for a short interval, are equally proper and striking:

> Poor naked wretches, wheresoe'er ye are,
> That bide the pelting of this pityless storm!
> How shall your houseless heads and unfed sides,
> Your loop'd and window'd raggedness, defend you
> From seasons such as these!

He concludes with a sentiment finely suited to his condition, and worthy to be written in characters of gold in the closet of every monarch upon earth:

> O! I have ta'en
> Too little care of this. Take physic, pomp!
> Expose thyself to feel what wretches feel;
> That thou may'st shake the superflux to them,
> And shew the Heav'ns more just!————

Lear being at last persuaded to take shelter in the hovel, the poet has artfully contrived to lodge there Edgar, the discarded son of Gloucester, who counterfeits the character and habit of a mad begger, haunted by an evil demon, and whose supposed sufferings are enumerated with an inimitable wildness of fancy; 'Whom the foul fiend hath led thro' fire, and thro' flame, thro' ford and whirlpool, o'er bog and quagmire; that hath laid knives under his pillow, and halters in his pew; set ratsbane by his porridge; made him proud of heart, to ride on a bay trotting horse over four inch'd bridges, to course his own shadow for a traitor.—Bless thy five wits, Tom's a cold!' The assumed madness of Edgar and the real distraction of Lear, form a judicious contrast.

Upon perceiving the nakedness and wretchedness of this figure, the poor king asks a question that I never could read without strong emotions of pity and admiration:

> What! have his daughters brought him to this pass?
> Couldst thou save nothing? Didst thou give them all?

And when Kent assures him, that the begger hath no daughters, he hastily answers;

> Death, traitor, nothing could have subdued nature
> To such a lowness, but his unkind daughters.

Afterwards, upon the calm contemplation of the misery of Edgar, he breaks out into the following serious and pathetic reflection: 'Thou wert better in thy grave, than to answer with thy uncovered body this extremity of the skies. Is man no more than this? Consider him well. Thou ow'st the worm no silk, the beast no hide, the sheep no wool, the cat no perfume. Ha! here's three of us are sophisticated. Thou art the thing itself: unaccommodated man is no more than such a poor, bare, forked animal as thou art. Off, off, you lendings! Come, unbutton here.'

Shakespeare has no where exhibited more inimitable strokes of his art, than in this uncommon scene; where he has so well conducted even the natural jargon of the begger, and the jestings of the fool, which in other hands must have sunk into burlesque, that they contribute to heighten the pathetic to a very high degree.

The heart of Lear having been agitated and torn by a conflict of such opposite and tumultuous passions, it is not wonderful that his 'wits should now begin to unsettle.' The first plain indication of the loss of his reason, is his calling Edgar a 'learned Theban;' and telling Kent, that 'he will keep still with his philosopher.' When he next appears, he imagines he is punishing his daughters. The imagery is extremely strong, and chills one with horror to read it.

> To have a thousand with red burning spits
> Come hizzing in upon them!———

As the fancies of lunatics have an extraordinary force and liveliness, and render the objects of their frenzy as it were present to their eyes, Lear actually thinks himself suddenly restored to his kingdom, and seated in judgment to try his daughters for their cruelties:

> I'll see their trial first; bring in the evidence.
> Thou robed man of justice take thy place;
> And thou, his yoke-fellow of equity,

> Bench by his side. You are of the commission,
> Sit you too. Arraign her first, 'tis Gonerill———
> And here's another, whose warpt looks proclaim
> What store her heart is made of.———

Here he imagines that Regan escapes out of his hands, and he eagerly exclaims,

> ———Stop her there.
> Arms, arms, sword, fire—Corruption in the place!
> False justicer, why hast thou let her 'scape?

A circumstance follows that is strangely moving indeed; for he fancies that his favourite domestic creatures, that used to fawn upon and caress him, and of which he was eminently fond, have now their tempers changed, and joined to insult him:

> ———The little dogs and all,
> Tray, Blanch, and Sweet-heart, see! they bark at me.

He again resumes his imaginary power, and orders them to anatomize Regan; 'See what breeds about her heart— Is there any cause in nature that makes these hard hearts? You, Sir,' speaking to Edgar, 'I entertain for one of my Hundred;' a circumstance most artfully introduced to remind us of the first affront he received, and to fix our thoughts on the causes of his distraction.

General criticism is on all subjects useless and unentertaining; but is more than commonly absurd with respect to Shakespeare, who must be accompanied step by step, and scene by scene, in his gradual developements of characters and passions, and whose finer features must be singly pointed out, if we would do compleat justice to his genuine beauties. It would have been easy to have declared, in general terms, 'that the madness of Lear was very natural and pathetic;' and the reader might then have escaped, what he may, perhaps, call a multitude of well known quotations: but then it had been impossible to exhibit a perfect picture of the secret workings and changes of Lear's mind, which vary in each succeeding passage, and which render an allegation of each particular sentiment absolutely necessary.

The Adventurer, No. 116. December 15, 1753.

I SHALL transiently observe, in conclusion of these remarks, that this drama is chargeable with considerable imperfections. The plot of Edmund against his brother, which distracts the attention, and destroys the unity of the fable; the cruel and horrid extinction of Glo'ster's eyes, which ought not to be exhibited on the stage; the utter improbability of Glo'ster's imagining, though blind, that he had leaped down Dover cliff; and some passages that are too turgid and full of strained metaphors; are faults which the warmest admirers of Shakespeare will find it difficult to excuse. I know not, also, whether the cruelty of the daughters is not painted with circumstances too savage and unnatural; for it is not sufficient to say, that this monstrous barbarity is founded on historical truth, if we recollect the just observation of Boileau,

Le vray peut quelquefois n'être pas vraisemblable.
Some truths may be too strong to be believed.—SOMES.

From The Adventurer, No. 122. January 5, 1754.

HENRY HOME, LORD KAMES[1]

Dramatic Representation of Passion

THIS descriptive manner of representing passion, is a very cold entertainment: our sympathy is not raised by description; we must first be lulled into a dream of reality, and every thing must appear as passing in our sight. Unhappy is the player of genius who acts a capital part in what may be termed a *descriptive tragedy*: after assuming the very passion that is to be represented, how is he cramped in action, when he must utter, not the sentiments of the passion he feels, but a cold description in the language of a bystander? It is this imperfection, I am persuaded, in the bulk of our plays, that confines our stage almost entirely to Shakespear, notwithstanding his many irregularities. In our late English tragedies, we sometimes find sentiments tolerably well adapted to a plain passion: but we must not, in any of them, expect a sentiment expressive of character; and, upon that very account, our late performances of the dramatic kind are for the most part intolerably insipid.

Elements of Criticism, chap. XVI.

[Kames proceeds to illustrate the difference between 'sentiments that appear the legitimate offspring of passion' and sentiments that are 'descriptive only, and illegitimate', by instances from Shakespeare and Corneille.]

[1] Henry Home of Kames (1696–1782) was generally known as 'Lord Kames', the judicial title which he took when raised to the Scottish bench in 1752.
Elements of Criticism was published in Edinburgh in 1762. It went into many editions, the fifth, 1774 (which has been used for the above extracts), being the last to appear in the author's lifetime. Benjamin Heath in the Dedication of *A Revisal of Shakespear's Text*, published in 1765 before Johnson's edition, describes Kames as 'the truest judge and most intelligent admirer of Shakespear'.

SHAKESPEAR is superior to all other writers in delineating passion. It is difficult to say in what part he most excels, whether in moulding every passion to peculiarity of character, in discovering the sentiments that proceed from various tones of passion, or in expressing properly every different sentiment: he disgusts not his reader with general declamation and unmeaning words, too common in other writers: his sentiments are adjusted to the peculiar character and circumstances of the speaker; and the propriety is not less perfect between his sentiments and his diction. That this is no exaggeration, will be evident to every one of taste, upon comparing Shakespear with other writers in similar passages. If upon any occasion he fall below himself, it is in those scenes where passion enters not: by endeavouring in that case to raise his dialogue above the style of ordinary conversation, he sometimes deviates into intricate thought and obscure expression: sometimes, to throw his language out of the familiar, he employs rhyme. But may it not in some measure excuse Shakespear, I shall not say his works, that he had no pattern, in his own or in any living language, of dialogue fitted for the theatre? At the same time, it ought not to escape observation, that the stream clears in its progress, and that in his later plays he has attained the purity and perfection of dialogue; an observation that, with greater certainty than tradition, will direct us to arrange his plays in the order of time. This ought to be considered, by those who rigidly exaggerate every blemish of the finest genius for the drama ever the world enjoy'd: they ought also for their own sake to consider, that it is easier to discover his blemishes, which lie generally at the surface, than his beauties, which cannot be truly relished but by those who dive deep into human nature. One thing must be evident to the meanest capacity, that where-ever passion is to be display'd,

Nature shows itself mighty in him, and is conspicuous
by the most delicate propriety of sentiment and expression.[1]

Chap. XVII.

Shakespeare's Style

ABSTRACT or general terms have no good effect in any
composition for amusement; because it is only of particular objects that images can be formed. Shakespear's
style in that respect is excellent: every article in his descriptions is particular, as in nature; and if accidentally
a vague expression slip in, the blemish is discernible by
the bluntness of its impression. . . . It was one of Homer's
advantages, that he wrote before general terms were
multiplied: the superior genius of Shakespear displays
itself in avoiding them after they were multiplied.

Chap. XXI.

[1] The critics seem not perfectly to comprehend the genius of
Shakespear. His plays are defective in the mechanical part,
which is less the work of genius than of experience; and is not
otherwise brought to perfection but by diligently observing
the errors of former compositions. Shakespeare excels all the
ancients and moderns, in knowledge of human nature, and in
unfolding even the most obscure and refined emotions. This is
a rare faculty, and of the greatest importance in a dramatic
author; and it is that faculty which makes him surpass all other
writers in the comic as well as tragic vein.

GEORGE, LORD LYTTELTON

DIALOGUES OF THE DEAD

Boileau—Pope

Boileau. . . . But I am still more angry with you for your edition of Shakespear. The office of an *editor* was below you, and your mind was unfit for the drudgery it requires. Would any body think of employing a Raphael to clean an old picture?

Pope. The principal cause of my undertaking that task was zeal for the honour of Shakespear: and, if you knew all his beauties as well as I, you would not wonder at this zeal. No other author had ever so copious, so bold, so *creative* an imagination, with so perfect a knowledge of the passions, the humours, and sentiments of mankind. He painted all characters, from kings down to peasants, with equal truth and equal force. If human nature were destroyed, and no monument were left of it except his works, other beings might know *what man was* from those writings.

Boileau. You say he painted all characters, from kings down to peasants, with equal truth and equal force. I can't deny that he did so: but I wish he had not jumbled those characters together, in the composition of his pictures, as he has frequently done.

Pope. The strange mixture of tragedy, comedy, and farce, in the same play, nay sometimes in the same scene, I acknowledge to be quite inexcusable. But this was the taste of the times when Shakespear wrote.

Boileau. A great genius ought to guide, not servilely follow, the taste of his contemporaries.

Pope. Consider from how thick a darkness of barbarism the genius of Shakespear broke forth! What were the English, and what (let me ask you) were the French dramatic performances, in the age when he flourished? The advances he made towards the highest perfection both of tragedy and comedy are amazing! In the principal points, in the power of exciting terror and pity, or raising laughter in an audience, none yet has excelled him, and very few have equalled.

Boileau. Do you think that he was equal in comedy to Molière?

Pope. In *comic force* I do: but in the fine and delicate strokes of satire, and what is called *genteel comedy*, he was greatly inferior to that admirable writer. There is nothing in him to compare with the *Misanthrope*, the *École des Femmes*, or *Tartuffe*.

Boileau. This, Mr. Pope, is a great deal for an Englishman to acknowledge. A veneration for Shakespear seems to be a part of your national religion, and the only part in which even your men of sense are fanatics.

Pope. He who can read Shakespear, and be cool enough for all the accuracy of sober criticism, has more of reason than taste.

Boileau. I join with you in admiring him as a prodigy of genius, though I find the most shocking absurdities in his plays; absurdities which no critic of my nation can pardon.

Pope. We will be satisfied with your feeling the excellence of his beauties.

From Dialogues of the Dead, *Dialogue XIV.*[1]

[1] Only the opening remarks of Boileau and Pope in this extract are found in the first edition of the *Dialogues of the Dead*, 1760. The greater part of it was added in the fourth edition, 1765.

SAMUEL JOHNSON

WHEN Learning's Triumph o'er her barb'rous Foes
First rear'd the Stage, immortal SHAKESPEAR rose;
Each Change of many-colour'd Life he drew,
Exhausted Worlds, and then imagin'd new:
Existence saw him spurn her bounded Reign,
And panting Time toil'd after him in vain:
His pow'rful Strokes presiding Truth impress'd,
And unresisted Passion storm'd the Breast.

From the Prologue spoken by Mr. Garrick at the
Opening of the Theatre in Drury-Lane, 1747.

BUT the Truth is, that a very small Part of the Reputation of this mighty Genius depends upon the naked
Plot, or Story of his Plays. He lived in an Age when the
Books of Chivalry were yet popular, and when therefore the Minds of his Auditors were not accustomed to
balance Probabilities, or to examine nicely the Proportion between Causes and Effects. It was sufficient to
recommend a Story, that it was far removed from common Life, that its Changes were frequent, and its Close
pathetic.

This Disposition of the Age concurred so happily with
the Imagination of *Shakespear* that he had no Desire to
reform it, and indeed to this he was indebted for the
licentious Variety, by which he has made his Plays more
entertaining than those of any other Author.

He had looked with great Attention on the Scenes of
Nature; but his chief Skill was in Human Actions, Pas-
sions, and Habits; he was therefore delighted with such
Tales as afforded numerous Incidents, and exhibited
many Characters, in many Changes of Situation. These
Characters are so copiously diversified, and some of

them so justly pursued, that his Works may be con-
sidered as a Map of Life, a faithful Miniature of human
Transactions, and he that has read *Shakespear* with
Attention, will perhaps find little new in the crouded
World.

Among his other Excellencies it ought to be remarked,
because it has hitherto been unnoticed, that his *Heroes
are Men*, that the Love and Hatred, the Hopes and Fears
of his chief Personages are such as are common to other
human Beings, and not like those which later Times
have exhibited, peculiar to Phantoms that strut upon the
Stage.

It is not perhaps very necessary to enquire whether
the Vehicle of so much Delight and Instruction be a
Story probable, or unlikely, native, or foreign. *Shakespear*'s Excellence is not the Fiction of a Tale, but the
Representation of Life; and his Reputation is therefore
safe, till Human Nature shall be changed.

> *From the Dedication to* Shakespear Illustrated: or
> the Novels and Histories, On which the Plays
> of Shakespear Are Founded, 1753, *written by
> Johnson for the authoress,* Mrs. Charlotte Lennox.[1]

[1] The quotations from the Drury-Lane Prologue and the
Dedication to *Shakespear Illustrated* are given as representative of
Johnson's criticism before the publication of his deliberate and
mature opinions in his edition of Shakespeare (October, 1765).
In 1745 he had brought out *Miscellaneous Observations on the
Tragedy of Macbeth . . . To which is affix'd, Proposals for a New
Edition of Shakespear, with a Specimen;* and in 1756 he issued his
new *Proposals for Printing the Dramatic Works of William Shakespeare.* There is a notable paragraph on Shakespeare, 'that trans-
cendent and unbounded genius,' in the essay on tragi-comedy
in *The Rambler,* No. 156 (September 14, 1751); and Shakespeare's diction, with illustrations from *Macbeth,* is the main
topic of No. 168. Later criticisms, made in conversation, are
recorded by Boswell.

Preface to Shakespeare[1]

(1765)

THAT praises are without reason lavished on the dead, and that the honours due only to excellence are paid to antiquity, is a complaint likely to be always continued by those, who, being able to add nothing to truth, hope for eminence from the heresies of paradox; or those, who, being forced by disappointment upon consolatory expedients, are willing to hope from posterity what the present age refuses, and flatter themselves that the regard which is yet denied by envy, will be at last bestowed by time.

Antiquity, like every other quality that attracts the notice of mankind, has undoubtedly votaries that reverence it, not from reason, but from prejudice. Some seem to admire indiscriminately whatever has been long preserved, without considering that time has sometimes co-operated with chance; all perhaps are more willing to honour past than present excellence; and the mind contemplates genius through the shades of age, as the eye surveys the sun through artificial opacity. The great contention of criticism is to find the faults of the moderns, and the beauties of the ancients. While an authour is yet living we estimate his powers by his worst performance, and when he is dead we rate them by his best.

To works, however, of which the excellence is not absolute and definite, but gradual and comparative; to works not raised upon principles demonstrative and scientifick, but appealing wholly to observation and

---

[1] Portions of this Preface dealing with the editors of Shakespeare and the history of the text of the plays are here omitted. Recent reprints of the complete Preface will be found in Sir Walter Raleigh's *Johnson on Shakespeare*, 1908, and in the editor's *Eighteenth Century Essays on Shakespeare*, 1903.

experience, no other test can be applied than length of duration and continuance of esteem. What mankind have long possessed they have often examined and compared, and if they persist to value the possession, it is because frequent comparisons have confirmed opinion in its favour. As among the works of nature no man can properly call a river deep or a mountain high, without the knowledge of many mountains and many rivers; so in the productions of genius, nothing can be stiled excellent till it has been compared with other works of the same kind. Demonstration immediately displays its power, and has nothing to hope or fear from the flux of years; but works tentative and experimental must be estimated by their proportion to the general and collective ability of man, as it is discovered in a long succession of endeavours. Of the first building that was raised, it might be with certainty determined that it was round or square, but whether it was spacious or lofty must have been referred to time. The Pythagorean scale of numbers was at once discovered to be perfect; but the poems of *Homer* we yet know not to transcend the common limits of human intelligence, but by remarking, that nation after nation, and century after century, has been able to do little more than transpose his incidents, new name his characters, and paraphrase his sentiments.

The reverence due to writings that have long subsisted arises therefore not from any credulous confidence in the superior wisdom of past ages, or gloomy persuasion of the degeneracy of mankind, but is the consequence of acknowledged and indubitable positions, that what has been longest known has been most considered, and what is most considered is best understood.

The Poet, of whose works I have undertaken the revision, may now begin to assume the dignity of an ancient, and claim the privilege of established fame and prescriptive veneration. He has long outlived his century, the term commonly fixed as the test of literary merit. Whatever advantages he might once derive from personal allusions, local customs, or temporary opinions, have for many years been lost; and every topick of merriment or motive of sorrow, which the modes of artificial life afforded him, now only obscure the scenes which they once illuminated. The effects of favour and competition are at an end; the tradition of his friendships and his enmities has perished; his works support no opinion with arguments, nor supply any faction with invectives; they can neither indulge vanity nor gratify malignity, but are read without any other reason than the desire of pleasure, and are therefore praised only as pleasure is obtained; yet, thus unassisted by interest or passion, they have past through variations of taste and changes of manners, and, as they devolved from one generation to another, have received new honours at every transmission.

But because human judgment, though it be gradually gaining upon certainty, never becomes infallible; and approbation, though long continued, may yet be only the approbation of prejudice or fashion; it is proper to inquire, by what peculiarities of excellence *Shakespeare* has gained and kept the favour of his countrymen.

Nothing can please many, and please long, but just representations of general nature. Particular manners can be known to few, and therefore few only can judge how nearly they are copied. The irregular combinations of fanciful invention may delight a-while, by that novelty of which the common satiety of life sends us all in quest; but the pleasures of sudden wonder are soon exhausted, and the mind can only repose on the stability of truth.

Shakespeare is above all writers, at least above all modern writers, the poet of nature; the poet that holds

up to his readers a faithful mirrour of manners and of
life. His characters are not modified by the customs of
particular places, unpractised by the rest of the world;
by the peculiarities of studies or professions, which can
operate but upon small numbers; or by the accidents
of transient fashions or temporary opinions: they are
the genuine progeny of common humanity, such as the
world will always supply, and observation will always
find. His persons act and speak by the influence of those
general passions and principles by which all minds are
agitated, and the whole system of life is continued in
motion. In the writings of other poets a character is too
often an individual; in those of *Shakespeare* it is commonly a species.

It is from this wide extension of design that so much
instruction is derived. It is this which fills the plays of
Shakespeare with practical axioms and domestick wisdom. It was said of *Euripides*, that every verse was a
precept; and it may be said of *Shakespeare*, that from
his works may be collected a system of civil and oecono-
mical prudence. Yet his real power is not shewn in the
splendour of particular passages, but by the progress of
his fable, and the tenour of his dialogue; and he that tries
to recommend him by select quotations, will succeed
like the pedant in *Hierocles*, who, when he offered his
house to sale, carried a brick in his pocket as a specimen.

It will not easily be imagined how much *Shakespeare*
excells in accommodating his sentiments to real life,
but by comparing him with other authours. It was
observed of the ancient schools of declamation, that the
more diligently they were frequented, the more was the
student disqualified for the world, because he found
nothing there which he should ever meet in any other
place. The same remark may be applied to every stage
but that of *Shakespeare*. The theatre, when it is under

any other direction, is peopled by such characters as were never seen, conversing in a language which was never heard, upon topicks which will never arise in the commerce of mankind. But the dialogue of this authour is often so evidently determined by the incident which produces it, and is pursued with so much ease and simplicity, that it seems scarcely to claim the merit of fiction, but to have been gleaned by diligent selection out of common conversation, and common occurrences.

Upon every other stage the universal agent is love, by whose power all good and evil is distributed, and every action quickened or retarded. To bring a lover, a lady and a rival into the fable; to entangle them in contradictory obligations, perplex them with oppositions of interest, and harrass them with violence of desires inconsistent with each other; to make them meet in rapture and part in agony; to fill their mouths with hyperbolical joy and outrageous sorrow; to distress them as nothing human ever was distressed; to deliver them as nothing human ever was delivered, is the business of a modern dramatist. For this probability is violated, life is misrepresented, and language is depraved. But love is only one of many passions; and as it has no great influence upon the sum of life, it has little operation in the dramas of a poet, who caught his ideas from the living world, and exhibited only what he saw before him. He knew, that any other passion, as it was regular or exorbitant, was a cause of happiness or calamity.

Characters thus ample and general were not easily discriminated and preserved, yet perhaps no poet ever kept his personages more distinct from each other. I will not say with *Pope*, that every speech may be assigned to the proper speaker, because many speeches there are which have nothing characteristical; but perhaps, though some may be equally adapted to every person, it will be difficult to find, any that can be properly transferred from the present possessor to another claimant. The choice is right, when there is reason for choice.

Other dramatists can only gain attention by hyperbolical or aggravated characters, by fabulous and unexampled excellence or depravity, as the writers of barbarous romances invigorated the reader by a giant and a dwarf; and he that should form his expectations of human affairs from the play, or from the tale, would be equally deceived. *Shakespeare* has no heroes; his scenes are occupied only by men, who act and speak as the reader thinks that he should himself have spoken or acted on the same occasion: Even where the agency is supernatural the dialogue is level with life. Other writers disguise the most natural passions and most frequent incidents; so that he who contemplates them in the book will not know them in the world: *Shakespeare* approximates the remote, and familiarizes the wonderful; the event which he represents will not happen, but if it were possible, its effects would probably be such as he has assigned; and it may be said, that he has not only shewn human nature as it acts in real exigencies, but as it would be found in trials, to which it cannot be exposed.

This therefore is the praise of *Shakespeare*, that his drama is the mirrour of life; that he who has mazed his imagination, in following the phantoms which other writers raise up before him, may here be cured of his delirious extasies, by reading human sentiments in human language; by scenes from which a hermit may estimate the transactions of the world, and a confessor predict the progress of the passions.

His adherence to general nature has exposed him to the censure of criticks, who form their judgments upon narrower principles. *Dennis* and *Rhymer* think his

Romans not sufficiently Roman; and *Voltaire* censures his kings as not completely royal. *Dennis* is offended, that *Menenius*, a senator of *Rome*, should play the buffoon; and *Voltaire* perhaps thinks decency violated when the *Danish* Usurper is represented as a drunkard. But *Shakespeare* always makes nature predominate over accident; and if he preserves the essential character, is not very careful of distinctions super-induced and adventitious. His story requires Romans or kings, but he thinks only on men. He knew that *Rome*, like every other city, had men of all dispositions; and wanting a buffoon, he went into the senate-house for that which the senate-house would certainly have afforded him. He was inclined to shew an usurper and a murderer not only odious but despicable, he therefore added drunkenness to his other qualities, knowing that kings love wine like other men, and that wine exerts its natural power upon kings. These are the petty cavils of petty minds; a poet overlooks the casual distinction of country and condition, as a painter, satisfied with the figure, neglects the drapery.

The censure which he has incurred by mixing comick and tragick scenes, as it extends to all his works, deserves more consideration. Let the fact be first stated, and then examined.

Shakespeare's plays are not in the rigorous and critical sense either tragedies or comedies, but compositions of a distinct kind; exhibiting the real state of sublunary nature, which partakes of good and evil, joy and sorrow, mingled with endless variety of proportion and innumerable modes of combination; and expressing the course of the world, in which the loss of one is the gain of another; in which, at the same time, the reveller is hasting to his wine, and the mourner burying his friend; in which the malignity of one is sometimes defeated by the frolick of another; and many mischiefs and many benefits are done and hindered without design.

Out of this chaos of mingled purposes and casualties the ancient poets, according to the laws which custom had prescribed, selected some the crimes of men, and some their absurdities; some the momentous vicissitudes of life, and some the lighter occurrences; some the terrours of distress, and some the gayeties of prosperity. Thus rose the two modes of imitation, known by the names of *tragedy* and *comedy*, compositions intended to promote different ends by contrary means, and considered as so little allied, that I do not recollect among the *Greeks* or *Romans* a single writer who attempted both.

Shakespeare has united the powers of exciting laughter and sorrow not only in one mind but in one composition. Almost all his plays are divided between serious and ludicrous characters, and, in the successive evolutions of the design, sometimes produce seriousness and sorrow, and sometimes levity and laughter.

That this is a practice contrary to the rules of criticism will be readily allowed; but there is always an appeal open from criticism to nature. The end of writing is to instruct; the end of poetry is to instruct by pleasing. That the mingled drama may convey all the instruction of tragedy or comedy cannot be denied, because it includes both in its alterations of exhibition, and approaches nearer than either to the appearance of life, by shewing how great machinations and slender designs may promote or obviate one another, and the high and the low co-operate in the general system by unavoidable concatenation.

It is objected, that by this change of scenes the passions are interrupted in their progression, and that the principal event, being not advanced by a due gradation of preparatory incidents, wants at last the power to move, which constitutes the perfection of dramatick poetry. This reasoning is so specious, that it is received as true even by those who in daily experience feel it to be false. The interchanges of mingled scenes seldom fail to produce the intended vicissitudes of passion. Fiction cannot move so much, but that the attention may be easily transferred; and though it must be allowed that pleasing melancholy be sometimes interrupted by unwelcome levity, yet let it be considered likewise, that melancholy is often not pleasing, and that the disturbance of one man may be the relief of another; that different auditors have different habitudes; and that, upon the whole, all pleasure consists in variety.

The players, who in their edition divided our authour's works into comedies, histories, and tragedies, seem not to have distinguished the three kinds, by any very exact or definite ideas.

An action which ended happily to the principal persons, however serious or distressful through its intermediate incidents, in their opinion constituted a comedy. This idea of a comedy continued long amongst us, and plays were written, which, by changing the catastrophe, were tragedies to-day and comedies to-morrow.

Tragedy was not in those times a poem of more general dignity or elevation than comedy; it required only a calamitous conclusion, with which the common criticism of that age was satisfied, whatever lighter pleasure it afforded in its progress.

History was a series of actions, with no other than chronological succession, independent on each other, and without any tendency to introduce or regulate the conclusion. It is not always very nicely distinguished from tragedy. There is not much nearer approach to unity of action in the tragedy of *Antony and Cleopatra*,

than in the history of *Richard the Second*. But a history
might be continued through many plays; as it had no
plan, it had no limits.

Through all these denominations of the drama, *Shakespeare*'s mode of composition is the same; an interchange
of seriousness and merriment, by which the mind is
softened at one time, and exhilarated at another. But
whatever be his purpose, whether to gladden or depress,
or to conduct the story, without vehemence or emotion,
through tracts of easy and familiar dialogue, he never
fails to attain his purpose; as he commands us, we laugh
or mourn, or sit silent with quiet expectation, in tranquillity without indifference.

When *Shakespeare*'s plan is understood, most of the
criticisms of *Rhymer* and *Voltaire* vanish away. The play
of *Hamlet* is opened, without impropriety, by two
sentinels; *Iago* bellows at *Brabantio*'s window, without
injury to the scheme of the play, though in terms which
a modern audience would not easily endure; the character of *Polonius* is seasonable and useful; and the Grave-
diggers themselves may be heard with applause.

Shakespeare engaged in dramatick poetry with the
world open before him; the rules of the ancients were
yet known to few; the publick judgment was unformed;
he had no example of such fame as might force him
upon imitation, nor criticks of such authority as might
restrain his extravagance: He therefore indulged his
natural disposition, and his disposition, as *Rhymer* has
remarked, led him to comedy. In tragedy he often
writes with great appearance of toil and study, what is
written at last with little felicity; but in his comick scenes,
he seems to produce without labour, what no labour
can improve. In tragedy he is always struggling after
some occasion to be comick, but in comedy he seems to
repose, or to luxuriate, as in a mode of thinking con-

genial to his nature. In his tragick scenes there is always
something wanting, but his comedy often surpasses expectation or desire. His comedy pleases by the thoughts
and the language, and his tragedy for the greater part
by incident and action. His tragedy seems to be skill,
his comedy to be instinct.

The force of his comick scenes has suffered little diminution from the changes made by a century and a half,
in manners or in words. As his personages act upon
principles arising from genuine passion, very little modified by particular forms, their pleasures and vexations
are communicable to all times and to all places; they are
natural, and therefore durable; the adventitious peculiarities of personal habits, are only superficial dies, bright
and pleasing for a little while, yet soon fading to a dim
tinct, without any remains of former lustre; but the
discriminations of true passion are the colours of nature;
they pervade the whole mass, and can only perish with
the body that exhibits them. The accidental compositions of heterogeneous modes are dissolved by the
chance which combined them; but the uniform simplicity of primitive qualities neither admits increase, nor
suffers decay. The sand heaped by one flood is scattered
by another, but the rock always continues in its place.
The stream of time, which is continually washing the
dissoluble fabricks of other poets, passes without injury
by the adamant of *Shakespeare*.

If there be, what I believe there is, in every nation, a
stile which never becomes obsolete, a certain mode of
phraseology so consonant and congenial to the analogy
and principles of its respective language as to remain
settled and unaltered; this style is probably to be sought in
the common intercourse of life, among those who speak
only to be understood, without ambition of elegance.
The polite are always catching modish innovations,

and the learned depart from established forms of speech, in hope of finding or making better; those who wish for distinction forsake the vulgar, when the vulgar is right; but there is a conversation above grossness and below refinement, where propriety resides, and where this poet seems to have gathered his comick dialogue. He is therefore more agreeable to the ears of the present age than any other authour equally remote, and among his other excellencies deserves to be studied as one of the original masters of our language.

These observations are to be considered not as unexceptionably constant, but as containing general and predominant truth. *Shakespeare*'s familiar dialogue is affirmed to be smooth and clear, yet not wholly without ruggedness or difficulty; as a country may be eminently fruitful, though it has spots unfit for cultivation: His characters are praised as natural, though their sentiments are sometimes forced, and their actions improbable; as the earth upon the whole is spherical, though its surface is varied with protuberances and cavities.

Shakespeare with his excellencies has likewise faults, and faults sufficient to obscure and overwhelm any other merit. I shall shew them in the proportion in which they appear to me, without envious malignity or superstitious veneration. No question can be more innocently discussed than a dead poet's pretensions to renown; and little regard is due to that bigotry which sets candour higher than truth.

His first defect is that to which may be imputed most of the evil in books or in men. He sacrifices virtue to convenience, and is so much more careful to please than to instruct, that he seems to write without any moral purpose. From his writings indeed a system of social duty may be selected, for he that thinks reasonably must think morally; but his precepts and axioms drop casually from him; he makes no just distribution of good or evil, nor is always careful to shew in the virtuous a disapprobation of the wicked; he carries his persons indifferently through right and wrong, and at the close dismisses them without further care, and leaves their examples to operate by chance. This fault the barbarity of his age cannot extenuate; for it is always a writer's duty to make the world better, and justice is a virtue independant on time or place.

The plots are often so loosely formed, that a very slight consideration may improve them, and so carelessly pursued, that he seems not always fully to comprehend his own design. He omits opportunities of instructing or delighting which the train of his story seems to force upon him, and apparently rejects those exhibitions which would be more affecting, for the sake of those which are more easy.

It may be observed, that in many of his plays the latter part is evidently neglected. When he found himself near the end of his work, and in view of his reward, he shortened the labour, to snatch the profit. He therefore remits his efforts where he should most vigorously exert them, and his catastrophe is improbably produced or imperfectly represented.

He had no regard to distinction of time or place, but gives to one age or nation, without scruple, the customs, institutions, and opinions of another, at the expence not only of likelihood, but of possibility. These faults *Pope* has endeavoured, with more zeal than judgment, to transfer to his imagined interpolators. We need not wonder to find *Hector* quoting *Aristotle*, when we see the loves of *Theseus* and *Hippolyta* combined with the *Gothick* mythology of fairies. *Shakespeare*, indeed, was not the only violator of chronology, for in the same age *Sidney*, who wanted not the advantages of learning, has, in his *Arcadia*, confounded the pastoral with the feudal times, the days of innocence, quiet and security, with those of turbulence, violence and adventure.

In his comick scenes he is seldom very successful, when he engages his characters in reciprocations of smartness and contests of sarcasm; their jests are commonly gross, and their pleasantry licentious; neither his gentlemen nor his ladies have much delicacy, nor are sufficiently distinguished from his clowns by any appearance of refined manners. Whether he represented the real conversation of his time is not easy to determine; the reign of *Elizabeth* is commonly supposed to have been a time of stateliness, formality and reserve, yet perhaps the relaxations of that severity were not very elegant. There must, however, have been always some modes of gayety preferable to others, and a writer ought to chuse the best.

In tragedy his performance seems constantly to be worse, as his labour is more. The effusions of passion which exigence forces out are for the most part striking and energetick; but whenever he solicits his invention, or strains his faculties, the offspring of his throes is tumour, meanness, tediousness, and obscurity.

In narration he affects a disproportionate pomp of diction and a wearisome train of circumlocution, and tells the incident imperfectly in many words, which might have been more plainly delivered in few. Narration in dramatick poetry is naturally tedious, as it is unanimated and inactive, and obstructs the progress of the action: is should therefore always be rapid, and enlivened by frequent interruption. *Shakespeare* found it an encumbrance, and instead of lightening it by brevity, endeavoured to recommend it by dignity and splendour.

His declamations or set speeches are commonly cold

and weak, for his power was the power of nature; when he endeavoured, like other tragick writers, to catch opportunities of amplification, and instead of inquiring what the occasion demanded, to show how much his stores of knowledge could supply, he seldom escapes without the pity or resentment of his reader.

It is incident to him to be now and then entangled with an unwieldy sentiment, which he cannot well express, and will not reject; he struggles with it a while, and if it continues stubborn, comprises it in words such as occur, and leaves it to be disentangled and evolved by those who have more leisure to bestow upon it.

Not that always where the language is intricate the thought is subtle, or the image always great where the line is bulky; the equality of words to things is very often neglected, and trivial sentiments and vulgar ideas disappoint the attention, to which they are recommended by sonorous epithets and swelling figures.

But the admirers of this great poet have never less reason to indulge their hopes of supreme excellence, than when he seems fully resolved to sink them in dejection, and mollify them with tender emotions by the fall of greatness, the danger of innocence, or the crosses of love. He is not long soft and pathetick without some idle conceit, or contemptible equivocation. He no sooner begins to move, than he counteracts himself; and terrour and pity, as they are rising in the mind, are checked and blasted by sudden frigidity.

A quibble is to *Shakespeare*, what luminous vapours are to the traveller; he follows it at all adventures, it is sure to lead him out of his way, and sure to engulf him in the mire. It has some malignant power over his mind, and its fascinations are irresistible. Whatever be the dignity or profundity of his disquisition, whether he be enlarging knowledge or exalting affection, whether he be amusing attention with incidents, or enchaining it in suspense, let but a quibble spring up before him, and he leaves his work unfinished. A quibble is the golden apple for which he will always turn aside from his career, or stoop from his elevation. A quibble, poor and barren as it is, gave him such delight, that he was content to purchase it, by the sacrifice of reason, propriety and truth. A quibble was to him the fatal *Cleopatra* for which he lost the world, and was content to lose it.

It will be thought strange, that, in enumerating the defects of this writer, I have not yet mentioned his neglect of the unities; his violation of those laws which have been instituted and established by the joint authority of poets and of criticks.

For his other deviations from the art of writing I resign him to critical justice, without making any other demand in his favour, than that which must be indulged to all human excellence; that his virtues be rated with his failings: But, from the censure which this irregularity may bring upon him, I shall, with due reverence to that learning which I must oppose, adventure to try how I can defend him.

His histories, being neither tragedies nor comedies, are not subject to any of their laws; nothing more is necessary to all the praise which they expect, than that the changes of action be so prepared as to be understood, that the incidents be various and affecting, and the characters consistent, natural and distinct. No other unity is intended, and therefore none is to be sought.

In his other works he has well enough preserved the unity of action. He has not, indeed, an intrigue regularly perplexed and regularly unravelled; he does not endeavour to hide his design only to discover it, for this is seldom the order of real events, and *Shakespeare* is the poet of nature: But his plan has commonly what

Aristotle requires, a beginning, a middle, and an end; one event is concatenated with another, and the conclusion follows by easy consequence. There are perhaps some incidents that might be spared, as in other poets there is much talk that only fills up time upon the stage; but the general system makes gradual advances, and the end of the play is the end of expectation.

To the unities of time and place he has shewn no regard, and perhaps a nearer view of the principles on which they stand will diminish their value, and withdraw from them the veneration which, from the time of *Corneille*, they have very generally received, by discovering that they have given more trouble to the poet, than pleasure to the auditor.

The necessity of observing the unities of time and place arises from the supposed necessity of making the drama credible. The criticks hold it impossible, that an action of months or years can be possibly believed to pass in three hours; or that the spectator can suppose himself to sit in the theatre, while ambassadors go and return between distant kings, while armies are levied and towns besieged, while an exile wanders and returns, or till he whom they saw courting his mistress, shall lament the untimely fall of his son. The mind revolts from evident falsehood, and fiction loses its force when it departs from the resemblance of reality.

From the narrow limitation of time necessarily arises the contraction of place. The spectator, who knows that he saw the first act at *Alexandria*, cannot suppose that he sees the next at *Rome*, at a distance to which not the dragons of *Medea* could, in so short a time, have transported him; he knows with certainty that he has not changed his place; and he knows that place cannot change itself; that what was a house cannot become a plain; that what was *Thebes* can never be *Persepolis*.

Such is the triumphant language with which a critick exults over the misery of an irregular poet, and exults commonly without resistance or reply. It is time therefore to tell him, by the authority of *Shakespeare*, that he assumes, as an unquestionable principle, a position, which, while his breath is forming it into words, his understanding pronounces to be false. It is false, that any representation is mistaken for reality; that any dramatick fable in its materiality was ever credible, or, for a single moment, was ever credited.

The objection arising from the impossibility of passing the first hour at *Alexandria*, and the next at *Rome*, supposes, that when the play opens the spectator really imagines himself at *Alexandria*, and believes that his walk to the theatre has been a voyage to *Egypt*, and that he lives in the days of *Antony* and *Cleopatra*. Surely he that imagines this may imagine more. He that can take the stage at one time for the palace of the *Ptolemies*, may take it in half an hour for the promontory of *Actium*. Delusion, if delusion be admitted, has no certain limitation; if the spectator can be once persuaded, that his old acquaintance are *Alexander* and *Cæsar*, that a room illuminated with candles is the plain of *Pharsalia*, or the bank of *Granicus*, he is in a state of elevation above the reach of reason, or of truth, and from the heights of empyrean poetry, may despise the circumscriptions of terrestrial nature. There is no reason why a mind thus wandering in extasy should count the clock, or why an hour should not be a century in that calenture of the brains that can make the stage a field.

The truth is, that the spectators are always in their senses, and know, from the first act to the last, that the stage is only a stage, and that the players are only players. They came to hear a certain number of lines recited with just gesture and elegant modulation. The lines relate to some action, and an action must be in some place; but the different actions that compleat a story may be in places very remote from each other; and where is the absurdity of allowing that space to represent first *Athens*, and then *Sicily*, which was always known to be neither *Sicily* nor *Athens*, but a modern theatre?

By supposition, as place is introduced, time may be extended; the time required by the fable elapses for the most part between the acts; for, of so much of the action as is represented, the real and poetical duration is the same. If, in the first act, preparations for war against *Mithridates* are represented to be made in *Rome*, the event of the war may, without absurdity, be represented, in the catastrophe, as happening in *Pontus*; we know that there is neither war, nor preparation for war; we know that we are neither in *Rome* nor *Pontus*; that neither *Mithridates* nor *Lucullus* are before us. The drama exhibits successive imitations of successive actions, and why may not the second imitation represent an action that happened years after the first; if it be so connected with it, that nothing but time can be supposed to intervene. Time is, of all modes of existence, most obsequious to the imagination; a lapse of years is as easily conceived as a passage of hours. In contemplation we easily contract the time of real actions, and therefore willingly permit it to be contracted when we only see their imitation.

It will be asked, how the drama moves, if it is not credited. It is credited with all the credit due to a drama. It is credited, whenever it moves, as a just picture of a real original; as representing to the auditor what he would himself feel, if he were to do or suffer what is there feigned to be suffered or to be done. The reflection that strikes the heart is not, that the evils before us are real evils, but that they are evils to which we ourselves may be exposed. If there be any fallacy, it is not that we fancy the players, but that we fancy ourselves unhappy for a moment; but we rather lament the possibility than suppose the presence of misery, as a mother weeps over her babe, when she remembers that death may take it from her. The delight of tragedy proceeds from our consciousness of fiction; if we thought murders and treasons real, they would please no more.

Imitations produce pain or pleasure, not because they are mistaken for realities, but because they bring realities to mind. When the imagination is recreated by a painted landscape, the trees are not supposed capable to give us shade, or the fountains coolness; but we consider, how we should be pleased with such fountains playing beside us, and such woods waving over us. We are agitated in reading the history of *Henry* the Fifth, yet no man takes his book for the field of *Agencourt*. A dramatick exhibition is a book recited with concomitants that encrease or diminish its effect. Familiar comedy is often more powerful on the theatre, than in the page; imperial tragedy is always less. The humour of *Petruchio* may be heightened by grimace; but what voice or what gesture can hope to add dignity or force to the soliloquy of *Cato*.

A play read, affects the mind like a play acted. It is therefore evident, that the action is not supposed to be real, and it follows that between the acts a longer or shorter time may be allowed to pass, and that no more account of space or duration is to be taken by the auditor of a drama, than by the reader of a narrative, before whom may pass in an hour the life of a hero, or the revolutions of an empire.

Whether *Shakespeare* knew the unities, and rejected them by design, or deviated from them by happy ignorance, it is, I think, impossible to decide, and useless to enquire. We may reasonably suppose, that, when he

rose to notice, he did not want the counsels and admonitions of scholars and criticks, and that he at last deliberately persisted in a practice, which he might have begun
by chance. As nothing is essential to the fable, but unity
of action, and as the unities of time and place arise
evidently from false assumptions, and, by circumscrib-
ing the extent of the drama, lessen its variety, I cannot
think it much to be lamented, that they were not known
by him, or not observed: Nor, if such another poet
could arise, should I very vehemently reproach him,
that his first act passed at *Venice*, and his next in *Cyprus*.
Such violations of rules merely positive, become the
comprehensive genius of *Shakespeare*, and such censures
are suitable to the minute and slender criticism of
Voltaire:

> *Non usque adeo permiscuit imis*
> *Longus summa dies, ut non, si voce Metelli*
> *Serventur leges, malint a Cæsare tolli.*

Yet when I speak thus slightly of dramatick rules, I
cannot but recollect how much wit and learning may
be produced against me; before such authorities I am
afraid to stand, not that I think the present question one
of those that are to be decided by mere authority, but
because it is to be suspected, that these precepts have not
been so easily received but for better reasons than I have
yet been able to find. The result of my enquiries, in
which it would be ludicrous to boast of impartiality, is,
that the unities of time and place are not essential to a
just drama, that though they may sometimes conduce
to pleasure, they are always to be sacrificed to the nobler
beauties of variety and instruction; and that a play,
written with nice observation of critical rules, is to be
contemplated as an elaborate curiosity, as the product
of superfluous and ostentatious art, by which is shewn,
rather what is possible, than what is necessary.

He that, without diminution of any other excellence, shall preserve all the unities unbroken, deserves the like applause with the architect, who shall display all the orders of architecture in a citadel, without any deduction from its strength; but the principal beauty of a citadel is to exclude the enemy; and the greatest graces of a play, are to copy nature and instruct life.

Perhaps, what I have here not dogmatically but deliberately written, may recal the principles of the drama to a new examination. I am almost frighted at my own temerity; and when I estimate the fame and the strength of those that maintain the contrary opinion, am ready to sink down in reverential silence; as *Æneas* withdrew from the defence of *Troy*, when he saw *Neptune* shaking the wall, and *Juno* heading the besiegers.

Those whom my arguments cannot persuade to give their approbation to the judgment of *Shakespeare*, will easily, if they consider the condition of his life, make some allowance for his ignorance.

Every man's performances, to be rightly estimated, must be compared with the state of the age in which he lived, and with his own particular opportunities; and though to the reader a book be not worse or better for the circumstances of the authour, yet as there is always a silent reference of human works to human abilities, and as the enquiry, how far man may extend his designs, or how high he may rate his native force, is of far greater dignity than in what rank we shall place any particular performance, curiosity is always busy to discover the instruments, as well as to survey the workmanship, to know how much is to be ascribed to original powers, and how much to casual and adventitious help. The palaces of *Peru* or *Mexico* were certainly mean and incommodious habitations, if compared to the houses of *European* monarchs; yet who could forbear to view them with astonishment, who remembered that they were built without the use of iron?

The *English* nation, in the time of *Shakespeare*, was yet struggling to emerge from barbarity. The philology of *Italy* had been transplanted hither in the reign of *Henry* the Eighth; and the learned languages had been successfully cultivated by *Lilly*, *Linacer*, and *More*; by *Pole*, *Cheke*, and *Gardiner*; and afterwards by *Smith*, *Clerk*, *Haddon*, and *Ascham*. Greek was now taught to boys in the principal schools; and those who united elegance with learning, read, with great diligence, the *Italian* and *Spanish* poets. But literature was yet confined to professed scholars, or to men and women of high rank. The publick was gross and dark; and to be able to read and write, was an accomplishment still valued for its rarity.

Nations, like individuals, have their infancy. A people newly awakened to literary curiosity, being yet unacquainted with the true state of things, knows not how to judge of that which is proposed as its resemblance. Whatever is remote from common appearances is always welcome to vulgar, as to childish credulity; and of a country unenlightened by learning, the whole people is the vulgar. The study of those who then aspired to plebeian learning was laid out upon adventures, giants, dragons, and enchantments. *The Death of Arthur* was the favourite volume.

The mind, which has feasted on the luxurious wonders of fiction, has no taste of the insipidity of truth. A play which imitated only the common occurrences of the world, would, upon the admirers of *Palmerin* and *Guy of Warwick*, have made little impression; he that wrote for such an audience was under the necessity of looking round for strange events and fabulous transactions, and that incredibility, by which maturer knowledge is offended, was the chief recommendation of writings, to unskilful curiosity.

Our authour's plots are generally borrowed from novels, and it is reasonable to suppose, that he chose the most popular, such as were read by many, and related by more; for his audience could not have followed him through the intricacies of the drama, had they not held the thread of the story in their hands.

The stories, which we now find only in remoter authours, were in his time accessible and familiar. The fable of *As you like it*, which is supposed to be copied from *Chaucer*'s Gamelyn, was a little pamphlet of those times; and old Mr. *Cibber* remembered the tale of *Hamlet* in plain *English* prose, which the criticks have now to seek in *Saxo Grammaticus*.

His *English* histories he took from *English* chronicles and *English* ballads; and as the ancient writers were made known to his countrymen by versions, they supplied him with new subjects; he dilated some of *Plutarch*'s lives into plays, when they had been translated by *North*.

His plots, whether historical or fabulous, are always crouded with incidents, by which the attention of a rude people was more easily caught than by sentiment or argumentation; and such is the power of the marvellous even over those who despise it, that every man finds his mind more strongly seized by the tragedies of *Shakespeare* than of any other writer; others please us by particular speeches, but he always makes us anxious for the event, and has perhaps excelled all but *Homer* in securing the first purpose of a writer, by exciting restless and unquenchable curiosity, and compelling him that reads his work to read it through.

The shows and bustle with which his plays abound have the same original. As knowledge advances, pleasure passes from the eye to the ear, but returns, as it declines, from the ear to the eye. Those to whom our authour's labours were exhibited had more skill in pomps or processions than in poetical language, and perhaps wanted some visible and discriminated events, as comments on the dialogue. He knew how he should most please; and whether his practice is more agreeable to nature, or whether his example has prejudiced the nation, we still find that on our stage something must be done as well as said, and inactive declamation is very coldly heard, however musical or elegant, passionate or sublime.

Voltaire expresses his wonder, that our authour's extravagances are endured by a nation, which has seen the tragedy of *Cato*. Let him be answered, that *Addison* speaks the language of poets, and *Shakespeare*, of men. We find in *Cato* innumerable beauties which enamour us of its authour, but we see nothing that acquaints us with human sentiments or human actions; we place it with the fairest and the noblest progeny which judgment propagates by conjunction with learning, but *Othello* is the vigorous and vivacious offspring of observation impregnated by genius. *Cato* affords a splendid exhibition of artificial and fictitious manners, and delivers just and noble sentiments, in diction easy, elevated and harmonious, but its hopes and fears communicate no vibration to the heart; the composition refers us only to the writer; we pronounce the name of *Cato*, but we think on *Addison*.

The work of a correct and regular writer is a garden accurately formed and diligently planted, varied with shades, and scented with flowers; the composition of *Shakespeare* is a forest, in which oaks extend their branches, and pines tower in the air, interspersed sometimes with weeds and brambles, and sometimes giving shelter to myrtles and to roses; filling the eye with awful pomp, and gratifying the mind with endless diversity.

Other poets display cabinets of precious rarities, minutely finished, wrought into shape, and polished unto brightness. *Shakespeare* opens a mine which contains gold and diamonds in unexhaustible plenty, though clouded by incrustations, debased by impurities, and mingled with a mass of meaner minerals.

It has been much disputed, whether *Shakespeare* owed his excellence to his own native force, or whether he had the common helps of scholastick education, the precepts of critical science, and the examples of ancient authours.

There has always prevailed a tradition, that *Shakespeare* wanted learning, that he had no regular education, nor much skill in the dead languages. *Johnson*, his friend, affirms, that *he had small Latin, and no[1] Greek*; who, besides that he had no imaginable temptation to falsehood, wrote at a time when the character and acquisitions of *Shakespeare* were known to multitudes. His evidence ought therefore to decide the controversy, unless some testimony of equal force could be opposed.

Some have imagined, that they have discovered deep learning in many imitations of old writers; but the examples which I have known urged, were drawn from books translated in his time; or were such easy coincidencies of thought, as will happen to all who consider the same subjects; or such remarks on life or axioms of morality as float in conversation, and are transmitted through the world in proverbial sentences.

I have found it remarked, that, in this important sentence, *Go before, I'll follow*, we read a translation of, *I prae, sequar*. I have been told, that when *Caliban*, after a pleasing dream, says, *I cry'd to sleep again*, the authour imitates *Anacreon*, who had, like every other man, the same wish on the same occasion.

[1] Corrected to 'less' in the edition of 1773.

There are a few passages which may pass for imitations, but so few, that the exception only confirms the rule; he obtained them from accidental quotations, or by oral communication, and as he used what he had, would have used more if he had obtained it.

The *Comedy of Errors* is confessedly taken from the *Menæchmi* of *Plautus*; from the only play of *Plautus* which was then in *English*. What can be more probable, than that he who copied that, would have copied more; but that those which were not translated were inaccessible?

Whether he knew the modern languages is uncertain. That his plays have some *French* scenes proves but little; he might easily procure them to be written, and probably, even though he had known the language in the common degree, he could not have written it without assistance. In the story of *Romeo* and *Juliet* he is observed to have followed the *English* translation, where it deviates from the *Italian*; but this on the other part proves nothing against his knowledge of the original. He was to copy, not what he knew himself, but what was known to his audience.

It is most likely that he had learned *Latin* sufficiently to make him acquainted with construction, but that he never advanced to an easy perusal of the *Roman* authours. Concerning his skill in modern languages, I can find no sufficient ground of determination; but as no imitations of *French* or *Italian* authours have been discovered, though the *Italian* poetry was then high in esteem, I am inclined to believe, that he read little more than *English*, and chose for his fables only such tales as he found translated.

That much knowledge is scattered over his works is very justly observed by *Pope*, but it is often such knowledge as books did not supply. He that will understand

Shakespeare, must not be content to study him in the closet, he must look for his meaning sometimes among the sports of the field, and sometimes among the manufactures of the shop.

There is however proof enough that he was a very diligent reader, nor was our language then so indigent of books, but that he might very liberally indulge his curiosity without excursion into foreign literature. Many of the *Roman* authours were translated, and some of the *Greek*; the reformation had filled the kingdom with theological learning; most of the topicks of human disquisition had found *English* writers; and poetry had been cultivated, not only with diligence, but success. This was a stock of knowledge sufficient for a mind so capable of appropriating and improving it.

But the greater part of his excellence was the product of his own genius. He found the *English* stage in a state of the utmost rudeness; no essays either in tragedy or comedy had appeared, from which it could be discovered to what degree of delight either one or other might be carried. Neither character nor dialogue were yet understood. *Shakespeare* may be truly said to have introduced them both amongst us, and in some of his happier scenes to have carried them both to the utmost height.

By what gradations of improvement he proceeded, is not easily known; for the chronology of his works is yet unsettled. *Rowe* is of opinion, that *perhaps we are not to look for his beginning, like those of other writers, in his least perfect works; art had so little, and nature so large a share in what he did, that for aught I know*, says he, *the performances of his youth, as they were the most vigorous, were the best.* But the power of nature is only the power of using to any certain purpose the materials which diligence procures, or opportunity supplies. Nature gives no man knowledge, and when images are collected by study and experience, can only assist in combining or applying them. *Shakespeare*, however favoured by nature, could impart only what he had learned; and as he must increase his ideas, like other mortals, by gradual acquisition, he, like them, grew wiser as he grew older, could display life better, as he knew it more, and instruct with more efficacy, as he was himself more amply instructed.

There is a vigilance of observation and accuracy of distinction which books and precepts cannot confer; from this almost all original and native excellence proceeds. *Shakespeare* must have looked upon mankind with perspicacity, in the highest degree curious and attentive. Other writers borrow their characters from preceding writers, and diversify them only by the accidental appendages of present manners; the dress is a little varied, but the body is the same. Our authour had both matter and form to provide; for except the characters of *Chaucer*, to whom I think he is not much indebted, there were no writers in *English*, and perhaps not many in other modern languages, which shewed life in its native colours.

The contest about the original benevolence or malignity of man had not yet commenced. Speculation had not yet attempted to analyse the mind, to trace the passions to their sources, to unfold the seminal principles of vice and virtue, or sound the depths of the heart for the motives of action. All those enquiries, which from the time that human nature became the fashionable study, have been made sometimes with nice discernment, but often with idle subtilty, were yet unattempted. The tales, with which the infancy of learning was satisfied, exhibited only the superficial appearances of action, related the events but omitted the causes, and were formed for such as delighted in wonders rather than in

truth. Mankind was not then to be studied in the closet; he that would know the world, was under the necessity of gleaning his own remarks, by mingling as he could in its business and amusements.

Boyle congratulated himself upon his high birth, because it favoured his curiosity, by facilitating his access. *Shakespeare* had no such advantage; he came to *London* a needy adventurer, and lived for a time by very mean employments. Many works of genius and learning have been performed in states of life, that appear very little favourable to thought or to enquiry; so many, that he who considers them is inclined to think that he sees enterprise and perseverance predominating over all external agency, and bidding help and hindrance vanish before them. The genius of *Shakespeare* was not to be depressed by the weight of poverty, nor limited by the narrow conversation to which men in want are inevitably condemned; the incumbrances of his fortune were shaken from his mind, *as dewdrops from a lion's mane.*

Though he had so many difficulties to encounter, and so little assistance to surmount them, he has been able to obtain an exact knowledge of many modes of life, and many casts of native dispositions; to vary them with great multiplicity; to mark them by nice distinctions; and to shew them in full view by proper combinations. In this part of his performances he had none to imitate, but has himself been imitated by all succeeding writers; and it may be doubted, whether from all his successors more maxims of theoretical knowledge, or more rules of practical prudence, can be collected, than he alone has given to his country.

Nor was his attention confined to the actions of men; he was an exact surveyor of the inanimate world; his descriptions have always some peculiarities, gathered by contemplating things as they really exist. It may be observed, that the oldest poets of many nations preserve their reputation, and that the following generations of wit, after a short celebrity, sink into oblivion. The first, whoever they be, must take their sentiments and descriptions immediately from knowledge; the resemblance is therefore just, their descriptions are verified by every eye, and their sentiments acknowledged by every breast. Those whom their fame invites to the same studies, copy partly them, and partly nature, till the books of one age gain such authority, as to stand in the place of nature to another, and imitation, always deviating a little, becomes at last capricious and casual. *Shakespeare*, whether life or nature be his subject, shews plainly, that he has seen with his own eyes; he gives the image which he receives, not weakened or distorted by the intervention of any other mind; the ignorant feel his representations to be just, and the learned see that they are compleat.

Perhaps it would not be easy to find any authour, except *Homer*, who invented so much as *Shakespeare*, who so much advanced the studies which he cultivated, or effused so much novelty upon his age or country. The form, the characters, the language, and the shows of the *English* drama are his. *He seems*, says *Dennis*, *to have been the very original of our* English *tragical harmony, that is, the harmony of blank verse, diversified often by dissyllable and trissyllable terminations. For the diversity distinguishes it from heroick harmony, and by bringing it nearer to common use makes it more proper to gain attention, and more fit for action and dialogue. Such verse we make when we are writing prose; we make such verse in common conversation.*

I know not whether this praise is rigorously just. The dissyllable termination, which the critick rightly appropriates to the drama, is to be found, though, I think, not in *Gorboduc* which is confessedly before our authour; yet in *Hieronnymo*, of which the date is not certain, but which there is reason to believe at least as old as his earliest plays. This however is certain, that he is the first who taught either tragedy or comedy to please, there being no theatrical piece of any older writer, of which the name is known, except to antiquaries and collectors of books, which are sought because they are scarce, and would not have been scarce, had they been much esteemed.

To him we must ascribe the praise, unless *Spenser* may divide it with him, of having first discovered to how much smoothness and harmony the *English* language could be softened. He has speeches, perhaps sometimes scenes, which have all the delicacy of *Rowe*, without his effeminacy. He endeavours indeed commonly to strike by the force and vigour of his dialogue, but he never executes his purpose better, than when he tries to sooth by softness.

Yet it must be at last confessed, that as we owe every thing to him, he owes something to us; that, if much of his praise is paid by perception and judgment, much is likewise given by custom and veneration. We fix our eyes upon his graces, and turn them from his deformities, and endure in him what we should in another loath or despise. If we endured without praising, respect for the father of our drama might excuse us; but I have seen, in the book of some modern critick, a collection of anomalies, which shew that he has corrupted language by every mode of depravation, but which his admirer has accumulated as a monument of honour.

He has scenes of undoubted and perpetual excellence, but perhaps not one play, which, if it were now exhibited as the work of a contemporary writer, would be heard to the conclusion. I am indeed far from thinking.

that his works were wrought to his own ideas of perfection; when they were such as would satisfy the audience, they satisfied the writer. It is seldom that authours, though more studious of fame than *Shakespeare*, rise much above the standard of their own age; to add a little of what is best will always be sufficient for present praise, and those who find themselves exalted into fame, are willing to credit their encomiasts, and to spare the labour of contending with themselves.

It does not appear, that *Shakespeare* thought his works worthy of posterity, that he levied any ideal tribute upon future times, or had any further prospect, than of present popularity and present profit. When his plays had been acted, his hope was at an end; he solicited no addition of honour from the reader. He therefore made no scruple to repeat the same jests in many dialogues, or to entangle different plots by the same knot of perplexity, which may be at least forgiven him, by those who recollect, that of *Congreve*'s four comedies, two are concluded by a marriage in a mask, by a deception, which perhaps never happened, and which, whether likely or not, he did not invent.

So careless was this great poet of future fame, that, though he retired to ease and plenty, while he was yet little *declined into the vale of years*, before he could be disgusted with fatigue, or disabled by infirmity, he made no collection of his works, nor desired to rescue those that had been already published from the depravations that obscured them, or secure to the rest a better destiny, by giving them to the world in their genuine state.

Of the plays which bear the name of *Shakespeare* in the late editions, the greater part were not published till about seven years after his death, and the few which appeared in his life are apparently thrust into the world without the care of the authour, and therefore probably without his knowledge.

Of all the publishers, clandestine or professed, their negligence and unskilfulness has by the late revisers been sufficiently shown. The faults of all are indeed numerous and gross, and have not only corrupted many passages perhaps beyond recovery, but have brought others into suspicion, which are only obscured by obsolete phraseology, or by the writer's unskilfulness and affectation. To alter is more easy than to explain, and temerity is a more common quality than diligence. Those who saw that they must employ conjecture to a certain degree, were willing to indulge it a little further. Had the authour published his own works, we should have sat quietly down to disentangle his intricacies, and clear his obscurities; but now we tear what we cannot loose, and eject what we happen not to understand.

The faults are more than could have happened without the concurrence of many causes. The stile of *Shakespeare* was in itself ungrammatical, perplexed and obscure; his works were transcribed for the players by those who may be supposed to have seldom understood them; they were transmitted by copiers equally unskilful, who still multiplied errours; they were perhaps sometimes mutilated by the actors, for the sake of shortening the speeches; and were at last printed without correction of the press. . . .

After the labours of all the editors, I found many passages which appeared to me likely to obstruct the greater number of readers, and thought it my duty to facilitate their passage. It is impossible for an expositor not to write too little for some, and too much for others. He can only judge what is necessary by his own experience; and how long soever he may deliberate, will at last explain many lines which the learned will think impossible to be mistaken, and omit many for which the ignorant will want his help. These are censures merely relative, and must be quietly endured. I have endeavoured to be neither superfluously copious, nor scrupulously reserved, and hope that I have made my authour's meaning accessible to many who before were frighted from perusing him, and contributed something to the publick, by diffusing innocent and rational pleasure.

The compleat explanation of an authour not systematick and consequential, but desultory and vagrant, abounding in casual allusions and light hints, is not to be expected from any single scholiast. All personal reflections, when names are suppressed, must be in a few years irrecoverably obliterated; and customs, too minute to attract the notice of law, such as modes of dress, formalities of conversation, rules of visits, disposition of furniture, and practices of ceremony, which naturally find places in familiar dialogue, are so fugitive and unsubstantial, that they are not easily retained or recovered. What can be known, will be collected by chance, from the recesses of obscure and obsolete papers, perused commonly with some other view. Of this knowledge every man has some, and none has much; but when an authour has engaged the publick attention, those who can add any thing to his illustration, communicate their discoveries, and time produces what had eluded diligence.

To time I have been obliged to resign many passages, which, though I did not understand them, will perhaps hereafter be explained, having, I hope, illustrated some, which others have neglected or mistaken, sometimes by short remarks, or marginal directions, such as every editor has added at his will, and often by comments more laborious than the matter will seem to deserve:

but that which is most difficult is not always most important, and to an editor nothing is a trifle by which his authour is obscured.

The poetical beauties or defects I have not been very diligent to observe. Some plays have more, and some fewer judicial observations, not in proportion to their difference of merit, but because I gave this part of my design to chance and to caprice. The reader, I believe, is seldom pleased to find his opinion anticipated; it is natural to delight more in what we find or make, than in what we receive. Judgment, like other faculties, is improved by practice, and its advancement is hindered by submission to dictatorial decisions, as the memory grows torpid by the use of a table book. Some initiation is however necessary; of all skill, part is infused by precept, and part is obtained by habit; I have therefore shewn so much as may enable the candidate of criticism to discover the rest.

To the end of most plays, I have added short strictures, containing a general censure of faults, or praise of excellence; in which I know not how much I have concurred with the current opinion; but I have not, by any affectation of singularity, deviated from it. Nothing is minutely and particularly examined, and therefore it is to be supposed, that in the plays which are condemned there is much to be praised, and in those which are praised much to be condemned. . .

Conjecture, though it be sometimes unavoidable, I have not wantonly nor licentiously indulged. It has been my settled principle, that the reading of the ancient books is probably true, and therefore is not to be disturbed for the sake of elegance, perspicuity, or mere improvement of the sense. For though much credit is not due to the fidelity, nor any to the judgment of the first publishers, yet they who had the copy before their eyes were more likely to read it right, than we who read it only by imagination. But it is evident that they have often made strange mistakes by ignorance or negligence, and that therefore something may be properly attempted by criticism, keeping the middle way between presumption and timidity.

Such criticism I have attempted to practise, and where any passage appeared inextricably perplexed, have endeavoured to discover how it may be recalled to sense, with least violence. But my first labour is, always to turn the old text on every side, and try if there be any interstice, through which light can find its way; nor would *Huetius* himself condemn me, as refusing the trouble of research, for the ambition of alteration. In this modest industry I have not been unsuccessful. I have rescued many lines from the violations of temerity, and secured many scenes from the inroads of correction. I have adopted the *Roman* sentiment, that it is more honourable to save a citizen, than to kill an enemy, and have been more careful to protect than to attack. . . .

As I practised conjecture more, I learned to trust it less; and after I had printed a few plays, resolved to insert none of my own readings in the text. Upon this caution I now congratulate myself, for every day encreases my doubt of my emendations. . . .

Perhaps I may not be more censured for doing wrong, than for doing little; for raising in the publick expectations, which at last I have not answered. The expectation of ignorance is indefinite, and that of knowledge is often tyrannical. It is hard to satisfy those who know not what to demand, or those who demand by design what they think impossible to be done. I have indeed disappointed no opinion more than my own; yet I have endeavoured to perform my task with no slight solicitude. Not a single passage in the whole work has appeared to me corrupt, which I have not attempted to restore; or obscure, which I have not endeavoured to illustrate. In many I have failed like others; and from many, after all my efforts, I have retreated, and confessed the repulse. I have not passed over, with affected superiority, what is equally difficult to the reader and to myself, but where I could not instruct him, have owned my ignorance. I might easily have accumulated a mass of seeming learning upon easy scenes; but it ought not to be imputed to negligence, that, where nothing was necessary, nothing has been done, or that, where others have said enough, I have said no more.

Notes are often necessary, but they are necessary evils. Let him, that is yet unacquainted with the powers of *Shakespeare*, and who desires to feel the highest pleasure that the drama can give, read every play from the first scene to the last, with utter negligence of all his commentators. When his fancy is once on the wing, let it not stoop at correction or explanation. When his attention is strongly engaged, let it disdain alike to turn aside to the name of *Theobald* and of *Pope*. Let him read on through brightness and obscurity, through integrity and corruption; let him preserve his comprehension of the dialogue and his interest in the fable. And when the pleasures of novelty have ceased, let him attempt exactness, and read the commentators.

Particular passages are cleared by notes, but the general effect of the work is weakened. The mind is refrigerated by interruption; the thoughts are diverted from the principal subject; the reader is weary, he suspects not why; and at last throws away the book, which he has too diligently studied.

Parts are not to be examined till the whole has been surveyed; there is a kind of intellectual remoteness necessary for the comprehension of any great work in its full design and its true proportions; a close approach shews the smaller niceties, but the beauty of the whole is discerned no longer.

It is not very grateful to consider how little the succession of editors has added to this authour's power of pleasing. He was read, admired, studied, and imitated, while he was yet deformed with all the improprieties which ignorance and neglect could accumulate upon him; while the reading was yet not rectified, nor his allusions understood; yet then did *Dryden* pronounce 'that *Shakespeare* was the man, who, of all modern and perhaps ancient poets, had the largest and most comprehensive soul. All the images of nature were still present to him, and he drew them not laboriously, but luckily: When he describes any thing, you more than see it, you feel it too. Those who accuse him to have wanted learning, give him the greater commendation: he was naturally learned: he needed not the spectacles of books to read nature; he looked inwards, and found her there. I cannot say he is every where alike; were he so, I should do him injury to compare him with the greatest of mankind. He is many times flat and insipid; his comick wit degenerating into clenches, his serious swelling into bombast. But he is always great, when some great occasion is presented to him: No man can say, he ever had a fit subject for his wit, and did not then raise himself as high above the rest of poets,

'*Quantum lenta solent inter viburna cupressi.*'

It is to be lamented, that such a writer should want a commentary; that his language should become obsolete, or his sentiments obscure. But it is vain to carry wishes beyond the condition of human things; that which must happen to all, has happened to *Shakespeare*, by accident and time; and more than has been suffered by

any other writer since the use of types, has been suffered
by him through his own negligence of fame, or perhaps
by that superiority of mind, which despised its own performances, when it compared them with its powers,
and judged those works unworthy to be preserved,
which the criticks of following ages were to contend
for the fame of restoring and explaining.

Among these candidates of inferiour fame, I am now
to stand the judgment of the publick; and wish that I
could confidently produce my commentary as equal to
the encouragement which I have had the honour of
receiving. Every work of this kind is by its nature deficient, and I should feel little solicitude about the sentence, were it to be pronounced only by the skilful and
the learned.

Henry IV

NONE of *Shakespeare*'s plays are more read than the first
and second parts of *Henry* the fourth. Perhaps no authour has ever in two plays afforded so much delight.
The great events are interesting, for the fate of kingdoms
depends upon them; the slighter occurrences are diverting, and, except one or two, sufficiently probable; the
incidents are multiplied with wonderful fertility of invention, and the characters diversified with the utmost
nicety of discernment, and the profoundest skill in the
nature of man.

The prince, who is the hero both of the comick and
tragick part, is a young man of great abilities and violent
passions, whose sentiments are right, though his actions
are wrong; whose virtues are obscured by negligence,
and whose understanding is dissipated by levity. In his
idle hours he is rather loose than wicked, and when the
occasion forces out his latent qualities, he is great without effort, and brave without tumult. The trifler is

roused into a hero, and the hero again reposes in the
trifler. This character is great, original, and just.

Piercy is a rugged soldier, cholerick, and quarrelsome,
and has only the soldier's virtues, generosity and courage.

But *Falstaff* unimitated, unimitable *Falstaff*, how shall
I describe thee? Thou compound of sense and vice; of
sense which may be admired but not esteemed, of vice
which may be despised, but hardly detested. *Falstaff* is
a character loaded with faults, and with those faults
which naturally produce contempt. He is a thief, and a
glutton, a coward, and a boaster, always ready to cheat
the weak, and prey upon the poor; to terrify the timo-
rous and insult the defenceless. At once obsequious and
malignant, he satirises in their absence those whom he
lives by flattering. He is familiar with the prince only
as an agent of vice, but of this familiarity he is so proud
as not only to be supercilious and haughty with common
men, but to think his interest of importance to the duke
of *Lancaster*. Yet the man thus corrupt, thus despicable,
makes himself necessary to the prince that despises him,
by the most pleasing of all qualities, perpetual gaiety, by
an unfailing power of exciting laughter, which is the
more freely indulged, as his wit is not of the splendid or
ambitious kind, but consists in easy escapes and sallies
of levity, which make sport but raise no envy. It must
be observed that he is stained with no enormous or
sanguinary crimes, so that his licentiousness is not so
offensive but that it may be borne for his mirth.

The moral to be drawn from this representation is,
that no man is more dangerous than he that with a will
to corrupt, hath the power to please; and that neither
wit nor honesty ought to think themselves safe with
such a companion when they see *Henry* seduced by
Falstaff.

Edition of Shakespeare, 1765, vol. iv, pp. 355-6.

King Lear

THE Tragedy of *Lear* is deservedly celebrated among
the dramas of *Shakespeare*. There is perhaps no play
which keeps the attention so strongly fixed; which so
much agitates our passions and interests our curiosity.
The artful involutions of distinct interests, the striking
opposition of contrary characters, the sudden changes of
fortune, and the quick succession of events, fill the mind
with a perpetual tumult of indignation, pity, and hope.
There is no scene which does not contribute to the aggra-
vation of the distress or conduct of the action, and scarce
a line which does not conduce to the progress of the
scene. So powerful is the current of the poet's imagination, that the mind, which once ventures within it, is
hurried irresistibly along.

On the seeming improbability of *Lear*'s conduct it
may be observed, that he is represented according to
histories at that time vulgarly received as true. And perhaps if we turn our thoughts upon the barbarity and
ignorance of the age to which this story is referred, it
will appear not so unlikely as while we estimate *Lear*'s
manners by our own. Such preference of one daughter
to another, or resignation of dominion on such conditions, would be yet credible, if told of a petty prince of
Guinea or *Madagascar*. *Shakespeare*, indeed, by the mention of his Earls and Dukes, has given us the idea of times
more civilised, and of life regulated by softer manners;
and the truth is, that though he so nicely discriminates, and
so minutely describes the characters of men, he commonly
neglects and confounds the characters of ages, by mingling customs ancient and modern, *English* and foreign.

My learned friend Mr. *Warton*, who has in the *Adventurer* very minutely criticised this play, remarks, that the
instances of cruelty are too savage and shocking, and

that the intervention of *Edmund* destroys the simplicity
of the story. These objections may, I think, be answered,
by repeating, that the cruelty of the daughters is an
historical fact, to which the poet has added little, having
only drawn it into a series by dialogue and action. But
I am not able to apologise with equal plausibility for the
extrusion of *Gloucester's* eyes, which seems an act too
horrid to be endured in dramatick exhibition, and such
as must always compel the mind to relieve its distress by
incredulity. Yet let it be remembered that our authour
well knew what would please the audience for which
he wrote.

The injury done by *Edmund* to the simplicity of the
action is abundantly recompensed by the addition of
variety, by the art with which he is made to co-operate
with the chief design, and the opportunity which he
gives the poet of combining perfidy with perfidy, and
connecting the wicked son with the wicked daughters, to
impress this important moral, that villany is never at a stop,
that crimes lead to crimes, and at last terminate in ruin.

But though this moral be incidentally enforced,
Shakespeare has suffered the virtue of *Cordelia* to perish
in a just cause, contrary to the natural ideas of justice,
to the hope of the reader, and, what is yet more strange,
to the faith of chronicles. Yet this conduct is justified
by the Spectator, who blames *Tate* for giving *Cordelia*
success and happiness in his alteration, and declares,
that, in his opinion, *the tragedy has lost half its beauty.*
Dennis has remarked, whether justly or not, that, to
secure the favourable reception of *Cato, the town was
poisoned with much false and abominable criticism,* and that
endeavours had been used to discredit and decry poetical
justice. A play in which the wicked prosper, and the
virtuous miscarry, may doubtless be good, because it is
a just representation of the common events of human

life: but since all reasonable beings naturally love justice, I cannot easily be persuaded, that the observation of justice makes a play worse; or, that if other excellencies are equal, the audience will not always rise better pleased from the final triumph of persecuted virtue.

In the present case the publick has decided. *Cordelia*, from the time of *Tate*, has always retired with victory and felicity. And, if my sensations could add any thing to the general suffrage, I might relate, that I was many years ago so shocked by *Cordelia's* death, that I know not whether I ever endured to read again the last scenes of the play till I undertook to revise them as an editor.

There is another controversy among the criticks concerning this play. It is disputed whether the predominant image in *Lear's* disordered mind be the loss of his kingdom or the cruelty of his daughters. Mr. *Murphy*, a very judicious critick, has evinced by induction of particular passages, that the cruelty of his daughters is the primary source of his distress, and that the loss of royalty affects him only as a secondary and subordinate evil; He observes with great justness, that *Lear* would move our compassion but little, did we not rather consider the injured father than the degraded king.[1] . .

Vol. vi, pp. 158–60.

Hamlet

Polonius is a man bred in courts, exercised in business, stored with observation, confident of his knowledge,

---

[1] Arthur Murphy had made *King Lear* the subject of his *Gray's-Inn Journal* for January 12, 1754. 'I am really surprized,' he said, 'that the Critic in the *Adventurer* should impute the Madness of *Lear* to the Loss of Royalty. The Behaviour of his Children is always uppermost in his Thoughts, and we perceive it working upon his Passions, till at Length his Mind settles into a fixt Attention to that single Object. This, I think, will appear in a critical Examination of the Play.'

proud of his eloquence, and declining into dotage. His mode of oratory is truly represented as designed to ridicule the practice of those times, of prefaces that made no introduction, and of method that embarrassed rather than explained. This part of his character is accidental, the rest is natural. Such a man is positive and confident, because he knows that his mind was once strong, and knows not that it is become weak. Such a man excels in general principles, but fails in the particular application. He is knowing in retrospect, and ignorant in foresight. While he depends upon his memory, and can draw from his repositories of knowledge, he utters weighty sentences, and gives useful counsel; but as the mind in its enfeebled state cannot be kept long busy and intent, the old man is subject to sudden dereliction of his faculties, he loses the order of his ideas, and entangles himself in his own thoughts, till he recovers the leading principle, and falls again into his former train. This idea of dotage encroaching upon wisdom, will solve all the phænomena of the character of *Polonius*.

Vol. viii, p. 183.

IF the dramas of *Shakespeare* were to be characterised, each by the particular excellence which distinguishes it from the rest, we must allow to the tragedy of *Hamlet* the praise of variety. The incidents are so numerous, that the argument of the play would make a long tale. The scenes are interchangeably diversified with merriment and solemnity; with merriment that includes judicious and instructive observations, and solemnity, not strained by poetical violence above the natural sentiments of man. New characters appear from time to time in continual succession, exhibiting various forms of life and particular modes of conversation. The pretended madness of *Hamlet* causes much mirth, the mournful distraction of *Ophelia* fills the heart with tenderness, and every personage produces the effect intended, from the apparition that in the first act chills the blood with horror, to the fop in the last, that exposes affectation to just contempt.

The conduct is perhaps not wholly secure against objections. The action is indeed for the most part in continual progression, but there are some scenes which neither forward nor retard it. Of the feigned madness of *Hamlet* there appears no adequate cause, for he does nothing which he might not have done with the reputation of sanity. He plays the madman most, when he treats *Ophelia* with so much rudeness, which seems to be useless and wanton cruelty.

Hamlet is, through the whole play, rather an instrument than an agent. After he has, by the stratagem of the play, convicted the King, he makes no attempt to punish him, and his death is at last effected by an incident which *Hamlet* has no part in producing.

The catastrophe is not very happily produced; the exchange of weapons is rather an expedient of necessity, than a stroke of art. A scheme might easily have been formed, to kill *Hamlet* with the dagger, and *Laertes* with the bowl.

The poet is accused of having shewn little regard to poetical justice, and may be charged with equal neglect of poetical probability. The apparition left the regions of the dead to little purpose; the revenge which he demands is not obtained but by the death of him that was required to take it; and the gratification which would arise from the destruction of an usurper and a murderer, is abated by the untimely death of *Ophelia*, the young, the beautiful, the harmless, and the pious.

P. 311.

Othello

THE beauties of this play impress themselves so strongly upon the attention of the reader, that they can draw no aid from critical illustration. The fiery openness of *Othello*, magnanimous, artless, and credulous, boundless in his confidence, ardent in his affection, inflexible in his resolution, and obdurate in his revenge; the cool malignity of *Iago*, silent in his resentment, subtle in his designs, and studious at once of his interest and his vengeance; the soft simplicity of *Desdemona*, confident of merit, and conscious of innocence, her artless perseverance in her suit, and her slowness to suspect that she can be suspected, are such proofs of *Shakespeare*'s skill in human nature, as, I suppose, it is vain to seek in any modern writer. The gradual progress which *Iago* makes in the Moor's conviction, and the circumstances which he employs to inflame him, are so artfully natural, that, though it will perhaps not be said of him as he says of himself, that he is *a man not easily jealous*, yet we cannot but pity him when at last we find him *perplexed in the extreme*.

There is always danger lest wickedness conjoined with abilities should steal upon esteem, though it misses of approbation; but the character of *Iago* is so conducted, that he is from the first scene to the last hated and despised.

Even the inferiour characters of this play would be very conspicuous in any other piece, not only for their justness but their strength. *Cassio* is brave, benevolent, and honest, ruined only by his want of stubbornness to resist an insidious invitation. *Rodorigo*'s suspicious credulity, and impatient submission to the cheats which he sees practised upon him, and which by persuasion he suffers to be repeated, exhibit a strong picture of a weak mind

betrayed by unlawful desires, to a false friend; and the
virtue of Æmilia is such as we often find, worn loosely,
but not cast off, easy to commit small crimes, but quickened and alarmed at atrocious villanies.

The Scenes from the beginning to the end are busy,
varied by happy interchanges, and regularly promoting
the progression of the story; and the narrative in the end,
though it tells but what is known already, yet is necessary to produce the death of *Othello*.

Had the scene opened in *Cyprus*, and the preceding
incidents been occasionally related, there had been little
wanting to a drama of the most exact and scrupulous
regularity.

Pp. 472–3.

THOMAS WHATELY

Remarks on some of the Characters of Shakespeare. By the Author of *Observations on
Modern Gardening*. M.DCC.LXXXV[1]

EVERY Play of Shakespeare abounds with instances of
his excellence in distinguishing characters. It would be
difficult to determine which is the most striking of
all that he drew; but his merit will appear most con-
spicuously by comparing two opposite characters, who
happen to be placed in similar circumstances:—not that
on such occasions he marks them more strongly than
on others, but because the contrast makes the distinction
more apparent; and of these none seem to agree so much
in situation, and to differ so much in disposition, as
RICHARD THE THIRD and MACBETH. Both are soldiers,

[1] Thomas Whately—Under-Secretary of State under Lord
North, 1771-2—died in 1772. This essay was brought out by
his brother, the Rev. Dr. Joseph Whately, after it had remained
at least fifteen years in manuscript. The short preface states that
the author 'intended to have gone through eight or ten of the
principal characters of Shakespeare in the same manner, but suspended his design, in order to finish his *Observations on Modern
Gardening*, first published in the year 1770; immediately after
which time, he was engaged in such an active scene of public
life, as left him but little leisure to attend to the *Belles Lettres*;
and in the year 1772 he died. The ensuing pages must therefore
be considered as a *Fragment* only of a greater work, and that also
destitute of the last corrections of the Author.' A second edition
was published in 1808; and a third in 1839, with a preface by
Archbishop Whately, the author's nephew. The present reprint
is from the edition of 1785, but has corrections from the edition
of 1808. It has been found necessary for reasons of space to make
several omissions, but they do not affect the general character
of the work, which, apart from its intrinsic merits, is important
as the earliest volume devoted exclusively to the minute analysis
of Shakespeare characters.

both usurpers; both attain the throne by the same means, by treason and murther; and both lose it too in the same manner, in battle against the person claiming it as lawful heir. Perfidy, violence, and tyranny are common to both; and those only, their obvious qualities, would have been attributed indiscriminately to both by an ordinary dramatic writer. But Shakespeare, in conformity to the truth of history as far as it led him, and by improving upon the fables which have been blended with it, has ascribed opposite principles and motives to the same designs and actions, and various effects to the operation of the same events upon different tempers. Richard and Macbeth, as represented by him, agree in nothing but their fortunes.

The periods of history, from which the subjects are taken, are such as at the best can be depended on only for some principal facts; but not for the minute detail, by which characters are unravelled. That of Macbeth is too distant to be particular; that of Richard, too full of discord and animosity to be true: and antiquity has not feigned more circumstances of horror in the one, than party violence has given credit to in the other. Fiction has even gone so far as to introduce supernatural fables into both stories: the usurpation of Macbeth is said to have been foretold by some witches; and the tyranny of Richard by omens attending his birth. From these fables, Shakespeare, unrestrained and indeed uninformed by history, seems to have taken the hint of their several characters; and he has adapted their dispositions so as to give to such fictions, in the days he wrote, a shew of probability. The first thought of acceding to the throne is suggested, and success in the attempt is promised, to Macbeth by the witches: he is therefore represented as a man, whose natural temper would have deterred him from such a design, if he had not been immediately tempted, and strongly impelled to it. Richard, on the other hand, brought with him into the world the signs of ambition and cruelty: his disposition, therefore, is suited to those symptoms; and he is not discouraged from indulging it by the improbability of succeeding, or by any difficulties and dangers which obstruct his way.

Agreeably to these ideas, Macbeth appears to be a man not destitute of the feelings of humanity. His lady gives him that character:

> —————I fear thy nature;
> It is too full o' th' milk of human kindness,
> To catch the nearest way.——

Which apprehension was well founded; for his reluctance to commit the murther is owing in a great measure to reflexions which arise from sensibility:

> —————— He's here in double trust:
> First, as I am his kinsman and his subject;
> Strong both against the deed; then, as his host,
> Who should against his murtherer shut the door,
> Not bear the knife myself.——

Immediately after he tells Lady Macbeth,

> We will proceed no further in this business;
> He hath honour'd me of late.

And thus giving way to his natural feelings of kindred, hospitality, and gratitude, he for a while lays aside his purpose.

A man of such a disposition will esteem, as they ought to be esteemed, all gentle and amiable qualities in another: and therefore Macbeth is affected by the mild virtues of Duncan; and reveres them in his sovereign when he stifles them in himself. That

> —————This Duncan
> Hath borne his faculties so meekly; hath been
> So clear in his great office,——

is one of his reasons against the murther: and when he is tortured with the thought of Banquo's issue succeeding him in the throne, he aggravates his misery by observing, that,

> For them the gracious Duncan have I murther'd:

which epithet of *gracious* would not have occurred to one who was not struck with the particular merit it expresses.

The frequent references to the prophecy in favour of Banquo's issue, is another symptom of the same disposition: for it is not always from fear, but sometimes from envy, that he alludes to it: and being himself very susceptible of those domestic affections, which raise a desire and love of posterity, he repines at the succession assured to the family of his rival, and which in his estimation seems more valuable than his own actual possession. He therefore reproaches the sisters for their partiality, when

> Upon my head they plac'd a fruitless crown,
> And put a barren sceptre in my gripe,
> Thence to be wrench'd with an unlineal hand,
> No son of mine succeeding. If 'tis so,
> For Banquo's issue have I 'fil'd my mind,
> For them the gracious Duncan have I murther'd;
> Put rancours in the vessel of my peace
> Only for them; and mine eternal jewel
> Given to the common enemy of man,
> To make them kings, the seed of Banquo kings!
> Rather than so, come, Fate, into the list,
> And champion me to the utterance.——

Thus, in a variety of instances, does the tenderness in his character shew itself; and one who has these feelings, though he may have no principles, cannot easily be induced to commit a murther. The intervention of a supernatural cause accounts for his acting so contrary to his disposition. But that alone is not sufficient to prevail entirely over his nature: the instigations of his wife are also necessary to keep him to his purpose; and she, knowing his temper, not only stimulates his courage to the deed, but sensible that, besides a backwardness in daring, he had a degree of softness which wanted hardening, endeavours to remove all remains of humanity from his breast, by the horrid comparison she makes between him and herself:

> ———— I have given suck, and know
> How tender 'tis to love the babe that milks me:
> I would, while it was smiling in my face,
> Have pluck'd my nipple from his boneless gums,
> And dash'd the brains out, had I but so sworn
> As you have done to this.————

The argument is, that the strongest and most natural affections are to be stifled upon so great an occasion: and such an argument is proper to persuade one who is liable to be swayed by them; but is no incentive either to his courage or his ambition.

Richard is in all these particulars the very reverse to Macbeth. He is totally destitute of every softer feeling:

> I that have neither pity, love, nor fear,

is the character he gives of himself, and which he preserves throughout; insensible to his habitudes with a brother, to his connexion with a wife, to the piety of the king, and the innocence of the babes, whom he murthers. The deformity of his body was supposed to indicate a similar depravity of mind; and Shakespeare makes great use both of that, and of the current stories of the times concerning the circumstances of his birth, to intimate that his actions proceeded not from the occasion, but from a savageness of nature. Henry therefore tells him,

> Thy mother felt more than a mother's pain,
> And yet brought forth less than a mother's hope;
> To wit, an indigested, deform'd lump,
> Not like the fruit of such a goodly tree.

> Teeth hadst thou in thy head when thou wast born,
> To signify thou cam'st to bite the world;
> And, if the rest be true which I have heard,
> Thou cam'st into the world with thy legs forward.

Which violent invective does not affect Richard as a re-proach; it serves him only for a pretence to commit the murther he came resolved on; and his answer while he is killing Henry is,

> I'll hear no more; die, prophet, in thy speech!
> For this, among the rest, was I ordain'd.

Immediately afterwards he resumes the subject himself; and, priding himself that the signs given at his birth were verified in his conduct, he says,

> Indeed 'tis true that Henry told me of;
> For I have often heard my mother say,
> I came into the world with my legs forward.
> Had I not reason, think ye, to make haste,
> And seek their ruin that usurp'd our right?
> The midwife wonder'd; and the women cry'd,
> O Jesus bless us! he is born with teeth!
> And so I was; which plainly signified
> That I should snarl, and bite, and play the dog.
> Then, since the Heavens have shap'd my body so,
> Let Hell make crook'd my mind to answer it.

Several other passages to the same effect imply that he has a natural propensity to evil; crimes are his delight: but Macbeth is always in an agony when he thinks of them. He is sensible, before he proceeds, of

> —— the heat-oppressed brain.

He feels

> —— the present horror of the time
> Which now suits with it.——

And immediately after he has committed the murther, he is

> —— afraid to think what he has done.

He is pensive even while he is enjoying the effect of his
crimes; but Richard is in spirits merely at the prospect
of committing them; and what is effort in the one, is
sport to the other. An extraordinary gaiety of heart
shews itself upon those occasions, which to Macbeth
seem most awful; and whether he forms or executes,
contemplates the means, or looks back on the success,
of the most wicked and desperate designs, they are at all
times to him subjects of merriment. Upon parting from
his brother, he bids him

> Go, tread the path that thou shalt ne'er return;
> Simple, plain Clarence! I do love thee so,
> That I will shortly send thy soul to Heaven,
> If Heaven will take the present at our hands.

His amusement, when he is meditating the murther of
his nephews, is the application of some proverbs to their
discourse and situation:

> So wise so young, they say, do ne'er live long.

And,

> Short summer lightly has a forward spring.

His ironical address to Tyrrel,

> Dar'st thou resolve to kill a friend of mine?

is agreeable to the rest of his deportment: and his pleasantry does not forsake him when he considers some of his
worst deeds, after he has committed them; for the terms
in which he mentions them are, that,

> The sons of Edward sleep in Abraham's bosom;
> And Ann my wife hath bid the world good night.

But he gives a still greater loose to his humour, when his
deformity, and the omens attending his birth, are alluded

to, either by himself or by others, as symptoms of the wickedness of his nature. . . .

But the characters of Richard and Macbeth are marked not only by opposite qualities; but even the same qualities in each differ so much in the cause, the kind, and the degree, that the distinction in them is as evident as in the others. Ambition is common to both; but in Macbeth it proceeds only from vanity, which is flattered and satisfied by the splendor of a throne: in Richard it is founded upon pride; his ruling passion is the lust of power:

> —— this earth affords no joy to him,
> But to command, to check, and to o'erbear.

And so great is that joy, that he enumerates among the delights of war,

> To fright the souls of fearful adversaries;

which is a pleasure brave men do not very sensibly feel; they rather value

> ———— Battles
> Nobly, hardly fought.———

But, in Richard, the sentiments natural to his high courage are lost in the greater satisfaction of trampling on mankind, and seeing even those whom he despises crouching beneath him: at the same time, to submit himself to any authority, is incompatible with his eager desire of ruling over all; nothing less than the first place can satiate his love of dominion: he declares that he shall

> Count himself but bad, till he is best:

and,

> While I live account this world but hell,
> Until the mis-shap'd trunk that bears this head
> Be round impaled with a glorious crown.

Which crown he hardly ever mentions, except in

swelling terms of exultation; and which, even after he
has obtained it, he calls

> The high imperial type of this earth's glory.

But the crown is not Macbeth's pursuit through life:
he had never thought of it till it was suggested to him
by the witches; he receives their promise, and the subsequent earnest of the truth of it, with calmness. But
his wife, whose thoughts are always more aspiring,
hears the tidings with rapture, and greets him with the
most extravagant congratulations; she complains of his
moderation; the utmost merit she can allow him is, that
he is

> ———— not without ambition.

But it is cold and faint, for the subject of it is that of a
weak mind; it is only pre-eminence of place, not dominion. He never carries his idea beyond the honour of
the situation he aims at; and therefore he considers it as
a situation which Lady Macbeth will partake of equally
with him: and in his letter tells her,

> This have I thought good to deliver thee, my dearest
> partner of greatness, that thou might'st not lose the dues
> of rejoicing, by being ignorant of what greatness is pro-
> mis'd thee.

But it was his rank alone, not his power, in which she
could share: and that indeed is all which he afterwards
seems to think he had attained by his usurpation. He
styles himself,

> ———— high-plac'd Macbeth:

but in no other light does he ever contemplate his advancement with satisfaction; and when he finds that it is
not attended with that adulation and respect which he
had promised himself, and which would have soothed

his vanity, he sinks under the disappointment, and complains that

> —————— my way of life
> Is fallen into the sear, the yellow leaf;
> And that which should accompany old age,
> As honour, love, obedience, troops of friends,
> I must not look to have.—————

These blessings, so desirable to him, are widely different from the pursuits of Richard. He wishes not to gain the affections, but to secure the submission of his subjects, and is happy to see men shrink under his controul. But Macbeth, on the contrary, reckons among the miseries of his condition

> —————— mouth-honour, breath,
> Which the poor heart would fain deny, but dare not:

and pities the wretch who fears him.

The towering ambition of Richard, and the weakness of that passion in Macbeth, are further instances wherein Shakespeare has accommodated their characters to the fabulous parts of their stories. The necessity for the most extraordinary incitements to stimulate the latter, thereby becomes apparent; and the meaning of the omens, which attended the birth of the former, is explained. Upon the same principle, a distinction still stronger is made in the article of courage, though both are possessed of it even to an eminent degree; but in Richard it is intrepidity, and in Macbeth no more than resolution: in him it proceeds from exertion, not from nature; in enterprise he betrays a degree of fear, though he is able, when occasion requires, to stifle and subdue it. When he and his wife are concerting the murther, his doubt,

> —————— If we should fail,

is a difficulty raised by apprehension; and as soon as that is removed by the contrivance of Lady Macbeth, to make the officers drunk, and lay the crime upon them, he runs with violence into the other extreme of confidence, and cries out, with a rapture unusual to him,

> ——Bring forth men-children only!
> For thy undaunted metal should compose
> Nothing but males. Will it not be received,
> When we have mark'd with blood these sleepy two
> Of his own chamber, and us'd their very daggers,
> That they have done it?——

Which question he puts to her, who but the moment before had suggested the thought of

> His spongy officers, who shall bear the guilt
> Of our great quell.——

And his asking it again proceeds from that extravagance, with which a delivery from apprehension and doubt is always accompanied. Then summoning all his fortitude, he says,

> I am settled, and bend up
> Each corporal agent to this terrible feat;

and proceeds to the bloody business without any further recoils. But a certain degree of restlessness and anxiety still continues, such as is constantly felt by a man, not naturally very bold, worked up to a momentous atchievement. His imagination dwells entirely on the circumstances of horror which surround him; the vision of the dagger; the darkness and the stillness of the night; and the terrors and the prayers of the chamberlains. Lady Macbeth, who is cool and undismayed, attends to the business only; considers of the place where she had laid the daggers ready; the impossibility of his missing them; and is afraid of nothing but a disappointment.

She is earnest and eager; he is uneasy and impatient, and
therefore wishes it over:

> I go, and it is done; the bell invites me;
> Hear it not, Duncan, for it is a knell
> Which summons thee to heaven or to hell.

But a resolution, thus forced, cannot hold longer than
the immediate occasion for it: the moment after that is
accomplished for which it was necessary, his thoughts take
the contrary turn, and he cries out in agony and despair,

Wake, Duncan, with this knocking: would thou could'st!

That courage, which had supported him while he was
settled and bent up, forsakes him so immediately after he
has performed the *terrible feat* for which it had been
exerted, that he forgets the favourite circumstance of
laying it on the officers of the bed-chamber; and when
reminded of it, he refuses to return and complete his
work, acknowledging that

> I am afraid to think what I have done;
> Look on't again I dare not.——

His disordered senses deceive him, and his debilitated
spirits fail him; he owns that

> —— every noise appals him.

He listens when nothing stirs; he mistakes the sounds he
does hear; he is so confused, as not to distinguish whence
the knocking proceeds. She, who is more calm, knows
that it is at the south entry; she gives clear and direct
answers to all the incoherent questions he asks her: but
he returns none to that which she puts to him; and
though after some time, and when necessity again urges
him to recollect himself, he recovers so far as to conceal
his distress, yet he still is not able to divert his thoughts
from it. . . .

Nothing can be conceived more directly opposite to
the agitations of Macbeth's mind, than the serenity of
Richard in parallel circumstances. Upon the murther of
the Prince of Wales, he immediately resolves on the
assassination of Henry; and stays only to say to Clarence,

> *Rich.* Clarence, excuse me to the king my brother;
> I'll hence to London, on a serious matter:
> Ere ye come there, be sure to hear some news.
> *Cla.* What? What?
> *Rich.* The Tower, man, the Tower! I'll root them
> out.

It is a thought of his own, which just then occurs to him:
he determines upon it without hesitation; it requires no
consideration, and admits of no delay: he is eager to put
it in execution; but his eagerness proceeds from ardor,
not from anxiety; and is not hurry, but dispatch. He
does not wait to communicate to the king his brother; he
only hints the thought, as he had conceived it, to Clarence; and supposes that the name alone of the Tower
will sufficiently indicate his business there. When come
thither, he proceeds directly without relenting; it is not
to him, as to Macbeth, *a terrible feat*, but only *a serious
matter:* and

> Sir, leave us to ourselves, we must confer,

is all the preparation he makes for it; and indeed with
him it is little more than a conference with an enemy:
his animosity and his insolence are the same, both before
and after the assassination; and nothing retards, staggers,
or alarms him. The humour which breaks from him,
upon this and other occasions, has been taken notice of
already, as a mark of his depravity; it is at the same time
a proof of his calmness, and of the composure he preserves when he does not indulge himself in ridicule. It
is with the most unfeeling steadiness that he tells the first

tidings of the death of Clarence to Edward, when, on
the Queen's intercession in his favour, he occasionally
introduces it as a notorious fact, and tells her,

> Who knows not that the gentle duke is dead?
> You do him injury to scorn his corse.

He feels no remorse for the deed, nor fear of discovery;
and therefore does not drop a word which can betray
him, but artfully endeavours to impute it to others; and,
without the least appearance of ostentation, makes the
most natural and most pertinent reflections upon the
fruits of rashness, and the vengeance of God against such
offenders. . . .

He never deviates; but throughout the whole progress
of his reiterated crimes, he is not once daunted at the
danger, discouraged by the difficulties, nor disconcerted
by the accidents attending them; nor ever shocked either
at the idea or the reflection.

Macbeth indeed commits subsequent murthers with
less agitation than that of Duncan: but this is no inconsistency in his character; on the contrary, it confirms the
principles upon which it is formed; for besides his being
hardened to the deeds of death, he is impelled to the perpetration of them by other motives than those which
instigated him to assassinate his sovereign. In the one he
sought to gratify his ambition; the rest are for his security: and he gets rid of fear by guilt, which, to a mind
so constituted, may be the less uneasy sensation of the
two. . . .

But Macbeth wants no disguise of his natural disposition, for it is not bad; he does not affect more piety than
he has: on the contrary, a part of his distress arises from
a real sense of religion; which, in the passages already
quoted, makes him regret that he could not join with
the chamberlains in prayer for God's blessing; and be-

wail that he has *given his eternal jewel to the common enemy of man.* He continually reproaches himself for his deeds; no use can harden him; confidence cannot silence, and even despair cannot stifle the cries of his conscience. By the first murther he committed he *put rancours in the vessel of his peace*; and of the last he owns to Macduff,

> —— my soul is too much charg'd
> With blood of thine already.——

How heavily it was charged with his crimes, appears from his asking the physician,

> Canst thou not minister to a mind diseas'd,
> Pluck from the memory a rooted sorrow,
> Raze out the written troubles of the brain,
> And, with some sweet oblivious antidote,
> Cleanse the stuff'd bosom of that perilous stuff,
> Which weighs upon the heart?

For though it is the disorder of Lady Macbeth that gives occasion to these questions, yet the feeling with which he describes the sensations he wishes to be removed; the longing he expresses for the means of doing it; the plaintive measure of the lines; and the rage into which he bursts, when he says,

> Throw physic to the dogs, I'll none of it——

upon being told that

> —— therein the patient
> Must minister unto himself,——

evidently shew, that, in his own mind, he is all the while making the application to himself. His credulity in the mysterious assurances of safety, which the incantations of the witches had procured, proceeds from superstition. He considers those who give him such assurances as

> —— spirits that know
> All mortal consequences:——

and yet he condemns all intercourse with them, at the
very time that he seeks it; and he calls his own application to the sisters a resolution

                                    —— to know,
        By the worst means, the worst.——

Conscious therefore of all these feelings, he has no occasion to assume the appearance, but is obliged to conceal
the force of them: and Lady Macbeth finds it necessary
more than once to suggest to him the precautions proper
to hide the agitations of his mind. After the murther of
Duncan, she bids him,

        Get on your night-gown, lest occasion call us,
        And shew us to be watchers. Be not lost
        So poorly in your thoughts.——

and while he is meditating the death of Banquo, she says
to him.

        Come on;——
        Gentle my lord, sleek o'er your rugged looks;
        Be bright and jovial with your friends to-night.

Which kind of disguise is all that is wanting to him;
and yet, when he had assumed it, he in both instances
betrays himself: in the first, by his too guarded conversation with Macduff and Lenox, which has been
quoted already; and in the last, by an over-acted regard
for Banquo, of whose absence from the feast he affects
to complain, that he may not be suspected of knowing
the cause of it, though at the same time he very un-
guardedly drops an allusion to that cause, when he says,

        Here had we now our country's honour roof'd,
        Were the grac'd person of our Banquo present;
        Whom may I rather challenge for unkindness,
        Than pity for mischance!——

This he says before the ghost rises; and after it is vanished, he, from the same consciousness, reassumes the same affectation; and as soon as he is recovered, drinks

> —— to the general joy of the whole table;
> And to our dear friend Banquo, whom we miss;
> Would he were here!——

Richard is able to put on a general character, directly the reverse of his disposition; and it is ready to him upon every occasion. But Macbeth cannot effectually conceal his sensations, when it is most necessary to conceal them; nor act a part which does not belong to him with any degree of consistency: and the same weakness of mind, which disqualifies him from maintaining such a force upon his nature, shews itself still further in that hesitation and dullness to dare, which he feels in himself, and allows in others. . . .

A mind so framed and so tortured as that of Macbeth, when the hour of extremity presses upon him, can find no refuge but in despair; and the expression of that despair by Shakespeare is perhaps one of the finest pictures that ever was exhibited. It is wildness, inconsistency, and disorder, to such a degree, and so apparent, that

> Some say he's mad; others, who lesser hate him,
> Do call it valiant fury: but for certain,
> He cannot buckle his distemper'd cause
> Within the belt of rule.——

It is presumption without hope, and confidence without courage: that confidence rests upon his superstition; he buoys himself up with it against all the dangers that threaten him, and yet sinks upon every fresh alarm. . . .

But his seeming composure is not resignation; it is passion still; it is one of the irregularities of despair, which sometimes overwhelms him, at other times starts into rage, and is at all times intemperate and extravagant. The resolution with which he bore up against the

desertion of the Thanes, fails him, upon meeting the
messenger who comes to tell him the numbers of the
enemy: when he receives the confirmation of that news,
his dejection turns into fury, and he declares,

> I'll fight, till from my bones my flesh is hack'd.

He then impetuously gives his orders, to

> Send out more horses; skirr the country round;
> Hang those that talk of fear.———

He repeats them afterwards with impatience. Though
the enemy is still at a distance, he calls for his armour;
notwithstanding Seyton's remonstrance, that *it is not
needed yet*, he persists in putting it on; he calls for it again
eagerly afterwards; he bids the person who is assisting
him, *dispatch*; then, the moment it is on, he pulls it off
again, and directs his attendants *to bring it after him*. In
the midst of all this violence and hurry, the melancholy
which preys upon him shews itself, by the sympathy he
expresses so feelingly, when the diseased mind of Lady
Macbeth is mentioned; and yet neither the troubles of
his conscience, nor his concern for her, can divert his
attention from the distress of his situation. He tells her
physician, that *the Thanes fly from him*; and betrays to
him, whose assistance he could not want, and in whom
he did not mean to place any particular confidence, his
apprehensions of the English forces. After he has forbid
those about him to bring him any more reports, he
anxiously enquires for news; he dreads every danger
which he supposes he scorns; at last he recurs to his
superstition, as to the only relief from his agony; and
concludes the agitated scene, as he had begun it, with
declaring that he

> ——— will not be afraid of death or bane,
> Till Birnam forest come to Dunsinane.

At his next appearance, he gives his orders, and considers his situation more calmly; but still there is no spirit in him. If he is for a short time sedate, it is because

> ——— he has surfeited with horrors;
> Direness, familiar to his slaughterous thoughts,
> Cannot now start him.———

He appears composed, only because he is become almost indifferent to every thing: he is hardly affected by the death of the Queen, whom he tenderly loved: he checks himself for wishing she had lived longer; for he is weary himself of life, which in his estimation now

> Is but a walking shadow; a poor player,
> That struts and frets his hour upon the stage,
> And then is heard no more: it is a tale
> Told by an idiot, full of sound and fury,
> Signifying nothing.———

Yet though he grows more careless about his fate, he cannot reconcile himself to it; he still flatters himself that he shall escape, even after he has found *the equivocation of the fiend*. When Birnam wood appeared to come towards Dunsinane, he trusts to the other assurance; and believes that he

> ——— bears a charmed life, which must not yield
> To one of woman born.———

His confidence however begins to fail him; he raves as soon as he perceives that he has reason to doubt of the promises which had been made to him, and says,

> If this which he avouches does appear,
> There is no flying hence, nor tarrying here.
> I 'gin to be a-weary of the sun,
> And wish the state o' th' world were now undone.—
> Ring the alarum bell:—Blow, wind! come, wrack!
> At least we'll die with harness on our back.

But sensible, at last, that he is driven to extremity,
and that

> They've tied him to a stake; he cannot fly,
> But, bear-like, he must fight the course,

he summons all his fortitude; and, agreeably to the manliness of character to which he had always formed himself, behaves with more temper and spirit during the
battle than he had before. He is so well recovered from
the disorder he had been in, that the natural sensibility of
his disposition finds even in the field an opportunity to
work; where he declines to fight with Macduff, not from
fear, but from a consciousness of the wrongs he had
done to him: he therefore answers his provoking challenge, only by saying,

> Of all men else I have avoided thee:
> But get thee back; my soul is too much charg'd
> With blood of thine already.——

and then patiently endeavours to persuade this injured
adversary to desist from so unequal a combat; for he is
confident that it must be fatal to Macduff, and therefore
tells him,

> ——— thou losest labour;
> As easy may'st thou the intrenchant air
> With thy keen sword impress, as make me bleed:
> Let fall thy blade on vulnerable crests;
> I bear a charmed life.——

But his reliance on this charm being taken away by the
explanation given by Macduff, and every hope now
failing him, though he wishes not to fight, yet his sense
of honour being touched by the threat, to be made *the
shew and gaze of the time*, and all his passions being
now lost in despair, his habits recur to govern him; he

disdains the thought of disgrace, and dies as becomes
a soldier. His last words are,

> —— I will not yield,
> To kiss the ground before young Malcolm's feet,
> And to be baited by the rabble's curse.
> Tho' Birnam wood be come to Dunsinane,
> And thou oppos'd, being of no woman born,
> Yet will I try the last. Before my body
> I throw my warlike shield: lay on, Macduff!
> And damn'd be he that first cries, *Hold, enough.*

If this behaviour of Macbeth required, it would receive illustration, by comparing it with that of Richard
in circumstances not very different. When he is to fight
for his crown and for his life, he prepares for the crisis
with the most perfect evenness of temper; and rises, as
the danger thickens, into ardour, without once starting
out into intemperance, or ever sinking into dejection.
Though he is so far from being supported, that he is depressed, as much as a brave spirit can be depressed, by
supernatural means, and instead of having a superstitious confidence, he is threatened by all the ghosts of all
whom he has murthered, that they will *sit heavy on his
soul to-morrow,* yet he soon shakes off the impression
they had made, and is again as gallant as ever. Before
their appearance he feels a presentiment of his fate; he
observes that he

> —— has not that alacrity of spirit,
> Nor cheer of mind, that he was wont to have:

and upon signifying his intention of lying in Bosworth
field that night, the reflexion of *where to-morrow?* occurs
to him; but he pushes it aside by answering, *Well, all's
one for that:* and he struggles against the lowness of spirits
which he feels, but cannot account for, by calling for
a bowl of wine, and applying to business. Instead of

giving way to it in himself, he attends to every symptom of dejection in others, and endeavours to dispel
them. He asks,

> My lord of Surry, why look you so sad?

He enquires,

> Saw'st thou the melancholy lord Northumberland?

and *is satisfied* upon being told, that he and Surry were
busied in *cheering up the soldiers*. He adverts to every
circumstance which can dishearten or encourage his
attendants or his troops, and observes upon them accordingly. When he perceives the gloominess of the morning, and that the sun might probably not be seen that
day, his observation is,

> Not shine to-day? why, what is that to me
> More than to Richmond? for the self-same heaven,
> That frowns on me, looks sadly upon him.

He takes notice of the superiority of his numbers; he
points out the circumstance that

> —— the king's name is a tower of strength,
> Which they upon the adverse faction want.

He represents the enemy as a troop only of banditti; he
urges the inexperience of Richmond; and he animates
his soldiers with their

> —— ancient word of courage, fair St. George;

the effect of which he had before intimated to the Duke
of Norfolk; when, having explained to him the disposition he intended, he asks him,

> This, and St. George to boot! what think'st thou, Norfolk?

He deliberately, and after having *surveyed the vantage of
the ground*, forms that disposition by himself; for which
purpose he calls for ink and paper, and, being informed
that it is ready, directs his guard to watch, and his

attendants to leave him; but, before he retires, he issues
the necessary orders. They are not, like those of Macbeth, general and violent, but temperate and particular;
delivered coolly, and distinctly given to different persons.
To the Duke of Norfolk he trusts the mounting of the
guard during the night, and bids him be ready himself
early in the morning. He directs Catesby to

—— send out a pursuivant at arms
To Stanley's regiment; bid him bring his power
Before sun-rising.——

He bids his menial servants,

Saddle white Surry for the field to-morrow;
Look that my staves be sound, and not too heavy.

And, instead of hastily putting on, and as hastily pulling
off his armour, he quietly asks,

What, is my beaver easier than it was?
And all my armour laid into my tent?

directing them to come about midnight to help to arm
him. He is attentive to every circumstance preparatory
to the battle; and preserves throughout a calmness and
presence of mind which denote his intrepidity. He does
not lose it upon being told, that *the foe vaunts in the field*;
but recollecting the orders he had given overnight, now
calls for the execution of them, by directing Lord Stanley
to be sent for, and his own horse to be caparisoned. He
tells the Duke of Norfolk, who is next in command to
himself, the disposition he had formed; and every thing
being in readiness, he then makes a speech to encourage
his soldiers: but on hearing the enemy's drum, he concludes with,

Fight, gentlemen of England! fight, bold yeomen!
Draw, archers, draw your arrows to the head!
Spur your proud horses hard, and ride in blood;
Amaze the welkin with your broken staves!

But even in this sally of ardour he is not hurried away
by a blind impetuosity, but still gives orders, and distinguishes the persons to whom he addresses them.
From this moment he is all on fire; and, possessed entirely with the great objects around him, others of lesser
note are below his attention. Swelling himself with
courage, and inspiring his troops with confidence of
victory, he rushes on the enemy. It is not a formed sense
of honour, nor a cold fear of disgrace, which impels
him to fight; but a natural high spirit, and bravery exult-
ing in danger: and being sensible that the competition
is only personal between him and Richmond, he directs
all his efforts to the destruction of his rival; endeavours
himself to single him out; and *seeking him in the throat
of death, he sets his own life upon the cast*. Five times foiled
in his aim, unhorsed, and surrounded with foes, he still
persists *to stand the hazard of the die*; and, having *enacted
more wonders than a man*, loses his life in an attempt so
worthy of himself.

Thus, from the beginning of their history to their last
moments, are the characters of Macbeth and Richard
preserved entire and distinct: and though probably Shakespeare, when he was drawing the one, had no attention to
the other; yet, as he conceived them to be widely different,
expressed his conceptions exactly, and copied both from
nature, they necessarily became contrasts to each other;
and, by seeing them together, that contrast is more
apparent, especially where the comparison is not between opposite qualities, but arises from the different
degrees, or from a particular display, or total omission,
of the same quality. This last must often happen, as the
character of Macbeth is much more complicated than
that of Richard; and therefore, when they are set in
opposition, the judgement of the poet shews itself as

much in what he has left out of the latter as in what he has inserted. The picture of Macbeth is also, for the same reason, much the more highly finished of the two; for it required a greater variety, and a greater delicacy of painting, to express and to blend with consistency all the several properties which are ascribed to him. That of Richard is marked by more careless strokes, but they are, notwithstanding, perfectly just. Much bad composition may indeed be found in the part; it is a fault from which the best of Shakespeare's plays are not exempt, and with which this Play particularly abounds; and the taste of the age in which he wrote, though it may afford some excuse, yet cannot entirely vindicate the exceptionable passages. After every reasonable allowance, they must still remain blemishes ever to be lamented; but happily, for the most part, they only obscure, they do not disfigure his draughts from nature. Through whole speeches and scenes, character is often wanting; but in the worst instances of this kind, Shakespeare is but insipid; he is not inconsistent; and in his peculiar excellence of drawing characters, though he often neglects to exert his talents, he is very rarely guilty of perverting them.

WILLIAM RICHARDSON

Shakespeare's Characters

UPON the whole, it is manifest, that a great portion of the delight we receive from poetry and fine writing, depends no less on the state of our own minds, than on the intrinsic excellence of the performance. It is also obvious, that, though the description of a passion or affection may give us pleasure, whether it be described by the agent or the spectator, yet, to those who would apply the inventions of the poet to the uses of philosophical investigation, it is far from being of equal utility with a passion exactly imitated. The talent of imitation is very different from that of description, and far superior.[1]

No writer has hitherto appeared who possesses in a more eminent degree than Shakespeare, the power of imitating the passions. All of them seem familiar to him; the boisterous no less than the gentle; the benign no less than the malignant. There are several writers, as there are many players, who are successful in imitating some particular passions, but who appear stiff, aukward, and unnatural, in the expression of others. Some are capable of exhibiting very striking representations of resolute and intrepid natures, but cannot so easily bend themselves to those that are softer and more complacent. Others, again, seem full of amiable affection and tenderness, but cannot exalt themselves to the boldness of the hero, or magnanimity of the patriot. The genius of Shakespeare is unlimited. Possessing extreme

---

[1] The author of the Elements of Criticism is, if I mistake not, the first writer who has taken any notice of this important distinction between the imitation and description of a passion.

sensibility, and uncommonly susceptible, he is the Proteus of the drama; he changes himself into every character, and enters easily into every condition of human
nature.

> O youths and virgins! O declining eld!
> O pale misfortune's slaves! O ye who dwell
> Unknown with humble quiet! Ye who wait
> In courts, and fill the golden seats of kings:
> O sons of sport and pleasure! O thou wretch
> That weep'st for jealous love, and the sore wound
> Of conscious guilt, or death's rapacious hand
> That left thee void of hope! O ye who mourn
> In exile! Ye who thro' th' embattled field
> Seek bright renown; or who for nobler palms
> Contend, the leaders of a public cause!
> Hath not his faithful tongue
> Told you the fashion of your own estate,
> The secrets of your bosom?   (*Akenside.*)

Many dramatic writers of different ages are capable,
occasionally, of breaking out with great fervour of
genius in the natural language of strong emotion. No
writer of antiquity is more distinguished for abilities of
this kind than Euripides. His whole heart and soul seem
torn and agitated by the force of the passion he imitates.
He ceases to be Euripides; he is Medea; he is Orestes.
Shakespeare, however, is most eminently distinguished,
not only by these occasional sallies, but by imitating the
passion in all its aspects, by pursuing it through all its
windings and labyrinths, by moderating or accelerating
its impetuosity according to the influence of other principles and of external events, and finally by combining
it in a judicious manner with other passions and propensities, or by setting it aptly in opposition. He thus
unites the two essential powers of dramatic invention,
that of forming characters; and that of imitating, in their

natural expressions, the passions and affections of which
they are composed. It is, therefore, my intention to
examine some of his remarkable characters, and to
analyze their component parts: An exercise no less adapted to improve the heart, than to inform the understanding. It is obvious that my design by no means coincides
with that of the ingenious author of the Essay on the
Writings and Genius of Shakespeare, whose success in
rescuing the fame of our poet from the attacks of partial
criticism, and in drawing the attention of the public to
various excellences in his works which might otherwise
have escaped the notice they deserve, gives her a just
title to the reputation she has acquired. My intention is
to make poetry subservient to philosophy, and to employ it in tracing the principles of human conduct. The
design surely is laudable: Of the execution, I have no
right to determine.

> *From the Introduction to* A Philosophical Analysis
> and Illustration of some of Shakespeare's Re-
> markable Characters, 1774.[1]

[1] This volume deals with Macbeth, Hamlet, Jaques, and
Imogen, and is the first published work devoted specifically and
exclusively to the 'philosophical' examination of Shakespeare's
characters. It was followed in 1784 by a second series dealing
with Richard III, King Lear, and Timon of Athens, and in 1789
by an essay on Falstaff and on Shakespeare's Female Characters.
Richardson was Professor of Humanity in the University of
Glasgow from 1773 till his death in 1814.

Mrs. Elizabeth Montagu's *Essay on the Writings and Genius of
Shakespeare, . . . with Some Remarks upon the Misrepresentations
of Mons. de Voltaire* was published in 1769.

MAURICE MORGANN

An Essay on the Dramatic Character of Sir John Falstaff. MDCCLXXVII[1]

PREFACE

THE following sheets were written in consequence of a friendly conversation, turning by some chance upon the Character of FALSTAFF, wherein the Writer, maintaining contrary to the general Opinion, that, this Character was not intended to be shewn as a Coward, he was challenged to deliver and support that Opinion from the Press, with an engagement, now he fears forgotten, for it was three years ago, that he should be answered thro' the same channel: Thus stimulated, these papers were almost wholly written in a very short time, but not without those attentions, whether successful or not, which seemed necessary to carry them beyond the Press into the hands of the Public. From the influence of the foregoing circumstances it is, that the Writer has gener-ally assumed rather the character and tone of an Advo-cate than of an Inquirer;—though if he had not first *inquired* and been *convinced*, he should never have attemp-ted to have amused either himself or others with the subject.—The impulse of the occasion, however, being passed, the papers were thrown by, and almost for-gotten: But having been looked into of late by some

---

[1] Only representative passages of this remarkable essay are given here. Modern reprints of the complete text will be found in the Oxford Library of Prose and Poetry (ed. W. A. Gill, 1912), and in the editor's *Eighteenth Century Essays on Shake-speare*, 1903.

The essay was written in 1774, though not published till 1777. Other editions appeared in 1820 and 1825.

friends, who observing that the Writer had not enlarged
so far for the sake of FALSTAFF alone, but that the Argument was made subservient to Critical amusement,
persuaded him to revise and convey it to the Press. This
has been accordingly done, though he fears something
too hastily, as he found it proper to add, while the papers
were in the course of printing, some considerations on
the *Whole* Character of FALSTAFF; which ought to have
been accompanied by a slight reform of a few preceding
passages, which may seem, in consequence of this addition, to contain too favourable a representation of his
Morals.

The vindication of FALSTAFF's Courage is truly no
otherwise the object than some old fantastic Oak, or
grotesque Rock, may be the object of a morning's ride;
yet being proposed as such, may serve to limit the distance, and shape the course: The real object is Exercise,
and the Delight which a rich, beautiful, picturesque, and
perhaps unknown Country, may excite from every side.
Such an Exercise may admit of some little excursion,
keeping however the Road in view; but seems to exclude every appearance of labour and of toil.—Under
the impression of such Feelings the Writer has endeavoured to preserve to his Text a certain lightness of air,
and chearfulness of tone; but is sensible however that
the manner of discussion does not *every where*, particularly near the commencement, sufficiently correspond
with his design.—If the Book shall be fortunate enough
to obtain another Impression, a separation may be made;
and such of the heavier parts as cannot be wholly dis-
pensed with, sink to their more proper station,—a
Note.

He is fearful likewise that he may have erred in the
other extreme; and that having thought himself intitled,
even in argument, to a certain degree of playful discus-

sion, may have pushed it, in a few places, even to levity. This error might be yet more easily reformed than the other.—The Book is perhaps, as it stands, too bulky for the subject; but if the Reader knew how many pressing considerations, as it grew into size, the Author resisted, which yet seemed intitled to be heard, he would the more readily excuse him.

The whole is a mere Experiment, and the Writer considers it as such: It may have the advantages, but it is likewise attended with all the difficulties and dangers, of *Novelty*.

ON THE DRAMATIC CHARACTER OF
SIR JOHN FALSTAFF

THE ideas which I have formed concerning the Courage and Military Character of the Dramatic Sir *John Falstaff*, are so different from those which I find generally to prevail in the world, that I shall take the liberty of stating my sentiments on the subject; in hope that some person as unengaged as myself, will either correct and reform my error in this respect; or, joining himself to my opinion, redeem me from, what I may call, the reproach of singularity.

I am to avow then, that I do not clearly discern that Sir *John Falstaff* deserves to bear the character so generally given him of an absolute Coward; or, in other words, that I do not conceive *Shakespeare* ever meant to make Cowardice an essential part of his constitution.

I know how universally the contrary opinion prevails; and I know what respect and deference are due to the public voice. But if to the avowal of this singularity, I add all the reasons that have led me to it, and acknowledge myself to be wholly in the judgment of the public, I shall hope to avoid the censure of too much forwardness or indecorum.

It must, in the first place, be admitted that the appearances in this case are singularly strong and striking; and so they had need be, to become the ground of so general a censure. We see this extraordinary Character, almost in the first moment of our acquaintance with him, involved in circumstances of apparent dishonour; and we hear him familiarly called *Coward* by his most intimate companions. We see him, on occasion of the robbery at *Gads-Hill*, in the very act of running away from the Prince and *Poins*; and we behold him, on another of more honourable obligation, in open day light, in battle, and acting in his profession as a Soldier, escaping from *Douglas* even out of the world as it were; counterfeiting death, and deserting his very existence; and we find him on the former occasion, betrayed into those *lies* and *braggadocioes*, which are the usual concomitants of Cowardice in Military men, and pretenders to valour. These are not only in themselves strong circumstances, but they are moreover thrust forward, prest upon our notice as the subject of our mirth, as the great business of the scene: No wonder, therefore, that the word should go forth that *Falstaff* is exhibited as a character of Cowardice and dishonour.

What there is to the contrary of this, it is my business to discover. Much, I think, will presently appear; but it lies so dispersed, is so latent, and so purposely obscured, that the reader must have some patience whilst I collect it into one body, and make it the object of a steady and regular contemplation.

But what have we to do, may my readers exclaim, with principles *so latent, so obscured?* In Dramatic composition the *Impression* is the *Fact*; and the Writer, who, meaning to impress one thing, has impressed another, is unworthy of observation.

It is a very unpleasant thing to have, in the first setting

out, so many and so strong prejudices to contend with. All that one can do in such case, is, to pray the reader to have a little patience in the commencement; and to reserve his censure, if it must pass, for the conclusion. Under his gracious allowance, therefore, I presume to declare it, as my opinion, that Cowardice *is not the Impression*, which the *whole* character of *Falstaff* is calculated to make on the minds of an unprejudiced audience; tho' there be, I confess, a great deal of something in the *composition* likely enough to puzzle, and consequently to mislead the Understanding.—The reader will perceive that I distinguish between *mental Impressions*, and the *Understanding*.—I wish to avoid every thing that looks like subtlety and refinement; but this is a distinction, which we all comprehend.—There are none of us unconscious of certain feelings or sensations of mind, which do not seem to have passed thro' the Understanding; the effects, I suppose, of some secret influences from without, acting upon a certain mental sense, and producing feelings and passions in just correspondence to the force and variety of those influences on the one hand, and to the quickness of our sensibility on the other. Be the cause, however, what it may, the fact is undoubtedly so; which is all I am concerned in. And it is equally a fact, which every man's experience may avouch, that the Understanding and those feelings are frequently at variance. The latter often arise from the most minute circumstances, and frequently from such as the Understanding cannot estimate, or even recognize; whereas the Understanding delights in abstraction, and in general propositions; which, however true considered as such, are very seldom, I had like to have said *never*, perfectly applicable to any particular case. And hence, among other causes, it is, that we often condemn or applaud characters and actions on the credit of some logical process, while our hearts revolt, and would fain lead us to a very different conclusion.

The Understanding seems for the most part to take cognizance of *actions* only, and from these to infer *motives* and *character*; but the sense we have been speaking of proceeds in a contrary course; and determines of *actions* from certain *first principles of character*, which seem wholly out of the reach of the Understanding. We cannot indeed do otherwise than admit that there must be distinct principles of character in every distinct individual: The manifest variety even in the minds of infants will oblige us to this. But what *are* these first principles of character? Not the objects, I am persuaded, of the Understanding; and yet we take as strong Impressions of them as if we could compare and assort them in a syllogism. We often love or hate at first sight; and indeed, in general, dislike or approve by some secret reference to these *principles*; and we judge even of conduct, not from any idea of abstract good or evil in the nature of actions, but by refering those actions to a supposed original character in the man himself. I do not mean that we *talk* thus; we could not indeed, if we would, explain ourselves in detail on this head; we can neither account for Impressions and passions, nor communicate them to others by *words:* Tones and looks will sometimes convey the *passion* strangely, but the *Impression* is incommunicable. The same causes may produce it indeed at the same time in many, but it is the separate possession of each, and not in its nature transferable: It is an imperfect sort of instinct, and proportionably dumb.—We might indeed, if we chose it, candidly confess to one another, that we are greatly swayed by these feelings, and are by no means so *rational* in all points as we could wish; but this would be a betraying of the interests of that high faculty, the Understanding, which

we so value ourselves upon, and which we more pecu-
liarly call our own. This, we think, must not be; and so
we huddle up the matter, concealing it as much as possible, both from ourselves and others. In Books indeed,
wherein character, motive, and action, are all alike
subjected to the Understanding, it is generally a very
clear case; and we make decisions compounded of them
all: And thus we are willing to approve of *Candide*, tho'
he kills my Lord the Inquisitor, and runs thro' the body
the Baron of *Thunder-ten-tronchk* the son of his patron,
and the brother of his beloved *Cunégonde*: But in real
life, I believe, *my Lords the Judges* would be apt to inform
the *Gentlemen of the Jury*, that my *Lord the Inquisitor* was
ill killed; as *Candide* did not proceed on the urgency of
the moment, but on the speculation only of future evil.
And indeed this clear perception, in Novels and Plays,
of the union of character and action not seen in nature,
is the principal defect of such compositions, and what
renders them but ill pictures of human life, and wretched
guides of conduct.

But if there was *one man* in the world, who could
make a more perfect draught of real nature, and steal
such Impressions on his audience, without their special
notice, as should keep their hold in spite of any error of
their Understanding, and should thereupon venture to
introduce an apparent incongruity of character and
action, for ends which I shall presently endeavour to
explain; such an imitation would be worth our nicest
curiosity and attention. But in such a case as this, the
reader might expect that he should find us all talking
the language of the Understanding only; that is, censuring the action with very little conscientious investigation even of *that*; and transferring the censure, in every
odious colour, to the actor himself; how much soever
our hearts and affections might secretly revolt: For as

to the *Impression*, we have already observed that it has
no tongue; nor is its operation and influence likely to
be made the subject of conference and communication.

It is not to the *Courage* only of *Falstaff* that we think
these observations will apply: No part whatever of his
character seems to be fully settled in our minds; at least
there is something strangely incongruous in our discourse and affections concerning him. We all like *Old
Jack*; yet, by some strange perverse fate, we all abuse him,
and deny him the possession of any one single good or
respectable quality. There is something extraordinary
in this: It must be a strange art in *Shakespeare* which can
draw our liking and good will towards so offensive an
object. He has wit, it will be said; chearfulness and
humour of the most characteristic and captivating sort.
And is this enough? Is the humour and gaiety of vice
so very captivating? Is the wit, characteristic of baseness
and every ill quality capable of attaching the heart and
winning the affections? Or does not the apparency of
such humour, and the flashes of such wit, by more
strongly disclosing the deformity of character, but the
more effectually excite our hatred and contempt of the
man? And yet this is not our *feeling* of *Falstaff*'s character. When he has ceased to amuse us, we find no
emotions of disgust; we can scarcely forgive the ingratitude of the Prince in the new-born virtue of the King,
and we curse the severity of that poetic justice which
consigns our old good-natured delightful companion to
the custody of the *warden*, and the dishonours of the
Fleet.

I am willing, however, to admit that if a Dramatic
writer will but preserve to any character the qualities of
a strong mind, particularly Courage and ability, that it
will be afterwards no very difficult task (as I may have

occasion to explain) to discharge that *disgust* which arises from vicious manners; and even to attach us (if such character should contain any quality productive of chearfulness and laughter) to the cause and subject of our mirth with some degree of affection.

But the question which I am to consider is of a very different nature: It is a question of fact, and concerning a quality which forms the basis of every respectable character; a quality which is the very essence of a Military man; and which is held up to us, in almost every Comic incident of the Play, as the subject of our observation. It is strange then that it should now be a question, whether *Falstaff* is, or is not a man of Courage; and whether we do in fact contemn him for the want, or respect him for the possession of that quality: And yet I believe the reader will find that he has by no means decided this question, even for himself.—If then it should turn out, that this difficulty has arisen out of the Art of *Shakespeare*, who has contrived to make secret Impressions upon us of Courage, and to preserve those Impressions in favour of a character which was to be held up for sport and laughter on account of actions of apparent Cowardice and dishonour, we shall have less occasion to wonder, as *Shakespeare* is a Name which contains All of Dramatic artifice and genius.

If in this place the reader shall peevishly and prematurely object that the observations and distinctions I have laboured to establish, are wholly unapplicable; he being himself unconscious of ever having received any such Impression; what can be done in so nice a case, but to refer him to the following pages; by the number of which he may judge how very much I respect his objection, and by the variety of those proofs, which I shall employ to induce him to part with it; and to recognize in its stead certain feelings, concealed and covered over perhaps, but not erazed, by time, reasoning, and authority.

In the mean while, it may not perhaps be easy for him to resolve how it comes about, that, whilst we look upon *Falstaff* as a character of the like nature with that of *Parolles* or of *Bobadil*, we should preserve for him a great degree of respect and good-will, and yet feel the highest disdain and contempt of the others, tho' they are all involved in similar situations. The reader, I believe, would wonder extremely to find either *Parolles* or *Bobadil* possess himself in danger: What then can be the cause that we are not at all surprized at the gaiety and ease of *Falstaff* under the most trying circumstances; and that we never think of charging *Shakespeare* with departing, on this account, from the truth and coherence of character? Perhaps, after all, the *real* character of *Falstaff* may be different from his *apparent* one; and possibly this difference between reality and appearance, whilst it accounts at once for our liking and our censure, may be the true point of humour in the character, and the source of all our laughter and delight. We may chance to find, if we will but examine a little into the nature of those circumstances which have accidentally involved him, that he was intended to be drawn as a character of much Natural courage and resolution; and be obliged thereupon to repeal those decisions, which may have been made upon the credit of some general tho' unapplicable propositions; the common source of error in other and higher matters. A little reflection may perhaps bring us round again to the point of our departure, and unite our Understandings to our instinct. —Let us then for a moment *suspend* at least our decisions, and candidly and coolly inquire if Sir *John Falstaff* be, indeed, what he has so often been called by critic and commentator, male and female,—a *Constitutional Coward.*

It will scarcely be possible to consider the Courage of *Falstaff* as wholly detached from his other qualities: But I write not professedly of any part of his character, but what is included under the term, *Courage*; however I may incidentally throw some lights on the whole.— The reader will not need to be told that this Inquiry will resolve itself of course into a Critique on the genius, the arts, and the conduct of *Shakespeare*: For what is *Falstaff*, what *Lear*, what *Hamlet*, or *Othello*, but different modifications of *Shakespeare*'s thought? It is true that this Inquiry is narrowed almost to a single point: But general criticism is as uninstructive as it is easy: *Shakespeare* deserves to be considered in detail;—a task hitherto unattempted.

It may be proper, in the first place, to take a short view of all the parts of *Falstaff*'s Character, and then proceed to discover, if we can, what *Impressions*, as to Courage or Cowardice, he had made on the persons of the Drama: After which we will examine, in course, such evidence, either of *persons* or *facts*, as are relative to the matter; and account as we may for those appearances, which seem to have led to the opinion of his Constitutional Cowardice.

The scene of the robbery, and the disgraces attending it, which stand first in the Play, and introduce us to the knowledge of *Falstaff*, I shall beg leave (as I think this scene to have been the source of much unreasonable prejudice) to *reserve* till we are more fully acquainted with the whole character of *Falstaff*; and I shall therefore hope that the reader will not for a time advert to it, or to the jests of the *Prince* or of *Poins* in consequence of that unlucky adventure.

In drawing out the parts of *Falstaff*'s character, with which I shall begin this Inquiry, I shall take the liberty of putting Constitutional bravery into his composition;

but the reader will be pleased to consider what I shall say in that respect as spoken hypothetically for the present, to be retained, or discharged out of it, as he shall finally determine.

To me then it appears that the leading quality in *Falstaff*'s character, and that from which all the rest take their colour, is a high degree of wit and humour, accompanied with great natural vigour and alacrity of mind. This quality so accompanied, led him probably very early into life, and made him highly acceptable to society; so acceptable, as to make it seem unnecessary for him to acquire any other virtue. Hence, perhaps, his continued debaucheries and dissipations of every kind.—He seems, by nature, to have had a mind free of malice or any evil principle; but he never took the trouble of acquiring any good one. He found himself esteemed and beloved with all his faults; nay *for* his faults, which were all connected with humour, and for the most part, grew out of it. As he had, possibly, no vices but such as he thought might be openly professed, so he appeared more dissolute thro' ostentation. To the character of wit and humour, to which all his other qualities seem to have conformed themselves, he appears to have added a very necessary support, *that* of the profession of a *Soldier*. He had from nature, as I presume to say, a spirit of boldness and enterprise; which in a Military age, tho' employment was only occasional, kept him always above contempt, secured him an honourable reception among the Great, and suited best both with his particular mode of humour and of vice. Thus living continually in society, nay even in Taverns, and indulging himself, and being indulged by others, in every debauchery; drinking, whoring, gluttony, and ease; assuming a liberty of fiction, necessary perhaps to his wit, and often falling into falsity and lies, he seems

to have set, by degrees, all sober reputation at defiance;
and finding eternal resources in his wit, he borrows,
shifts, defrauds, and even robs, without dishonour.—
Laughter and approbation attend his greatest excesses;
and being governed visibly by no settled bad principle
or ill design, fun and humour account for and cover all.
By degrees, however, and thro' indulgence, he acquires
bad habits, becomes an humourist, grows enormously
corpulent, and falls into the infirmities of age; yet never
quits, all the time, one single levity or vice of youth, or
loses any of that chearfulness of mind, which had enabled
him to pass thro' this course with ease to himself and
delight to others; and thus, at last, mixing youth and age,
enterprize and corpulency, wit and folly, poverty and
expence, title and buffoonery, innocence as to purpose,
and wickedness as to practice; neither incurring hatred
by bad principle, or contempt by Cowardice, yet involved in circumstances productive of imputation in
both; a butt and a wit, a humourist and a man of humour, a touchstone and a laughing stock, a jester and a
jest, has Sir *John Falstaff*, taken at that period of his life
in which we see him, become the most perfect Comic
character that perhaps ever was exhibited.

It may not possibly be wholly amiss to remark in this
place, that if Sir *John Falstaff* had possessed any of that
Cardinal quality, Prudence, alike the guardian of virtue
and the protector of vice; that quality, from the possession or the absence of which, the character and fate of
men in this life take, I think, their colour, and not from
real vice or virtue; if he had considered his wit not as
principal but *accessary* only; as the instrument of power,
and not as power itself; if he had had much baseness to
hide, if he had had less of what may be called mellowness
or good humour, or less of health and spirit; if he had
spurred and rode the world with his wit, instead of

suffering the world, boys and all, to ride him;—he might, without any other essential change, have been the admiration and not the jest of mankind:—Or if he had lived in our day, and instead of attaching himself to one Prince, had renounced *all* friendship and *all* attachment, and had let himself out as the ready instrument and Zany of every successive Minister, he might possibly have acquired the high honour of marking his shroud or decorating his coffin with the living rays of an Irish at least, if not a British Coronet: Instead of which, tho' enforcing laughter from every disposition, he appears, now, as such a character, which every wise man will pity and avoid, every knave will censure, and every fool will fear: And accordingly *Shakespeare*, ever true to nature, has made *Harry* desert, and *Lancaster* censure him:—He dies where he lived, in a Tavern, broken-hearted, without a friend; and his final exit is given up to the derision of fools. Nor have his misfortunes ended here; the scandal arising from the misapplication of his wit and talents seems immortal. He has met with as little justice or mercy from his final judges the critics, as from his companions of the Drama. With our cheeks still red with laughter, we ungratefully as unjustly censure him as a coward by nature, and a rascal upon principle: Tho', if this were so, it might be hoped, for our own credit, that we should behold him rather with disgust and disapprobation than with pleasure and delight.

But to remember our question—*Is Falstaff a constitutional coward?*

With respect to every infirmity, except that of Cowardice, we must take him as at the period in which he is represented to us. If we see him dissipated, fat,—it is enough;—we have nothing to do with his youth, when he might perhaps have been modest, chaste, 'and not an Eagle's talon in the waist.' But *Constitu-tional Courage* extends to a man's whole life, makes a part of his nature, and is not to be taken up or deserted like a mere Moral quality. It is true, there is a Courage founded upon *principle*, or rather a principle independent of Courage, which will sometimes operate in spite of nature; a principle, which prefers death to shame, but which always refers itself, in conformity to its own nature, to the prevailing modes of honour, and the fashions of the age.—But Natural courage is another thing: It is independent of opinion; It adapts itself to occasions, preserves itself under every shape, and can avail itself of flight as well as of action.—In the last war, some Indians of America perceiving a line of Highlanders to keep their station under every disadvantage, and under a fire which they could not effectually return, were so miserably mistaken in our points of honour as to conjecture, from observation on the habit and stability of those troops, that they were indeed the women of England, who wanted courage to run away.—That Courage which is founded in nature and constitution, *Falstaff*, as I presume to say, possessed;—but I am ready to allow, that the principle already mentioned, so far as it refers to reputation only, began with every other Moral quality to lose its hold on him in his old age; that is, at the time of life in which he is represented to us; a period, as it should seem, approaching to *seventy*.—The truth is that he had drollery enough to support himself in credit without the point of honour, and had address enough to make even the preservation of his life a point of drollery. The reader knows I allude, tho' something prematurely, to his fictitious death in the battle of Shrewsbury. This incident is generally construed to the disadvantage of *Falstaff*: It is a transaction which bears the external marks of Cowardice: It is also aggravated to the spectators by the idle tricks of the Player, who practises on this occasion all the attitudes and wild apprehensions of fear; more ambitious, as it should seem, of representing a Caliban than a *Falstaff*; or indeed rather a poor unweildy miserable Tortoise than either.—The painful Comedian lies spread out on his belly, and not only covers himself all over with his robe as with a shell, but forms a kind of round Tortoise-back by I know not what stuffing or contrivance; in addition to which, he alternately lifts up, and depresses, and dodges his head, and looks to the one side and to the other, so much with the piteous aspect of that animal, that one would not be sorry to see the ambitious imitator calipashed in his robe, and served up for the entertainment of the gallery.— There is no hint for this mummery in the Play: Whatever there may be of dishonour in *Falstaff*'s conduct, he neither does or says any thing on this occasion which indicates terror or disorder of mind: On the contrary, this very act is a proof of his having all his wits about him, and is a stratagem, such as it is, not improper for a buffoon, whose fate would be singularly hard, if he should not be allowed to avail himself of his Character when it might serve him in most stead. We must remember, in extenuation, that the executive, the destroying hand of *Douglas* was over him: '*It was time to counterfeit, or that hot termagant Scot had paid him scot and lot too.*' He had but one choice; he was obliged to pass thro' the ceremony of dying either in jest or in earnest; and we shall not be surprized at the event, when we remember his propensities to the former.—Life (and especially the life of *Falstaff*) might be a jest; but he could see no joke whatever in dying: To be chopfallen was, with him, to lose both life and character together: He saw the point of honour, as well as every thing else, in ridiculous lights, and began to renounce its tyranny.

But I am too much in advance, and must retreat for more advantage. I should not forget how much opinion is against me, and that I am to make my way by the mere force and weight of evidence; without which I must not hope to possess myself of the reader: No address, no insinuation will avail. To this evidence, then, I now resort. The Courage of *Falstaff* is my Theme: And no passage will I spare from which any thing can be inferred as relative to this point. It would be as vain as injudicious to attempt concealment: How could I escape detection? The Play is in every one's memory, and a single passage remembered in detection would tell, in the mind of the partial observer, for fifty times its real weight. Indeed this argument would be void of all excuse if it declined any difficulty; if it did not meet, if it did not challenge opposition. Every passage then shall be produced from which, in my opinion, any inference, favourable or unfavourable, has or can be drawn;—but not methodically, not formally, as texts for comment, but as chance or convenience shall lead the way; but in what shape soever, they shall be always distinguishingly marked for notice. And so with that attention to truth and candour which ought to accompany even our lightest amusements I proceed to offer such proof as the case will admit, that *Courage* is a part of *Falstaff*'s *Character*, that it belonged to his constitution, and was manifest in the conduct and practice of his whole life. . . .

I cannot foresee the temper of the reader, nor whether he be content to go along with me in these kind of observations. Some of the incidents which I have drawn out of the Play may appear too minute, whilst yet they refer to principles, which may seem too general. Many points require explanation; something should be said of the nature of *Shakespeare*'s Dramatic

characters;[1] by what arts they were formed, and wherein
they differ from those of other writers; something likewise more professedly of *Shakespeare* himself, and of the

---

[1] The reader must be sensible of something in the composition of *Shakespeare*'s characters, which renders them essentially
different from those drawn by other writers. The characters
of every Drama must indeed be grouped; but in the groupes of
other poets the parts which are not seen, do not in fact exist.
But there is a certain roundness and integrity in the forms of
Shakespeare, which give them an independence as well as a
relation, insomuch that we often meet with passages, which
tho' perfectly felt, cannot be sufficiently explained in words,
without unfolding the whole character of the speaker: And this
I may be obliged to do in respect to that of *Lancaster*, in order
to account for some words spoken by him in censure of *Falstaff*.
. . . Something which may be thought too heavy for the *text*,
I shall add *here*, as a conjecture concerning the composition of
Shakespeare's characters: Not that they were the effect, I believe,
so much of a minute and laborious attention, as of a certain
comprehensive energy of mind, involving within itself all the
effects of system and of labour.

Bodies of all kinds, whether of metals, plants, or animals, are
supposed to possess certain first principles of *being*, and to have
an existence independent of the accidents, which form their
magnitude or growth: Those accidents are supposed to be
drawn in from the surrounding elements, but not indiscriminately; each plant and each animal, imbibes those things only,
which are proper to its own distinct nature, and which have
besides such a secret relation to each other as to be capable of
forming a perfect union and coalescence: But so variously are
the surrounding elements mingled and disposed, that each particular body, even of those under the same species, has yet some
peculiar of its own. *Shakespeare* appears to have considered the
being and growth of the human mind as analogous to this
system: There are certain qualities and capacities, which he
seems to have considered as first principles; the chief of which
are certain energies of courage and activity, according to their
degrees; together with different degrees and sorts of sensibilities,
and a capacity, varying likewise in the *degree*, of discernment
and intelligence. The rest of the composition is drawn in from
an atmosphere of surrounding things; that is, from the various
influences of the different laws, religions and governments in

peculiar character of his genius. After such a review we may not perhaps think any consideration arising out of the world; and from those of the different ranks and inequalities in society; and from the different professions of men, encouraging or repressing passions of particular sorts, and inducing different modes of thinking and habits of life; and he seems to have known intuitively what those influences in particular were which this or that original constitution would most freely imbibe, and which would most easily associate and coalesce. But all these things being, in different situations, very differently disposed, and those differences exactly discerned by him, he found no difficulty in marking every individual, even among characters of the same sort, with something peculiar and distinct.—Climate and complexion demand their influence, '*Be thus when thou art dead, and I will kill thee, and love thee after,*' is a sentiment characteristic of, and fit only to be uttered by a *Moor*.

But it was not enough for *Shakespeare* to have formed his characters with the most perfect truth and coherence; it was further necessary that he should possess a wonderful facility of compressing, as it were, his own spirit into these images, and of giving alternate animation to the forms. This was not to be done *from without*; he must have *felt* every varied situation, and have spoken thro' the organ he had formed. Such an intuitive comprehension of things and such a facility, must unite to produce a *Shakespeare*. The reader will not now be surprised if I affirm that those characters in *Shakespeare*, which are seen only in part, are yet capable of being unfolded and understood in the whole; every part being in fact relative, and inferring all the rest. It is true that the point of action or sentiment, which we are most concerned in, is always held out for our special notice. But who does not perceive that there is a peculiarity about it, which conveys a relish of the whole? And very frequently, when no particular point presses, he boldly makes a character act and speak from those parts of the composition, which are *inferred* only, and not distinctly shewn. This produces a wonderful effect: it seems to carry us beyond the poet to nature itself, and gives an integrity and truth to facts and character, which they could not otherwise obtain: And this is in reality that art in *Shakespeare*, which being withdrawn from our notice, we more emphatically call *nature*. A felt propriety and truth from causes unseen, I take to be the highest point of Poetic composition. If the characters of *Shakespeare* are thus *whole*, and as it were original, while those of almost all other writers are mere imitation, it may be fit to the Play, or out of general nature, either as too minute or too extensive.

Shakespeare is in truth, an author whose mimic creation agrees in general so perfectly with that of nature, that it is not only wonderful in the great, but opens another scene of amazement to the discoveries of the microscope. We have been charged indeed by a Foreign writer with an overmuch admiring of this *Barbarian*: Whether we have admired with knowledge, or have blindly followed those feelings of affection which we could not resist, I cannot tell; but certain it is, that to the labours of his Editors he has not been overmuch obliged. They are however for the most part of the first rank in literary fame; but some of them had possessions of their own in Parnassus, of an extent too great and important to allow of a very diligent attention to the interests of others; and among those Critics more professionally so, the ablest and the best has unfortunately looked more to the praise of ingenious than of just conjecture. The character of his emendations are not so much that of *right* or *wrong*, as that, being in the extreme, they are always *Warburtonian*. Another has since undertaken the custody of our author, whom he seems to consider as a sort of wild Proteus or madman, and accordingly knocks him down with the butt-end of his critical staff, as often as he exceeds that line of sober discretion, which this learned Editor appears to have chalked out for him: Yet is this Editor notwithstanding 'a man take him for all in all,' very highly respectable for his genius and his learning. What however may be chiefly complained of in these gentlemen is, that having

consider them rather as Historic than Dramatic beings; and, when occasion requires, to account for their conduct from the *whole* of character, from general principles, from latent motives, and from policies not avowed.

erected themselves into the condition, as it were, of guardians and trustees of *Shakespeare*, they have never undertaken to discharge the disgraceful incumbrances of some wretched productions, which have long hung heavy on his fame. Besides the evidence of taste, which indeed is not communicable, there are yet other and more general proofs that these incumbrances were not incurred by *Shakespeare*: The *Latin* sentences dispersed thro' the imputed trash is, I think, of itself a decisive one. *Love's Labour lost* contains a very conclusive one of another kind; tho' the very last Editor has, I believe, in his critical sagacity, suppressed the evidence, and withdrawn the record.

Yet whatever may be the neglect of some, or the censure of others, there are those, who firmly believe that this wild, this uncultivated Barbarian, has not yet obtained one half of his fame; and who trust that some new Stagyrite will arise, who instead of pecking at the surface of things will enter into the inward soul of his compositions, and expel by the force of congenial feelings, those foreign impurities which have stained and disgraced his page. And as to those *spots* which will still remain, they may perhaps become invisible to those who shall seek them thro' the medium of his beauties, instead of looking for those beauties, as is too frequently done, thro' the smoke of some real or imputed obscurity. When the hand of time shall have brushed off his present Editors and Commentators, and when the very name of *Voltaire*, and even the memory of the language in which he has written, shall be no more, the *Apalachian* mountains, the banks of the *Ohio*, and the plains of *Sciota* shall resound with the accents of this Barbarian: In his native tongue he shall roll the genuine passions of nature; nor shall the griefs of *Lear* be alleviated, or the charms and wit of *Rosalind* be abated by time. There is indeed nothing perishable about him, except that very learning which he is said so much to want. He had not, it is true, enough for the demands of the age in which he lived, but he had perhaps too much for the reach of his genius, and the interest of his fame. *Milton* and he will carry the decayed remnants and fripperies of antient mythology into more distant ages than they are by their own force intitled to extend; and the metamorphoses of *Ovid*, upheld by them, lay in a new claim to unmerited immortality.

Shakespeare is a name so interesting, that it is excusable to stop a moment, nay it would be indecent to pass him without the tribute of some admiration. He differs essentially from all other writers: Him we may profess rather to feel than to understand; and it is safer to say, on many occasions, that we are possessed by him, than that we possess him. And no wonder;—He scatters the seeds of things, the principles of character and action, with so cunning a hand yet with so careless an air, and, master of our feelings, submits himself so little to our judgment, that every thing seems superior. We discern not his course, we see no connection of cause and effect, we are rapt in ignorant admiration, and claim no kindred with his abilities. All the incidents, all the parts, look like chance, whilst we feel and are sensible that the whole is design. His Characters not only act and speak in strict conformity to nature, but in strict relation to us; just so much is shewn as is requisite, just so much is impressed; he commands every passage to our heads and to our hearts, and moulds us as he pleases, and that with so much ease, that he never betrays his own exertions. We see these Characters act from the mingled motives of passion, reason, interest, habit and complection, in all their proportions, when they are supposed to know it not themselves; and we are made to acknowledge that their actions and sentiments are, from those motives, the necessary result. He at once blends and distinguishes every thing;—every thing is complicated, every thing is plain. I restrain the further expressions of my admiration lest they should not seem applicable to man; but it is really astonishing that a mere human being, a part of humanity only, should so perfectly comprehend the whole; and that he should possess such exquisite art, that whilst every woman and every child shall feel the whole effect, his learned Editors and Commentators should yet so very frequently mistake or seem ignorant of the cause. A sceptre or a straw are in his hands of equal efficacy; he needs no selection; he converts every thing into excellence; nothing is too great, nothing is too base. Is a character efficient like *Richard*, it is every thing we can wish: Is it otherwise, like *Hamlet*, it is productive of equal admiration: Action produces one mode of excellence and inaction another: The Chronicle, the Novel, or the Ballad; the king, or the beggar, the hero, the madman, the sot or the fool; it is all one;—nothing is worse, nothing is better: The same genius pervades and is equally admirable in all. Or, is a character to be shewn in progressive change, and the events of years comprized within the hour;—with what a Magic hand does he prepare and scatter his spells! The Understanding must, in the first place, be subdued; and lo! how the rooted prejudices of the child spring up to confound the man! The Weird sisters rise, and order is extinguished. The laws of nature give way, and leave nothing in our minds but wildness and horror. No pause is allowed us for reflection: Horrid sentiment, furious guilt and compunction, air-drawn daggers, murders, ghosts, and inchantment, shake and *possess us wholly*. In the mean time the *process* is completed. *Macbeth* changes under our eye, *the milk of human kindness is converted to gall; he*

has supped full of horrors, and his *May of life is fallen into
the sear, the yellow leaf*; whilst we, the fools of amazement, are insensible to the shifting of place and the lapse
of time, and till the curtain drops, never once wake to
the truth of things, or recognize the laws of existence.—
On such an occasion, a fellow, like *Rymer*, waking from
his trance, shall lift up his Constable's staff, and charge
this great Magician, this daring *practicer of arts inhibited*,
in the name of *Aristotle*, to surrender; whilst *Aristotle*
himself, disowning his wretched Officer, would fall
prostrate at his feet and acknowledge his supremacy.—
O supreme of Dramatic excellence! (*might he say,*) not
to me be imputed the insolence of fools. The bards of
Greece were confined within the narrow circle of the
Chorus, and hence they found themselves constrained to
practice, for the most part, the precision, and copy the
details of nature. I followed them, and knew not that a
larger circle might be drawn, and the Drama extended
to the whole reach of human genius. Convinced, I see
that a more compendious *nature* may be obtained; a
nature of *effects* only, to which neither the relations of
place, or continuity of time, are always essential. Nature,
condescending to the faculties and apprehensions of
man, has drawn through human life a regular chain of
visible causes and effects: But Poetry delights in surprize,
conceals her steps, seizes at once upon the heart, and
obtains the Sublime of things without betraying the
rounds of her ascent: True Poesy is *magic*, not *nature*; an
effect from causes hidden or unknown. To the Magician
I prescribed no laws; his law and his power are one; his
power is his law. Him, who neither imitates, nor is
within the reach of imitation, no precedent can or ought
to bind, no limits to contain. If his end is obtained, who
shall question his course? Means, whether apparent or
hidden, are justified in poesy by success; but then most

perfect and most admirable when most concealed.[1]—
But whither am I going! This copious and delightful

[1] These observations have brought me so near to the regions
of Poetic *magic*, (using the word here in its strict and proper
sense, and not loosely as in the *text*) that tho' they lie not directly
in my course, I yet may be allowed in this place to point the
reader that way. A felt propriety, or truth of art, from an unseen, tho' supposed adequate cause, we call *nature*. A like feeling
of propriety and truth, supposed without a cause, or as seeming
to be derived from causes inadequate, fantastic, and absurd,—
such as wands, circles, incantations, and so forth,—we call by
the general name *magic*, including all the train of superstition,
witches, ghosts, fairies, and the rest.—*Reason* is confined to the
line of visible existence; our *passions* and our *fancy* extend far
beyond into the *obscure*; but however lawless their operations
may seem, the images they so wildly form have yet a relation
to truth, and are the shadows at least, however fantastic, of
reality. I am not investigating but passing this subject, and must
therefore leave behind me much curious speculation. Of Per-
sonifications however we should observe that those which are
made out of abstract ideas are the creatures of the Understanding
only: Thus, of the mixed modes, virtue, beauty, wisdom and
others,—what are they but very obscure ideas of *qualities* considered as abstracted from any *subject* whatever? The mind cannot steadily contemplate such an abstraction: What then does
it do?—Invent or imagine a subject in order to support these
qualities; and hence we get the Nymphs or Goddesses of virtue,
of beauty, or of wisdom; the very obscurity of the ideas being
the cause of their conversion into sensible objects, with precision
both of feature and of form. But as reason has its personifica-
tions, so has *passion*.—Every passion has its Object, tho' often
distant and obscure;—to be brought nearer then, and rendered
more distinct, it is personified; and Fancy fantastically decks, or
aggravates the *form*, and adds 'a local habitation and a name.'
But passion is the *dupe* of its own artifice, and *realises* the image
it had formed. The Grecian theology was mixed of both these
kinds of personification. Of the images produced by passion it
must be observed that they are the images, for the most part, not
of the passions themselves, but of their remote effects. *Guilt*
looks through the medium, and beholds a devil; *fear*, spectres of
every sort; *hope*, a smiling cherub; *malice* and *envy* see hags, and
witches, and inchanters dire; whilst the innocent and the young,
behold with fearful delight the tripping fairy, whose shadowy

topic has drawn me far beyond my design: I hasten back to my subject, and am guarded, for a time at least, against any further temptation to digress.

form the moon gilds with its softest beams.—Extravagant as all this appears, it has its laws so precise that we are sensible both of a local and temporary, and of an universal magic; the first derived from the general nature of the human mind, influenced by particular habits, institutions, and climate; and the latter from the same general nature abstracted from those considerations: Of the first sort the *machinery* in *Macbeth* is a very striking instance; a machinery, which, however exquisite at the time, has already lost more than half its force; and the Gallery now laughs in some places where it ought to shudder:—But the magic of the *Tempest* is lasting and universal.

There is besides a species of writing for which we have no term of art, and which holds a middle place between nature and magic; I mean where fancy either alone, or mingled with reason, or reason assuming the appearance of fancy, governs some real existence; but the whole of this art is pourtrayed in a single Play; in the real madness of *Lear*, in the assumed wildness of *Edgar*, and in the Professional *Fantasque* of the *Fool*, all operating to contrast and heighten each other. There is yet another feat in this kind, which *Shakespeare* has performed;—he has personified *malice* in his *Caliban*; a character kneaded up of three distinct natures, the diabolical, the human, and the brute. The rest of his preternatural beings are images of *effects* only, and cannot subsist but in a surrounding atmosphere of those passions, from which they are derived. *Caliban* is the passion itself, or rather a compound of malice, servility, and lust, *substantiated*; and therefore best shewn in contrast with the lightness of *Ariel* and the innocence of *Miranda*.—*Witches* are sometimes substantial existences, supposed to be possessed by, or allyed to the unsubstantial; but the Witches in *Macbeth* are a gross sort of shadows, 'bubbles of the earth,' as they are finely called by *Banquo*.—*Ghosts* differ from other imaginary beings in this, that they belong to no element, have no specific nature or character, and are effects, however harsh the expression, supposed without a cause; the reason of which is that they are not the creation of the poet but the servile copies or transcripts of popular imagination, connected with supposed reality and religion. Should the poet assign the true cause, and call them the mere painting or *coinage of the brain*, he would disappoint his own end, and destroy the

I was considering the dignity of *Falstaff* so far as it might seem connected with, or productive of military merit, and I have assigned him *reputation* at least, if not *fame*, noble connection, birth, attendants, title, and an honourable pension; every one of them presumptive proofs of Military merit, and motives of action. What deduction is to be made on these articles, and why they are so much obscured may, perhaps, hereafter appear.

I have now gone through the examination of all the persons of the Drama from whose mouths any thing can be drawn relative to the Courage of *Falstaff*, excepting the *Prince* and *Poins*, whose evidence I have begged leave to *reserve*, and excepting a very severe censure passed on him by Lord *John* of *Lancaster*, which I shall presently consider: But I must first observe, that setting aside the jests of the *Prince* and *Poins*, and this censure of *Lancaster*, there is not one expression uttered by any character in the Drama that can be construed into any impeachment of *Falstaff*'s Courage;—an observation made before as respecting some of the Witnesses;—it is now extended to all: And though this silence be a negative proof only, it cannot, in my opinion, under the circumstances of the case, and whilst uncontradicted by facts, be too much relied on. If *Falstaff* had been intended for the character of a *Miles Gloriosus*, his behaviour ought, and therefore would have been commented upon by others. *Shakespeare* seldom trusts to the apprehensions of his

being he had raised. Should he assign fictitious causes, and add a specific nature, and a local habitation, it would not be endured; or the effect would be lost by the conversion of one being into another. The approach to reality in this case defeats all the arts and managements of fiction.—The whole play of the *Tempest* is of so high and superior a nature that *Dryden*, who had attempted to imitate in vain, might well exclaim that

'—*Shakespeare*'s *magic* could not copied be,
Within that circle none durst walk but He.'

audience; his characters interpret for one another continually, and when we least suspect such artful and secret management: The conduct of *Shakespeare* in this respect is admirable, and I could point out a thousand passages which might put to shame the advocates of a formal Chorus, and prove that there is as little of necessity as grace in so mechanic a contrivance.[1] But I confine my censure of the Chorus to its supposed use of comment and interpretation only. . . .

Tho' I have considered *Falstaff*'s character as relative only to one single quality, yet so much has been said, that it cannot escape the reader's notice that he is a character made up by *Shakespeare* wholly of incongruities;—a man at once young and old, enterprizing and fat, a dupe and a wit, harmless and wicked, weak in principle and resolute by constitution, cowardly in appearance and brave in reality; a knave without malice, a lyar without deceit; and a knight, a gentleman, and a soldier, without either dignity, decency, or honour: This is a character, which, though it may be decompounded, could not, I believe, have been formed, nor the ingredients of it duly mingled upon any receipt whatever: It required the hand of *Shakespeare* himself to give to every particular part a relish of the whole, and of the whole to every particular part;—alike the same incongruous, identical *Falstaff*, whether to the grave Chief Justice he vainly talks of his youth, and offers to *caper for a thousand*; or cries to Mrs. *Doll*, '*I am old, I am old*,' though she is seated on his lap, and he is courting her for busses. How *Shakespeare* could furnish out sentiment of so extraordinary a composition, and supply it with such appropriated and characteristic language, humour and wit, I cannot tell; but I may, however,

[1] Ænobarbus, in Anthony and Cleopatra, is in effect the Chorus of the Play; as Menenius Agrippa is of Coriolanus.

venture to infer, and that confidently, that he who so well understood the uses of incongruity, and that laughter was to be raised by the opposition of qualities in the same man, and not by their agreement or conformity, would never have attempted to raise mirth by shewing us Cowardice in a Coward unattended by Pretence, and softened by every excuse of age, corpulence, and infirmity: And of this we cannot have a more striking proof than his furnishing this very character, on one instance of real terror, however excusable, with boast, braggadocio, and pretence, exceeding that of all other stage Cowards the whole length of his superior wit, humour, and invention.

What then upon the whole shall be said but that *Shakespeare* has made certain Impressions, or produced certain effects, of which he has thought fit to conceal or obscure the cause? How he has done this, and for what special ends, we shall now presume to guess.—Before the period in which *Shakespeare* wrote, the fools and Zanys of the stage were drawn out of the coarsest and cheapest materials: Some essential folly, with a dash of knave and coxcomb, did the feat. But *Shakespeare*, who delighted in difficulties, was resolved to furnish a richer repast, and to give to one eminent buffoon the high relish of wit, humour, birth, dignity, and Courage. But this was a process which required the nicest hand, and the utmost management and address: These enumerated qualities are, in their own nature, productive of *respect*; an Impression the most opposite to laughter that can be. This Impression then, it was, at all adventures, necessary to with-hold; which could not perhaps well be without dressing up these qualities in fantastic forms, and colours not their own; and thereby cheating the eye with shews of baseness and of folly, whilst he stole as it were upon the palate a richer and a fuller *goût*. To this end, what arts, what contrivances, has he not practised! How has he steeped this singular character in bad habits for fifty years together, and brought him forth saturated with every folly and with every vice not destructive of his essential character, or incompatible with his own primary design! For this end, he has deprived *Falstaff* of every good principle; and for another, which will be presently mentioned, he has concealed every bad one. He has given him also every infirmity of body that is not likely to awaken our compassion, and which is most proper to render both his better qualities and his vices ridiculous: He has associated levity and debauch with *age*, corpulence and inactivity with *courage*, and has roguishly coupled the gout with *Military honours*, and a *pension* with the *pox*. He has likewise involved this character in situations, out of which neither wit or Courage can extricate him with honour. The surprize at *Gads-hill* might have betrayed a hero into flight, and the encounter with *Douglas* left him no choice but death or stratagem. If he plays an after-game, and endeavours to redeem his ill fortune by lies and braggadocio, his ground fails him; no wit, no evasion will avail: Or is he likely to appear respectable in his person, rank, and demeanor, how is that respect abated or discharged! *Shakespeare* has given him a kind of state indeed; but of what is it composed: Of that fustian cowardly rascal *Pistol*, and his yoke-fellow of few words the equally deedless *Nym*; of his cup-bearer the fiery *Trigon*, whose zeal burns in his nose, *Bardolph*; and of the boy, who bears the purse with *seven groats and two-pence*;—a boy who was given him on purpose to set him off, and whom he walks *before*, according to his own description, '*like a sow that had overwhelmed all her litter but one.*'

But it was not enough to render *Falstaff* ridiculous in his figure, situations, and equipage; *still his respectable* qualities would have come forth, at least occasionally, to spoil our mirth; or they might have burst the intervention of such slight impediments, and have every where shone through: It was necessary then to go farther, and throw on him that substantial ridicule, which only the incongruities of real vice can furnish; of vice, which was to be so mixed and blended with his frame as to give a durable character and colour to the whole.

But it may here be necessary to detain the reader a moment in order to apprize him of my further intention; without which, I might hazard that good understanding, which I hope has hitherto been preserved between us.

I have 'till now looked only to the Courage of *Falstaff*, a quality which having been denied, in terms, to belong to his constitution, I have endeavoured to vindicate to the Understandings of my readers; the Impression on their Feelings (in which all Dramatic truth consists) being already, as I have supposed, in favour of the character. In the pursuit of this subject I have taken the general Impression of the whole character pretty much, I suppose, like other men; and, when occasion has required, have so transmitted it to the reader; joining in the common Feeling of *Falstaff*'s pleasantry, his apparent freedom from ill principle, and his companionable wit and good humour: With a stage character, in the article of exhibition, we have nothing more to do; for in fact what is it but an Impression; an appearance, which we are to consider as a reality; and which we may venture to applaud or condemn as such, without further inquiry or investigation? But if we would account for our Impressions, or for certain sentiments or actions in a character, not derived from its apparent principles, yet appearing, we know not why, natural, we are then compelled to look farther, and examine if there be not something more in the character than is *shewn*; something inferred, which is not brought under our special notice: In short, we must look to the art of the writer, and to the principles of human nature, to discover the hidden causes of such effects.—Now this is a very different matter—The former considerations respected the Impression only, without regard to the Understanding; but this question relates to the Understanding alone. It is true that there are but few Dramatic characters which will bear this kind of investigation, as not being drawn in exact conformity to those principles of general nature to which we must refer. But this is not the case with regard to the characters of *Shakespeare*; they are struck out *whole*, by some happy art which I cannot clearly comprehend, out of the general mass of things, from the block as it were of nature: And it is, I think, an easier thing to give a just draught of man from these Theatric forms, which I cannot help considering as originals, than by drawing from real life, amidst so much intricacy, obliquity, and disguise. If therefore, for further proofs of *Falstaff*'s Courage, or for the sake of curious speculation, or for both, I change my position, and look to causes instead of effects, the reader must not be surprized if he finds the former *Falstaff* vanish like a dream, and another, of more disgustful form, presented to his view; one, whose final punishment we shall be so far from regretting, that we ourselves shall be ready to consign him to a severer doom.

The reader will very easily apprehend that a character, which we might wholly disapprove of, considered as existing in human life, may yet be thrown on the stage into certain peculiar situations, and be compressed by external influences into such temporary appearances, as may render such character for a time highly acceptable and entertaining, and even more distinguished for qualities, which on this supposition would be accidents only, than another character really possessing those qualities, but which, under the pressure of the same situation and influences, would be distorted into a different form, or totally lost in timidity and weakness. If therefore the character before us will admit of this kind of investigation, our Inquiry will not be without some dignity, considered as extending to the principles of human nature, and to the genius and arts of Him, who has best caught every various form of the human mind, and transmitted them with the greatest happiness and fidelity. . . .

Such, I think, is the true character of this extraordinary buffoon; and from hence we may discern for what special purposes *Shakespeare* has given him talents and qualities, which were to be afterwards obscured, and perverted to ends opposite to their nature; it was clearly to furnish out a Stage buffoon of a peculiar sort; a kind of Game-bull which would stand the baiting thro' a hundred Plays, and produce equal sport, whether he is pinned down occasionally by *Hal* or *Poins*, or tosses such mongrils as *Bardolph*, or the Justices, sprawling in the air. There is in truth no such thing as totally demolishing *Falstaff*; he has so much of the invulnerable in his frame that no ridicule can destroy him; he is safe even in defeat, and seems to rise, like another *Antæus*, with recruited vigour from every fall; in this as in every other respect, unlike *Parolles* or *Bobadil*: They fall by the first shaft of ridicule, but *Falstaff* is a butt on which we may empty the whole quiver, whilst the substance of his character remains unimpaired. His ill habits, and the accidents of age and corpulence, are no part of his essential constitution; they come forward indeed on our eye, and solicit our notice, but they are second natures, not *first*; mere shadows, we pursue them in vain; *Falstaff*

himself has a distinct and separate subsistence; he laughs
at the chace, and when the sport is over, gathers them
with unruffled feather under his wing: And hence it is
that he is made to undergo not one detection only, but
a series of detections; that he is not formed for one Play
only, but was intended originally at least for two; and
the author we are told, was doubtful if he should not
extend him yet farther, and engage him in the wars with
France. This he might well have done, for there is nothing perishable in the nature of *Falstaff*: He might have
involved him, by the vicious part of his character, in new
difficulties and unlucky situations, and have enabled him,
by the better part, to have scrambled through, abiding
and retorting the jests and laughter of every beholder.

But whatever we may be told concerning the intention of *Shakespeare* to extend this character farther, there
is a manifest preparation near the end of the second part
of Henry IV. for his disgrace: The disguise is taken off,
and he begins openly to pander to the excesses of the
Prince, intitling himself to the character afterwards
given him of being *the tutor and the feeder of his riots*. '*I
will fetch off,*' (says he) '*these Justices.—I will devise matter
enough out of this* Shallow *to keep the Prince in continual
laughter the wearing out of six fashions.—If the young* dace
be a bait for the old pike,' (speaking with reference to his
own designs upon *Shallow*) '*I see no reason in the law of
nature but I may snap at him.*'—This is shewing himself
abominably dissolute: The laborious arts of fraud,
which he practices on *Shallow* to induce the loan of a
thousand pound, create *disgust*; and the more, as we are
sensible this money was never likely to be *paid back*, as
we are told that *was*, of which the travellers had been
robbed. It is true we feel no pain for *Shallow*, he being
a very bad character, as would fully appear, if he were
unfolded; but *Falstaff*'s deliberation in fraud is not on

that account more excusable.—The event of the old King's death draws him out almost into detestation.—'*Master* Robert Shallow, *chuse what office thou wilt in the land,—'tis thine.—I am fortune's steward.—Let us take any man's horses.—The laws of England are at my commandment.—Happy are they who have been my friends;—and woe to my* Lord Chief Justice.'—After this we ought not to complain if we see Poetic justice duly executed upon him, and that he is finally given up to shame and dishonour.

But it is remarkable that, during this process, we are not acquainted with the success of *Falstaff*'s designs upon *Shallow* 'till the moment of his disgrace. '*If I had had time,*' (says he to *Shallow,* as the King is approaching,) '*to have made new liveries, I would have bestowed the thousand pounds I borrowed of you;*'—and the first word he utters after this period is, '*Master* Shallow, *I owe you a thousand pounds:*' We may from hence very reasonably presume, that *Shakespeare* meant to connect this fraud with the punishment of *Falstaff,* as a more avowed ground of censure and dishonour: Nor ought the consideration that this passage contains the most exquisite comic humour and propriety in another view, to diminish the truth of this observation.

But however just it might be to demolish *Falstaff* in this way, by opening to us his bad principles it was by no means *convenient.* If we had been to have seen a single representation of him only, it might have been proper enough; but as he was to be shewn from night to night, and from age to age, the disgust arising from the *close,* would by degrees have spread itself over the whole character; reference would be had throughout to his bad principles, and he would have become less acceptable as he was more known: And yet it was necessary to bring him, like all other stage characters, to some conclusion. Every play must be wound up by some event, which may shut in the characters and the action. If some *hero* obtains a crown, or a mistress, involving therein the fortune of others, we are satisfied;—we do not desire to be afterwards admitted of his council, or his bedchamber: Or if through jealousy, causeless or well founded, *another* kills a beloved wife, and himself after,—there is no more to be said;—they are dead, and there an end; Or if in the scenes of Comedy, parties are engaged, and plots formed, for the furthering or preventing the completion of that great article Cuckoldom, we expect to be satisfied in the point as far as the nature of so nice a case will permit, or at least to see such a manifest *disposition* as will leave us in no doubt of the event. By the bye, I cannot but think that the Comic writers of the last age treated this matter as of more importance, and made more bustle about it, than the temper of the present times will well bear; and it is therefore to be hoped that the Dramatic authors of the present day, some of whom, to the best of my judgment, are deserving of great praise, will consider and treat this business, rather as a common and natural incident arising out of modern manners, than as worthy to be held forth as the great object and sole end of the Play.

But whatever be the question, or whatever the character, the curtain must not only be dropt before the eyes, but over the minds of the spectators, and nothing left for further examination and curiosity.—But how was this to be done in regard to *Falstaff*? He was not involved in the fortune of the Play; he was engaged in no action which, as to him, was to be compleated; he had reference to no system, he was attracted to no center; he passes thro' the Play as a lawless meteor, and we wish to know what course he is afterwards likely to take: He is detected and disgraced, it is true; but he lives by detection, and thrives on disgrace; and we are desirous

to see him detected and disgraced again. The *Fleet*
might be no bad scene of further amusement;—he carries
all within him, *and what matter where, if he be still the
same,* possessing the same force of mind, the same wit,
and the same incongruity. This, *Shakespeare* was fully
sensible of, and knew that this character could not be
compleatly dismissed but by death.—'Our author, (says
the Epilogue to the Second Part of Henry IV.) will continue the story with Sir *John* in it, and make you merry
with fair *Catherine* of *France;* where, for any thing I
know, *Falstaff* shall dye of a sweat, unless already he be
killed with your hard opinions.' If it had been prudent
in *Shakespeare* to have killed *Falstaff* with *hard opinion,*
he had the means in his hand to effect it;—but dye, it
seems, he must, in one form or another, and a *sweat*
would have been no unsuitable catastrophe. However
we have reason to be satisfied as it is;—his death was
worthy of his birth and of his life: '*He was born,* he says,
'*about three o'clock in the afternoon with a white head, and
something a round belly.*' But if he came into the world
in the evening with these marks of age, he departs out
of it in the morning in all the follies and vanities of
youth;—'*He was shaked* (we are told) '*of a burning quoti-
dian tertian;—the young King had run bad humours on the
knight;—his heart was fracted and corroborate; and a' parted
just between twelve and one, even at the turning of the tide,
yielding the crow a pudding, and passing directly into* Arthur's
bosom, if ever man went into the bosom of Arthur.'—So
ended this singular buffoon; and with him ends an Essay,
on which the reader is left to bestow what character he
pleases: An Essay professing to treat of the Courage of
Falstaff, but extending itself to his Whole character; to
the arts and genius of his Poetic-Maker, SHAKESPEARE;
and thro' him sometimes, with ambitious aim, even to
the principles of human nature itself.

CHARLES LAMB

On the Tragedies of Shakspeare, considered with reference to their fitness for Stage Representation[1]

TAKING a turn the other day in the Abbey, I was struck with the affected attitude of a figure, which I do not remember to have seen before, and which upon examination proved to be a whole-length of the celebrated Mr. Garrick. Though I would not go so far with some good catholics abroad as to shut players altogether out of consecrated ground, yet I own I was not a little scandalized at the introduction of theatrical airs and gestures into a place set apart to remind us of the saddest realities. Going nearer, I found inscribed under this harlequin figure the following lines:—

> To paint fair Nature, by divine command,
> Her magic pencil in his glowing hand,
> A Shakspeare rose: then, to expand his fame
> Wide o'er this breathing world, a Garrick came.
> Though sunk in death the forms the Poet drew,
> The Actor's genius bade them breathe anew;
> Though, like the bard himself, in night they lay,
> Immortal Garrick call'd them back to day:
> And till Eternity with pow'r sublime
> Shall mark the mortal hour of hoary Time,
> Shakspeare and Garrick like twin-stars shall shine,
> And earth irradiate with a beam divine.

It would be an insult to my readers' understandings to attempt any thing like a criticism on this farrago of false thoughts and nonsense. But the reflection it led me into was a kind of wonder, how, from the days of the actor here celebrated to our own, it should have been

[1] First published in *The Reflector*, 1811; here printed from *The Works of Charles Lamb*, 1818. vol. ii, pp. 1–36.

the fashion to compliment every performer in his turn, that has had the luck to please the town in any of the great characters of Shakspeare, with the notion of pos- sessing a *mind congenial with the poet's:* how people should come thus unaccountably to confound the power of originating poetical images and conceptions with the faculty of being able to read or recite the same when put into words;[1] or what connection that absolute mastery over the heart and soul of man, which a great dramatic poet possesses, has with those low tricks upon the eye and ear, which a player by observing a few general effects, which some common passion, as grief, anger, &c. usually has upon the gestures and exterior, can so easily compass. To know the internal workings and movements of a great mind, of an Othello or a Hamlet for instance, the *when* and the *why* and the *how far* they should be moved; to what pitch a passion is be- coming; to give the reins and to pull in the curb exactly at the moment when the drawing in or the slackening is most graceful; seems to demand a reach of intellect of a vastly different extent from that which is employed upon the bare imitation of the signs of these passions in the countenance or gesture, which signs are usually observed to be most lively and emphatic in the weaker sort of minds, and which signs can after all but indicate some passion, as I said before, anger, or grief, generally; but of the motives and grounds of the passion, wherein it differs from the same passion in low and vulgar natures,

---

[1] It is observable that we fall into this confusion only in *dramatic* recitations. We never dream that the gentleman who reads Lucretius in public with great applause, is therefore a great poet and philosopher; nor do we find that Tom Davies, the bookseller, who is recorded to have recited the Paradise Lost better than any man in England in his day (though I cannot help thinking there must be some mistake in this tradition) was there- fore, by his intimate friends, set upon a level with **Milton.**

of these the actor can give no more idea by his face or
gesture than the eye (without a metaphor) can speak,
or the muscles utter intelligible sounds. But such is the
instantaneous nature of the impressions which we take
in at the eye and ear at a playhouse, compared with the
slow apprehension oftentimes of the understanding in
reading, that we are apt not only to sink the play-writer
in the consideration which we pay to the actor, but
even to identify in our minds in a perverse manner, the
actor with the character which he represents. It is difficult for a frequent playgoer to disembarrass the idea of
Hamlet from the person and voice of Mr. K. We speak
of Lady Macbeth, while we are in reality thinking of
Mrs. S. Nor is this confusion incidental alone to un-
lettered persons, who, not possessing the advantage of
reading, are necessarily dependent upon the stage-player
for all the pleasure which they can receive from the
drama, and to whom the very idea of *what an author is*
cannot be made comprehensible without some pain and
perplexity of mind: the error is one from which persons
otherwise not meanly lettered, find it almost impossible
to extricate themselves.

Never let me be so ungrateful as to forget the very
high degree of satisfaction which I received some years
back from seeing for the first time a tragedy of Shakspeare performed, in which those two great performers
sustained the principal parts. It seemed to embody and
realize conceptions which had hitherto assumed no distinct shape. But dearly do we pay all our life after for
this juvenile pleasure, this sense of distinctness. When
the novelty is past, we find to our cost that instead of
realizing an idea, we have only materialized and brought
down a fine vision to the standard of flesh and blood.
We have let go a dream, in quest of an unattainable substance.

How cruelly this operates upon the mind, to have its free conceptions thus crampt and pressed down to the measure of a strait-lacing actuality, may be judged from that delightful sensation of freshness, with which we turn to those plays of Shakspeare which have escaped being performed, and to those passages in the acting plays of the same writer which have happily been left out in the performance. How far the very custom of hearing any thing *spouted*, withers and blows upon a fine passage, may be seen in those speeches from Henry the Fifth, &c. which are current in the mouths of school-boys from their being to be found in *Enfield Speakers*, and such kind of books. I confess myself utterly unable to appreciate that celebrated soliloquy in Hamlet, be-ginning 'To be or not to be', or to tell whether it be good, bad, or indifferent, it has been so handled and pawed about by declamatory boys and men, and torn so inhumanly from its living place and principle of con-tinuity in the play, till it is become to me a perfect dead member.

It may seem a paradox, but I cannot help being of opinion that the plays of Shakspeare are less calculated for performance on a stage, than those of almost any other dramatist whatever. Their distinguishing excel-lence is a reason that they should be so. There is so much in them, which comes not under the province of act-ing, with which eye, and tone, and gesture, have nothing to do.

The glory of the scenic art is to personate passion, and the turn of passion; and the more coarse and palpable the passion is, the more hold upon the eyes and ears of the spectators the performer obviously possesses. For this reason, scolding scenes, scenes where two persons talk themselves into a fit of fury, and then in a surprising manner talk themselves out of it again, have always been

H

the most popular upon our stage. And the reason is plain, because the spectators are here most palpably appealed to, they are the proper judges in this war of words, they are the legitimate ring that should be formed round such 'intellectual prize-fighters'. Talking is the direct object of the imitation here. But in all the best dramas, and in Shakspeare above all, how obvious it is, that the form of *speaking*, whether it be in soliloquy or dialogue, is only a medium, and often a highly artificial one, for putting the reader or spectator into possession of that knowledge of the inner structure and workings of mind in a character, which he could otherwise never have arrived at *in that form of composition* by any gift short of intuition. We do here as we do with novels written in the *epistolary form*. How many improprieties, perfect solecisms in letter-writing, do we put up with in Clarissa and other books, for the sake of the delight which that form upon the whole gives us.

But the practice of stage representation reduces every thing to a controversy of elocution. Every character, from the boisterous blasphemings of Bajazet to the shrinking timidity of womanhood, must play the orator. The love-dialogues of Romeo and Juliet, those silver-sweet sounds of lovers' tongues by night; the more intimate and sacred sweetness of nuptial colloquy between an Othello or a Posthumus with their married wives, all those delicacies which are so delightful in the reading, as when we read of those youthful dalliances in Paradise—

———As beseem'd
Fair couple link'd in happy nuptial league,
Alone:

by the inherent fault of stage representation, how are these things sullied and turned from their very nature by being exposed to a large assembly; when such speeches as Imogen addresses to her lord, come drawling out of the mouth of a hired actress, whose courtship, though nominally addressed to the personated Posthumus, is manifestly aimed at the spectators, who are to judge of her endearments and her returns of love.

The character of Hamlet is perhaps that by which, since the days of Betterton, a succession of popular performers have had the greatest ambition to distinguish themselves. The length of the part may be one of their reasons. But for the character itself, we find it in a play, and therefore we judge it a fit subject of dramatic representation. The play itself abounds in maxims and reflexions beyond any other, and therefore we consider it as a proper vehicle for conveying moral instruction. But Hamlet himself—what does he suffer meanwhile by being dragged forth as a public schoolmaster, to give lectures to the crowd! Why, nine parts in ten of what Hamlet does, are transactions between himself and his moral sense, they are the effusions of his solitary musings, which he retires to holes and corners and the most sequestered parts of the palace to pour forth; or rather, they are the silent meditations with which his bosom is bursting, reduced to *words* for the sake of the reader, who must else remain ignorant of what is passing there. These profound sorrows, these light-and-noise-abhorring ruminations, which the tongue scarce dares utter to deaf walls and chambers, how can they be represented by a gesticulating actor, who comes and mouths them out before an audience, making four hundred people his confidants at once? I say not that it is the fault of the actor so to do; he must pronounce them *ore rotundo*, he must accompany them with his eye, he must insinuate them into his auditory by some trick of eye, tone, or gesture, or he fails. *He must be thinking all the while of his appearance, because he knows that all the while the spectators are judging of it.* And this is the way to represent the shy, negligent, retiring Hamlet.

It is true that there is no other mode of conveying a vast quantity of thought and feeling to a great portion of the audience, who otherwise would never earn it for themselves by reading, and the intellectual acquisition gained this way may, for aught I know, be inestimable; but I am not arguing that Hamlet should not be acted, but how much Hamlet is made another thing by being acted. I have heard much of the wonders which Garrick performed in this part; but as I never saw him, I must have leave to doubt whether the representation of such a character came within the province of his art. Those who tell me of him, speak of his eye, of the magic of his eye, and of his commanding voice: physical properties, vastly desirable in an actor, and without which he can never insinuate meaning into an auditory,—but what have they to do with Hamlet? what have they to do with intellect? In fact, the things aimed at in theatrical representation, are to arrest the spectator's eye upon the form and the gesture, and so to gain a more favourable hearing to what is spoken: it is not what the character is, but how he looks; not what he says, but how he speaks it. I see no reason to think that if the play of Hamlet were written over again by some such writer as Banks or Lillo, retaining the process of the story, but totally omitting all the poetry of it, all the divine features of Shakspeare, his stupendous intellect; and only taking care to give us enough of passionate dialogue, which Banks or Lillo were never at a loss to furnish; I see not how the effect could be much different upon an audience, nor how the actor has it in his power to represent Shakspeare to us differently from his representation of Banks or Lillo. Hamlet would still be a youthful accomplished prince, and must be gracefully personated; he might be puzzled in his mind, wavering in his conduct, seemingly-cruel to Ophelia, he might see a ghost, and start at it, and address it kindly when he found it to be his father; all this in the poorest and most homely language of the servilest creeper after nature that ever consulted the palate of an audience; without troubling Shakspeare for the matter: and I see not but there would be room for all the power which an actor has, to display itself. All the passions and changes of passion might remain: for those are much less difficult to write or act than is thought, it is a trick easy to be attained, it is but rising or falling a note or two in the voice, a whisper with a significant foreboding look to announce its approach, and so contagious the counterfeit appearance of any emotion is, that let the words be what they will, the look and tone shall carry it off and make it pass for deep skill in the passions.

It is common for people to talk of Shakspeare's plays being *so natural;* that every body can understand him. They are natural indeed, they are grounded deep in nature, so deep that the depth of them lies out of the reach of most of us. You shall hear the same persons say that George Barnwell is very natural, and Othello is very natural, that they are both very deep; and to them they are the same kind of thing. At the one they sit and shed tears, because a good sort of young man is tempted by a naughty woman to commit *a trifling peccadillo,* the murder of an uncle or so,[1] that is all, and so comes to an

---

[1] If this note could hope to meet the eye of any of the Managers, I would intreat and beg of them, in the name of both the Galleries, that this insult upon the morality of the common people of London should cease to be eternally repeated in the holiday weeks. Why are the 'Prentices of this famous and well-governed city, instead of an amusement, to be treated over and over again with the nauseous sermon of George Barnwell? Why *at the end of their vistoes* are we to place the *gallows?* Were

untimely end, which is *so moving;* and at the other, because a blackamoor in a fit of jealousy kills his innocent white wife: and the odds are that ninety-nine out of a hundred would willingly behold the same catastrophe happen to both the heroes, and have thought the rope more due to Othello than to Barnwell. For of the texture of Othello's mind, the inward construction marvellously laid open with all its strengths and weaknesses, its heroic confidences and its human misgivings, its agonies of hate springing from the depths of love, they see no more than the spectators at a cheaper rate, who pay their pennies a-piece to look through the man's telescope in Leicester-fields, see into the inward plot and topography of the moon. Some dim thing or other they see, they see an actor personating a passion, of grief, or anger, for instance, and they recognize it as a copy of the usual external effects of such passions; or at least as being true to *that symbol of the emotion which passes current at the theatre for it,* for it is often no more than that: but of the grounds of the passion, its correspondence to a great or heroic nature, which is the only worthy object of tragedy,—that common auditors know any thing of this, or can have any such notions dinned into them by the mere strength of an actor's lungs,—that apprehensions foreign to them should be thus infused into them by storm, I can neither believe, nor understand how it can be possible.

We talk of Shakspeare's admirable observation of

I an uncle, I should not much like a nephew of mine to have such an example placed before his eyes. It is really making uncle-murder too trivial to exhibit it as done upon such slight motives;—it is attributing too much to such characters as Millwood;—it is putting things into the heads of good young men, which they would never otherwise have dreamed of. Uncles that think any thing of their lives, should fairly petition the Chamberlain against it.

life, when we should feel, that not from a petty inquisition into those cheap and every-day characters which surrounded him, as they surround us, but from his own mind, which was, to borrow a phrase of Ben Jonson's, the very 'sphere of humanity', he fetched those images of virtue and of knowledge, of which every one of us recognizing a part, think we comprehend in our natures the whole; and oftentimes mistake the powers which he positively creates in us, for nothing more than indigenous faculties of our own minds which only waited the application of corresponding virtues in him to return a full and clear echo of the same.

To return to Hamlet.—Among the distinguishing features of that wonderful character, one of the most interesting (yet painful) is that soreness of mind which makes him treat the intrusions of Polonius with harshness, and that asperity which he puts on in his interviews with Ophelia. These tokens of an unhinged mind (if they be not mixed in the latter case with a profound artifice of love, to alienate Ophelia by affected discourtesies, so to prepare her mind for the breaking off of that loving intercourse, which can no longer find a place amidst business so serious as that which he has to do) are parts of his character, which to reconcile with our admiration of Hamlet, the most patient consideration of his situation is no more than necessary; they are what we *forgive afterwards*, and explain by the whole of his character, but *at the time* they are harsh and unpleasant. Yet such is the actor's necessity of giving strong blows to the audience, that I have never seen a player in this character, who did not exaggerate and strain to the utmost these ambiguous features,—these temporary deformities in the character. They make him express a vulgar scorn at Polonius which utterly degrades his gentility, and which no explanation can render palateable; they make him shew contempt,

and curl up the nose at Ophelia's father,—contempt in
its very grossest and most hateful form; but they get
applause by it: it is natural, people say; that is, the words
are scornful, and the actor expresses scorn, and that they
can judge of: but why so much scorn, and of that sort,
they never think of asking.

So to Ophelia.—All the Hamlets that I have ever
seen, rant and rave at her as if she had committed some
great crime, and the audience are highly pleased, because
the words of the part are satirical, and they are enforced
by the strongest expression of satirical indignation of
which the face and voice are capable. But then, whether
Hamlet is likely to have put on such brutal appearances
to a lady whom he loved so dearly, is never thought on.
The truth is, that in all such deep affections as had subsisted between Hamlet and Ophelia, there is a stock of
supererogatory love, (if I may venture to use the expression) which in any great grief of heart, especially where
that which preys upon the mind cannot be communicated, confers a kind of indulgence upon the grieved
party to express itself, even to its heart's dearest object,
in the language of a temporary alienation; but it is not
alienation, it is a distraction purely, and so it always
makes itself to be felt by that object: it is not anger, but
grief assuming the appearance of anger,—love awk-
wardly counterfeiting hate, as sweet countenances when
they try to frown: but such sternness and fierce disgust
as Hamlet is made to shew, is no counterfeit, but the
real face of absolute aversion,—of irreconcileable alienation. It may be said he puts on the madman; but then
he should only so far put on this counterfeit lunacy as
his own real distraction will give him leave; that is,
incompletely, imperfectly; not in that confirmed, practised way, like a master of his art, or as Dame Quickly
would say, 'like one of those harlotry players.'

I mean no disrespect to any actor, but the sort of pleasure which Shakspeare's plays give in the acting seems to me not at all to differ from that which the audience receive from those of other writers; and, *they being in themselves essentially so different from all others,* I must conclude that there is something in the nature of acting which levels all distinctions. And in fact, who does not speak indifferently of the Gamester and of Macbeth as fine stage performances, and praise the Mrs. Beverley in the same way as the Lady Macbeth of Mrs. S.? Belvidera, and Calista, and Isabella, and Euphrasia, are they less liked than Imogen, or than Juliet, or than Desdemona? Are they not spoken of and remembered in the same way? Is not the female performer as great (as they call it) in one as in the other? Did not Garrick shine, and was he not ambitious of shining in every drawling tragedy that his wretched day produced,— the productions of the Hills and the Murphys and the Browns,—and shall he have that honour to dwell in our minds for ever as an inseparable concomitant with Shakspeare? A kindred mind! O who can read that affecting sonnet of Shakspeare which alludes to his profession as a player:—

Oh for my sake do you with Fortune chide,
The guilty goddess of my harmful deeds,
That did not better for my life provide
Than public means which public custom breeds—
Thence comes it that my name receives a brand;
And almost thence my nature is subdued
To what it works in, like the dyer's hand—

Or that other confession:—

Alas! 'tis true, I have gone here and there,
And made myself a motly to thy view,
Gor'd mine own thoughts, sold cheap what is most
    dear—

Who can read these instances of jealous self-watchfulness in our sweet Shakspeare, and dream of any congeniality between him and one that, by every tradition of him, appears to have been as mere a player as ever existed; to have had his mind tainted with the lowest players' vices,—envy and jealousy, and miserable cravings after applause; one who in the exercise of his profession was jealous even of the women-performers that stood in his way; a manager full of managerial tricks and stratagems and finesse: that any resemblance should be dreamed of between him and Shakspeare,—Shakspeare who, in the plenitude and consciousness of his own powers, could with that noble modesty, which we can neither imitate nor appreciate, express himself thus of his own sense of his own defects:—

> Wishing me like to one more rich in hope,
> Featur'd like him, like him with friends possest;
> Desiring *this man's art, and that man's scope.*

I am almost disposed to deny to Garrick the merit of being an admirer of Shakspeare. A true lover of his excellencies he certainly was not; for would any true lover of them have admitted into his matchless scenes such ribald trash as Tate and Cibber, and the rest of them, that

> With their darkness durst affront his light.

have foisted into the acting plays of Shakspeare? I believe it impossible that he could have had a proper reverence for Shakspeare, and have condescended to go through that interpolated scene in Richard the Third, in which Richard tries to break his wife's heart by telling her he loves another woman, and says, 'if she survives this she is immortal.' Yet I doubt not he delivered this vulgar stuff with as much anxiety of emphasis as any of the genuine parts: and for acting, it is as well calculated

as any. But we have seen the part of Richard lately produce great fame to an actor by his manner of playing it,
and it lets us into the secret of acting, and of popular
judgments of Shakspeare derived from acting. Not one
of the spectators who have witnessed Mr. C.'s exertions
in that part, but has come away with a proper conviction that Richard is a very wicked man, and kills little
children in their beds, with something like the pleasure
which the giants and ogres in children's books are represented to have taken in that practice; moreover, that
he is very close and shrewd and devilish cunning, for
you could see that by his eye.

But is in fact this the impression we have in reading
the Richard of Shakspeare? Do we feel any thing like
disgust, as we do at that butcher-like representation of
him that passes for him on the stage? A horror at his
crimes blends with the effect which we feel, but how is
it qualified, how is it carried off, by the rich intellect
which he displays, his resources, his wit, his buoyant
spirits, his vast knowledge and insight into characters,
the poetry of his part,—not an atom of all which is made
perceivable in Mr. C.'s way of acting it. Nothing but
his crimes, his actions, is visible; they are prominent and
staring; the murderer stands out, but where is the lofty
genius, the man of vast capacity,—the profound, the
witty, accomplished Richard?

The truth is, the Characters of Shakspeare are so much
the objects of meditation rather than of interest or curiosity as to their actions, that while we are reading any of
his great criminal characters,—Macbeth, Richard, even
Iago,—we think not so much of the crimes which they
commit, as of the ambition, the aspiring spirit, the intellectual activity, which prompts them to overleap those
moral fences. Barnwell is a wretched murderer; there
is a certain fitness between his neck and the rope; he is

the legitimate heir to the gallows; nobody who thinks at all can think of any alleviating circumstances in his case to make him a fit object of mercy. Or to take an instance from the higher tragedy, what else but a mere assassin is Glenalvon! Do we think of any thing but of the crime which he commits, and the rack which he deserves? That is all which we really think about him. Whereas in corresponding characters in Shakspeare so little do the actions comparatively affect us, that while the impulses, the inner mind in all its perverted greatness, solely seems real and is exclusively attended to, the crime is comparatively nothing. But when we see these things represented, the acts which they do are comparatively every thing, their impulses nothing. The state of sublime emotion into which we are elevated by those images of night and horror which Macbeth is made to utter, that solemn prelude with which he entertains the time till the bell shall strike which is to call him to murder Duncan,— when we no longer read it in a book, when we have given up that vantage-ground of abstraction which reading possesses over seeing, and come to see a man in his bodily shape before our eyes actually preparing to commit a murder, if the acting be true and impressive, as I have witnessed it in Mr. K.'s performance of that part, the painful anxiety about the act, the natural longing to prevent it while it yet seems unperpetrated, the too close pressing semblance of reality, give a pain and an uneasiness which totally destroy all the delight which the words in the book convey, where the deed doing never presses upon us with the painful sense of presence: it rather seems to belong to history,—to something past and inevitable, if it has any thing to do with time at all. The sublime images, the poetry alone, is that which is present to our minds in the reading.

So to see Lear acted,—to see an old man tottering

about the stage with a walking-stick, turned out of doors by his daughters in a rainy night, has nothing in it but what is painful and disgusting. We want to take him into shelter and relieve him. That is all the feeling which the acting of Lear ever produced in me. But the Lear of Shakspeare cannot be acted. The contemptible machinery by which they mimic the storm which he goes out in, is not more inadequate to represent the horrors of the real elements, than any actor can be to represent Lear: they might more easily propose to personate the Satan of Milton upon a stage, or one of Michael Angelo's terrible figures. The greatness of Lear is not in corporal dimension, but in intellectual: the explosions of his passion are terrible as a volcano: they are storms turning up and disclosing to the bottom that sea, his mind, with all its vast riches. It is his mind which is laid bare. This case of flesh and blood seems too insignificant to be thought on; even as he himself neglects it. On the stage we see nothing but corporal infirmities and weakness, the impotence of rage; while we read it, we see not Lear, but we are Lear,—we are in his mind, we are sustained by a grandeur which baffles the malice of daughters and storms; in the aberrations of his reason, we discover a mighty irregular power of reasoning, immethodized from the ordinary purposes of life, but exerting its powers, as the wind blows where it listeth, at will upon the corruptions and abuses of mankind. What have looks, or tones, to do with that sublime identification of his age with that of the *heavens themselves*, when in his reproaches to them for conniving at the injustice of his children, he reminds them that 'they themselves are old'. What gesture shall we appropriate to this? What has the voice or the eye to do with such things? But the play is beyond all art, as the tamperings with it shew: it is too hard and stony; it must have

love-scenes, and a happy ending. It is not enough that
Cordelia is a daughter, she must shine as a lover too.
Tate has put his hook in the nostrils of this Leviathan,
for Garrick and his followers, the showmen of the scene,
to draw the mighty beast about more easily. A happy
ending!—as if the living martyrdom that Lear had gone
through,—the flaying of his feelings alive, did not make
a fair dismissal from the stage of life the only decorous
thing for him. If he is to live and be happy after, if he
could sustain this world's burden after, why all this
pudder and preparation,—why torment us with all this
unnecessary sympathy? As if the childish pleasure of
getting his gilt robes and sceptre again could tempt him
to act over again his misused station,—as if at his years,
and with his experience, any thing was left but to die.

Lear is essentially impossible to be represented on a
stage. But how many dramatic personages are there in
Shakspeare, which though more tractable and feasible
(if I may so speak) than Lear, yet from some circumstance, some adjunct to their character, are improper to
be shewn to our bodily eye. Othello for instance. Nothing can be more soothing, more flattering to the nobler
parts of our natures, than to read of a young Venetian
lady of highest extraction, through the force of love and
from a sense of merit in him whom she loved, laying
aside every consideration of kindred, and country, and
colour, and wedding with *a coal-black Moor*—(for such
he is represented, in the imperfect state of knowledge
respecting foreign countries in those days, compared
with our own, or in compliance with popular notions,
though the Moors are now well enough known to be
by many shades less unworthy of a white woman's
fancy)—it is the perfect triumph of virtue over accidents,
of the imagination over the senses. She sees Othello's
colour in his mind. But upon the stage, when the

imagination is no longer the ruling faculty, but we are left to our poor unassisted senses, I appeal to every one that has seen Othello played, whether he did not, on the contrary, sink Othello's mind in his colour; whether he did not find something extremely revolting in the court-ship and wedded caresses of Othello and Desdemona; and whether the actual sight of the thing did not over-weigh all that beautiful compromise which we make in read-ing;—and the reason it should do so is obvious, because there is just so much reality presented to our senses as to give a perception of disagreement, with not enough of belief in the internal motives,—all that which is unseen, —to overpower and reconcile the first and obvious pre-judices.[1] What we see upon a stage is body and bodily action; what we are conscious of in reading is almost exclusively the mind, and its movements: and this I think may sufficiently account for the very different sort of delight with which the same play so often affects us in the reading and the seeing.

It requires little reflection to perceive, that if those characters in Shakspeare which are within the precincts of nature, have yet something in them which appeals too exclusively to the imagination, to admit of their be-ing made objects to the senses without suffering a change and a diminution,—that still stronger the objection

[1] The error of supposing that because Othello's colour does not offend us in the reading, it should also not offend us in the seeing, is just such a fallacy as supposing that an Adam and Eve in a picture shall affect us just as they do in the poem. But in the poem we for a while have Paradisaical senses given us, which vanish when we see a man and his wife without clothes in the picture. The painters themselves feel this, as is apparent by the aukward shifts they have recourse to, to make them look not quite naked; by a sort of prophetic anachronism, antedating the invention of fig-leaves. So in the reading of the play, we see with Desdemona's eyes; in the seeing of it, we are forced to look with our own.

must lie against representing another line of characters, which Shakspeare has introduced to give a wildness and a supernatural elevation to his scenes, as if
to remove them still farther from that assimilation to
common life in which their excellence is vulgarly supposed to consist. When we read the incantations of those
terrible beings the Witches in Macbeth, though some of
the ingredients of their hellish composition savour of the
grotesque, yet is the effect upon us other than the most
serious and appalling that can be imagined? Do we not
feel spell-bound as Macbeth was? Can any mirth accompany a sense of their presence? We might as well laugh
under a consciousness of the principle of Evil himself
being truly and really present with us. But attempt to
bring these beings on to a stage, and you turn them instantly into so many old women, that men and children
are to laugh at. Contrary to the old saying, that 'seeing
is believing', the sight actually destroys the faith; and
the mirth in which we indulge at their expense, when
we see these creatures upon a stage, seems to be a sort
of indemnification which we make to ourselves for the
terror which they put us in when reading made them
an object of belief,—when we surrendered up our reason
to the poet, as children to their nurses and their elders;
and we laugh at our fears, as children who thought they
saw something in the dark, triumph when the bringing
in of a candle discovers the vanity of their fears. For
this exposure of supernatural agents upon a stage is truly
bringing in a candle to expose their own delusiveness.
It is the solitary taper and the book that generates a faith
in these terrors: a ghost by chandelier light, and in good
company, deceives no spectators,—a ghost that can be
measured by the eye, and his human dimensions made
out at leisure. The sight of a well-lighted house, and a
well-dressed audience, shall arm the most nervous child

against any apprehensions: as Tom Brown says of the impenetrable skin of Achilles with his impenetrable armour over it, 'Bully Dawson would have fought the devil with such advantages.'

Much has been said, and deservedly, in reprobation of the vile mixture which Dryden has thrown into the Tempest: doubtless without some such vicious alloy, the impure ears of that age would never have sate out to hear so much innocence of love as is contained in the sweet courtship of Ferdinand and Miranda. But is the Tempest of Shakspeare at all a subject for stage representation? It is one thing to read of an enchanter, and to believe the wondrous tale while we are reading it; but to have a conjuror brought before us in his conjuring-gown, with his spirits about him, which none but himself and some hundred of favoured spectators before the curtain are supposed to see, involves such a quantity of the *hateful incredible*, that all our reverence for the author cannot hinder us from perceiving such gross attempts upon the senses to be in the highest degree childish and inefficient. Spirits and fairies cannot be represented, they cannot even be painted,—they can only be believed. But the elaborate and anxious provision of scenery, which the luxury of the age demands, in these cases works a quite contrary effect to what is intended. That which in comedy, or plays of familiar life, adds so much to the life of the imitation, in plays which appeal to the higher faculties, positively destroys the illusion which it is introduced to aid. A parlour or a drawing-room,—a library opening into a garden,—a garden with an alcove in it,—a street, or the piazza of Covent-garden, does well enough in a scene; we are content to give as much credit to it as it demands; or rather, we think little about it,—it is little more than reading at the top of a page, 'Scene, a Garden;' we do not imagine ourselves there, but we readily admit the imitation of familiar objects. But to think by the help of painted trees and caverns, which we know to be painted, to transport our minds to Prospero, and his island and his lonely cell;[1] or by the aid of a fiddle dexterously thrown in, in an interval of speaking, to make us believe that we hear those supernatural noises of which the isle was full:—the Orrery Lecturer at the Haymarket might as well hope, by his musical glasses cleverly stationed out of sight behind his apparatus, to make us believe that we do indeed hear the chrystal spheres ring out that chime, which if it were to inwrap our fancy long, Milton thinks,

> Time would run back and fetch the age of gold,
> And speckled vanity
> Would sicken soon and die,
> And leprous Sin would melt from earthly mould;
> Yea Hell itself would pass away,
> And leave its dolorous mansions to the peering day.

The Garden of Eden, with our first parents in it, is not more impossible to be shewn on a stage, than the Enchanted Isle, with its no less interesting and innocent first settlers.

The subject of Scenery is closely connected with that of the Dresses, which are so anxiously attended to on our stage. I remember the last time I saw Macbeth played, the discrepancy I felt at the changes of garment which he varied,—the shiftings and re-shiftings, like a Romish priest at mass. The luxury of stage-improvements, and the importunity of the public eye, require this. The coronation robe of the Scottish monarch was

---

[1] It will be said these things are done in pictures. But pictures and scenes are very different things. Painting is a world of itself, but in scene-painting there is the attempt to deceive; and there is the discordancy, never to be got over, between painted scenes and real people.

fairly a counterpart to that which our King wears when
he goes to the Parliament-house,—just so full and cum-
bersome, and set out with ermine and pearls. And if
things must be represented, I see not what to find fault
with in this. But in reading, what robe are we conscious
of? Some dim images of royalty—a crown and sceptre,
may float before our eyes, but who shall describe the
fashion of it? Do we see in our mind's eye what Webb
or any other robe-maker could pattern? This is the inevitable consequence of imitating every thing, to make
all things natural. Whereas the reading of a tragedy is a
fine abstraction. It presents to the fancy just so much of
external appearances as to make us feel that we are among
flesh and blood, while by far the greater and better part
of our imagination is employed upon the thoughts and
internal machinery of the character. But in acting,
scenery, dress, the most contemptible things, call upon
us to judge of their naturalness.

Perhaps it would be no bad similitude, to liken the
pleasure which we take in seeing one of these fine plays
acted, compared with that quiet delight which we find
in the reading of it, to the different feelings with which
a reviewer, and a man that is not a reviewer, reads a fine
poem. The accursed critical habit,—the being called
upon to judge and pronounce, must make it quite a
different thing to the former. In seeing these plays acted,
we are affected just as judges. When Hamlet compares
the two pictures of Gertrude's first and second husband,
who wants to see the pictures? But in the acting, a
miniature must be lugged out; which we know not to
be the picture, but only to shew how finely a miniature
may be represented. This shewing of every thing, levels
all things: it makes tricks, bows, and curtesies, of importance. Mrs. S. never got more fame by any thing
than by the manner in which she dismisses the guests in

the banquet-scene in Macbeth: it is as much remembered as any of her thrilling tones or impressive looks. But does such a trifle as this enter into the imaginations of the readers of that wild and wonderful scene? Does not the mind dismiss the feasters as rapidly as it can? Does it care about the gracefulness of the doing it? But by acting, and judging of acting, all these non-essentials are raised into an importance, injurious to the main interest of the play.

I have confined my observations to the tragic parts of Shakspeare. It would be no very difficult task to extend the enquiry to his comedies; and to shew why Falstaff, Shallow, Sir Hugh Evans, and the rest, are equally incompatible with stage representation. The length to which this Essay has run, will make it, I am afraid, sufficiently distasteful to the Amateurs of the Theatre, without going any deeper into the subject at present.

SAMUEL TAYLOR COLERIDGE

The specific symptoms of poetic power elucidated in a critical analysis of Shakspeare's 'Venus and Adonis', and 'Lucrece'

IN the application of these principles to purposes of practical criticism as employed in the appraisal of works more or less imperfect, I have endeavoured to discover what the qualities in a poem are, which may be deemed promises and specific symptoms of poetic power, as distinguished from general talent determined to poetic composition by accidental motives, by an act of the will, rather than by the inspiration of a genial and productive nature. In this investigation, I could not, I thought, do better, than keep before me the earliest work of the greatest genius that perhaps human nature has yet produced, our *myriad-minded*[1] Shakspeare. I mean the 'Venus and Adonis', and the 'Lucrece'; works which give at once strong promises of the strength, and yet obvious proofs of the immaturity, of his genius. From these I abstracted the following marks, as characteristics of original poetic genius in general.

1. In the 'Venus and Adonis', the first and most obvious excellence is the perfect sweetness of the versification; its adaptation to the subject; and the power displayed in varying the march of the words without passing into a loftier and more majestic rhythm than was demanded by the thoughts, or permitted by the propriety of preserving a sense of melody predominant.

[1] 'Ἀνὴρ μυριόνους, a phrase which I have borrowed from a Greek monk, who applies it to a Patriarch of Constantinople. I might have said, that I have *reclaimed*, rather than borrowed it: for it seems to belong to Shakspeare, 'de jure singulari, et ex privilegie naturae.'

The delight in richness and sweetness of sound, even to a faulty excess, if it be evidently original, and not the result of an easily imitable mechanism, I regard as a highly favourable promise in the compositions of a young man. 'The man that hath not music in his soul' can indeed never be a genuine poet. Imagery (even taken from nature, much more when transplanted from books, as travels, voyages, and works of natural history); affecting incidents; just thoughts; interesting personal or domestic feelings; and with these the art of their combination or intertexture in the form of a poem; may all by incessant effort be acquired as a trade, by a man of talents and much reading, who, as I once before observed, has mistaken an intense desire of poetic reputation for a natural poetic genius; the love of the arbitrary end for a possession of the peculiar means. But the sense of musical delight, with the power of producing it, is a gift of imagination; and this together with the power of reducing multitude into unity of effect, and modifying a series of thoughts by some one predominant thought or feeling, may be cultivated and improved, but can never be learned. It is in these that 'Poeta nascitur non fit.'

2. A second promise of genius is the choice of subjects very remote from the private interests and circumstances of the writer himself. At least I have found, that where the subject is taken immediately from the author's personal sensations and experiences, the excellence of a particular poem is but an equivocal mark, and often a fallacious pledge, of genuine poetic power. We may perhaps remember the tale of the statuary, who had acquired considerable reputation for the legs of his goddesses, though the rest of the statue accorded but indifferently with ideal beauty; till his wife, elated by her husband's praises, modestly acknowledged that she herself had been his constant model. In the 'Venus and

Adonis' this proof of poetic power exists even to excess.
It is throughout as if a superior spirit more intuitive,
more intimately conscious, even than the characters
themselves, not only of every outward look and act, but
of the flux and reflux of the mind in all its subtlest
thoughts and feelings, were placing the whole before
our view; himself meanwhile unparticipating in the
passions, and actuated only by that pleasureable excitement, which had resulted from the energetic fervour
of his own spirit in so vividly exhibiting, what it had
so accurately and profoundly contemplated. I think, I
should have conjectured from these poems, that even
then the great instinct, which impelled the poet to the
drama, was secretly working in him, prompting him by
a series and never broken chain of imagery, always vivid
and, because unbroken, often minute; by the highest
effort of the picturesque in words, of which words are
capable, higher perhaps than was ever realized by any
other poet, even Dante not excepted; to provide a substitute for that visual language, that constant intervention
and running comment by tone, look and gesture, which
in his dramatic works he was entitled to expect from the
players. His Venus and Adonis seem at once the characters themselves, and the whole representation of those
characters by the most consummate actors. You seem
to be *told* nothing, but to see and hear everything.
Hence it is, that from the perpetual activity of attention
required on the part of the reader; from the rapid flow,
the quick change, and the playful nature of the thoughts
and images; and above all from the alienation, and, if I
may hazard such an expression, the utter *aloofness* of the
poet's own feelings, from those of which he is at once
the painter and the analyst; that though the very subject
cannot but detract from the pleasure of a delicate mind,
yet never was poem less dangerous on a moral account.

Instead of doing as Ariosto, and as, still more offensively, Wieland has done, instead of degrading and deforming passion into appetite, the trials of love into the struggles of concupiscence; Shakspeare has here represented the animal impulse itself, so as to preclude all sympathy with it, by dissipating the reader's notice among the thousand outward images, and now beautiful, now fanciful circumstances, which form its dresses and its scenery; or by diverting our attention from the main subject by those frequent witty or profound reflections, which the poet's ever active mind has deduced from, or connected with, the imagery and the incidents. The reader is forced into too much action to sympathize with the merely passive of our nature. As little can a mind thus roused and awakened be brooded on by mean and indistinct emotion, as the low, lazy mist can creep upon the surface of a lake, while a strong gale is driving it onward in waves and billows.

3. It has been before observed that images, however beautiful, though faithfully copied from nature, and as accurately represented in words, do not of themselves characterize the poet. They become proofs of original genius only as far as they are modified by a predominant passion; or by associated thoughts or images awakened by that passion; or when they have the effect of reducing multitude to unity, or succession to an instant; or lastly, when a human and intellectual life is transferred to them from the poet's own spirit,

Which shoots its being through earth, sea, and air.

In the two following lines for instance, there is nothing objectionable, nothing which would preclude them from forming, in their proper place, part of a descriptive poem:

Behold yon row of pines, that shorn and bow'd
Bend from the sea-blast, seen at twilight eve.

But with a small alteration of rhythm, the same words would be equally in their place in a book of topography, or in a descriptive tour. The same image will rise into a semblance of poetry if thus conveyed:

> Yon row of bleak and visionary pines,
> By twilight glimpse discerned, mark! how they flee
> From the fierce sea-blast, all their tresses wild
> Streaming before them.

I have given this as an illustration, by no means as an instance, of that particular excellence which I had in view, and in which Shakspeare even in his earliest, as in his latest, works surpasses all other poets. It is by this, that he still gives a dignity and a passion to the objects which he presents. Unaided by any previous excitement, they burst upon us at once in life and in power.

> Full many a glorious morning have I seen
> *Flatter* the mountain tops with sovereign eye.
>   Shakspeare's Sonnet 33rd.

> Not mine own fears, nor the prophetic soul
> Of the wide world dreaming on things to come—

> .   .   .   .
> .   .   .   .

> The mortal moon hath her eclipse endur'd,
> And the sad augurs mock their own presage;
> Incertainties now crown themselves assur'd,
> And Peace proclaims olives of endless age.
> Now with the drops of this most balmy time
> My love looks fresh, and DEATH to me subscribes!
> Since spite of him, I'll live in this poor rhyme,
> While he insults o'er dull and speechless tribes.
> And thou in this shalt find thy monument,
> When tyrants' crests, and tombs of brass are spent.
>   Sonnet 107.

As of higher worth, so doubtless still more characteristic of poetic genius does the imagery become, when

it moulds and colors itself to the circumstances, passion,
or character, present and foremost in the mind. For unrivalled instances of this excellence, the reader's own
memory will refer him to the LEAR, OTHELLO, in short
to which not of the *great, ever living, dead man's* dramatic works? 'Inopem me copia fecit.' How true it is to
nature, he has himself finely expressed in the instance of
love in Sonnet 98.

From you have I been absent in the spring,
When proud pied April drest in all its trim
Hath put a spirit of youth in every thing,
That heavy Saturn laugh'd and leap'd with him.
Yet nor the lays of birds, nor the sweet smell
Of different flowers in odour and in hue,
Could make me any summer's story tell,
Or from their proud lap pluck them, where they grew:
Nor did I wonder at the lilies white,
Nor praise the deep vermilion in the rose;
They were, tho' sweet, but figures of delight,
Drawn after you, you pattern of all those.
Yet seem'd it winter still, and, you away,
As with your shadow I with these did play!

Scarcely less sure, or if a less valuable, not less indispensable mark

Γονίμου μὲν ποιητοῦ——
——ὅστις ῥῆμα γενναῖον λάκοι,

will the imagery supply, when, with more than the
power of the painter, the poet gives us the liveliest image
of succession with the feeling of simultaneousness!

With this, he breaketh from the sweet embrace
Of those fair arms, that held him to her heart,
And homeward through the dark lawns runs apace:
Look! how a bright star shooteth from the sky,
So glides he in the night from Venus' eye.

4. The last character I shall mention, which would

prove indeed but little, except as taken conjointly with the former; yet without which the former could scarce exist in a high degree, and (even if this were possible) would give promises only of transitory flashes and a meteoric power; is DEPTH, and ENERGY of THOUGHT. No man was ever yet a great poet, without being at the same time a profound philosopher. For poetry is the blossom and the fragrancy of all human knowledge, human thoughts, human passions, emotions, language. In Shakspeare's *poems* the creative power and the intellectual energy wrestle as in a war embrace. Each in its excess of strength seems to threaten the extinction of the other. At length in the DRAMA they were reconciled, and fought each with its shield before the breast of the other. Or like two rapid streams, that, at their first meeting within narrow and rocky banks, mutually strive to repel each other and intermix reluctantly and in tumult; but soon finding a wider channel and more yielding shores blend, and dilate, and flow on in one current and with one voice. The 'Venus and Adonis' did not perhaps allow the display of the deeper passions. But the story of Lucretia seems to favor, and even demand their intensest workings. And yet we find in *Shakspeare's* management of the tale neither pathos, nor any other *dramatic* quality. There is the same minute and faithful imagery as in the former poem, in the same vivid colours, inspirited by the same impetuous vigour of thought, and diverging and contracting with the same activity of the assimilative and of the modifying faculties; and with a yet larger display, a yet wider range of knowledge and reflection; and lastly, with the same perfect dominion, often *domination*, over the whole world of language. What then shall we say? even this; that Shakspeare, no mere child of nature; no automaton of genius; no passive vehicle of inspiration possessed by the spirit, not possessing it; first studied patiently, meditated deeply, understood minutely, till knowledge, become habitual and intuitive, wedded itself to his habitual feelings, and at length gave birth to that stupendous power, by which he stands alone, with no equal or second in his own class; to that power which seated him on one of the two glory-smitten summits of the poetic mountain, with Milton as his compeer, not rival. While the former darts himself forth, and passes into all the forms of human character and passion, the one Proteus of the fire and the flood; the other attracts all forms and things to himself, into the unity of his own IDEAL. All things and modes of action shape themselves anew in the being of MILTON; while SHAKSPEARE becomes all things, yet for ever remaining himself. O what great men hast thou not produced, England! my country! truly indeed—

> Must *we* be free or die, who speak the tongue,
> Which SHAKSPEARE spake; the faith and morals hold,
> Which MILTON held. In every thing we are sprung
> Of earth's first blood, have titles manifold!
>
> WORDSWORTH.

From Biographia Literaria, 1817, Chap. XV.

Shakspeare as a Poet generally

CLOTHED in radiant armour, and authorized by titles sure and manifold, as a poet, Shakspeare came forward to demand the throne of fame, as the dramatic poet of England. His excellencies compelled even his contemporaries to seat him on that throne, although there were giants in those days contending for the same honor. Hereafter I would fain endeavour to make out the title of the English drama as created by, and existing in, Shakspeare, and its right to the supremacy of dramatic excellence in general. But he had shown himself a poet,

previously to his appearance as a dramatic poet; and had
no *Lear*, no *Othello*, no *Henry IV.*, no *Twelfth Night*
ever appeared, we must have admitted that Shakspeare
possessed the chief, if not every, requisite of a poet,—
deep feeling and exquisite sense of beauty, both as
exhibited to the eye in the combinations of form, and to
the ear in sweet and appropriate melody; that these feelings were under the command of his own will; that in
his very first productions he projected his mind out of
his own particular being, and felt, and made others feel,
on subjects no way connected with himself, except by
force of contemplation and that sublime faculty by
which a great mind becomes that, on which it meditates.
To this must be added that affectionate love of nature
and natural objects, without which no man could have
observed so steadily, or painted so truly and passion-
ately, the very minutest beauties of the external world:—

> And when thou hast on foot the purblind hare,
> Mark the poor wretch; to overshoot his troubles,
> How he outruns the wind, and with what care,
> He cranks and crosses with a thousand doubles;
> The many musits through the which he goes
> Are like a labyrinth to amaze his foes.
>
> Sometimes he runs among the flock of sheep,
> To make the cunning hounds mistake their smell;
> And sometime where earth-delving conies keep,
> To stop the loud pursuers in their yell;
> And sometime sorteth with a herd of deer:
> Danger deviseth shifts, wit waits on fear.
>
> For there his smell with others' being mingled.
> The hot scent-snuffing hounds are driven to doubt,
> Ceasing their clamorous cry, till they have singled,
> With much ado, the cold fault cleanly out,
> Then do they spend their mouths; echo replies.
> As if another chase were in the skies.

> By this poor Wat far off, upon a hill,
> Stands on his hinder legs with listening ear,
> To hearken if his foes pursue him still:
> Anon their loud alarums he doth hear,
> And now his grief may be compared well
> To one sore-sick, that hears the passing bell.
>
> Then shalt thou see the dew-bedabbled wretch
> Turn, and return, indenting with the way:
> Each envious briar his weary legs doth scratch,
> Each shadow makes him stop, each murmur stay.
> For misery is trodden on by many,
> And being low, never relieved by any.
>
> *Venus and Adonis.*

And the preceding description:—

> But, lo! from forth a copse that neighbours by,
> A breeding jennet, lusty, young and proud, &c.

is much more admirable, but in parts less fitted for quotation.

Moreover Shakspeare had shown that he possessed fancy, considered as the faculty of bringing together images dissimilar in the main by some one point or more of likeness, as in such a passage as this:—

> Full gently now she takes him by the hand,
> A lily prisoned in a jail of snow,
> Or ivory in an alabaster band:
> So white a friend ingirts so white a foe!   *Ib.*

And still mounting the intellectual ladder, he had as unequivocally proved the indwelling in his mind of imagination, or the power by which one image or feeling is made to modify many others, and by a sort of fusion to force many into one;—that which afterwards showed itself in such might and energy in Lear, where the deep anguish of a father spreads the feeling of ingratitude and cruelty over the very elements of heaven; —and which, combining many circumstances into one

moment of consciousness, tends to produce that ultimate end of all human thought and human feeling,
unity, and thereby the reduction of the spirit to its principle and fountain, who is alone truly one. Various are
the workings of this the greatest faculty of the human
mind, both passionate and tranquil. In its tranquil and
purely pleasurable operation, it acts chiefly by creating
out of many things, as they would have appeared in the
description of an ordinary mind, detailed in unimpassioned succession, a oneness, even as nature, the greatest
of poets, acts upon us, when we open our eyes upon an
extended prospect. Thus the flight of Adonis in the
dusk of the evening:—

> Look! how a bright star shooteth from the sky;
> So glides he in the night from Venus' eye!

How many images and feelings are here brought together without effort and without discord, in the beauty
of Adonis, the rapidity of his flight, the yearning, yet
hopelessness, of the enamored gazer, while a shadowy
ideal character is thrown over the whole! Or this power
acts by impressing the stamp of humanity, and of human feelings, on inanimate or mere natural objects:—

> Lo! here the gentle lark, weary of rest,
> From his moist cabinet mounts up on high,
> And wakes the morning, from whose silver breast
> The sun ariseth in his majesty,
> Who doth the world so gloriously behold,
> The cedar-tops and hills seem burnish'd gold.

Or again, it acts by so carrying on the eye of the
reader as to make him almost lose the consciousness of
words,—to make him see every thing flashed, as Wordsworth has grandly and appropriately said,—

> *Flashed* upon that inward eye
> Which is the bliss of solitude;—

and this without exciting any painful or laborious attention, without any anatomy of description, (a fault not uncommon in descriptive poetry)—but with the sweetness and easy movement of nature. This energy is an absolute essential of poetry, and of itself would constitute a poet, though not one of the highest class;—it is, however, a most hopeful symptom, and the Venus and Adonis is one continued specimen of it.

In this beautiful poem there is an endless activity of thought in all the possible associations of thought with thought, thought with feeling, or with words, of feelings with feelings, and of words with words.

> Even as the sun, with purple-colour'd face,
> Had ta'en his last leave of the weeping morn,
> Rose-cheek'd Adonis hied him to the chase:
> Hunting he loved, but love he laughed to scorn.
> Sick-thoughted Venus makes amain unto him,
> And like a bold-faced suitor 'gins to woo him.

Remark the humanizing imagery and circumstances of the first two lines, and the activity of thought in the play of words in the fourth line. The whole stanza presents at once the time, the appearance of the morning, and the two persons distinctly characterized, and in six simple verses puts the reader in possession of the whole argument of the poem.

> Over one arm the lusty courser's rein,
> Under the other was the tender boy,
> Who blush'd and pouted in a dull disdain,
> With leaden appetite, unapt to toy,
> She red and hot, as coals of glowing fire,
> He red for shame, but frosty to desire:—

This stanza and the two following afford good instances of that poetic power, which I mentioned above, of making every thing present to the imagination—both the forms, and the passions which modify those forms, either actually, as in the representations of love, or anger, or other human affections; or imaginatively, by the different manner in which inanimate objects, or objects unimpassioned themselves, are caused to be seen by the mind in moments of strong excitement, and according to the kind of the excitement,—whether of jealousy, or rage, or love, in the only appropriate sense of the word, or of the lower impulses of our nature, or finally of the poetic feeling itself. It is, perhaps, chiefly in the power of producing and reproducing the latter that the poet stands distinct.

The subject of the *Venus and Adonis* is unpleasing; but the poem itself is for that very reason the more illustrative of Shakspeare. There are men who can write passages of deepest pathos and even sublimity on circumstances personal to themselves and stimulative of their own passions; but they are not, therefore, on this account poets. Read that magnificent burst of woman's patriotism and exultation, Deborah's song of victory; it is glorious, but nature is the poet there. It is quite another matter to become all things and yet remain the same,—to make the changeful god be felt in the river, the lion and the flame;—this it is, that is the true imagination. Shakspeare writes in this poem, as if he were of another planet, charming you to gaze on the movements of *Venus and Adonis*, as you would on the twinkling dances of two vernal butterflies.

Finally, in this poem and the *Rape of Lucrece*, Shakspeare gave ample proof of his possession of a most profound, energetic, and philosophical mind, without which he might have pleased, but could not have been a great dramatic poet. Chance and the necessity of his genius combined to lead him to the drama his proper

I

province; in his conquest of which we should consider both the difficulties which opposed him, and the advantages by which he was assisted.

Lectures.[1]

Shakspeare's Judgment equal to his Genius

THUS then Shakspeare appears, from his *Venus and Adonis* and *Rape of Lucrece* alone, apart from all his great works, to have possessed all the conditions of the true poet. Let me now proceed to destroy, as far as may be in my power, the popular notion that he was a great dramatist by mere instinct, that he grew immortal in his own despite, and sank below men of second or third-rate power, when he attempted aught beside the drama —even as bees construct their cells and manufacture their honey to admirable perfection; but would in vain attempt to build a nest. Now this mode of reconciling a compelled sense of inferiority with a feeling of pride, began in a few pedants, who having read that Sophocles was the great model of tragedy, and Aristotle the infallible dictator of its rules, and finding that the *Lear*, *Hamlet*, *Othello* and other master-pieces were neither in imitation of Sophocles, nor in obedience to Aristotle, —and not having (with one or two exceptions) the

---

[1] Coleridge's 'Lectures' are not preserved as they were delivered. It was his habit to write out only portions of them and to make many notes, then to study the 'mass of material', and then to speak extempore. The fragments which remain cannot all be assigned to the same date, though most of them probably belong to the series delivered in London in 1818. They were printed in H. N. Coleridge's edition of his uncle's *Literary Remains*, 1836–39. Much additional matter is included in Ashe's collection of Coleridge's *Lectures and Notes on Shakspere and Other English Poets*, 1883.

In the extracts from the 'Lectures' the spelling 'Shakspeare' has been adopted throughout. It is the spelling in the *Biographia Literaria*, which Coleridge himself saw through the press.

courage to affirm, that the delight which their country received from generation to generation, in defiance of the alterations of circumstances and habits, was wholly groundless,—took upon them, as a happy medium and refuge, to talk of Shakspeare as a sort of beautiful *lusus naturæ*, a delightful monster,—wild, indeed, and without taste or judgment, but like the inspired idiots so much venerated in the East, uttering, amid the strangest follies, the sublimest truths. In nine places out of ten in which I find his awful name mentioned, it is with some epithet of 'wild,' 'irregular,' 'pure child of nature,' &c. If all this be true, we must submit to it; though to a thinking mind it cannot but be painful to find any excellence, merely human, thrown out of all human analogy, and thereby leaving us neither rules for imitation, nor motives to imitate;—but if false, it is a dangerous falsehood;—for it affords a refuge to secret self-conceit, —enables a vain man at once to escape his reader's indignation by general swoln panegyrics, and merely by his *ipse dixit* to treat, as contemptible, what he has not intellect enough to comprehend, or soul to feel, without assigning any reason, or referring his opinion to any demonstrative principle;—thus leaving Shakspeare as a sort of grand Lama, adored indeed, and his very excrements prized as relics, but with no authority or real influence. I grieve that every late voluminous edition of his works would enable me to substantiate the present charge with a variety of facts one tenth of which would of themselves exhaust the time allotted to me. Every critic, who has or has not made a collection of black letter books—in itself a useful and respectable amusement,—puts on the seven-league boots of self-opinion, and strides at once from an illustrator into a supreme judge, and blind and deaf, fills his three-ounce phial at the waters of Niagara; and determines

positively the greatness of the cataract to be neither
more nor less than his three-ounce phial has been able
to receive.

I think this a very serious subject. It is my earnest
desire—my passionate endeavour,—to enforce at various
times and by various arguments and instances the close
and reciprocal connexion of just taste with pure morality.
Without that acquaintance with the heart of man, or
that docility and childlike gladness to be made acquainted
with it, which those only can have, who dare look at
their own hearts—and that with a steadiness which religion only has the power of reconciling with sincere
humility;—without this, and the modesty produced by
it, I am deeply convinced that no man, however wide
his erudition, however patient his antiquarian researches,
can possibly understand, or be worthy of understanding,
the writings of Shakspeare.

Assuredly that criticism of Shakspeare will alone be
genial which is reverential. The Englishman, who without reverence, a proud and affectionate reverence, can
utter the name of William Shakspeare, stands disqualified for the office of critic. He wants one at least of the
very senses, the language of which he is to employ, and
will discourse at best, but as a blind man, while the
whole harmonious creation of light and shade with all
its subtle interchange of deepening and dissolving colours
rises in silence to the silent *fiat* of the uprising Apollo.
However inferior in ability I may be to some who have
followed me, I own I am proud that I was the first in
time who publicly demonstrated to the full extent of the
position, that the supposed irregularity and extravagances
of Shakspeare were the mere dreams of a pedantry
that arraigned the eagle because it had not the dimensions of the swan. In all the successive courses of lectures
delivered by me, since my first attempt at the Royal

Institution, it has been, and it still remains, my object, to prove that in all points from the most important to the most minute, the judgment of Shakspeare is commensurate with his genius,—nay, that his genius reveals itself in his judgment, as in its most exalted form. And the more gladly do I recur to this subject from the clear conviction, that to judge aright, and with distinct consciousness of the grounds of our judgment, concerning the works of Shakspeare, implies the power and the means of judging rightly of all other works of intellect, those of abstract science alone excepted.

It is a painful truth that not only individuals, but even whole nations, are ofttimes so enslaved to the habits of their education and immediate circumstances, as not to judge disinterestedly even on those subjects, the very pleasure arising from which consists in its disinterestedness, namely, on subjects of taste and polite literature. Instead of deciding concerning their own modes and customs by any rule of reason, nothing appears rational, becoming, or beautiful to them, but what coincides with the peculiarities of their education. In this narrow circle, individuals may attain to exquisite discrimination, as the French critics have done in their own literature; but a true critic can no more be such without placing himself on some central point, from which he may command the whole, that is, some general rule, which, founded in reason, or the faculties common to all men, must therefore apply to each,—than an astronomer can explain the movements of the solar system without taking his stand in the sun. And let me remark, that this will not tend to produce despotism, but, on the contrary, true tolerance, in the critic. He will, indeed, require, as the spirit and substance of a work, something true in human nature itself, and independent of all circumstances; but in the mode of applying it, he will

estimate genius and judgment according to the felicity
with which the imperishable soul of intellect shall have
adapted itself to the age, the place, and the existing manners. The error he will expose, lies in reversing this,
and holding up the mere circumstances as perpetual to
the utter neglect of the power which can alone animate
them. For art cannot exist without, or apart from,
nature; and what has man of his own to give to his
fellow-man, but his own thoughts and feelings, and his
observations so far as they are modified by his own
thoughts or feelings?

Let me, then, once more submit this question to minds
emancipated alike from national, or party, or sectarian
prejudice:—Are the plays of Shakspeare works of rude
uncultivated genius, in which the splendour of the parts
compensates, if aught can compensate, for the barbarous
shapelessness and irregularity of the whole?—Or is the
form equally admirable with the matter, and the judgment of the great poet, not less deserving our wonder
than his genius?—Or, again, to repeat the question in
other words:—Is Shakspeare a great dramatic poet on
account only of those beauties and excellencies which he
possesses in common with the ancients, but with dimi-
nished claims to our love and honour to the full extent
of his differences from them?—Or are these very differences additional proofs of poetic wisdom, at once results
and symbols of living power as contrasted with lifeless
mechanism—of free and rival originality as contradis-
tinguished from servile imitation, or, more accurately,
a blind copying of effects, instead of a true imitation of
the essential principles?—Imagine not that I am about
to oppose genius to rules. No! the comparative value
of these rules is the very cause to be tried. The spirit of
poetry, like all other living powers, must of necessity
circumscribe itself by rules, were it only to unite power

with beauty. It must embody in order to reveal itself;
but a living body is of necessity an organized one; and
what is organization but the connexion of parts in and
for a whole, so that each part is at once end and means?
—This is no discovery of criticism;—it is a necessity
of the human mind; and all nations have felt and obeyed
it, in the invention of metre, and measured sounds, as
the vehicle and *involucrum* of poetry—itself a fellow-
growth from the same life,—even as the bark is to the
tree!

No work of true genius dares want its appropriate
form, neither indeed is there any danger of this. As it
must not, so genius cannot, be lawless; for it is even this
that constitutes it genius—the power of acting creatively
under laws of its own origination. How then comes it
that not only single *Zoili*, but whole nations have combined in unhesitating condemnation of our great dramatist, as a sort of African nature, rich in beautiful monsters
—as a wild heath where islands of fertility look the greener
from the surrounding waste, where the loveliest plants
now shine out among unsightly weeds, and now are
choked by their parasitic growth, so intertwined that we
cannot disentangle the weed without snapping the flower?
—In this statement I have had no reference to the vulgar
abuse of Voltaire, save as far as his charges are coincident
with the decisions of Shakspeare's own commentators
and (so they would tell you) almost idolatrous admirers.
The true ground of the mistake lies in the confounding
mechanical regularity with organic form. The form is
mechanic, when on any given material we impress a
pre-determined form, not necessarily arising out of the
properties of the material;—as when to a mass of wet
clay we give whatever shape we wish it to retain when
hardened. The organic form, on the other hand, is in-
nate; it shapes, as it developes, itself from within, and

the fulness of its development is one and the same with the perfection of its outward form. Such as the life is, such is the form. Nature, the prime genial artist, inexhaustible in diverse powers, is equally inexhaustible in forms;—each exterior is the physiognomy of the being within,—its true image reflected and thrown out from the concave mirror;—and even such is the appropriate excellence of her chosen poet, of our own Shakspeare, —himself a nature humanized, a genial understanding directing self-consciously a power and an implicit wisdom deeper even than our consciousness.

I greatly dislike beauties and selections in general; but as proof positive of his unrivalled excellence, I should like to try Shakspeare by this criterion. Make out your amplest catalogue of all the human faculties, as reason or the moral law, the will, the feeling of the coincidence of the two (a feeling *sui generis et demonstratio demonstrationum*) called the conscience the understanding or prudence, wit, fancy, imagination, judgment,—and then of the objects on which these are to be employed, as the beauties, the terrors, and the seeming caprices of nature, the realities and the capabilities, that is, the actual and the ideal, of the human mind, conceived as an individual or as a social being, as in innocence or in guilt, in a play-paradise, or in a war-field of temptation;—and then compare with Shakspeare under each of these heads all or any of the writers in prose and verse that have ever lived! Who, that is competent to judge, doubts the result?—And ask your own hearts,—ask your own common-sense—to conceive the possibility of this man being —I say not, the drunken savage of that wretched sciolist, whom Frenchmen, to their shame, have honoured before their elder and better worthies,—but the anomalous, the wild, the irregular, genius of our daily criticism! What! are we to have miracles in sport?—Or, I speak

reverently, does God choose idiots by whom to convey
divine truths to man?

Lectures.

Recapitulation and Summary of the Characteristics of Shakspeare's Dramas

HAVING intimated that times and manners lend their
form and pressure to genius, let me once more draw a
slight parallel between the ancient and modern stage,
the stages of Greece and of England. The Greeks were
polytheists; their religion was local; almost the only
object of all their knowledge, art and taste, was their
gods; and, accordingly, their productions were, if the
expression may be allowed, statuesque, whilst those of
the moderns are picturesque. The Greeks reared a structure, which in its parts, and as a whole, filled the mind
with the calm and elevated impression of perfect beauty
and symmetrical proportion. The moderns also produced a whole, a more striking whole; but it was by
blending materials and fusing the parts together. And
as the Pantheon is to York Minster or Westminster
Abbey, so is Sophocles compared with Shakspeare; in
the one a completeness, a satisfaction, an excellence, on
which the mind rests with complacency; in the other a
multitude of interlaced materials, great and little, magnificent and mean, accompanied, indeed, with the sense
of a falling short of perfection, and yet, at the same time,
so promising of our social and individual progression,
that we would not, if we could, exchange it for that
repose of the mind which dwells on the forms of symmetry in the acquiescent admiration of grace. This
general characteristic of the ancient and modern drama
might be illustrated by a parallel of the ancient and
modern music;—the one consisting of melody arising
from a succession only of pleasing sounds,—the modern

embracing harmony also, the result of combination and the effect of a whole.

I have said, and I say it again, that great as was the genius of Shakspeare, his judgment was at least equal to it. Of this any one will be convinced, who attentively considers those points in which the dramas of Greece and England differ, from the dissimilitude of circumstances by which each was modified and influenced. The Greek stage had its origin in the ceremonies of a sacrifice, such as of the goat to Bacchus, whom we most erroneously regard as merely the jolly god of wine;—for among the ancients he was venerable, as the symbol of that power which acts without our consciousness in the vital energies of nature,—the *vinum mundi*,—as Apollo was that of the conscious agency of our intellectual being. The heroes of old under the influences of this Bacchic enthusiasm performed more than human actions; —hence tales of the favorite champions soon passed into dialogue. On the Greek stage the chorus was always before the audience; the curtain was never dropped, as we should say; and change of place being therefore, in general, impossible, the absurd notion of condemning it merely as improbable in itself was never entertained by any one. If we can believe ourselves at Thebes in one act, we may believe ourselves at Athens in the next. If a story lasts twenty-four hours or twenty-four years, it is equally improbable. There seems to be no just boundary but what the feelings prescribe. But on the Greek stage where the same persons were perpetually before the audience, great judgment was necessary in venturing on any such change. The poets never, therefore, attempted to impose on the senses by bringing places to men, but they did bring men to places, as in the well known instance in the Eumenides, where during an evident retirement of the chorus from the orchestra, the scene is changed to Athens, and Orestes is first introduced in the temple of Minerva, and the chorus of Furies come in afterwards in pursuit of him.

In the Greek drama there were no formal divisions into scenes and acts; there were no means, therefore, of allowing for the necessary lapse of time between one part of the dialogue and another, and unity of time in a strict sense was, of course, impossible. To overcome that difficulty of accounting for time, which is effected on the modern stage by dropping a curtain, the judgment and great genius of the ancients supplied music and measured motion, and with the lyric ode filled up the vacuity. In the story of the Agamemnon of Æschylus, the capture of Troy is supposed to be announced by a fire lighted on the Asiatic shore, and the transmission of the signal by successive beacons to Mycenæ. The signal is first seen at the 21st line, and the herald from Troy itself enters at the 486th, and Agamemnon himself at the 783rd line. But the practical absurdity of this was not felt by the audience, who, in imagination stretched minutes into hours, while they listened to the lofty narrative odes of the chorus which almost entirely fill up the interspace. Another fact deserves attention here, namely, that regularly on the Greek stage a drama, or acted story, consisted in reality of three dramas, called together a trilogy, and performed consecutively in the course of one day. Now you may conceive a tragedy of Shakspeare's as a trilogy connected in one single representation. Divide *Lear* into three parts, and each would be a play with the ancients; or take the three Æschylean dramas of Agamemnon, and divide them into, or call them, as many acts, and they together would be one play. The first act would comprise the usurpation of Ægisthus, and the murder of Agamemnon; the second, the revenge of Orestes, and the murder of his mother;

and the third, the penance and absolution of Orestes;—occupying a period of twenty-two years.

The stage in Shakspeare's time was a naked room with a blanket for a curtain; but he made it a field for monarchs. The law of unity, which has its foundations, not in the factitious necessity of custom, but in nature itself, the unity of feeling, is every where and at all times observed by Shakspeare in his plays. Read *Romeo and Juliet*;—all is youth and spring;—youth with its follies, its virtues, its precipitancies;—spring with its odours, its flowers, and its transiency; it is one and the same feeling that commences, goes through, and ends the play. The old men, the Capulets and the Montagues, are not common old men; they have an eagerness, a heartiness, a vehemence, the effect of spring; with Romeo, his change of passion, his sudden marriage, and his rash death, are all the effects of youth;—whilst in Juliet love has all that is tender and melancholy in the nightingale, all that is voluptuous in the rose, with whatever is sweet in the freshness of spring; but it ends with a long deep sigh like the last breeze of the Italian evening. This unity of feeling and character pervades every drama of Shakspeare.

It seems to me that his plays are distinguished from those of all other dramatic poets by the following characteristics:

1. Expectation in preference to surprise. It is like the true reading of the passage;—'God said, Let there be light, and there was *light*;'—not there *was* light. As the feeling with which we startle at a shooting star, compared with that of watching the sunrise at the pre-established moment, such and so low is surprise compared with expectation.

2. Signal adherence to the great law of nature, that all opposites tend to attract and temper each other. Passion

in Shakspeare generally displays libertinism, but involves morality; and if there are exceptions to this, they are, independently of their intrinsic value, all of them indicative of individual character, and, like the farewell admonitions of a parent, have an end beyond the parental relation. Thus the Countess's beautiful precepts to Bertram, by elevating her character, raise that of Helena her favorite, and soften down the point in her which Shakspeare does not mean us not to see, but to see and to forgive, and at length to justify. And so it is in Polonius, who is the personified memory of wisdom no longer actually possessed. This admirable character is always misrepresented on the stage. Shakspeare never intended to exhibit him as a buffoon; for although it was natural that Hamlet,—a young man of fire and genius, detesting formality, and disliking Polonius on political grounds, as imagining that he had assisted his uncle in his usurpation,—should express himself satirically,—yet this must not be taken as exactly the poet's conception of him. In Polonius a certain induration of character had arisen from long habits of business; but take his advice to Laertes, and Ophelia's reverence for his memory, and we shall see that he was meant to be represented as a statesman somewhat past his faculties,—his recollections of life all full of wisdom, and showing a knowledge of human nature, whilst what immediately takes place before him, and escapes from him, is indicative of weakness.

But as in Homer all the deities are in armour, even Venus; so in Shakspeare all the characters are strong. Hence real folly and dulness are made by him the vehicles of wisdom. There is no difficulty for one being a fool to imitate a fool; but to be, remain, and speak like a wise man and a great wit, and yet so as to give a vivid representation of a veritable fool,—*hic labor, hoc opus est.*

A drunken constable is not uncommon, nor hard to draw; but see and examine what goes to make up a Dogberry.

3. Keeping at all times in the high road of life. Shakspeare has no innocent adulteries, no interesting incests, no virtuous vice;—he never renders that amiable which religion and reason alike teach us to detest, or clothes impurity in the garb of virtue, like Beaumont and Fletcher, the Kotzebues of the day. Shakspeare's fathers are roused by ingratitude, his husbands stung by unfaithfulness; in him, in short, the affections are wounded in those points in which all may, nay, must, feel. Let the morality of Shakspeare be contrasted with that of the writers of his own, or the succeeding, age, or of those of the present day, who boast their superiority in this respect. No one can dispute that the result of such a comparison is altogether in favour of Shakspeare;—even the letters of women of high rank in his age were often coarser than his writings. If he occasionally disgusts a keen sense of delicacy, he never injures the mind; he neither excites, nor flatters, passion, in order to degrade the subject of it; he does not use the faulty thing for a faulty purpose, nor carries on warfare against virtue, by causing wickedness to appear as no wickedness, through the medium of a morbid sympathy with the unfortunate. In Shakspeare vice never walks as in twilight; nothing is purposely out of its place;—he inverts not the order of nature and propriety,—does not make every magistrate a drunkard or glutton, nor every poor man weak, humane, and temperate; he has no benevolent butchers, nor any sentimental rat-catchers.

4. Independence of the dramatic interest on the plot. The interest in the plot is always in fact on account of the characters, not *vice versa*, as in almost all other writers; the plot is a mere canvass and no more. Hence arises the

true justification of the same stratagem being used in regard to Benedict and Beatrice,—the vanity in each being
alike. Take away from the *Much Ado About Nothing* all
that which is not indispensable to the plot, either as having little to do with it, or, at best, like Dogberry and
his comrades, forced into the service, when any other
less ingeniously absurd watchmen and night-constables
would have answered the mere necessities of the action;
—take away Benedict, Beatrice, Dogberry, and the reaction of the former on the character of Hero,—and
what will remain? In other writers the main agent of
the plot is always the prominent character; in Shakspeare it is so, or is not so, as the character is in itself calculated, or not calculated, to form the plot. Don John
is the main-spring of the plot of this play; but he is
merely shown and then withdrawn.

5. Independence of the interest on the story as the
ground-work of the plot. Hence Shakspeare never took
the trouble of inventing stories. It was enough for him
to select from those that had been already invented or
recorded such as had one or other, or both, of two re-
commendations, namely, suitableness to his particular
purpose, and their being parts of popular tradition,—
names of which we had often heard, and of their fortunes, and as to which all we wanted was, to see the man
himself. So it is just the man himself, the Lear, the Shylock, the Richard, that Shakspeare makes us for the
first time acquainted with. Omit the first scene in *Lear*,
and yet every thing will remain; so the first and second
scenes in the *Merchant of Venice*. Indeed it is universally
true.

6. Interfusion of the lyrical—that which in its very
essence is poetical—not only with the dramatic, as in the
plays of Metastasio, where at the end of the scene comes
the *aria* as the *exit* speech of the character,—but also in

and through the dramatic. Songs in Shakspeare are introduced as songs only, just as songs are in real life, beautifully as some of them are characteristic of the person who has sung or called for them, as Desdemona's 'Willow,' and Ophelia's wild snatches, and the sweet carollings in *As You Like It*. But the whole of the *Midsummer Night's Dream* is one continued specimen of the dramatized lyrical. And observe how exquisitely the dramatic of Hotspur;—

> Marry, and I'm glad on't with all my heart;
> I had rather be a kitten and cry—mew, &c.

melts away into the lyric of Mortimer;—

> I understand thy looks: that pretty Welsh
> Which thou pourest down from these swelling heavens,
> I am too perfect in, &c.
>
> Henry IV. part i. act iii. sc. i.

7. The characters of the *dramatis personæ*, like those in real life, are to be inferred by the reader;—they are not told to him. And it is well worth remarking that Shakspeare's characters, like those in real life, are very commonly misunderstood, and almost always understood by different persons in different ways. The causes are the same in either case. If you take only what the friends of the character say, you may be deceived, and still more so, if that which his enemies say; nay, even the character himself sees himself through the medium of his character, and not exactly as he is. Take all together, not omitting a shrewd hint from the clown or the fool, and perhaps your impression will be right; and you may know whether you have in fact discovered the poet's own idea, by all the speeches receiving light from it, and attesting its reality by reflecting it.

Lastly, in Shakspeare the heterogeneous is united, as it is in nature. You must not suppose a pressure or

passion always acting on or in the character;—passion in
Shakspeare is that by which the individual is distinguished
from others, not that which makes a different kind of
him. Shakspeare followed the main march of the human
affections. He entered into no analysis of the passions
or faiths of men, but assured himself that such and such
passions and faiths were grounded in our common nature, and not in the mere accidents of ignorance or
disease. This is an important consideration, and constitutes our Shakspeare the morning star, the guide and
the pioneer, of true philosophy.

Lectures.

The Tempest

THE *Tempest* is a specimen of the purely romantic
drama, in which the interest is not historical, or dependent upon fidelity of portraiture, or the natural connexion
of events,—but is a birth of the imagination, and rests
only on the coaptation and union of the elements granted
to, or assumed by, the poet. It is a species of drama
which owes no allegiance to time or space, and in which,
therefore, errors of chronology and geography—no
mortal sins in any species—are venial faults, and count
for nothing. It addresses itself entirely to the imaginative faculty; and although the illusion may be assisted
by the effect on the senses of the complicated scenery
and decorations of modern times, yet this sort of assistance is dangerous. For the principal and only genuine
excitement ought to come from within,—from the
moved and sympathetic imagination; whereas, where
so much is addressed to the mere external senses of seeing
and hearing, the spiritual vision is apt to languish, and
the attraction from without will withdraw the mind
from the proper and only legitimate interest which is
intended to spring from within.

The romance opens with a busy scene admirably appropriate to the kind of drama, and giving, as it were, the key-note to the whole harmony. It prepares and initiates the excitement required for the entire piece, and yet does not demand any thing from the spectators, which their previous habits had not fitted them to understand. It is the bustle of a tempest, from which the real horrors are abstracted;—therefore it is poetical, though not in strictness natural—(the distinction to which I have so often alluded)—and is purposely restrained from concentering the interest on itself, but used merely as an induction or tuning for what is to follow.

In the second scene, Prospero's speeches, till the entrance of Ariel, contain the finest example, I remember, of retrospective narration for the purpose of exciting immediate interest, and putting the audience in possession of all the information necessary for the understanding of the plot. Observe, too, the perfect probability of the moment chosen by Prospero (the very Shakspeare himself, as it were, of the tempest) to open out the truth to his daughter, his own romantic bearing, and how completely any thing that might have been disagreeable to us in the magician, is reconciled and shaded in the humanity and natural feelings of the father. In the very first speech of Miranda the simplicity and tenderness of her character are at once laid open;—it would have been lost in direct contact with the agitation of the first scene. The opinion once prevailed, but, happily, is now abandoned, that Fletcher alone wrote for women;—the truth is, that with very few, and those partial, exceptions, the female characters in the plays of Beaumont and Fletcher are, when of the light kind, not decent; when heroic, complete viragos. But in Shakspeare all the elements of womanhood are holy, and there is the sweet, yet dignified feeling of all that *continuates* society, as sense of ancestry and of sex, with a purity unassailable by sophistry, because it rests not in the analytic processes, but in that sane equipoise of the faculties, during which the feelings are representative of all past experience,—not of the individual only, but of all those by whom she has been educated, and their predecessors even up to the first mother that lived. Shakspeare saw that the want of prominence, which Pope notices for sarcasm, was the blessed beauty of the woman's character, and knew that it arose not from any deficiency, but from the more exquisite harmony of all the parts of the moral being constituting one living total of head and heart. He has drawn it, indeed, in all its distinctive energies of faith, patience, constancy, fortitude,—shown in all of them as following the heart, which gives its results by a nice tact and happy intuition, without the intervention of the discursive faculty,—sees all things in and by the light of the affections, and errs, if it ever err, in the exaggerations of love alone. In all the Shakspearian women there is essentially the same foundation and principle; the distinct individuality and variety are merely the result of the modification of circumstances, whether in Miranda the maiden, in Imogen the wife, or in Katharine the queen.

But to return. The appearance and characters of the super or ultra-natural servants are finely contrasted. Ariel has in every thing the airy tint which gives the name; and it is worthy of remark that Miranda is never directly brought into comparison with Ariel, lest the natural and human of the one and the supernatural of the other should tend to neutralize each other; Caliban, on the other hand, is all earth, all condensed and gross in feelings and images; he has the dawnings of understanding without reason or the moral sense, and in him, as in some brute animals, this advance to the intellectual faculties,

without the moral sense, is marked by the appearance
of vice. For it is in the primacy of the moral being only
that man is truly human; in his intellectual powers he is
certainly approached by the brutes, and, man's whole
system duly considered, those powers cannot be considered other than means to an end, that is, to morality.

In this sense, as it proceeds, is displayed the impression
made by Ferdinand and Miranda on each other; it is love
at first sight;—

> at the first sight
> They have chang'd eyes:—

and it appears to me, that in all cases of real love, it is at
one moment that it takes place. That moment may have
been prepared by previous esteem, admiration, or even
affection,—yet love seems to require a momentary act
of volition, by which a tacit bond of devotion is im-
posed,—a bond not to be thereafter broken without
violating what should be sacred in our nature. How
finely is the true Shakspearian scene contrasted with
Dryden's vulgar alteration of it, in which a mere ludicrous psychological experiment, as it were, is tried—
displaying nothing but indelicacy without passion.
Prospero's interruption of the courtship has often seemed
to me to have no sufficient motive; still his alleged
reason—

> lest too light winning
> Make the prize light—

is enough for the ethereal connexions of the romantic
imagination, although it would not be so for the historical. The whole courting scene, indeed, in the beginning
of the third act, between the lovers is a masterpiece; and
the first dawn of disobedience in the mind of Miranda
to the command of her father is very finely drawn, so
as to seem the working of the Scriptural command,

Thou shalt leave father and mother, &c. O! with what exquisite purity this scene is conceived and executed! Shakspeare may sometimes be gross, but I boldly say that he is always moral and modest. Alas! in this our day decency of manners is preserved at the expense of morality of heart, and delicacies for vice are allowed, whilst grossness against it is hypocritically, or at least morbidly, condemned.

In this play are admirably sketched the vices generally accompanying a low degree of civilization; and in the first scene of the second act Shakspeare has, as in many other places, shown the tendency in bad men to indulge in scorn and contemptuous expressions, as a mode of getting rid of their own uneasy feelings of inferiority to the good, and also, by making the good ridiculous, of rendering the transition of others to wickedness easy. Shakspeare never puts habitual scorn into the mouths of other than bad men, as here in the instances of Antonio and Sebastian. The scene of the intended assassination of Alonzo and Gonzalo is an exact counterpart of the scene between Macbeth and his lady, only pitched in a lower key throughout, as designed to be frustrated and concealed, and exhibiting the same profound management in the manner of familiarizing a mind, not immediately recipient, to the suggestion of guilt, by associating the proposed crime with something ludicrous or out of place,—something not habitually matter of reverence. By this kind of sophistry the imagination and fancy are first bribed to contemplate the suggested act, and at length to become acquainted with it. Observe how the effect of this scene is heightened by contrast with another counterpart of it in low life,—that between the conspirators Stephano, Caliban, and Trinculo in the second scene of the third act, in which there are the same essential characteristics.

In this play and in this scene of it are also shown the springs of the vulgar in politics,—of that kind of politics which is inwoven with human nature. In his treatment of this subject, wherever it occurs, Shakspeare is quite peculiar. In other writers we find the particular opinions of the individual; in Massinger it is rank republicanism; in Beaumont and Fletcher even *jure divino* principles are carried to excess;—but Shakspeare never promulgates any party tenets. He is always the philosopher and the moralist, but at the same time with a profound veneration for all the established institutions of society, and for those classes which form the permanent elements of the state—especially never introducing a professional character, as such, otherwise than as respectable. If he must have any name, he should be styled a philosophical aristocrat, delighting in those hereditary institutions which have a tendency to bind one age to another, and in that distinction of ranks, of which, although few may be in possession, all enjoy the advantages. Hence, again, you will observe the good nature with which he seems always to make sport with the passions and follies of a mob, as with an irrational animal. He is never angry with it, but hugely content with holding up its absurdities to its face; and sometimes you may trace a tone of almost affectionate superiority, something like that in which a father speaks of the rogueries of a child. See the good-humoured way in which he describes Stephano passing from the most licentious freedom to absolute despotism over Trinculo and Caliban. The truth is, Shakspeare's characters are all *genera* intensely individualized; the results of meditation, of which observation supplied the drapery and the colours necessary to combine them with each other. He had virtually surveyed all the great component powers and impulses of human nature,—had seen that their different combinations and subordinations were in fact the individualizers of men, and showed how their harmony was produced by reciprocal disproportions of excess or deficiency. The language in which these truths are expressed was not drawn from any set fashion, but from the profoundest depths of his moral being, and is therefore for all ages.

Lectures.

Antony and Cleopatra

SHAKSPEARE can be complimented only by comparison with himself: all other eulogies are either heterogeneous, as when they are in reference to Spenser or Milton; or they are flat truisms, as when he is gravely preferred to Corneille, Racine, or even his own immediate successors, Beaumont and Fletcher, Massinger and the rest. The highest praise, or rather form of praise, of this play, which I can offer in my own mind, is the doubt which the perusal always occasions in me, whether the *Antony and Cleopatra* is not, in all exhibitions of a giant power in its strength and vigour of maturity, a formidable rival of *Macbeth*, *Lear*, *Hamlet*, and *Othello*. *Feliciter audax* is the motto for its style comparatively with that of Shakspeare's other works, even as it is the general motto of all his works compared with those of other poets. Be it remembered, too, that this happy valiancy of style is but the representative and result of all the material excellences so expressed.

This play should be perused in mental contrast with *Romeo and Juliet*;—as the love of passion and appetite opposed to the love of affection and instinct. But the art displayed in the character of Cleopatra is profound; in this, especially, that the sense of criminality in her passion is lessened by our insight into its depth and energy, at the very moment that we cannot but perceive that the passion itself springs out of the habitual craving of a licentious nature, and that it is supported and reinforced by voluntary stimulus and sought-for associations, instead of blossoming out of spontaneous emotion.

Of all Shakspeare's historical plays, *Antony and Cleopatra* is by far the most wonderful. There is not one in which he has followed history so minutely, and yet there are few in which he impresses the notion of angelic strength so much;—perhaps none in which he impresses it more strongly. This is greatly owing to the manner in which the fiery force is sustained throughout, and to the numerous momentary flashes of nature counteracting the historic abstraction. As a wonderful specimen of the way in which Shakspeare lives up to the very end of this play, read the last part of the concluding scene. And if you would feel the judgment as well as the genius of Shakspeare in your heart's core, compare this astonishing drama with Dryden's *All For Love*.

Lectures.

Romeo and Juliet

I HAVE previously had occasion to speak at large on the subject of the three unities of time, place, and action, as applied to the drama in the abstract, and to the particular stage for which Shakspeare wrote, as far as he can be said to have written for any stage but that of the universal mind. I hope I have in some measure succeeded in demonstrating that the former two, instead of being rules, were mere inconveniences attached to the local peculiarities of the Athenian drama; that the last alone deserved the name of a principle, and that in the preservation of this unity Shakspeare stood pre-eminent. Yet, instead of unity of action, I should greatly prefer the more appropriate, though scholastic and uncouth,

words homogeneity, proportionateness, and totality of
interest,—expressions, which involve the distinction, or
rather the essential difference, betwixt the shaping skill
of mechanical talent, and the creative, productive, life-
power of inspired genius. In the former each part is
separately conceived, and then by a succeeding act put
together;—not as watches are made for wholesale,—
(for there each part supposes a pre-conception of the
whole in some mind)—but more like pictures on a
motley screen. Whence arises the harmony that strikes
us in the wildest natural landscapes,—in the relative
shapes of rocks, the harmony of colours in the heaths,
ferns, and lichens, the leaves of the beech and the oak,
the stems and rich brown branches of the birch and other
mountain trees, varying from verging autumn to returning spring,—compared with the visual effect from
the greater number of artificial plantations?—From this,
that the natural landscape is effected, as it were, by a
single energy modified *ab intra* in each component part.
And as this is the particular excellence of the Shakspearian drama generally, so is it especially characteristic
of the *Romeo and Juliet*.

The groundwork of the tale is altogether in family
life, and the events of the play have their first origin in
family feuds. Filmy as are the eyes of party-spirit, at
once dim and truculent, still there is commonly some
real or supposed object in view, or principle to be main-
tained; and though but the twisted wires on the plate
of rosin in the preparation for electrical pictures, it is still
a guide in some degree, an assimilation to an outline.
But in family quarrels, which have proved scarcely less
injurious to states, wilfulness, and precipitancy, and
passion from mere habit and custom, can alone be expected. With his accustomed judgment, Shakspeare has
begun by placing before us a lively picture of all the

impulses of the play; and as nature ever presents two
sides, one for Heraclitus, and one for Democritus, he
has, by way of prelude, shown the laughable absurdity
of the evil by the contagion of it reaching the servants,
who have so little to do with it, but who are under the
necessity of letting the superfluity of sensoreal power
fly off through the escape-valve of wit-combats, and of
quarrelling with weapons of sharper edge, all in humble
imitation of their masters. Yet there is a sort of unhired
fidelity, an *ourishness* about all this that makes it rest
pleasant on one's feelings. All the first scene, down to
the conclusion of the Prince's speech, is a motley dance
of all ranks and ages to one tune, as if the horn of Huon
had been playing behind the scenes.

Benvolio's speech—

Madam, an hour before the worshipp'd sun
Peer'd forth the golden window of the east—

and, far more strikingly, the following speech of old
Montague—

Many a morning hath he there been seen
With tears augmenting the fresh morning dew—

prove that Shakspeare meant the *Romeo and Juliet* to
approach to a poem, which, and indeed its early date,
may be also inferred from the multitude of rhyming
couplets throughout. And if we are right, from the internal evidence, in pronouncing this one of Shakspeare's
early dramas, it affords a strong instance of the fineness
of his insight into the nature of the passions, that Romeo
is introduced already love-bewildered. The necessity of
loving creates an object for itself in man and woman;
and yet there is a difference in this respect between the
sexes, though only to be known by a perception of it.
It would have displeased us if Juliet had been represented as already in love, or as fancying herself so;—

but no one, I believe, ever experiences any shock at
Romeo's forgetting his Rosaline, who had been a mere
name for the yearning of his youthful imagination, and
rushing into his passion for Juliet. Rosaline was a mere
creation of his fancy; and we should remark the boastful
positiveness of Romeo in a love of his own making,
which is never shown where love is really near the heart.

> When the devout religion of mine eye
> Maintains such falsehood, then turn tears to fires!
>
> . . . .
>
> One fairer than my love! the all-seeing sun
> Ne'er saw her match, since first the world begun.

The character of the Nurse is the nearest of any thing
in Shakspeare to a direct borrowing from mere observation; and the reason is, that as in infancy and childhood
the individual in nature is a representative of a class,—
just as in describing one larch tree, you generalize a
grove of them,—so it is nearly as much so in old age.
The generalization is done to the poet's hand. Here you
have the garrulity of age strengthened by the feelings
of a long-trusted servant, whose sympathy with the
mother's affections gives her privileges and rank in the
household; and observe the mode of connection by
accidents of time and place, and the childlike fondness
of repetition in a second childhood, and also that happy,
humble, ducking under, yet constant resurgence against,
the check of her superiors!—

> Yes, madam!—Yet I cannot choose but laugh, &c.

In the fourth scene we have Mercutio introduced to
us. O! how shall I describe that exquisite ebullience and
overflow of youthful life, wafted on over the laughing
waves of pleasure and prosperity, as a wanton beauty
that distorts the face on which she knows her lover is
gazing enraptured, and wrinkles her forehead in the

triumph of its smoothness! Wit ever wakeful, fancy busy and procreative as an insect, courage, an easy mind that, without cares of its own, is at once disposed to laugh away those of others, and yet to be interested in them,—these and all congenial qualities, melting into the common *copula* of them all, the man of rank and the gentleman, with all its excellencies and all its weaknesses, constitute the character of Mercutio!

Lectures.

Lear

OF all Shakspeare's plays *Macbeth* is the most rapid, *Hamlet* the slowest, in movement. *Lear* combines length with rapidity,—like the hurricane and the whirlpool, absorbing while it advances. It begins as a stormy day in summer, with brightness; but that brightness is lurid, and anticipates the tempest.

It was not without forethought, nor is it without its due significance, that the division of Lear's kingdom is in the first six lines of the play stated as a thing already determined in all its particulars, previously to the trial of professions, as the relative rewards of which the daughters were to be made to consider their several portions. The strange, yet by no means unnatural, mixture of selfishness, sensibility, and habit of feeling derived from, and fostered by, the particular rank and usages of the individual;—the intense desire of being intensely beloved,—selfish, and yet characteristic of the selfishness of a loving and kindly nature alone;—the self-supportless leaning for all pleasure on another's breast;—the craving after sympathy with a prodigal disinterestedness, frustrated by its own ostentation, and the mode and nature of its claims;—the anxiety, the distrust, the jealousy, which more or less accompany all selfish affections, and are amongst the surest contradistinctions of mere fondness from true love, and which originate Lear's eager wish to enjoy his daughters' violent professions, whilst the inveterate habits of sovereignty convert the wish into claim and positive right, and an incompliance with it into crime and treason;— these facts, these passions, these moral verities, on which the whole tragedy is founded, are all prepared for, and will to the retrospect be found implied, in these first four or five lines of the play. They let us know that the trial is but a trick; and that the grossness of the old king's rage is in part the natural result of a silly trick suddenly and most unexpectedly baffled and disappointed.

It may here be worthy of notice, that *Lear* is the only serious performance of Shakspeare, the interest and situations of which are derived from the assumption of a gross improbability; whereas Beaumont and Fletcher's tragedies are, almost all of them, founded on some out of the way accident or exception to the general experience of mankind. But observe the matchless judgment of our Shakspeare. First, improbable as the conduct of Lear is in the first scene, yet it was an old story rooted in the popular faith,—a thing taken for granted already, and consequently without any of the effects of improbability. Secondly, it is merely the canvass for the characters and passions,—a mere occasion for,—and not, in the manner of Beaumont and Fletcher, perpetually recurring as the cause, and *sine qua non* of,—the incidents and emotions. Let the first scene of this play have been lost, and let it only be understood that a fond father had been duped by hypocritical professions of love and duty on the part of two daughters to disinherit the third, previously, and deservedly, more dear to him;—and all the rest of the tragedy would retain its interest undiminished, and be perfectly intelligible. The accidental is no where the groundwork of the passions, but that which is catholic, which in all ages has been, and ever will be, close and native to the heart of man,—parental anguish from filial ingratitude, the genuineness of worth, though coffined in bluntness, and the execrable vileness of a smooth iniquity. Perhaps I ought to have added the *Merchant of Venice*; but here too the same remarks apply. It was an old tale; and substitute any other danger than that of the pound of flesh (the circumstance in which the improbability lies), yet all the situations and the emotions appertaining to them remain equally excellent and appropriate. Whereas take away from the *Mad Lover* of Beaumont and Fletcher the fantastic hypothesis of his engagement to cut out his own heart, and have it presented to his mistress, and all the main scenes must go with it. . . .

Act I. sc. 4. In Lear old age is itself a character,—its natural imperfections being increased by life-long habits of receiving a prompt obedience. Any addition of individuality would have been unnecessary and painful; for the relations of others to him, of wondrous fidelity and of frightful ingratitude, alone sufficiently distinguish him. Thus Lear becomes the open and ample play-room of nature's passions.

Knight. Since my young lady's going into France, Sir; the fool hath much pin'd away.

The Fool is no comic buffoon to make the groundlings laugh,—no forced condescension of Shakspeare's genius to the taste of his audience. Accordingly the poet prepares for his introduction, which he never does with any of his common clowns and fools, by bringing him into living connection with the pathos of the play. He is as wonderful a creation as Caliban;—his wild babblings, and inspired idiocy, articulate and gauge the horrors of the scene.

The monster Goneril prepares what is necessary, while the character of Albany renders a still more maddening grievance possible, namely, Regan and Cornwall in perfect sympathy of monstrosity. Not a sentiment, not an image, which can give pleasure on its own account, is admitted; whenever these creatures are introduced, and they are brought forward as little as possible, pure horror reigns throughout. In this scene and in all the earlier speeches of Lear, the one general sentiment of filial ingratitude prevails as the main spring of the feelings;—in this early stage the outward object causing the pressure on the mind, which is not yet sufficiently familiarized with the anguish for the imagination to work upon it. . . .

Act II. sc. 3. Edgar's assumed madness serves the great purpose of taking off part of the shock which would otherwise be caused by the true madness of Lear, and further displays the profound difference between the two. In every attempt at representing madness throughout the whole range of dramatic literature, with the single exception of Lear, it is mere lightheadedness, as especially in Otway. In Edgar's ravings Shakspeare all the while lets you see a fixed purpose, a practical end in view;—in Lear's, there is only the brooding of the one anguish, an eddy without progression. . . .

Act III. sc. 4. O, what a world's convention of agonies is here! All external nature in a storm, all moral nature convulsed,—the real madness of Lear, the feigned madness of Edgar, the babbling of the Fool, the desperate fidelity of Kent—surely such a scene was never conceived before or since! Take it but as a picture for the eye only, it is more terrific than any which a Michel Angelo, inspired by a Dante, could have conceived, and which none but a Michel Angelo could have executed. Or let it have been uttered to the blind, the howlings of

nature would seem converted into the voice of conscious
humanity. This scene ends with the first symptoms of
positive derangement; and the intervention of the fifth
scene is particularly judicious,—the interruption allowing an interval for Lear to appear in full madness in the
sixth scene.

Lectures.

Hamlet

IN Hamlet he seems to have wished to exemplify the
moral necessity of a due balance between our attention
to the objects of our senses, and our meditation on the
workings of our minds,—an *equilibrium* between the real
and the imaginary worlds. In Hamlet this balance is
disturbed: his thoughts, and the images of his fancy, are
far more vivid than his actual perceptions, and his very
perceptions, instantly passing through the *medium* of his
contemplations, acquire, as they pass, a form and a
colour not naturally their own. Hence we see a great,
an almost enormous, intellectual activity, and a proportionate aversion to real action, consequent upon it, with
all its symptoms and accompanying qualities. This character Shakspeare places in circumstances, under which
it is obliged to act on the spur of the moment:—Hamlet is brave and careless of death; but he vacillates from
sensibility, and procrastinates from thought, and loses
the power of action in the energy of resolve. Thus it is
that this tragedy presents a direct contrast to that of
Macbeth; the one proceeds with the utmost slowness,
the other with a crowded and breathless rapidity.

The effect of this overbalance of the imaginative
power is beautifully illustrated in the everlasting brood-
ings and superfluous activities of Hamlet's mind, which,
unseated from its healthy relation, is constantly occupied
with the world within, and abstracted from the world

without,—giving substance to shadows, and throwing
a mist over all commonplace actualities. It is the nature
of thought to be indefinite;—definiteness belongs to
external imagery alone. Hence it is that the sense of
sublimity arises, not from the sight of an outward object,
but from the beholder's reflection upon it;—not from
the sensuous impression, but from the imaginative
reflex. Few have seen a celebrated waterfall without
feeling something akin to disappointment: it is only
subsequently that the image comes back full into the
mind, and brings with it a train of grand or beautiful
associations. Hamlet feels this; his senses are in a state of
trance, and he looks upon external things as hierogly-
phics. His soliloquy—

> O! that this too too solid flesh would melt, &c.

springs from that craving after the indefinite—for that
which is not—which most easily besets men of genius;
and the self-delusion common to this temper of mind
is finely exemplified in the character which Hamlet
gives of himself:—

> —It cannot be
> But I am pigeon-livered, and lack gall
> To make oppression bitter.

He mistakes the seeing his chains for the breaking them,
delays action till action is of no use, and dies the victim
of mere circumstance and accident. . . .

But as of more importance, so more striking, is the
iudgment displayed by our truly dramatic poet, as well
as poet of the drama, in the management of his first
scenes. With the single exception of *Cymbeline*, they
either place before us at one glance both the past and
the future in some effect, which implies the continuance
and full agency of its cause, as in the feuds and party-
spirit of the servants of the two houses in the first scene

of *Romeo and Juliet*; or in the degrading passion for shews and public spectacles, and the overwhelming attachment for the newest successful war-chief in the Roman people, already become a populace, contrasted with the jealousy of the nobles in *Julius Cæsar*;—or they at once commence the action so as to excite a curiosity for the explanation in the following scenes, as in the storm of wind and waves, and the boatswain in the *Tempest*, instead of anticipating our curiosity, as in most other first scenes, and in too many other first acts;—or they act, by contrast of diction suited to the characters, at once to heighten the effect, and yet to give a naturalness to the language and rhythm of the principal personages, either as that of Prospero and Miranda by the appropriate lowness of the style,—or as in *King John*, by the equally appropriate stateliness of official harangues or narratives, so that the after blank verse seems to belong to the rank and quality of the speakers, and not to the poet;—or they strike at once the key-note, and give the predominant spirit of the play, as in the *Twelfth Night* and in *Macbeth*; —or finally, the first scene comprises all these advantages at once, as in *Hamlet*.

Compare the easy language of common life, in which this drama commences, with the direful music and wild wayward rhythm and abrupt lyrics of the opening of *Macbeth*. The tone is quite familiar;—there is no poetic description of night, no elaborate information conveyed by one speaker to another of what both had immediately before their senses—(such as the first distich in Addison's *Cato*, which is a translation into poetry of 'Past four o'clock and a dark morning!');—and yet nothing bordering on the comic on the one hand, nor any striving of the intellect on the other. It is precisely the language of sensation among men who feared no charge of effeminacy for feeling, what they had no want of resolution to bear. Yet the armour, the dead silence, the watchfulness that first interrupts it, the welcome relief of the guard, the cold, the broken expressions of compelled attention to bodily feelings still under control—all excellently accord with, and prepare for, the after gradual rise into tragedy;—but, above all, into a tragedy, the interest of which is as eminently *ad et apud intra*, as that of *Macbeth* is directly *ad extra*.

In all the best attested stories of ghosts and visions, as in that of Brutus, of Archbishop Cranmer, that of Benvenuto Cellini recorded by himself, and the vision of Galileo communicated by him to his favourite pupil Torricelli, the ghost-seers were in a state of cold or chilling damp from without, and of anxiety inwardly. It has been with all of them as with Francisco on his guard, —alone, in the depth and silence of the night;—' 'twas bitter cold, and they were sick at heart, and *not a mouse stirring.'* The attention to minute sounds,—naturally associated with the recollection of minute objects, and the more familiar and trifling, the more impressive from the unusualness of their producing any impression at all—gives a philosophic pertinency to this last image; but it has likewise its dramatic use and purpose. For its commonness in ordinary conversation tends to produce the sense of reality, and at once hides the poet, and yet approximates the reader or spectator to that state in which the highest poetry will appear, and in its component parts, though not in the whole composition, really is, the language of nature. If I should not speak it, I feel that I should be thinking it;—the voice only is the poet's,—the words are my own. That Shakspeare meant to put an effect in the actor's power in the very first words—'Who's there?'—is evident from the impatience expressed by the startled Francisco in the words that follow—'Nay, answer me: stand and unfold

yourself.' A brave man is never so peremptory, as when
he fears that he is afraid. Observe the gradual transition
from the silence and the still recent habit of listening in
Francisco's—'I think I hear them'—to the more cheerful
call out, which a good actor would observe, in the—
'Stand ho! Who is there?' Bernardo's inquiry after
Horatio, and the repetition of his name and in his own
presence indicate a respect or an eagerness that implies
him as one of the persons who are in the foreground;
and the scepticism attributed to him,—

> Horatio says, 'tis but our fantasy;
> And will not let belief take hold of him—

prepares us for Hamlet's after eulogy on him as one
whose blood and judgment were happily commingled.
The actor should also be careful to distinguish the expectation and gladness of Bernardo's 'Welcome, Horatio!' from the mere courtesy of his 'Welcome, good
Marcellus!'

Now observe the admirable indefiniteness of the
first opening out of the occasion of all this anxiety.
The preparation informative of the audience is just
as much as was precisely necessary, and no more;
—it begins with the uncertainty appertaining to a
question:—

Mar. What, has *this thing* appear'd again to-night?—

Even the word 'again' has its *credibilizing* effect. Then
Horatio, the representative of the ignorance of the audience, not himself, but by Marcellus to Bernardo, anticipates the common solution—' 'tis but our fantasy!'
upon which Marcellus rises into

> This dreaded sight, twice seen of us—

which immediately afterwards becomes 'this apparition,'
and that, too, an intelligent spirit, that is, to be spoken

to! Then comes the confirmation of Horatio's dis-
belief;—

       Tush! tush! 'twill not appear!—

and the silence, with which the scene opened, is again
restored in the shivering feeling of Horatio sitting down,
at such a time, and with the two eye-witnesses, to hear
a story of a ghost, and that, too, of a ghost which had
appeared twice before at the very same hour. In the
deep feeling which Bernardo has of the solemn nature
of what he is about to relate, he makes an effort to
master his own imaginative terrors by an elevation of
style,—itself a continuation of the effort,—and by turning off from the apparition, as from something which
would force him too deeply into himself, to the outward objects, the realities of nature, which had accompanied it:—

    Ber. Last night of all,
  When yon same star, that's westward from the pole
  Had made his course to illume that part of heaven
  Where now it burns, Marcellus and myself,
  The bell then beating one—

This passage seems to contradict the critical law that
what is told, makes a faint impression compared with
what is beholden; for it does indeed convey to the mind
more than the eye can see; whilst the interruption of the
narrative at the very moment, when we are most intensely listening for the sequel, and have our thoughts
diverted from the dreaded sight in expectation of the
desired, yet almost dreaded, tale—this gives all the sud-
denness and surprise of the original appearance;—

Mar. Peace, break thee off; look, where it comes again!—

Note the judgment displayed in having the two persons
present, who, as having seen the Ghost before, are

naturally eager in confirming their former opinions,—whilst the sceptic is silent, and after having been twice addressed by his friends, answers with two hasty syllables—'Most like,'—and a confession of horror:

—It harrows me with fear and wonder.

O heaven! words are wasted on those who feel, and to those who do not feel the exquisite judgment of Shakspeare in this scene, what can be said?—Hume himself could not but have had faith in this Ghost dramatically, let his anti-ghostism have been as strong as Sampson against other ghosts less powerfully raised. . . .

Act I. sc. 2. Hamlet's first soliloquy:—

O, that this too too solid flesh would melt,
Thaw, and resolve itself into a dew! &c.

This *tædium vitæ* is a common oppression on minds cast in the Hamlet mould, and is caused by disproportionate mental exertion, which necessitates exhaustion of bodily feeling. Where there is a just coincidence of external and internal action, pleasure is always the result; but where the former is deficient, and the mind's appetency of the ideal is unchecked, realities will seem cold and unmoving. In such cases, passion combines itself with the indefinite alone. In this mood of his mind the relation of the appearance of his father's spirit in arms is made all at once to Hamlet:—it is—Horatio's speech, in particular—a perfect model of the true style of dramatic narrative;—the purest poetry, and yet in the most natural language, equally remote from the ink-horn and the plough.

Lectures.

Hamlet's character is the prevalence of the abstracting and generalizing habit over the practical. He does not want courage, skill, will, or opportunity; but every

HAMLET 263

incident sets him thinking; and it is curious, and, at the same time strictly natural, that Hamlet, who all the play seems reason itself, should be impelled, at last, by mere accident to effect his object. I have a smack of Hamlet myself, if I may say so.

A maxim is a conclusion upon observation of matters of fact, and is merely retrospective: an Idea, or, if you like, a Principle, carries knowledge within itself, and is prospective. Polonius is a man of maxims. Whilst he is descanting on matters of past experience, as in that excellent speech to Laertes before he sets out on his travels, he is admirable; but when he comes to advise or project, he is a mere dotard. You see, Hamlet, as the man of ideas, despises him.

A man of maxims only is like a Cyclops with one eye, and that eye placed in the back of his head.

Table Talk, June 24, 1827.

Macbeth

Macbeth stands in contrast throughout with *Hamlet*; in the manner of opening more especially. In the latter, there is a gradual ascent from the simplest forms of conversation to the language of impassioned intellect,—yet the intellect still remaining the seat of passion: in the former, the invocation is at once made to the imagination and the emotions connected therewith. Hence the movement throughout is the most rapid of all Shakspeare's plays; and hence also, with the exception of the disgusting passage of the Porter (Act ii. sc. 3.), which I dare pledge myself to demonstrate to be an interpolation of the actors, there is not, to the best of my remembrance, a single pun or play on words in the whole drama. . . .

In *Hamlet* and *Macbeth* the scene opens with superstition;

but, in each it is not merely different, but opposite. In the first it is connected with the best and holiest feelings; in the second with the shadowy, turbulent, and unsanctified cravings of the individual will. Nor is the purpose the same; in the one the object is to excite, whilst in the other it is to mark a mind already excited. Superstition, of one sort or another, is natural to victorious generals; the instances are too notorious to need mentioning. There is so much of chance in warfare, and such vast events are connected with the acts of a single individual,—the representative, in truth, of the efforts of myriads, and yet to the public and, doubtless, to his own feelings, the aggregate of all,—that the proper temperament for generating or receiving superstitious impressions is naturally produced. Hope, the master element of a commanding genius, meeting with an active and combining intellect, and an imagination of just that degree of vividness which disquiets and impels the soul to try to realize its images, greatly increases the creative power of the mind; and hence the images become a satisfying world of themselves, as is the case in every poet and original philosopher:—but hope fully gratified, and yet the elementary basis of the passion remaining, becomes fear; and, indeed, the general, who must often feel, even though he may hide it from his own consciousness, how large a share chance had in his successes, may very naturally be irresolute in a new scene, where he knows that all will depend on his own act and election.

The Weird Sisters are as true a creation of Shakspeare's, as his Ariel and Caliban,—fates, furies, and materializing witches being the elements. They are wholly different from any representation of witches in the contemporary writers, and yet presented a sufficient external resemblance to the creatures of vulgar prejudice

to act immediately on the audience. Their character
consists in the imaginative disconnected from the good;
they are the shadowy obscure and fearfully anomalous
of physical nature, the lawless of human nature,—ele-
mental avengers without sex or kin:

> Fair is foul, and foul is fair;
> Hover thro' the fog and filthy air.

How much it were to be wished in playing Macbeth,
that an attempt should be made to introduce the flexile
character-mask of the ancient pantomime;—that Flax-
man would contribute his genius to the embodying and
making sensuously perceptible that of Shakspeare! . . .

Ib. sc. 5. Macbeth is described by Lady Macbeth so
as at the same time to reveal her own character. Could
he have every thing he wanted, he would rather have it
innocently;—ignorant, as alas! how many of us are,
that he who wishes a temporal end for itself, does in
truth will the means; and hence the danger of indulging
fancies. Lady Macbeth, like all in Shakspeare, is a class
individualized:—of high rank, left much alone, and
feeding herself with day-dreams of ambition, she mistakes the courage of fantasy for the power of bearing
the consequences of the realities of guilt. Hers is the
mock fortitude of a mind deluded by ambition; she
shames her husband with a superhuman audacity of
fancy which she cannot support, but sinks in the season
of remorse, and dies in suicidal agony. Her speech:

> Come, all you spirits
> That tend on mortal thoughts, unsex me here, &c.

is that of one who had habitually familiarized her imagination to dreadful conceptions, and was trying to do so
still more. Her invocations and requisitions are all the
false efforts of a mind accustomed only hitherto to the
shadows of the imagination, vivid enough to throw

the every-day substances of life into shadow, but never
as yet brought into direct contact with their own corre-
spondent realities. She evinces no womanly life, no
wifely joy, at the return of her husband, no pleased
terror at the thought of his past dangers, whilst Macbeth
bursts forth naturally—

> My dearest love—

and shrinks from the boldness with which she presents
his own thoughts to him. With consummate art she at
first uses as incentives the very circumstances, Duncan's
coming to their house, &c. which Macbeth's conscience
would most probably have adduced to her as motives of
abhorrence or repulsion. Yet Macbeth is not prepared:

> We will speak further.

Act II. sc. 3. This low soliloquy of the Porter and his
few speeches afterwards, I believe to have been written
for the mob by some other hand, perhaps with Shakspeare's consent; and that finding it take, he with
the remaining ink of a pen otherwise employed, just
interpolated the words—

> I'll devil-porter it no further: I had thought to have let
> in some of all professions, that go the primrose way to th'
> everlasting bonfire.

Of the rest not one syllable has the ever-present being
of Shakspeare.

Lectures.

Othello

Act I. sc. 1.

> *Rod.* What a full fortune does the *thick-lips* owe,
> If he can carry 't thus.

Roderigo turns off to Othello; and here comes one,
if not the only, seeming justification of our blackamoor

or negro Othello. Even if we supposed this an uninterrupted tradition of the theatre, and that Shakspeare himself, from want of scenes, and the experience that nothing could be made too marked for the senses of his audience, had practically sanctioned it,—would this prove aught concerning his own intention as a poet for all ages? Can we imagine him so utterly ignorant as to make a barbarous negro plead royal birth,—at a time, too, when negroes were not known except as slaves?—As for Iago's language to Brabantio, it implies merely that Othello was a Moor, that is, black. Though I think the rivalry of Roderigo sufficient to account for his wilful confusion of Moor and Negro,—yet, even if compelled to give this up, I should think it only adapted for the acting of the day, and should complain of an enormity built on a single word, in direct contradiction to Iago's 'Barbary horse.' Besides, if we could in good earnest believe Shakspeare ignorant of the distinction, still why should we adopt one disagreeable possibility instead of a ten times greater and more pleasing probability? It is a common error to mistake the epithets applied by the *dramatis personæ* to each other, as truly descriptive of what the audience ought to see or know. No doubt Desdemona saw Othello's visage in his mind; yet, as we are constituted, and most surely as an English audience was disposed in the beginning of the seventeenth century, it would be something monstrous to conceive this beautiful Venetian girl falling in love with a veritable negro. It would argue a disproportionateness, a want of balance, in Desdemona, which Shakspeare does not appear to have in the least contemplated. . . .

Act I. sc. 5. Iago's speech:—

Virtue? a fig! 'tis in ourselves, that we are thus, or thus, &c.

This speech comprises the passionless character of Iago.

It is all will in intellect; and therefore he is here a bold
partizan of a truth, but yet of a truth converted into a
falsehood by the absence of all the necessary modifications caused by the frail nature of man. And then comes
the last sentiment,—

Our raging motions, our carnal stings, our unbitted
lusts, whereof I take this, that you call—love, to be a sect
or scion!

Here is the true Iagoism of, alas! how many! Note
Iago's pride of mastery in the repetition of 'Go, make
money!' to his anticipated dupe, even stronger than his
love of lucre: and when Roderigo is completely won—

I am chang'd. I'll go sell all my land—

when the effect has been fully produced, the repetition
of triumph—

Go to; farewell; put money enough in your purse!

The remainder—Iago's soliloquy—the motive-hunting
of a motiveless malignity—how awful it is! Yea, whilst
he is still allowed to bear the divine image, it is too
fiendish for his own steady view,—for the lonely gaze
of a being next to devil, and only not quite devil,—and
yet a character which Shakspeare has attempted and
executed, without disgust and without scandal! . . .

Finally, let me repeat that Othello does not kill Desdemona in jealousy, but in a conviction forced upon
him by the almost superhuman art of Iago, such a conviction as any man would and must have entertained
who had believed Iago's honesty as Othello did. We,
the audience, know that Iago is a villain from the beginning; but in considering the essence of the Shakspearian Othello, we must perseveringly place ourselves
in his situation, and under his circumstances. Then we

shall immediately feel the fundamental difference between the solemn agony of the noble Moor, and the
wretched fishing jealousies of Leontes, and the morbid
suspiciousness of Leonatus, who is, in other respects, a
fine character. Othello had no life but in Desdemona:—
the belief that she, his angel, had fallen from the heaven
of her native innocence, wrought a civil war in his heart.
She is his counterpart; and, like him, is almost sanctified
in our eyes by her absolute unsuspiciousness, and holy
entireness of love. As the curtain drops, which do we
pity the most?

Lectures.

Othello must not be conceived as a negro, but a high
and chivalrous Moorish chief. Shakspeare learned the
spirit of the character from the Spanish poetry, which
was prevalent in England in his time. Jealousy does not
strike me as the point in his passion; I take it to be rather
an agony that the creature, whom he had believed
angelic, with whom he had garnered up his heart, and
whom he could not help still loving, should be proved
impure and worthless. It was a struggle *not* to love her.
It was a moral indignation and regret that virtue should
so fall:—'But yet the *pity* of it, Iago!—O Iago! the *pity*
of it, Iago!' In addition to this, his honour was concerned: Iago would not have succeeded but by hinting
that his honour was compromised. There is no ferocity
in Othello; his mind is majestic and composed. He
deliberately determines to die; and speaks his last speech
with a view of showing his attachment to the Venetian
State, though it had superseded him.

Table Talk, Dec. 29, 1822.

Lear is the most tremendous effort of Shakspeare as a
poet; *Hamlet* as a philosopher or meditater; and *Othello*

is the union of the two. There is something gigantic
and unformed in the former two; but in the latter,
everything assumes its due place and proportion, and
the whole mature powers of his mind are displayed in
admirable equilibrium.

Id.

I have often told you that I do not think there is any
jealousy, properly so called, in the character of Othello.
There is no predisposition to suspicion, which I take to
be an essential term in the definition of the word. Desdemona very truly told Emilia that he was not jealous,
that is, of a jealous habit, and he says so as truly of himself. Iago's suggestions, you see, are quite new to him;
they do not correspond with anything of a like nature
previously in his mind. If Desdemona had, in fact, been
guilty, no one would have thought of calling Othello's
conduct that of a jealous man. He could not act otherwise than he did with the lights he had; whereas jealousy
can never be strictly right. See how utterly unlike
Othello is to Leontes, in the *Winter's Tale*, or even to
Leonatus, in *Cymbeline*! The jealousy of the first proceeds from an evident trifle, and something like hatred
is mingled with it; and the conduct of Leonatus in
accepting the wager, and exposing his wife to the trial,
denotes a jealous temper already formed.

Id. June 24, 1827.

Shakspeare is the Spinozistic deity—an omnipresent
creativeness. Milton is the deity of prescience; he stands
ab extra, and drives a fiery chariot and four, making the
horses feel the iron curb which holds them in. Shakspeare's poetry is characterless; that is, it does not reflect
the individual Shakspeare; but John Milton himself is
in every line of the *Paradise Lost*. Shakspeare's rhymed

verses are excessively condensed,—epigrams with the point everywhere; but in his blank dramatic verse he is diffused, with a linked sweetness long drawn out. No one can understand Shakspeare's superiority fully until he has ascertained, by comparison, all that which he possessed in common with several other great dramatists of his age, and has then calculated the surplus which is entirely Shakspeare's own. His rhythm is so perfect, that you may be almost sure that you do not understand the real force of a line, if it does not run well as you read it. The necessary mental pause after every hemistich or imperfect line is always equal to the time that would have been taken in reading the complete verse.

Table Talk, May 12, 1830.

Shakspeare is of no age. It is idle to endeavour to support his phrases by quotations from Ben Jonson, Beaumont and Fletcher, &c. His language is entirely his own, and the younger dramatists imitated him. The construction of Shakspeare's sentences, whether in verse or prose, is the necessary and homogeneous vehicle of his peculiar manner of thinking. His is not the style of the age. More particularly, Shakspeare's blank verse is an absolutely new creation. Read Daniel—the admirable Daniel—in his *Civil Wars*, and *Triumphs of Hymen*. The style and language are just such as any very pure and manly writer of the present day—Wordsworth, for example—would use; it seems quite modern in comparison with the style of Shakspeare. Ben Jonson's blank verse is very masterly and individual, and perhaps Massinger's is even still nobler. In Beaumont and Fletcher it is constantly slipping into lyricisms.

I believe Shakspeare was not a whit more intelligible in his own day than he is now to an educated man, except for a few local allusions of no consequence. As

I said, he is of no age—nor, I may add, of any religion, or party, or profession. The body and substance of his works came out of the unfathomable depths of his own oceanic mind: his observation and reading, which was considerable, supplied him with the drapery of his figures.

Table Talk, March 15, 1834.

WILLIAM HAZLITT

Macbeth

MACBETH and *Lear*, *Othello* and *Hamlet*, are usually
reckoned Shakespear's four principal tragedies. *Lear*
stands first for the profound intensity of the passion;
Macbeth for the wildness of the imagination and the
rapidity of the action; *Othello* for the progressive interest and powerful alternations of feeling; *Hamlet* for
the refined developement of thought and sentiment.
If the force of genius shown in each of these works is
astonishing, their variety is not less so. They are like
different creations of the same mind, not one of which
has the slightest reference to the rest. This distinctness
and originality is indeed the necessary consequence of
truth and nature. Shakespear's genius alone appeared to
possess the resources of nature. He is 'your only *tragedy-
maker*. His plays have the force of things upon the mind.
What he represents is brought home to the bosom as a
part of our experience, implanted in the memory as if
we had known the places, persons, and things of which
he treats. MACBETH is like a record of a preternatural
and tragical event. It has the rugged severity of an old
chronicle with all that the imagination of the poet can
engraft upon traditional belief. The castle of Macbeth,
round which 'the air smells wooingly,' and where 'the
temple-haunting martlet builds,' has a real subsistence
in the mind; the Weird Sisters meet us in person on 'the
blasted heath;' the 'air-drawn dagger' moves slowly before our eyes; the 'gracious Duncan,' the 'blood-boltered
Banquo' stand before us; all that passed through the
mind of Macbeth passes, without the loss of a tittle,
through ours. All that could actually take place, and all

that is only possible to be conceived, what was said and what was done, the workings of passion, the spells of magic, are brought before us with the same absolute truth and vividness.—Shakespear excelled in the openings of his plays: that of MACBETH is the most striking of any. The wildness of the scenery, the sudden shifting of the situations and characters, the bustle, the expectations excited, are equally extraordinary. From the first entrance of the Witches and the description of them when they meet Macbeth,

> ——————What are these
> So wither'd and so wild in their attire,
> That look not like the inhabitants of th' earth
> And yet are on't?

the mind is prepared for all that follows.

This tragedy is alike distinguished for the lofty imagination it displays, and for the tumultuous vehemence of the action; and the one is made the moving principle of the other. The overwhelming pressure of preternatural agency urges on the tide of human passion with redoubled force. Macbeth himself appears driven along by the violence of his fate like a vessel drifting before a storm: he reels to and fro like a drunken man; he staggers under the weight of his own purposes and the suggestions of others; he stands at bay with his situation; and from the superstitious awe and breathless suspense into which the communications of the Weird Sisters throw him, is hurried on with daring impatience to verify their predictions, and with impious and bloody hand to tear aside the veil which hides the uncertainty of the future. He is not equal to the struggle with fate and conscience. He now 'bends up each corporal instrument to the terrible feat;' at other times his heart misgives him, and he is cowed and abashed by his success. 'The deed, no less

than the attempt, confounds him.' His mind is assailed
by the stings of remorse, and full of 'preternatural solicit-
ings.' His speeches and soliloquies are dark riddles on
human life, baffling solution, and entangling him in their
labyrinths. In thought he is absent and perplexed, sudden and desperate in act, from a distrust of his own
resolution. His energy springs from the anxiety and
agitation of his mind. His blindly rushing forward on
the objects of his ambition and revenge, or his recoiling
from them, equally betrays the harassed state of his feelings.—This part of his character is admirably set off by
being brought in connection with that of Lady Macbeth,
whose obdurate strength of will and masculine firmness
give her the ascendancy over her husband's faultering
virtue. She at once seizes on the opportunity that offers
for the accomplishment of all their wished-for greatness,
and never flinches from her object till all is over. The
magnitude of her resolution almost covers the magnitude of her guilt. She is a great bad woman, whom we
hate, but whom we fear more than we hate. She does
not excite our loathing and abhorrence like Regan and
Goneril. She is only wicked to gain a great end; and is
perhaps more distinguished by her commanding presence of mind and inexorable self-will, which do not
suffer her to be diverted from a bad purpose, when once
formed, by weak and womanly regrets, than by the
hardness of her heart or want of natural affections. The
impression which her lofty determination of character
makes on the mind of Macbeth is well described where
he exclaims,

——————Bring forth men children only;
For thy undaunted mettle should compose
Nothing but males!

Nor do the pains she is at to 'screw his courage to the

sticking-place,' the reproach to him, not to be 'lost so
poorly in himself,' the assurance that 'a little water clears
them of this deed,' show anything but her greater consistency in depravity. Her strong-nerved ambition
furnishes ribs of steel to 'the sides of his intent;' and she
is herself wound up to the execution of her baneful project with the same unshrinking fortitude in crime, that
in other circumstances she would probably have shewn
patience in suffering. The deliberate sacrifice of all other
considerations to the gaining 'for their future days and
nights sole sovereign sway and masterdom,' by the
murder of Duncan, is gorgeously expressed in her invocation on hearing of 'his fatal entrance under her
battlements:'—

> ————————Come all you spirits
> That tend on mortal thoughts, unsex me here:
> And fill me, from the crown to th' toe, top-full
> Of direst cruelty; make thick my blood,
> Stop up the access and passage to remorse,
> That no compunctious visitings of nature
> Shake my fell purpose, nor keep peace between
> The effect and it. Come to my woman's breasts,
> And take my milk for gall, you murthering ministers,
> Wherever in your sightless substances
> You wait on nature's mischief. Come, thick night!
> And pall thee in the dunnest smoke of hell,
> That my keen knife see not the wound it makes,
> Nor heav'n peep through the blanket of the dark,
> To cry, hold, hold!—

When she first hears that 'Duncan comes there to sleep,'
she is so overcome by the news, which is beyond her
utmost expectations, that she answers the messenger,
'Thou'rt mad to say it:' and on receiving her husband's
account of the predictions of the Witches, conscious of
his instability of purpose, and that her presence is neces-

ɔary to goad him on to the consummation of his promised
greatness, she exclaims—

> ————Hie thee hither,
> That I may pour my spirits in thine ear,
> And chastise with the valour of my tongue
> All that impedes thee from the golden round,
> Which fate and metaphysical aid doth seem
> To have thee crowned withal.

This swelling exultation and keen spirit of triumph, this
uncontroulable eagerness of anticipation, which seems
to dilate her form and take possession of all her faculties,
this solid, substantial flesh and blood display of passion,
exhibit a striking contrast to the cold, abstracted, gratu-
itous, servile malignity of the Witches, who are equally
instrumental in urging Macbeth to his fate for the mere
love of mischief, and from a disinterested delight in deformity and cruelty. They are hags of mischief, obscene
panders to iniquity, malicious from their impotence of
enjoyment, enamoured of destruction, because they are
themselves unreal, abortive, half-existences—who become sublime from their exemption from all human
sympathies and contempt for all human affairs, as Lady
Macbeth does by the force of passion! Her fault seems
to have been an excess of that strong principle of self-
interest and family aggrandisement, not amenable to
the common feelings of compassion and justice, which
is so marked a feature in barbarous nations and times.
A passing reflection of this kind, on the resemblance of
the sleeping king to her father, alone prevents her from
slaying Duncan with her own hand. . . .

MACBETH (generally speaking) is done upon a stronger
and more systematic principle of contrast than any other
of Shakespear's plays. It moves upon the verge of an
abyss, and is a constant struggle between life and death.
The action is desperate and the reaction is dreadful.

It is a huddling together of fierce extremes, a war of opposite natures which of them shall destroy the other. There is nothing but what has a violent end or violent beginnings. The lights and shades are laid on with a determined hand; the transitions from triumph to despair, from the height of terror to the repose of death, are sudden and startling; every passion brings in its fellow-contrary, and the thoughts pitch and jostle against each other as in the dark. The whole play is an unruly chaos of strange and forbidden things, where the ground rocks under our feet. Shakespear's genius here took its full swing, and trod upon the farthest bounds of nature and passion. This circumstance will account for the abruptness and violent antitheses of the style, the throes and labour which run through the expression, and from defects will turn them into beauties. 'So fair and foul a day I have not seen,' &c. 'Such welcome and unwelcome news together.' 'Men's lives are like the flowers in their caps, dying or ere they sicken.' 'Look like the innocent flower, but be the serpent under it.' The scene before the castle-gate follows the appearance of the Witches on the heath, and is followed by a midnight murder. Duncan is cut off betimes by treason leagued with witchcraft, and Macduff is ripped untimely from his mother's womb to avenge his death. Macbeth, after the death of Banquo, wishes for his presence in extravagant terms, 'To him and all we thirst,' and when his ghost appears, cries out, 'Avaunt and quit my sight,' and being gone, he is 'himself again.' Macbeth resolves to get rid of Macduff, that 'he may sleep in spite of thunder;' and cheers his wife on the doubtful intelligence of Banquo's taking-off with the encouragement—'Then be thou jocund: ere the bat has flown his cloistered flight; ere to black Hecate's summons the shard-born beetle has rung night's yawning peal, there shall be done—a deed of dreadful note.' In Lady Macbeth's speech 'Had he not resembled my father as he slept, I had done't,' there is murder and filial piety together; and in urging him to fulfil his vengeance against the defenceless king, her thoughts spare the blood neither of infants nor old age. The description of the Witches is full of the same contradictory principle; they 'rejoice when good kings bleed,' they are neither of the earth nor the air, but both; 'they should be women, but their beards forbid it;' they take all the pains possible to lead Macbeth on to the height of his ambition, only to betray him 'in deeper consequence,' and after showing him all the pomp of their art, discover their malignant delight in his disappointed hopes, by that bitter taunt, 'Why stands Macbeth thus amazedly?' We might multiply such instances everywhere.

The leading features in the character of Macbeth are striking enough, and they form what may be thought at first only a bold, rude, Gothic outline. By comparing it with other characters of the same author we shall perceive the absolute truth and identity which is observed in the midst of the giddy whirl and rapid career of events. Macbeth in Shakespear no more loses his identity of character in the fluctuations of fortune or the storm of passion, than Macbeth in himself would have lost the identity of his person. Thus he is as distinct a being from Richard III as it is possible to imagine, though these two characters in common hands, and indeed in the hands of any other poet, would have been a repetition of the same general idea, more or less exaggerated. For both are tyrants, usurpers, murderers, both aspiring and ambitious, both courageous, cruel, treacherous. But Richard is cruel from nature and constitution. Macbeth becomes so from accidental circumstances. Richard is from his birth deformed in body and mind, and naturally incapable of good. Macbeth is full of 'the milk of human kindness,' is frank, sociable, generous. He is tempted to the commission of guilt by golden opportunities, by the instigations of his wife, and by prophetic warnings. Fate and metaphysical aid conspire against his virtue and his loyalty. Richard on the contrary needs no prompter, but wades through a series of crimes to the height of his ambition from the ungovernable violence of his temper and a reckless love of mischief. He is never gay but in the prospect or in the success of his villainies: Macbeth is full of horror at the thoughts of the murder of Duncan, which he is with difficulty prevailed on to commit, and of remorse after its perpetration. Richard has no mixture of common humanity in his composition, no regard to kindred or posterity, he owns no fellowship with others, he is 'himself alone.' Macbeth is not destitute of feelings of sympathy, is accessible to pity, is even made in some measure the dupe of his uxoriousness, ranks the loss of friends, of the cordial love of his followers, and of his good name, among the causes which have made him weary of life, and regrets that he has ever seized the crown by unjust means, since he cannot transmit it to his posterity—

> For Banquo's issue have I fil'd my mind—
> For them the gracious Duncan have I murther'd
> To make them kings, the seed of Banquo kings.

In the agitation of his mind, he envies those whom he has sent to peace. 'Duncan is in his grave; after life's fitful fever he sleeps well.' It is true, he becomes more callous as he plunges deeper in guilt, 'direness is thus rendered familiar to his slaughterous thoughts'—and he in the end anticipates his wife in the boldness and bloodiness of his enterprises, while she for want of the same stimulus of action, 'is troubled with thick-coming fancies

that rob her of her rest,' goes mad and dies. Macbeth
endeavours to escape from reflection on his crimes by
repelling their consequences, and banishes remorse for
the past by the meditation of future mischief. This is
not the principle of Richard's cruelty, which displays
the wanton malice of a fiend as much as the frailty of
human passion. Macbeth is goaded on to acts of violence and retaliation by necessity; to Richard, blood is a
pastime.—There are other decisive differences inherent
in the two characters. Richard may be regarded as a
man of the world, a plotting, hardened knave, wholly
regardless of everything but his own ends, and the means
to secure them.—Not so Macbeth. The superstitions of
the age, the rude state of society, the local scenery and
customs, all give a wildness and imaginary grandeur to
his character. From the strangeness of the events that
surround him, he is full of amazement and fear; and
stands in doubt between the world of reality and the
world of fancy. He sees sights not shewn to mortal eye,
and hears unearthly music. All is tumult and disorder
within and without his mind; his purposes recoil upon
himself, are broken and disjointed; he is the double thrall
of his passions and his evil destiny. Richard is not a character either of imagination or pathos, but of pure self-
will. There is no conflict of opposite feelings in his
breast. The apparitions which he sees only haunt him in
his sleep; nor does he live like Macbeth in a waking
dream. Macbeth has considerable energy and manliness
of character; but then he is 'subject to all the skyey influences.' He is sure of nothing but the present moment.
Richard in the busy turbulence of his projects never loses
his self-possession, and makes use of every circumstance
that happens as an instrument of his long-reaching designs. In his last extremity we can only regard him as a
wild beast taken in the toils: while we never entirely lose

our concern for Macbeth; and he calls back all our sympathy by that fine close of thoughtful melancholy,

My way of life is fallen into the sear,
The yellow leaf; and that which should accompany old age,
As honour, troops of friends, I must not look to have;
But in their stead, curses not loud but deep,
Mouth-honour, breath, which the poor heart
Would fain deny, and dare not.

From Characters of Shakespear's Plays, 1817.[1]

Othello

IT has been said that tragedy purifies the affections by terror and pity. That is, it substitutes imaginary sympathy for mere selfishness. It gives us a high and permanent interest, beyond ourselves, in humanity as such. It raises the great, the remote, and the possible to an equality with the real, the little and the near. It makes man a partaker with his kind. It subdues and softens the stubbornness of his will. It teaches him that there are and have been others like himself, by shewing him as in a glass what they have felt, thought and done. It opens the chambers of the human heart. It leaves nothing indifferent to us that can affect our common nature. It excites our sensibility by exhibiting the passions wound up to the utmost pitch by the power of imagination or the temptation of circumstances; and corrects their fatal excesses in ourselves by pointing to the greater extent of sufferings and of crimes to which

---

[1] Hazlitt knew Whately's comparison of Macbeth and Richard III, which he considered 'an exceedingly ingenious piece of analytical criticism' (Preface to *Characters of Shakespear's Plays*). But he attributed it to 'a gentleman of the name of Mason,' confounding Whately's *Observations on Modern Gardening*, 1770, with George Mason's *Essay on Design in Gardening*, 1768.

they have led others. Tragedy creates a balance of the affections. It makes us thoughtful spectators in the lists of life. It is the refiner of the species; a discipline of humanity. The habitual study of poetry and works of imagination is one chief part of a well-grounded education. A taste for liberal art is necessary to complete the character of a gentleman. Science alone is hard and mechanical. It exercises the understanding upon things out of ourselves, while it leaves the affections unemployed, or engrossed with our own immediate, narrow interests.—OTHELLO furnishes an illustration of these remarks. It excites our sympathy in an extraordinary degree. The moral it conveys has a closer application to the concerns of human life than that of almost any other of Shakespear's plays. 'It comes directly home to the bosoms and business of men.' The pathos in *Lear* is indeed more dreadful and overpowering; but it is less natural, and less of every day's occurrence. We have not the same degree of sympathy with the passions described in *Macbeth*. The interest in *Hamlet* is more remote and reflex. That of OTHELLO is at once equally profound and affecting.

The picturesque contrasts of character in this play are almost as remarkable as the depth of the passion. The Moor Othello, the gentle Desdemona, the villain Iago, the good-natured Cassio, the fool Roderigo, present a range and variety of character as striking and palpable as that produced by the opposition of costume in a picture. Their distinguishing qualities stand out to the mind's eye, so that even when we are not thinking of their actions or sentiments, the idea of their persons is still as present to us as ever. These characters and the images they stamp upon the mind are the farthest asunder possible, the distance between them is immense: yet the compass of knowledge and invention which the poet has shown in embodying these extreme creations of his genius is only greater than the truth and felicity with which he has identified each character with itself, or blended their different qualities together in the same story. What a contrast the character of Othello forms to that of Iago! At the same time, the force of conception with which these two figures are opposed to each other is rendered still more intense by the complete consistency with which the traits of each character are brought out in a state of the highest finishing. The making one black and the other white, the one unprincipled, the other unfortunate in the extreme, would have answered the common purposes of effect, and satisfied the ambition of an ordinary painter of character. Shakespear has laboured the finer shades of difference in both with as much care and skill as if he had had to depend on the execution alone for the success of his design. On the other hand, Desdemona and Æmilia are not meant to be opposed with any thing like strong contrast to each other. Both are, to outward appearance, characters of common life, not more distinguished than women usually are, by difference of rank and situation. The difference of their thoughts and sentiments is however laid open, their minds are separated from each other by signs as plain and as little to be mistaken as the complexions of their husbands.

The movement of the passion in Othello is exceedingly different from that of Macbeth. In Macbeth there is a violent struggle between opposite feelings, between ambition and the stings of conscience, almost from first to last: in Othello, the doubtful conflict between contrary passions, though dreadful, continues only for a short time, and the chief interest is excited by the alternate ascendancy of different passions, by the entire and unforeseen change from the fondest love and most

unbounded confidence to the tortures of jealousy and the
madness of hatred. The revenge of Othello, after it has
once taken thorough possession of his mind, never quits
it, but grows stronger and stronger at every moment of
its delay. The nature of the Moor is noble, confiding,
tender, and generous; but his blood is of the most in-
flammable kind; and being once roused by a sense of his
wrongs, he is stopped by no considerations of remorse
or pity till he has given a loose to all the dictates of his
rage and his despair. It is in working his noble nature
up to this extremity through rapid but gradual transitions, in raising passion to its height from the smallest
beginnings and in spite of all obstacles, in painting the
expiring conflict between love and hatred, tenderness
and resentment, jealousy and remorse, in unfolding the
strength and the weakness of our nature, in uniting sublimity of thought with the anguish of the keenest woe,
in putting in motion the various impulses that agitate
this our mortal being, and at last blending them in that
noble tide of deep and sustained passion, impetuous but
majestic, that 'flows on to the Propontic, and knows no
ebb,' that Shakespear has shown the mastery of his
genius and of his power over the human heart. The
third act of OTHELLO is his finest display, not of knowledge or passion separately, but of the two combined, of
the knowledge of character with the expression of passion, of consummate art in the keeping up of appearances with the profound workings of nature, and the
convulsive movements of uncontroulable agony, of the
power of inflicting torture and of suffering it. Not only
is the tumult of passion in Othello's mind heaved up
from the very bottom of the soul, but every the slightest
undulation of feeling is seen on the surface, as it arises
from the impulses of imagination or the malicious suggestions of Iago. . . .

The character of Iago is one of the supererogations
of Shakespear's genius. Some persons, more nice than
wise, have thought this whole character unnatural, because his villainy is *without a sufficient motive*. Shakespear,
who was as good a philosopher as he was a poet, thought
otherwise. He knew that the love of power, which is
another name for the love of mischief, is natural to man.
He would know this as well or better than if it had been
demonstrated to him by a logical diagram, merely from
seeing children paddle in the dirt or kill flies for sport.
Iago in fact belongs to a class of character, common to
Shakespear and at the same time peculiar to him; whose
heads are as acute and active as their hearts are hard and
callous. Iago is to be sure an extreme instance of the
kind; that is to say, of diseased intellectual activity, with
the most perfect indifference to moral good or evil, or
rather with a decided preference of the latter, because it
falls more readily in with his favourite propensity, gives
greater zest to his thoughts and scope to his actions. He
is quite or nearly as indifferent to his own fate as to that
of others; he runs all risks for a trifling and doubtful
advantage; and is himself the dupe and victim of his
ruling passion—an insatiable craving after action of the
most difficult and dangerous kind. 'Our ancient' is a
philosopher, who fancies that a lie that kills has more
point in it than an alliteration or an antithesis; who thinks
a fatal experiment on the peace of a family a better thing
than watching the palpitations in the heart of a flea in a
microscope; who plots the ruin of his friends as an
exercise for his ingenuity, and stabs men in the dark to
prevent *ennui*. His gaiety, such as it is, arises from the
success of his treachery; his ease from the torture he has
inflicted on others. He is an amateur of tragedy in real
life; and instead of employing his invention on imaginary characters, or long-forgotten incidents, he takes the

bolder and more desperate course of getting up his plot at home, casts the principal parts among his nearest friends and connections, and rehearses it in downright earnest, with steady nerves and unabated resolution.

Id.

Hamlet

THIS is that Hamlet the Dane, whom we read of in our youth, and whom we may be said almost to remember in our after-years; he who made that famous soliloquy on life, who gave the advice to the players, who thought 'this goodly frame, the earth, a steril promontory, and this brave o'er-hanging firmament, the air, this majestical roof fretted with golden fire, a foul and pestilent congregation of vapours;' whom 'man delighted not, nor woman neither;' he who talked with the grave-diggers, and moralised on Yorick's skull; the school-fellow of Rosencrantz and Guildenstern at Wittenberg; the friend of Horatio; the lover of Ophelia; he that was mad and sent to England; the slow avenger of his father's death; who lived at the court of Horwendillus five hundred years before we were born, but all whose thoughts we seem to know as well as we do our own, because we have read them in Shakespear.

Hamlet is a name; his speeches and sayings but the idle coinage of the poet's brain. What then, are they not real? They are as real as our own thoughts. Their reality is in the reader's mind. It is *we* who are Hamlet. This play has a prophetic truth, which is above that of history. Whoever has become thoughtful and melancholy through his own mishaps or those of others; whoever has borne about with him the clouded brow of reflection, and thought himself 'too much i' th' sun;' whoever has seen the golden lamp of day dimmed by envious mists rising in his own breast, and could find in the world before him only a dull blank with nothing left remarkable in it; whoever has known 'the pangs of despised love, the insolence of office, or the spurns which patient merit of the unworthy takes;' he who has felt his mind sink within him, and sadness cling to his heart like a malady, who has had his hopes blighted and his youth staggered by the apparitions of strange things; who cannot be well at ease, while he sees evil hovering near him like a spectre; whose powers of action have been eaten up by thought, he to whom the universe seems infinite, and himself nothing; whose bitterness of soul makes him careless of consequences, and who goes to a play as his best resource to shove off, to a second remove, the evils of life by a mock representation of them—this is the true Hamlet.

We have been so used to this tragedy that we hardly know how to criticise it any more than we should know how to describe our own faces. But we must make such observations as we can. It is the one of Shakespear's plays that we think of the oftenest, because it abounds most in striking reflections on human life, and because the distresses of Hamlet are transferred, by the turn of his mind, to the general account of humanity. Whatever happens to him we apply to ourselves, because he applies it so himself as a means of general reasoning. He is a great moraliser; and what makes him worth attending to is, that he moralises on his own feelings and experience. He is not a common-place pedant. If *Lear* is distinguished by the greatest depth of passion, HAMLET is the most remarkable for the ingenuity, originality, and unstudied development of character. Shakespear had more magnanimity than any other poet, and he has shown more of it in this play than in any other. There is no attempt to force an interest: every thing is left for time and circumstances to unfold. The attention is

excited without effort, the incidents succeed each other
as matters of course, the characters think and speak and
act just as they might do, if left entirely to themselves.
There is no set purpose, no straining at a point. The
observations are suggested by the passing scene—the
gusts of passion come and go like sounds of music borne
on the wind. The whole play is an exact transcript of
what might be supposed to have taken place at the court
of Denmark, at the remote period of time fixed upon,
before the modern refinements in morals and manners
were heard of. It would have been interesting enough
to have been admitted as a bystander in such a scene, at
such a time, to have heard and witnessed something of
what was going on. But here we are more than spectators. We have not only 'the outward pageants and the
signs of grief;' but 'we have that within which passes
shew.' We read the thoughts of the heart, we catch the
passions living as they rise. Other dramatic writers give
us very fine versions and paraphrases of nature; but
Shakespear, together with his own comments, gives us
the original text, that we may judge for ourselves. This
is a very great advantage.

The character of Hamlet stands quite by itself. It is
not a character marked by strength of will or even of
passion, but by refinement of thought and sentiment.
Hamlet is as little of the hero as a man can well be: but
he is a young and princely novice, full of high enthusiasm
and quick sensibility—the sport of circumstances, ques-
tioning with fortune and refining on his own feelings,
and forced from the natural bias of his disposition by
the strangeness of his situation. He seems incapable of
deliberate action, and is only hurried into extremities
on the spur of the occasion, when he has no time to
reflect, as in the scene where he kills Polonius, and
again, where he alters the letters which Rosencrantz and

Guildenstern are taking with them to England, purporting
his death. At other times, when he is most bound to act,
he remains puzzled, undecided, and sceptical, dallies with
his purposes, till the occasion is lost, and finds out some
pretence to relapse into indolence and thoughtfulness
again. For this reason he refuses to kill the King when
he is at his prayers, and by a refinement in malice, which
is in truth only an excuse for his own want of resolution,
defers his revenge to a more fatal opportunity, when he
shall be engaged in some act 'that has no relish of salva-
tion in it.'

> He kneels and prays,
> And now I'll do't, and so he goes to heaven,
> And so am I reveng'd: *that would be scann'd.*
> He kill'd my father, and for that,
> I, his sole son, send him to heaven.
> Why, this is reward, not revenge.
> Up sword and know thou a more horrid time,
> When he is drunk, asleep, or in a rage.

He is the prince of philosophical speculators; and because he cannot have his revenge perfect, according to
the most refined idea his wish can form, he declines it
altogether. So he scruples to trust the suggestions of
the ghost, contrives the scene of the play to have surer
proof of his uncle's guilt, and then rests satisfied with
this confirmation of his suspicions, and the success of his
experiment, instead of acting upon it. Yet he is sensible
of his own weakness, taxes himself with it, and tries to
reason himself out of it. . . .

Still he does nothing; and this very speculation on his
own infirmity only affords him another occasion for
indulging it. It is not from any want of attachment to
his father or of abhorrence of his murder that Hamlet is
thus dilatory, but it is more to his taste to indulge his
imagination in reflecting upon the enormity of the

crime and refining on his schemes of vengeance, than to put them into immediate practice. His ruling passion is to think, not to act: and any vague pretext that flatters this propensity instantly diverts him from his previous purposes. . . .

We do not like to see our author's plays acted, and least of all, HAMLET. There is no play that suffers so much in being transferred to the stage. Hamlet himself seems hardly capable of being acted. Mr. Kemble unavoidably fails in this character from a want of ease and variety. The character of Hamlet is made up of undulating lines; it has the yielding flexibility of 'a wave o' th' sea.' Mr. Kemble plays it like a man in armour, with a determined inveteracy of purpose, in one undeviating straight line, which is as remote from the natural grace and refined susceptibility of the character, as the sharp angles and abrupt starts which Mr. Kean introduces into the part. Mr. Kean's Hamlet is as much too splenetic and rash as Mr. Kemble's is too deliberate and formal. His manner is too strong and pointed. He throws a severity, approaching to virulence, into the common observations and answers. There is nothing of this in Hamlet. He is, as it were, wrapped up in his reflections, and only *thinks aloud*. There should therefore be no attempt to impress what he says upon others by a studied exaggeration of emphasis or manner; no *talking at* his hearers. There should be as much of the gentleman and scholar as possible infused into the part, and as little of the actor. A pensive air of sadness should sit reluctantly upon his brow, but no appearance of fixed and sullen gloom. He is full of weakness and melancholy, but there is no harshness in his nature. He is the most amiable of misanthropes.

Id.

Lear

WE wish that we could pass this play over, and say nothing about it. All that we can say must fall far short of
the subject; or even of what we ourselves conceive of it.
To attempt to give a description of the play itself or of
its effect upon the mind, is mere impertinence: yet we
must say something.—It is then the best of all Shakespear's plays, for it is the one in which he was the most
in earnest. He was here fairly caught in the web of his
own imagination. The passion which he has taken as
his subject is that which strikes its root deepest into the
human heart; of which the bond is the hardest to be
unloosed; and the cancelling and tearing to pieces of
which gives the greatest revulsion to the frame. This
depth of nature, this force of passion, this tug and war
of the elements of our being, this firm faith in filial piety,
and the giddy anarchy and whirling tumult of the
thoughts at finding this prop failing it, the contrast between the fixed, immoveable basis of natural affection,
and the rapid, irregular starts of imagination, suddenly
wrenched from all its accustomed holds and resting-
places in the soul, this is what Shakespear has given, and
what nobody else but he could give. So we believe.—
The mind of Lear, staggering between the weight of
attachment and the hurried movements of passion, is
like a tall ship driven about by the winds, buffetted by
the furious waves, but that still rides above the storm,
having its anchor fixed in the bottom of the sea; or it is
like the sharp rock circled by the eddying whirlpool
that foams and beats against it, or like the solid promontory pushed from its basis by the force of an earthquake. . . .

It has been said, and we think justly, that the third act
of *Othello* and the first three acts of LEAR are Shakespear's

great masterpieces in the logic of passion: that they contain the highest examples not only of the force of individual passion, but of its dramatic vicissitudes and striking effects arising from the different circumstances and characters of the persons speaking. We see the ebb and flow of the feeling, its pauses and feverish starts, its impatience of opposition, its accumulating force when it has time to recollect itself, the manner in which it avails itself of every passing word or gesture, its haste to repel insinuation, the alternate contraction and dilatation of the soul, and all 'the dazzling fence of controversy' in this mortal combat with poisoned weapons, aimed at the heart, where each wound is fatal. We have seen in *Othello*, how the unsuspecting frankness and impetuous passions of the Moor are played upon and exasperated by the artful dexterity of Iago. In the present play, that which aggravates the sense of sympathy in the reader, and of uncontroulable anguish in the swoln heart of Lear, is the petrifying indifference, the cold, calculating, obdurate selfishness of his daughters. His keen passions seem whetted on their stony hearts. The contrast would be too painful, the shock too great, but for the intervention of the Fool, whose well-timed levity comes in to break the continuity of feeling when it can no longer be borne, and to bring into play again the fibres of the heart just as they are growing rigid from over-strained excitement. The imagination is glad to take refuge in the half-comic, half-serious comments of the Fool, just as the mind under the extreme anguish of a surgical operation vents itself in sallies of wit. The character was also a grotesque ornament of the barbarous times, in which alone the tragic ground-work of the story could be laid. In another point of view it is indispensable, inasmuch as while it is a diversion to the too great intensity of our disgust, it carries the pathos to the highest pitch of which it is capable, by showing the pitiable weakness of the old king's conduct and its irretrievable consequences in the most familiar point of view. Lear may well 'beat at the gate which let his folly in,' after, as the Fool says, 'he has made his daughters his mothers.' The character is dropped in the third act to make room for the entrance of Edgar as Mad Tom, which well accords with the increasing bustle and wildness of the incidents; and nothing can be more complete than the distinction between Lear's real and Edgar's assumed madness, while the resemblance in the cause of their distresses, from the severing of the nearest ties of natural affection, keeps up a unity of interest. Shakespear's mastery over his subject, if it was not art, was owing to a knowledge of the connecting links of the passions, and their effect upon the mind, still more wonderful than any systematic adherence to rules, and that antici-pated and outdid all the efforts of the most refined art, not inspired and rendered instinctive by genius.

Id.

Falstaff

IF Shakespear's fondness for the ludicrous sometimes led to faults in his tragedies (which was not often the case) he has made us amends by the character of Falstaff. This is perhaps the most substantial comic character that ever was invented. Sir John carries a most portly presence in the mind's eye; and in him, not to speak it profanely, 'we behold the fulness of the spirit of wit and humour bodily.' We are as well acquainted with his person as his mind, and his jokes come upon us with double force and relish from the quantity of flesh through which they make their way, as he shakes his fat sides with laughter, or 'lards the lean earth as he walks along.' Other comic characters seem, if we approach and handle them, to resolve themselves into air, 'into thin air;' but this is embodied and palpable to the grossest apprehension: it lies 'three fingers deep upon the ribs,' it plays about the lungs and diaphragm with all the force of animal enjoyment. His body is like a good estate to his mind, from which he receives rents and revenues of profit and pleasure in kind, according to its extent, and the richness of the soil. Wit is often a meagre substitute for pleasurable sensation; an effusion of spleen and petty spite at the comforts of others, from feeling none in itself. Falstaff's wit is an emanation of a fine constitution; an exuberance of good-humour and good-nature; an overflowing of his love of laughter and good-fellowship; a giving vent to his heart's ease, and over-contentment with himself and others. He would not be in character, if he were not so fat as he is; for there is the greatest keeping in the boundless luxury of his imagination and the pampered self-indulgence of his physical appetites. He manures and nourishes his mind with jests, as he does his body with sack and sugar. He carves out his jokes, as he would a capon or a haunch of venison, where there is *cut and come again;* and pours out upon them the oil of gladness. His tongue drops fatness, and in the chambers of his brain 'it snows of meat and drink.' He keeps up perpetual holiday and open house, and we live with him in a round of invitations to a rump and dozen. —Yet we are not to suppose that he was a mere sensualist. All this is as much in imagination as in reality. His sensuality does not engross and stupify his other faculties, but 'ascends me into the brain, clears away all the dull, crude vapours that environ it, and makes it full of nimble, fiery, and delectable shapes.' His imagination keeps up the ball after his senses have done with it. He seems to have even a greater enjoyment of the freedom from restraint, of good cheer, of his ease, of his vanity, in the ideal exaggerated description which he gives of them, than in fact. He never fails to enrich his discourse with allusions to eating and drinking, but we never see him at table. He carries his own larder about with him, and he is himself ' a tun of man.' His pulling out the bottle in the field of battle is a joke to show his contempt for glory accompanied with danger, his systematic adherence to his Epicurean philosophy in the most trying circumstances. Again, such is his deliberate exaggeration of his own vices, that it does not seem quite certain whether the account of his hostess's bill, found in his pocket, with such an out-of-the-way charge for capons and sack with only one halfpenny-worth of bread, was not put there by himself as a trick to humour the jest upon his favourite propensities, and as a conscious caricature of himself. He is represented as a liar, a braggart, a coward, a glutton, &c., and yet we are not offended but delighted with him; for he is all these as much to amuse others as to gratify himself. He openly assumes all these characters to shew the humourous part of them. The unrestrained indulgence of his own ease, appetites, and conveniences, has neither malice nor hypocrisy in it. In a word, he is an actor in himself almost as much as upon the stage, and we no more object to the character of Falstaff in a moral point of view than we should think of bringing an excellent comedian, who should represent him to the life, before one of the police offices. We only consider the number of pleasant lights in which he puts certain foibles (the more pleasant as they are opposed to the received rules and necessary restraints of society) and do not trouble ourselves about the consequences resulting from them, for no mischievous consequences do result. Sir John is old as well as fat, which gives a melancholy retrospective tinge to the character; and by the disparity between his inclinations and his capacity for enjoyment, makes it still more ludicrous and fantastical.

The secret of Falstaff's wit is for the most part a masterly presence of mind, an absolute self-possession, which nothing can disturb. His repartees are involuntary suggestions of his self-love; instinctive evasions of everything that threatens to interrupt the career of his triumphant jollity and self-complacency. His very size floats him out of all his difficulties in a sea of rich conceits; and he turns round on the pivot of his convenience, with every occasion and at a moment's warning. His natural repugnance to every unpleasant thought or circumstance, of itself makes light of objections, and provokes the most extravagant and licentious answers in his own justification. His indifference to truth puts no check upon his invention, and the more improbable and unexpected his contrivances are, the more happily does he seem to be delivered of them, the anticipation of their effect acting as a stimulus to the gaiety of his fancy. The success of one adventurous sally gives him spirits to undertake another: he deals always in round numbers, and his exaggerations and excuses are 'open, palpable, monstrous as the father that begets them.'

Id.

Midsummer Night's Dream

PUCK, or Robin Goodfellow, is the leader of the fairy band. He is the Ariel of the MIDSUMMER NIGHT'S DREAM; and yet as unlike as can be to the Ariel in the *Tempest*. No other poet could have made two such different characters out of the same fanciful materials and situations. Ariel is a minister of retribution, who is touched with the sense of pity at the woes he inflicts. Puck is a madcap sprite, full of wantonness and mischief, who laughs at those whom he misleads—'Lord, what fools these mortals be!' Ariel cleaves the air, and executes his mission with the zeal of a winged messenger; Puck is borne along on his fairy errand like the light and glittering gossamer before the breeze. He is, indeed, a most Epicurean little gentleman, dealing in quaint devices, and faring in dainty delights. Prospero and his world of spirits are a set of moralists: but with Oberon and his fairies we are launched at once into the empire of the butterflies. How beautifully is this race of beings contrasted with the men and women actors in the scene, by a single epithet which Titania gives to the latter, 'the human mortals!' It is astonishing that Shakespear should be considered, not only by foreigners, but by many of our own critics, as a gloomy and heavy writer, who painted nothing but 'gorgons and hydras, and chimeras dire.' His subtlety exceeds that of all other dramatic writers, insomuch that a celebrated person of the present day said that he regarded him rather as a metaphysician than a poet. His delicacy and sportive gaiety are infinite. In the MIDSUMMER NIGHT'S DREAM alone, we should imagine, there is more sweetness and beauty of description than in the whole range of French poetry put together. What we mean is this, that we will produce out of that single play ten passages, to which we do not think any ten passages in the works of the French poets can be opposed, displaying equal fancy and imagery. Shall we mention the remonstrance of Helena to Hermia, or Titania's description of her fairy train, or her disputes with Oberon about the Indian boy, or Puck's account of himself and his employments, or the Fairy Queen's exhortation to the elves to pay due attendance upon her favourite, Bottom; or Hippolita's description of a chase, or Theseus's answer? The two last are as heroical and spirited as the others are full of luscious tenderness. The reading of this play is like wandering in a grove by moonlight; the descriptions breathe a sweetness like odours thrown from beds of flowers. . . .

The MIDSUMMER NIGHT'S DREAM, when acted, is converted from a delightful fiction into a dull pantomime. All that is finest in the play is lost in the representation. The spectacle was grand; but the spirit was evaporated, the genius was fled.—Poetry and the stage do not agree well together. The attempt to reconcile them in this instance fails not only of effect, but of decorum. The *ideal* can have no place upon the stage, which is a picture without perspective; everything there is in the foreground. That which was merely an airy shape, a dream, a passing thought, immediately becomes an unmanageable reality. Where all is left to the imagination (as is the case in reading), every circumstance, near or remote, has an equal chance of being kept in mind, and tells accordingly to the mixed impression of all that has been suggested. But the imagination cannot sufficiently qualify the actual impressions of the senses. Any offence given to the eye is not to be got rid of by explanation. Thus Bottom's head in the play is a fantastic illusion, produced by magic spells: on the stage it is an ass's head, and nothing more; certainly a very strange costume for a gentleman to appear in. Fancy cannot be embodied any more than a simile can be painted; and it is as idle to attempt it as to personate *Wall* or *Moonshine*. Fairies are not incredible, but fairies six feet high are so. Monsters are not shocking, if they are seen at a proper distance. When ghosts appear at mid-day, when apparitions stalk along Cheapside, then may the MIDSUMMER NIGHT'S DREAM be represented without injury at Covent-garden or at Drury-lane. The boards of a theatre and the regions of fancy are not the same thing.

Id.

Twelfth Night; or, What You Will

THIS is justly considered as one of the most delightful of
Shakespear's comedies. It is full of sweetness and pleasantry. It is perhaps too good-natured for comedy. It
has little satire, and no spleen. It aims at the ludicrous
rather than the ridiculous. It makes us laugh at the follies
of mankind, not despise them, and still less bear any ill-
will towards them. Shakespear's comic genius resembles
the bee rather in its power of extracting sweets from
weeds or poisons, than in leaving a sting behind it. He
gives the most amusing exaggeration of the prevailing
foibles of his characters, but in a way that they themselves, instead of being offended at, would almost join in
to humour; he rather contrives opportunities for them to
show themselves off in the happiest lights, than renders
them contemptible in the perverse construction of the
wit or malice of others. There is a certain stage of society
in which people become conscious of their peculiarities
and absurdities, affect to disguise what they are, and set
up pretensions to what they are not. This gives rise to
a corresponding style of comedy, the object of which is
to detect the disguises of self-love, and to make reprisals
on these preposterous assumptions of vanity, by marking
the contrast between the real and the affected character
as severely as possible, and denying to those, who would
impose on us for what they are not, even the merit which
they have. This is the comedy of artificial life, of wit
and satire, such as we see it in Congreve, Wycherley,
Vanbrugh, &c. To this succeeds a state of society from
which the same sort of affectation and pretence are
banished by a greater knowledge of the world or by
their successful exposure on the stage; and which by
neutralising the materials of comic character, both
natural and artificial, leaves no comedy at all—but *the*

sentimental. Such is our modern comedy. There is a period in the progress of manners anterior to both these, in which the foibles and follies of individuals are of nature's planting, not the growth of art or study; in which they are therefore unconscious of them themselves, or care not who knows them, if they can but have their whim out; and in which, as there is no attempt at imposition, the spectators rather receive pleasure from humouring the inclinations of the persons they laugh at, than wish to give them pain by exposing their absurdity. This may be called the comedy of nature, and it is the comedy which we generally find in Shakespear.— Whether the analysis here given be just or not, the spirit of his comedies is evidently quite distinct from that of the authors above mentioned, as it is in its essence the same with that of Cervantes, and also very frequently of Molière, though he was more systematic in his extravagance than Shakespear. Shakespear's comedy is of a pastoral and poetical cast. Folly is indigenous to the soil, and shoots out with native, happy, unchecked luxuriance. Absurdity has every encouragement afforded it; and nonsense has room to flourish in. Nothing is stunted by the churlish, icy hand of indifference or severity. The poet runs riot in a conceit, and idolises a quibble. His whole object is to turn the meanest or rudest objects to a pleasurable account. The relish which he has of a pun, or of the quaint humour of a low character, does not interfere with the delight with which he describes a beautiful image, or the most refined love. The clown's forced jests do not spoil the sweetness of the character of Viola; the same house is big enough to hold Malvolio, the Countess, Maria, Sir Toby, and Sir Andrew Ague-cheek. For instance, nothing can fall much lower than this last character in intellect or morals: yet how are his weaknesses nursed and dandled by Sir

Toby into something 'high fantastical,' when on Sir
Andrew's commendation of himself for dancing and
fencing, Sir Toby answers—'Wherefore are these things
hid? Wherefore have these gifts a curtain before them?
Are they like to take dust like mistress Moll's picture?
Why dost thou not go to church in a galliard, and come
home in a coranto? My very walk should be a jig! I
would not so much as make water but in a cinque-pace.
What dost thou mean? Is this a world to hide virtues in?
I did think by the excellent constitution of thy leg, it was
framed under the star of a galliard!' How Sir Toby,
Sir Andrew, and the Clown afterwards *chirp over their
cups,* how they 'rouse the night-owl in a catch, that will
draw three souls out of one weaver!' What can be
better than Sir Toby's unanswerable answer to Malvolio,
'Dost thou think, because thou art virtuous, there shall
be no more cakes and ale?'—In a word, the best turn is
given to every thing, instead of the worst. There is a
constant infusion of the romantic and enthusiastic, in
proportion as the characters are natural and sincere:
whereas, in the more artificial style of comedy, everything gives way to ridicule and indifference, there being
nothing left but affectation on one side, and incredulity on the other. Much as we like Shakespear's
comedies, we cannot agree with Dr. Johnson that they
are better than his tragedies; nor do we like them half so
well. If his inclination to comedy sometimes led him to
trifle with the seriousness of tragedy, the poetical and
impassioned passages are the best parts of his comedies.
The great and secret charm of TWELFTH NIGHT is the
character of Viola. Much as we like catches and cakes
and ale, there is something that we like better. We have
a friendship for Sir Toby; we patronise Sir Andrew; we
have an understanding with the Clown, a sneaking kindness for Maria and her rogueries; we feel a regard for

Molvolio, and sympathise with his gravity, his smiles, his cross garters, his yellow stockings, and imprisonment in the stocks. But there is something that excites in us a stronger feeling than all this—it is Viola's confession of her love.

> *Duke.* What's her history?
> *Viola. A blank, my lord; she never told her love:*
> She let concealment, like a worm i' th' bud,
> Feed on her damask cheek: she pin'd in thought,
> And with a green and yellow melancholy,
> She sat like Patience on a monument,
> Smiling at grief. *Was not this love indeed?*
> We men may say more, swear more, but indeed,
> Our shews are more than will; for still we prove
> Much in our vows, but little in our love.
>   *Duke.* But died thy sister of her love, my boy?
>   *Viola.* I am all the daughters of my father's house,
> And all the brothers too;—and yet I know not.—

Shakespear alone could describe the effect of his own poetry.

> O, it came o'er the ear like the sweet south
> That breathes upon a bank of violets,
> Stealing and giving odour.

What we so much admire here is not the image of Patience on a monument, which has been generally quoted, but the lines before and after it. 'They give a very echo to the seat where love is throned.' How long ago it is since we first learnt to repeat them; and still, still they vibrate on the heart, like the sounds which the passing wind draws from the trembling strings of a harp left on some desert shore! There are other passages of not less impassioned sweetness. Such is Olivia's address to Sebastian, whom she supposes

to have already deceived her in a promise of
marriage:

> Blame not this haste of mine: if you mean well,
> Now go with me and with this holy man
> Into the chantry by: there before him,
> And underneath that consecrated roof,
> Plight me the full assurance of your faith,
> *That my most jealous and too doubtful soul*
> *May live at peace.*

Id.

The Heroines

IT is the peculiar excellence of Shakespear's heroines,
that they seem to exist only in their attachment to others.
They are pure abstractions of the affections. We think
as little of their persons as they do themselves, because
we are let into the secrets of their hearts, which are more
important. We are too much interested in their affairs
to stop to look at their faces, except by stealth and at
intervals. No one ever hit the true perfection of the
female character, the sense of weakness leaning on the
strength of its affections for support, so well as Shakespear—no one ever so well painted natural tenderness
free from affectation and disguise—no one else ever so
well shewed how delicacy and timidity, when driven
to extremity, grow romantic and extravagant; for the
romance of his heroines (in which they abound) is only
an excess of the habitual prejudices of their sex, scrupulous of being false to their vows, truant to their affections, and taught by the force of feeling when to forego
the forms of propriety for the essence of it. His women
were in this respect exquisite logicians; for there is nothing so logical as passion. They knew their own minds
exactly; and only followed up a favourite purpose, which
they had sworn to with their tongues, and which was

engraven on their hearts, into its untoward consequences. They were the prettiest little set of martyrs and confessors on record.—Cibber, in speaking of the early English stage, accounts for the want of prominence and theatrical display in Shakespear's female characters from the circumstance, that women in those days were not allowed to play the parts of women, which made it necessary to keep them a good deal in the back-ground. Does not this state of manners itself, which prevented their exhibiting themselves in public, and confined them to the relations and charities of domestic life, afford a truer explanation of the matter? His women are certainly very unlike stage-heroines; the reverse of tragedy-queens.

Id., Cymbeline.

Shakespeare's Genius

. . . IN comparing these four writers together, it might be said that Chaucer excels as the poet of manners, or of real life; Spenser, as the poet of romance; Shakespeare, as the poet of nature (in the largest use of the term); and Milton, as the poet of morality. Chaucer most frequently describes things as they are; Spenser, as we wish them to be; Shakespeare, as they would be; and Milton as they ought to be. As poets, and as great poets, imagination, that is, the power of feigning things according to nature, was common to them all: but the principle, or moving power, to which this faculty was most subservient in Chaucer, was habit, or inveterate prejudice; in Spenser, novelty, and the love of the marvellous; in Shakespeare, it was the force of passion, combined with every variety of possible circumstances; and in Milton, [combined] only with the highest. The characteristic of Chaucer is intensity; of Spenser, remoteness; of Milton, elevation; of Shakespeare, everything.—It has been said by some critic, that Shakespeare was distinguished from the other dramatic writers of his day only by his wit; that they had all his other qualities but that; that one writer had as much sense, another as much fancy, another as much knowledge of character, another the same depth of passion, and another as great a power of language. This statement is not true; nor is the inference from it well-founded, even if it were. This person does not seem to have been aware that, upon his own shewing, the great distinction of Shakespeare's genius was its virtually including the genius of all the great men of his age, and not its differing from them in one accidental particular. But to have done with such minute and literal trifling.

The striking peculiarity of Shakespeare's mind was its generic quality, its power of communication with all other minds—so that it contained a universe of thought and feeling within itself, and had no one peculiar bias or exclusive excellence more than another. He was just like any other man, but that he was like all other men. He was the least of an egotist that it was possible to be. He was nothing in himself, but he was all that others were, or that they could become. He not only had in himself the germs of every faculty and feeling, but he could follow them by anticipation, intuitively, into all their conceivable ramifications, through every change of fortune or conflict of passion, or turn of thought. He had 'a mind reflecting ages past' and present:—all the people that ever lived are there. There was no respect of persons with him. His genius shone equally on the evil and on the good, on the wise and the foolish, the monarch and the beggar. 'All corners of the earth, kings, queens, and states, maids, matrons, nay, the secrets of the grave,' are hardly hid from his searching glance. He was like the genius of humanity, changing places with all of us at pleasure, and playing with our purposes as with his own. He turned the globe round for his amusement, and surveyed the generations of men, and the individuals as they passed, with their different concerns, passions, follies, vices, virtues, actions, and motives—as well those that they knew, as those which they did not know, or acknowledge to themselves. The dreams of childhood, the ravings of despair, were the toys of his fancy. Airy beings waited at his call, and came at his bidding. Harmless fairies 'nodded to him, and did him curtesies:' and the night-hag bestrode the blast at the command of 'his so potent art.' The world of spirits lay open to him, like the world of real men and women: and there is the same truth in his delineations of the one as of the other; for if the preternatural characters he describes could be supposed to exist, they would speak, and feel, and act, as he makes them. He had only to think of any thing in order to become that thing, with all the circumstances belonging to it. When he conceived of a character, whether real or imaginary, he not only entered into all its thoughts and feelings, but seemed instantly, and as if by touching a secret spring, to be surrounded with all the same objects, 'subject to the same skyey influences,' the same local, outward, and unforeseen accidents which would occur in reality. Thus the character of Caliban not only stands before us with a language and manners of its own, but the scenery and situation of the enchanted island he inhabits, the traditions of the place, its strange noises, its hidden recesses, 'his frequent haunts and ancient neighbourhood,' are given with a miraculous truth of nature, and with all the familiarity of an old recollection. The whole 'coheres semblably together' in time, place, and circumstance. In reading this author, you do not merely learn what his characters say,—you see their persons. By

something expressed or understood, you are at no loss
to decipher their peculiar physiognomy, the meaning of
a look, the grouping, the bye-play, as we might see it on
the stage. A word, an epithet, paints a whole scene, or
throws us back whole years in the history of the person
represented. So (as it has been ingeniously remarked)
when Prospero describes himself as left alone in the boat
with his daughter, the epithet which he applies to her,
'Me and thy *crying* self,' flings the imagination instantly
back from the grown woman to the helpless condition
of infancy, and places the first and most trying scene of
his misfortunes before us, with all that he must have
suffered in the interval. How well the silent anguish of
Macduff is conveyed to the reader, by the friendly ex-
postulation of Malcolm:—'What! man, ne'er pull your
hat upon your brows.' Again, Hamlet, in the scene with
Rosencrantz and Guildenstern, somewhat abruptly concludes his fine soliloquy on life by saying, 'Man delights
not me, nor woman neither, though by your smiling
you seem to say so.' Which is explained by their answer—'My lord, we had no such stuff in our thoughts.
But we smiled to think, if you delight not in man, what
lenten entertainment the players shall receive from you,
whom we met on the way:'—as if while Hamlet was
making this speech, his two old schoolfellows from
Wittenberg had been really standing by, and he had
seen them smiling by stealth, at the idea of the players
crossing their minds. It is not 'a combination and a form'
of words, a set speech or two, a preconcerted theory of
a character, that will do this: but all the persons concerned must have been present in the poet's imagination,
as at a kind of rehearsal; and whatever would have passed
through their minds on the occasion, and have been observed by others, passed through his, and is made known
to the reader.—I may add in passing, that Shakespeare

always gives the best directions for the costume and carriage of his heroes. Thus to take one example, Ophelia gives the following account of Hamlet; and as Ophelia had seen Hamlet, I should think her word ought to be taken against that of any modern authority.

> *Ophelia.* My lord, as I was reading in my closet,
> Prince Hamlet, with his doublet all unbrac'd,
> No hat upon his head, his stockings loose,
> Ungartred, and down-gyved to his ancle,
> Pale as his shirt, his knees knocking each other,
> And with a look so piteous,
> As if he had been sent from hell
> To speak of horrors, thus he comes before me.
> *Polonius.* Mad for thy love!
> *Oph.* My lord, I do not know,
> But truly I do fear it.
> *Pol.* What said he?
> *Oph.* He took me by the wrist, and held me hard;
> Then goes he to the length of all his arm;
> And, with his other hand thus o'er his brow,
> He falls to such perusal of my face,
> As he would draw it: long staid he so;
> At last, a little shaking of my arm,
> And thrice his head thus waving up and down,
> He rais'd a sigh so piteous and profound,
> As it did seem to shatter all his bulk,
> And end his being. That done, he lets me go,
> And with his head over his shoulder turn'd,
> He seem'd to find his way without his eyes;
> For out of doors he went without their help,
> And to the last bended their light on me.
>
> Act II. Scene 1.

How after this airy, fantastic idea of irregular grace and bewildered melancholy any one can play Hamlet, as we have seen it played, with strut, and stare, and antic right-angled sharp-pointed gestures, it is difficult to say, unless it be that Hamlet is not bound, by the prompter's cue, to

study the part of Ophelia. The account of Ophelia's
death begins thus:

> There is a willow hanging o'er a brook,
> That shows its hoary leaves in the glassy stream.—

Now this is an instance of the same unconscious power
of mind which is as true to nature as itself. The leaves
of the willow are, in fact, white underneath, and it is
this part of them which would appear 'hoary' in the reflection in the brook. The same sort of intuitive power,
the same faculty of bringing every object in nature,
whether present or absent, before the mind's eye, is
observable in the speech of Cleopatra, when conjectur-
ing what were the employments of Antony in his absence:—'He's speaking now, or murmuring, where's my
serpent of old Nile?' How fine to make Cleopatra have
this consciousness of her own character, and to make
her feel that it is this for which Antony is in love with
her! She says, after the battle of Actium, when Antony
has resolved to risk another fight, 'It is my birth-day; I
had thought to have held it poor: but since my lord is
Antony again, I will be Cleopatra.' What other poet
would have thought of such a casual resource of the
imagination, or would have dared to avail himself of it?
The thing happens in the play as it might have happened
in fact.—That which, perhaps, more than any thing else
distinguishes the dramatic productions of Shakspeare
from all others, is this wonderful truth and individuality
of conception. Each of his characters is as much itself,
and as absolutely independent of the rest, as well as of
the author, as if they were living persons, not fictions
of the mind. The poet may be said, for the time, to
identify himself with the character he wishes to represent, and to pass from one to another, like the same soul
successively animating different bodies. By an art like

that of the ventriloquist, he throws his imagination out of himself, and makes every word appear to proceed from the mouth of the person in whose name it is given. His plays alone are properly expressions of the passions, not descriptions of them. His characters are real beings of flesh and blood; they speak like men, not like authors. One might suppose that he had stood by at the time, and overheard what passed. As in our dreams we hold conversations with ourselves, make remarks, or communicate intelligence, and have no idea of the answer which we shall receive, and which we ourselves make, till we hear it: so the dialogues in Shakespeare are carried on without any consciousness of what is to follow, without any appearance of preparation or premeditation. The gusts of passion come and go like sounds of music borne on the wind. Nothing is made out by formal inference and analogy, by climax and antithesis: all comes, or seems to come, immediately from nature. Each object and circumstance exists in his mind, as it would have existed in reality: each several train of thought and feeling goes on of itself, without confusion or effort. In the world of his imagination, everything has a life, a place, and being of its own!

Chaucer's characters are sufficiently distinct from one another, but they are too little varied in themselves, too much like identical propositions. They are consistent, but uniform; we get no new idea of them from first to last; they are not placed in different lights, nor are their subordinate *traits* brought out in new situations; they are like portraits or physiognomical studies, with the distinguishing features marked with inconceivable truth and precision, but that preserve the same unaltered air and attitude. Shakespeare's are historical figures, equally true and correct, but put into action, where every nerve and muscle is displayed in the struggle with others, with all the effect of collision and contrast, with every variety of light and shade. Chaucer's characters are narrative, Shakespeare's dramatic, Milton's epic. That is, Chaucer told only as much of his story as he pleased, as was required for a particular purpose. He answered for his characters himself. In Shakespeare they are introduced upon the stage, are liable to be asked all sorts of questions, and are forced to answer for themselves. In Chaucer we perceive a fixed essence of character. In Shakespeare there is a continual composition and decomposition of its elements, a fermentation of every particle in the whole mass, by its alternate affinity or antipathy to other principles which are brought in contact with it. Till the experiment is tried, we do not know the result, the turn which the character will take in its new circumstances. Milton took only a few simple principles of character, and raised them to the utmost conceivable grandeur, and refined them from every base alloy. His imagination, 'nigh sphered in Heaven,' claimed kindred only with what he saw from that height, and could raise to the same elevation with itself. He sat retired and kept his state alone, 'playing with wisdom;' while Shakespeare mingled with the crowd, and played the host, 'to make society the sweeter welcome.'

The passion in Shakespeare is of the same nature as his delineation of character. It is not some one habitual feeling or sentiment preying upon itself, growing out of itself, and moulding everything to itself; it is passion modified by passion, by all the other feelings to which the individual is liable, and to which others are liable with him; subject to all the fluctuations of caprice and accident; calling into play all the resources of the understanding and all the energies of the will; irritated by obstacles or yielding to them; rising from small beginnings to its utmost height; now drunk with hope, now

stung to madness, now sunk in despair, now blown to
air with a breath, now raging like a torrent. The human
soul is made the sport of fortune, the prey of adversity:
it is stretched on the wheel of destiny, in restless ecstasy.
The passions are in a state of projection. Years are melted
down to moments, and every instant teems with fate.
We know the results, we see the process. Thus after
Iago has been boasting to himself of the effect of his
poisonous suggestions on the mind of Othello, 'which,
with a little act upon the blood, will work like mines
of sulphur,' he adds:—

> Look where he comes! not poppy, nor mandragora
> Nor all the drowsy syrups of the East,
> Shall ever medicine thee to that sweet sleep
> Which thou ow'dst yesterday.

And he enters at this moment, like the crested serpent,
crowned with his wrongs and raging for revenge! The
whole depends upon the turn of a thought. A word,
a look, blows the spark of jealousy into a flame; and the
explosion is immediate and terrible as a volcano. The
dialogues in *Lear*, in *Macbeth*, that between Brutus and
Cassius, and nearly all those in Shakespeare, where the
interest is wrought up to its highest pitch, afford examples of this dramatic fluctuation of passion. The interest in Chaucer is quite different; it is like the course of
a river, strong, and full, and increasing. In Shakespeare,
on the contrary, it is like the sea, agitated this way and
that, and loud-lashed by furious storms; while in the
still pauses of the blast we distinguish only the cries of
despair, or the silence of death! Milton, on the other
hand, takes the imaginative part of passion—that which
remains after the event, which the mind reposes on
when all is over, which looks upon circumstances from
the remotest elevation of thought and fancy, and

abstracts them from the world of action to that of contemplation. The objects of dramatic poetry affect us by
sympathy, by their nearness to ourselves, as they take us
by surprise, or force us upon action, 'while rage with
rage doth sympathise': the objects of epic poetry affect
us through the medium of the imagination, by magnitude and distance, by their permanence and universality.
The one fills us with terror and pity, the other with
admiration and delight. There are certain objects that
strike the imagination, and inspire awe in the very idea
of them, independently of any dramatic interest, that is,
of any connection with the vicissitudes of human life.
For instance, we cannot think of the pyramids of Egypt,
of a Gothic ruin, or an old Roman encampment, without a certain emotion, a sense of power and sublimity
coming over the mind. The heavenly bodies that hang
over our heads wherever we go, and 'in their untroubled
element shall shine when we are laid in dust, and all our
cares forgotten,' affect us in the same way. Thus Satan's
address to the Sun has an epic, not a dramatic interest;
for though the second person in the dialogue makes no
answer and feels no concern, yet the eye of that vast
luminary is upon him, like the eye of heaven, and seems
conscious of what he says, like an universal presence.
Dramatic poetry and epic in their perfection, indeed,
approximate to and strengthen one another. Dramatic
poetry borrows aid from the dignity of persons and
things, as the heroic does from human passion, but in
theory they are distinct. When Richard II. calls for the
looking-glass to contemplate his faded majesty in it, and
bursts into that affecting exclamation: 'Oh that I were
a mockery-king of snow, to melt away before the sun
of Bolingbroke!' we have here the utmost force of human passion, combined with the ideas of regal splendour
and fallen power. When Milton says of Satan:

'———— His form had not yet lost
All her original brightness, nor appear'd
Less than archangel ruin'd, and th' excess
Of glory obscur'd;

the mixture of beauty, of grandeur, and pathos, from the sense of irreparable loss, of never-ending, unavailing regret, is perfect.

The great fault of a modern school of poetry is, that it is an experiment to reduce poetry to a mere effusion of natural sensibility; or what is worse, to divest it both of imaginary splendour and human passion, to surround the meanest objects with the morbid feelings and devouring egotism of the writers' own minds. Milton and Shakespeare did not so understand poetry. They gave a more liberal interpretation both to nature and art. They did not do all they could to get rid of the one and the other, to fill up the dreary void with the Moods of their own Minds. They owe their power over the human mind to their having had a deeper sense than others of what was grand in the objects of nature, or affecting in the events of human life. But to the men I speak of there is nothing interesting, nothing heroical, but themselves. To them the fall of gods or of great men is the same. They do not enter into the feeling. They cannot understand the terms. They are even debarred from the last poor, paltry consolation of an unmanly triumph over fallen greatness; for their minds reject, with a convulsive effort and intolerable loathing, the very idea that there ever was, or was thought to be, anything superior to themselves. All that has ever excited the attention or admiration of the world, they look upon with the most perfect indifference; and they are surprised to find that the world repays their indifference with scorn. 'With what measure they mete, it has been meted to them again.'——

Shakespeare's imagination is of the same plastic kind as his conception of character or passion. 'It glances from heaven to earth, from earth to heaven.' Its movement is rapid and devious. It unites the most opposite extremes; or, as Puck says, in boasting of his own feats, 'puts a girdle round about the earth in forty minutes.' He seems always hurrying from his subject, even while describing it; but the stroke, like the lightning's, is sure as it is sudden. He takes the widest possible range, but from that very range he has his choice of the greatest variety and aptitude of materials. He brings together images the most alike, but placed at the greatest distance from each other; that is, found in circumstances of the greatest dissimilitude. From the remoteness of his combinations, and the celerity with which they are effected, they coalesce the more indissolubly together. The more the thoughts are strangers to each other, and the longer they have been kept asunder, the more intimate does their union seem to become. Their felicity is equal to their force. Their likeness is made more dazzling by their novelty. They startle, and take the fancy prisoner in the same instant. I will mention one or two which are very striking, and not much known, out of *Troilus and Cressida*. Æneas says to Agamemnon:

> I ask that I may waken reverence,
> And on the cheek be ready with a blush
> Modest as morning, when she coldly eyes
> The youthful Phœbus.

Ulysses urging Achilles to shew himself in the field, says—

> No man is the lord of any thing,
> Till he communicate his parts to others:
> Nor doth he of himself know them for aught,
> Till he behold them formed in the applause,

> Where they're extended! which, like an arch
>   reverberates
> The voice again, or like a gate of steel
> Fronting the sun, receives and renders back
> Its figure and its heat.

Patroclus gives the indolent warrior the same advice:

> Rouse yourself; and the weak wanton Cupid
> Shall from your neck unloose his amorous fold,
> And like a dew-drop from the lion's mane
> Be shook to air.

Shakespeare's language and versification are like the rest of him. He has a magic power over words: they come winged at his bidding; and seem to know their places. They are struck out at a heat, on the spur of the occasion, and have all the truth and vividness which arise from an actual impression of the objects. His epithets and single phrases are like sparkles, thrown off from an imagination, fired by the whirling rapidity of its own motion. His language is hieroglyphical. It translates thoughts into visible images. It abounds in sudden transitions and elliptical expressions. This is the source of his mixed metaphors, which are only abbreviated forms of speech. These, however, give no pain from long custom. They have, in fact, become idioms in the language. They are the building, and not the scaffolding to thought. We take the meaning and effect of a well-known passage entire, and no more stop to scan and spell out the particular words and phrases than the syllables of which they are composed. In trying to recollect any other author, one sometimes stumbles, in case of failure, on a word as good. In Shakespeare, any other word but the true one, is sure to be wrong. If anybody, for instance, could not recollect the words of the following description,

> —— Light thickens,
> And the crow makes wing to the rooky wood

he would be greatly at a loss to substitute others for them equally expressive of the feeling. These remarks, however, are strictly applicable only to the impassioned parts of Shakespeare's language, which flowed from the warmth and originality of his imagination, and were his own. The language used for prose conversation and ordinary business is sometimes technical, and involved in the affectation of the time. Compare, for example, Othello's apology to the Senate, relating 'his whole course of love,' with some of the preceding parts relating to his appointment, and the official dispatches from Cyprus. In this respect, 'the business of the state does him offence.'—His versification is no less powerful, sweet, and varied. It has every occasional excellence, of sullen intricacy, crabbed and perplexed, or of the smoothest and loftiest expansion—from the ease and familiarity of measured conversation to the lyrical sounds

> ———— Of ditties highly penned,
> Sung by a fair queen in a summer's bower,
> With ravishing division to her lute.'

It is the only blank verse in the language, except Milton's, that for itself is readable. It is not stately and uniformly swelling like his, but varied and broken by the inequalities of the ground it has to pass over in its uncertain course,

> And so by many winding nooks it strays,
> With willing sport to the wild ocean.

It remains to speak of the faults of Shakespeare. They are not so many or so great as they have been represented; what there are, are chiefly owing to the following causes:—The universality of his genius was, perhaps, a disadvantage to his single works; the variety of his resources sometimes diverting him from applying them to the most effectual purposes. He might be said to combine the powers of Æschylus and Aristophanes, of Dante and Rabelais, in his own mind. If he had been only half what he was, he would perhaps have appeared greater. The natural ease and indifference of his temper made him sometimes less scrupulous than he might have been. He is relaxed and careless in critical places; he is in earnest throughout only in *Timon*, *Macbeth*, and *Lear*. Again, he had no models of acknowledged excellence constantly in view to stimulate his efforts, and, by all that appears, no love of fame. He wrote for the 'great vulgar and the small' in his time, not for posterity. If Queen Elizabeth and the maids of honour laughed heartily at his worst jokes, and the catcalls in the gallery were silent at his best passages, he went home satisfied, and slept the next night well. He did not trouble himself about Voltaire's criticisms. He was willing to take advantage of the ignorance of the age in many things, and if his plays pleased others, not to quarrel with them himself. His very facility of production would make him set less value on his own excellences, and not care to distinguish nicely between what he did well or ill. His blunders in chronology and geography do not amount to above half a dozen, and they are offences against chronology and geography, not against poetry. As to the unities, he was right in setting them at defiance. He was fonder of puns than became so great a man. His barbarisms were those of his age. His genius was his own. He had no objection to float down with the stream of common taste and opinion: he rose above it by his own buoyancy, and an impulse which he could not keep under, in spite of himself, or others, and 'his delights did show most dolphin-like.'

From Lectures on the English Poets, '*On Shakespeare and Milton*,' 1818 (with corrections from the second edition, 1819).

THE poet of nature is one who, from the elements of
beauty, of power, and of passion in his own breast,
sympathises with whatever is beautiful, and grand, and
impassioned in nature, in its simple majesty, in its immediate appeal to the senses, to the thoughts and hearts
of all men; so that the poet of nature, by the truth, and
depth, and harmony of his mind, may be said to hold
communion with the very soul of nature; to be identified with and to foreknow and to record the feelings of
all men at all times and places, as they are liable to the
same impressions, and to exert the same power over the
minds of his readers, that nature does. He sees things in
their eternal beauty, for he sees them as they are; he feels
them in their universal interest, for he feels them as they
affect the first principles of his and our common nature.
Such was Homer, such was Shakespeare, whose works
will last as long as nature, because they are a copy of the
indestructible forms and everlasting impulses of nature,
welling out from the bosom as from a perennial spring,
or stamped upon the senses by the hand of their maker.
The power of the imagination in them, is the representative power of all nature. It has its centre in the human
soul, and makes the circuit of the universe.

Id., 'On Dryden and Pope.'

Shakespeare's Contemporaries

WE affect to wonder at Shakespeare and one or two more
of that period, as solitary instances upon record; whereas
it is our own dearth of information that makes the waste;
for there is no time more populous of intellect, or more
prolific of intellectual wealth, than the one we are speaking of. Shakespeare did not look upon himself in this
light, as a sort of monster of poetical genius, or on his
contemporaries as 'less than smallest dwarfs,' when he

speaks with true, not false modesty, of himself and them, and of his wayward thoughts, 'desiring this man's art, and that man's scope.' We fancy that there were no such men, that could either add to or take any thing away from him, but such there were. He indeed overlooks and commands the admiration of posterity, but he does it from the *table-land* of the age in which he lived. He towered above his fellows, 'in shape and gesture proudly eminent;' but he was one of a race of giants—the tallest, the strongest, the most graceful and beautiful of them; but it was a common and a noble brood. He was not something sacred and aloof from the vulgar herd of men, but shook hands with nature and the circumstances of the time, and is distinguished from his immediate contemporaries, not in kind, but in degree and greater variety of excellence. He did not form a class or species by himself, but belonged to a class or species. His age was necessary to him; nor could he have been wrenched from his place, in the edifice of which he was so conspicuous a part, without equal injury to himself and it. Mr. Wordsworth says of Milton, that 'his soul was like a star, and dwelt apart.' This cannot be said with any propriety of Shakespear, who certainly moved in a constellation of bright luminaries, and 'drew after him a third part of the heavens.' If we allow, for argument's sake (or for truth's, which is better), that he was in himself equal to all his competitors put together; yet there was more dramatic excellence in that age than in the whole of the period that has elapsed since. If his contemporaries, with their united strength, would hardly make one Shakespear, certain it is that all his successors would not make half a one. With the exception of a single writer, Otway, and of a single play of his (*Venice Preserved*), there is nobody in tragedy and dramatic poetry (I do not here speak of comedy) to be compared to the great men of the age of Shakespear, and immediately after. They are a mighty phalanx of kindred spirits closing him round, moving in the same orbit, and impelled by the same causes in their whirling and eccentric career. They had the same faults and the same excellences; the same strength and depth and richness, the same truth of character, passion, imagination, thought and language, thrown, heaped, massed together without careful polishing or exact method, but poured out in unconcerned profusion from the lap of nature and genius in boundless and unrivalled magnificence. The sweetness of Deckar, the thought of Marston, the gravity of Chapman, the grace of Fletcher and his young-eyed wit, Jonson's learned sock, the flowing vein of Middleton, Heywood's ease, the pathos of Webster, and Marlow's deep designs, add a double lustre to the sweetness, thought, gravity, grace, wit, artless nature, copiousness, ease, pathos, and sublime conceptions of Shakespear's Muse. They are indeed the scale by which we can best ascend to the true knowledge and love of him. Our admiration of them does not lessen our relish for him: but, on the contrary, increases and confirms it.

From Lectures on the Dramatic Literature of the Age of Elizabeth, 'General View of the Subject,' 1820.

FRANCIS JEFFREY

Review of Hazlitt's 'Characters of Shakespear's Plays' in 'The Edinburgh Review' for August 1817[1]

. . . THE book, as we have already intimated, is written less to tell the reader what Mr. H. *knows* about Shakespeare or his writings, than to explain to them what he *feels* about them—and *why* he feels so—and thinks that all who profess to love poetry should feel so likewise. What we chiefly look for in such a work, accordingly, is a fine sense of the beauties of the author, and an eloquent exposition of them; and all this, and more, we think, may be found in the volume before us. There is nothing niggardly in Mr. H.'s praises, and nothing affected in his raptures. He seems animated throughout with a full and hearty sympathy with the delight which his author should inspire, and pours himself gladly out in explanation of it, with a fluency and ardour, obviously much more akin to enthusiasm than affectation. He seems pretty generally, indeed, in a state of happy intoxication—and has borrowed from his great original, not indeed the force or brilliancy of his fancy, but something of its playfulness, and a large share of his apparent joyousness and self-indulgence in its exercise. It is evidently a great pleasure to him to be fully possessed with the beauties of his author, and to follow the impulse of his unrestrained eagerness to impress them upon his readers.

[1] Jeffrey included this article in the selection from his writings published in 1844 under the title *Contributions to the Edinburgh Review*. He there added in a footnote that 'it presumes to direct attention but to one, and that, as I think, a comparatively neglected, aspect of his universal genius.'

When we have said that his observations are generally
right, we have said, in substance, that they are not generally original; for the beauties of Shakespeare are not of
so dim or equivocal a nature as to be visible only to
learned eyes—and undoubtedly his finest passages are
those which please all classes of readers, and are admired
for the same qualities by judges from every school of
criticism. Even with regard to those passages, however,
a skilful commentator will find something worth hearing to tell. Many persons are very sensible of the effect
of fine poetry on their feelings, who do not well know
how to refer these feelings to their causes; and it is always
a delightful thing to be made to see clearly the sources
from which our delight has proceeded—and to trace
back the mingled stream that has flowed upon our hearts,
to the remoter fountains from which it has been gathered.
And when this is done with warmth as well as precision,
and embodied in an eloquent description of the beauty
which is explained, it forms one of the most attractive,
and not the least instructive, of literary exercises.   In
all works of merit, however, and especially in all works
of original genius, there are a thousand retiring and less
obtrusive graces, which escape hasty and superficial
observers, and only give out their beauties to fond and
patient contemplation;—a thousand slight and harmo-
nizing touches, the merit and the effect of which are
equally imperceptible to vulgar eyes; and a thousand
indications of the continual presence of that poetical
spirit, which can only be recognised by those who are
in some measure under its influence, or have prepared
themselves to receive it, by worshipping meekly at the
shrines which it inhabits.

In the exposition of these, there is room enough for
originality,—and more room than Mr. H. has yet filled.
In many points, however, he has acquitted himself

excellently;—partly in the development of the principal
characters with which Shakespeare has peopled the fancies of all English readers—but principally, we think, in
the delicate sensibility with which he has traced, and the
natural eloquence with which he has pointed out that
fond familiarity with beautiful forms and images—that
eternal recurrence to what is sweet or majestic in the
simple aspects of nature—that indestructible love of
flowers and odours, and dews and clear waters, and soft
airs and sounds, and bright skies, and woodland soli-
tudes, and moonlight bowers, which are the Material
elements of Poetry—and that fine sense of their unde-
finable relation to mental emotion, which is its essence
and vivifying Soul—and which, in the midst of Shakespeare's most busy and atrocious scenes, falls like gleams
of sunshine on rocks and ruins—contrasting with all
that is rugged and repulsive, and reminding us of the
existence of purer and brighter elements!—which HE
ALONE has poured out from the richness of his own mind,
without effort or restraint; and contrived to intermingle
with the play of all the passions, and the vulgar course
of this world's affairs, without deserting for an instant
the proper business of the scene, or appearing to pause
or digress, from love of ornament or need of repose!
—HE ALONE, who, when the object requires it, is always
keen and worldly and practical—and who yet, without
changing his hand, or stopping his course, scatters
around him, as he goes, all sounds and shapes of sweetness—and conjures up landscapes of immortal fragrance
and freshness, and peoples them with Spirits of glorious
aspect and attractive grace—and is a thousand times
more full of fancy and imagery, and splendour, than
those who, in pursuit of such enchantments, have shrunk
back from the delineation of character or passion, and
declined the discussion of human duties and cares. More

full of wisdom and ridicule and sagacity, than all the
moralists and satirists that ever existed—he is more wild,
airy, and inventive, and more pathetic and fantastic,
than all the poets of all regions and ages of the world:
—and has all those elements so happily mixed up in him,
and bears his high faculties so temperately, that the
most severe reader cannot complain of him for want of
strength or of reason—nor the most sensitive for defect
of ornament or ingenuity. Every thing in him is in un-
measured abundance, and unequalled perfection—but
every thing so balanced and kept in subordination, as
not to jostle or disturb or take the place of another. The
most exquisite poetical conceptions, images, and descriptions, are given with such brevity, and introduced
with such skill, as merely to adorn, without loading the
sense they accompany. Although his sails are purple
and perfumed, and his prow of beaten gold, they waft
him on his voyage, not less, but more rapidly and directly
than if they had been composed of baser materials.
All his excellences, like those of Nature herself, are
thrown out together; and instead of interfering with,
support and recommend each other. His flowers are
not tied up in garlands, nor his fruits crushed into
baskets—but spring living from the soil, in all the dew
and freshness of youth; with the graceful foliage in
which they lurk, and the ample branches, the rough
and vigorous stem, and the wide-spreading roots on
which they depend, are present along with them,
and share, in their places, the equal care of their
Creator.

What other poet has put all the charm of a Moonlight
landscape into a single line?—and that by an image so
true to nature, and so simple, as to seem obvious to the
most common observation?—

See how the Moonlight SLEEPS on yonder bank!

Who else has expressed, in three lines, all that is picturesque
and lovely in a Summer's Dawn?—first setting before
our eyes, with magical precision, the visible appearances of the infant light, and then, by one graceful and
glorious image, pouring on our souls all the freshness,
cheerfulness, and sublimity of returning morning?—

> ——————— See, love! what envious streaks
> Do lace the severing clouds in yonder East!
> Night's candles[1] are burnt out,—and jocund Day
> Stands tiptoe on the misty mountain tops!

Where shall we find sweet sounds and odours so luxuri-
ously blended and illustrated, as in these few words of
sweetness and melody, where the author says of soft
music—

> O it came o'er my ear like the sweet South
> That breathes upon a bank of violets,
> Stealing and giving odour!

This is still finer, we think, than the noble speech on
Music in the *Merchant of Venice*, and only to be compared with the enchantments of Prospero's island;
where all the effects of sweet sounds are expressed in
miraculous numbers, and traced in their operation on

---

[1] If the advocates for the grand style object to this expression,
we shall not stop to defend it: But, to us, it seems equally beautiful, as it is obvious and natural, to a person coming out of a
lighted chamber into the pale dawn. The word candle, we
admit, is rather homely in modern language, while lamp is
sufficiently dignified for poetry. The moon hangs her silver
lamp on high, in every schoolboy's copy of verses; and she could
not be called the candle of heaven without manifest absurdity.
Such are the caprices of usage. Yet we like the passage before
us much better as it is, than if the candles were changed into
lamps. If we should read 'The lamps of heaven are quenched,'
or 'wax dim,' it appears to us that the whole charm of the expression would be lost: as our fancies would no longer be recalled
to the privacy of that dim-lighted chamber which the lovers
were so reluctantly leaving.

all the gradations of being, from the delicate Ariel to
the brutish Caliban, who, savage as he is, is still touched
with those supernatural harmonies; and thus exhorts
his less poetical associates—

> Be not afraid, the isle is full of noises,
> Sounds, and sweet airs, that give delight and hurt not.
> Sometimes a thousand twanging instruments
> Will hum about mine ears, and sometimes voices,
> That if I then had waked after long sleep,
> Would make me sleep again.

Observe, too, that this and the other poetical speeches
of this incarnate demon, are not mere ornaments of the
poet's fancy, but explain his character and describe his
situation more briefly and effectually, than any other
words could have done. In this play, indeed, and in the
Midsummer-Night's Dream, all Eden is unlocked before
us, and the whole treasury of natural and supernatural
beauty poured out profusely, to the delight of all our
faculties. We dare not trust ourselves with quotations;
but we refer to those plays generally—to the forest
scenes in *As You Like It*—the rustic parts of the *Winter's
Tale*—several entire scenes in *Cymbeline*, and in *Romeo
and Juliet*—and many passages in all the other plays—as
illustrating this love of nature and natural beauty of
which we have been speaking—the power it had over the
poet, and the power it imparted to him. Who else would
have thought, on the very threshold of treason and midnight murder, of bringing in so sweet and rural an image
as this, at the portal of that blood-stained castle of Macbeth?

> This guest of summer,
> The temple-haunting martlet, does approve
> By his loved masonry that heaven's breath
> Smells wooingly here. No jutting frieze,
> Buttress, nor coigne of vantage, but this bird
> Has made his pendent bed, and procreant cradle.

Nor is this brought in for the sake of an elaborate contrast between the peaceful innocence of this exterior,
and the guilt and horrors that are to be enacted within.
There is no hint of any such suggestion—but it is set
down from the pure love of nature and reality—because the kindled mind of the poet brought the
whole scene before his eyes, and he painted all that
he saw in his vision. The same taste predominates
in that emphatic exhortation to evil, where Lady
Macbeth says,

> —— Look like the innocent flower,
> But be the serpent under it.

And in that proud boast of the bloody Richard—

> But I was *born* so high:
> Our aery buildeth in the cedar's top,
> And dallies with the wind, and scorns the sun!

The same splendour of natural imagery, brought
simply and directly to bear upon stern and repulsive
passions, is to be found in the cynic rebukes of Apemantus to Timon.

> Will these moist trees
> That have out-liv'd the eagle, page thy heels,
> And skip when thou point'st out? will the cold
>   brook,
> Candied with ice, caudle thy morning taste
> To cure thine o'er-night's surfeit?

No one but Shakespeare would have thought of putting this noble picture into the taunting address of a
snappish misanthrope—any more than the following
into the mouth of a mercenary murderer.

> Their lips were four red roses on a stalk,
> And *in their summer beauty* kissed each other!

Or this delicious description of concealed love, into that
of a regretful and moralizing parent.

> But he, his own affections' Counsellor,
> Is to himself so secret and so close,
> As is the bud bit with an envious worm
> Ere he can spread his sweet leaves to the air,
> Or dedicate his beauty to the sun.

And yet all these are so far from being unnatural, that
they are no sooner put where they are, than we feel at
once their beauty and their effect; and acknowledge our
obligations to that exuberant genius which alone could
thus throw out graces and attractions where there seemed
to be neither room nor call for them. In the same spirit
of prodigality he puts this rapturous and passionate
exaltation of the beauty of Imogen, into the mouth of
one who is not even a lover.

>   —It is her breathing that
> Perfumes the chamber thus! the flame o' th' taper
> Bows towards her! and would under-peep her lids
> To see th' enclosed lights, now canopied
> Under the windows, white and azure, laced
> With blue of Heaven's own tinct!—on her left breast
> A mole cinque-spotted, like the crimson drops
> I' the bottom of a cowslip!

THOMAS DE QUINCEY

On the Knocking at the Gate in 'Macbeth'[1]

FROM my boyish days I had always felt a great perplexity on one point in *Macbeth*. It was this: the knocking at the gate, which succeeds to the murder of Duncan, produced to my feelings an effect for which I never could account. The effect was, that it reflected back upon the murderer a peculiar awfulness and a depth of solemnity; yet, however obstinately I endeavoured with my understanding to comprehend this, for many years I never could see *why* it should produce such an effect.

Here I pause for one moment, to exhort the reader never to pay any attention to his understanding, when it stands in opposition to any other faculty of his mind. The mere understanding, however useful and indispensable, is the meanest faculty in the human mind, and the most to be distrusted; and yet the great majority of people trust to nothing else, which may do for ordinary life, but not for philosophical purposes. Of this out of ten thousand instances that I might produce, I will cite one. Ask of any person whatsoever, who is not previously prepared for the demand by a knowledge of the perspective, to draw in the rudest way the commonest appearance which depends upon the laws of that science; as, for instance, to represent the effect of two walls standing at right angles to each other, or the appearance of the houses on each side of a street, as seen by a person looking down the street from one extremity. Now in all cases, unless the person has happened to observe in pictures how it is that artists produce these effects, he will be utterly unable to make the smallest approximation

[1] First published in *The London Magazine*, October 1823.

to it. Yet why? For he has actually seen the effect every day of his life. The reason is—that he allows his understanding to overrule his eyes. His understanding, which includes no intuitive knowledge of the laws of vision, can furnish him with no reason why a line which is known and can be proved to be a horizontal line, should not *appear* a horizontal line; a line that made any angle with the perpendicular, less than a right angle, would seem to him to indicate that his houses were all tumbling down together. Accordingly, he makes the line of his houses a horizontal line, and fails, of course, to produce the effect demanded. Here, then, is one instance out of many, in which not only the understanding is allowed to overrule the eyes, but where the understanding is positively allowed to obliterate the eyes, as it were; for not only does the man believe the evidence of his understanding in opposition to that of his eyes, but (what is monstrous!) the idiot is not aware that his eyes ever gave such evidence. He does not know that he has seen (and therefore *quoad* his consciousness has *not* seen) that which he *has* seen every day of his life.

But to return from this digression, my understanding could furnish no reason why the knocking at the gate in *Macbeth* should produce any effect, direct or reflected. In fact, my understanding said positively that it could *not* produce any effect. But I knew better; I felt that it did; and I waited and clung to the problem until further knowledge should enable me to solve it. At length, in 1812, Mr. Williams made his *début* on the stage of Ratcliffe Highway, and executed those unparalleled murders which have procured for him such a brilliant and undying reputation. On which murders, by the way, I must observe, that in one respect they have had an ill effect, by making the connoisseur in murder very fastidious in his taste, and dissatisfied by anything that has

been since done in that line. All other murders look
pale by the deep crimson of his; and, as an amateur once
said to me in a querulous tone, 'There has been absolutely
nothing *doing* since his time, or nothing that's worth
speaking of.' But this is wrong; for it is unreasonable
to expect all men to be great artists, and born with the
genius of Mr. Williams. Now it will be remembered,
that in the first of these murders (that of the Marrs), the
same incident (of a knocking at the door) soon after the
work of extermination was complete, did actually occur,
which the genius of Shakespeare has invented; and all
good judges, and the most eminent dilettanti, acknowledged the felicity of Shakespeare's suggestion, as soon
as it was actually realized. Here, then, was a fresh proof
that I was right in relying on my own feeling, in opposition to my understanding; and I again set myself to study
the problem; at length I solved it to my own satisfaction,
and my solution is this. Murder, in ordinary cases,
where the sympathy is wholly directed to the case of the
murdered person, is an incident of coarse and vulgar
horror; and for this reason, that it flings the interest
exclusively upon the natural but ignoble instinct by
which we cleave to life; an instinct which, as being indispensable to the primal law of self-preservation, is the
same in kind (though different in degree) amongst all
living creatures: this instinct, therefore, because it anni-
hilates all distinctions, and degrades the greatest of men
to the level of 'the poor beetle that we tread on', exhibits human nature in its most abject and humiliating
attitude. Such an attitude would little suit the purposes
of the poet. What then must he do? He must throw
the interest on the murderer. Our sympathy must be
with *him* (of course I mean a sympathy of comprehension, a sympathy by which we enter into his feelings,
and are made to understand them,—not a sympathy of

pity or approbation[1]). In the murdered person, all strife
of thought, all flux and reflux of passion and of purpose,
are crushed by one overwhelming panic; the fear of
instant death smites him 'with its petrific mace'. But in
the murderer, such a murderer as a poet will condescend
to, there must be raging some great storm of passion—
jealousy, ambition, vengeance, hatred—which will
create a hell within him; and into this hell we are to
look.

In *Macbeth*, for the sake of gratifying his own enormous and teeming faculty of creation, Shakspere has
introduced two murderers: and, as usual in his hands,
they are remarkably discriminated: but, though in Macbeth the strife of mind is greater than in his wife, the
tiger spirit not so awake, and his feelings caught chiefly
by contagion from her,—yet, as both were finally involved in the guilt of murder, the murderous mind of
necessity is finally to be presumed in both. This was to
be expressed; and on its own account, as well as to make
it a more proportionable antagonist to the unoffending
nature of their victim, 'the gracious Duncan,' and adequately to expound 'the deep damnation of his taking
off', this was to be expressed with peculiar energy. We
were to be made to feel that the human nature, i.e. the
divine nature of love and mercy, spread through the
hearts of all creatures, and seldom utterly withdrawn

---

[1] It seems almost ludicrous to guard and explain my use of a
word, in a situation where it would naturally explain itself.
But it has become necessary to do so, in consequence of the
unscholarlike use of the word sympathy, at present so general,
by which, instead of taking it in its proper sense, as the act of
reproducing in our minds the feelings of another, whether for
hatred, indignation, love, pity, or approbation, it is made a mere
synonyme of the word *pity*; and hence, instead of saying 'sympathy *with* another', many writers adopt the monstrous barbarism of 'sympathy *for* another'.

from man—was gone, vanished, extinct, and that the
fiendish nature had taken its place. And, as this effect is
marvellously accomplished in the *dialogues* and *soliloquies* themselves, so it is finally consummated by the
expedient under consideration; and it is to this that I
now solicit the reader's attention. If the reader has ever
witnessed a wife, daughter, or sister in a fainting fit, he
may chance to have observed that the most affecting
moment in such a spectacle is *that* in which a sigh and a
stirring announce the recommencement of suspended
life. Or, if the reader has ever been present in a vast
metropolis, on the day when some great national idol
was carried in funeral pomp to his grave, and chancing
to walk near the course through which it passed, has
felt powerfully in the silence and desertion of the streets,
and in the stagnation of ordinary business, the deep interest which at that moment was possessing the heart of
man—if all at once he should hear the death-like stillness
broken up by the sound of wheels rattling away from
the scene, and making known that the transitory vision
was dissolved, he will be aware that at no moment was
his sense of the complete suspension and pause in ordinary human concerns so full and affecting, as at that
moment when the suspension ceases, and the goings-on
of human life are suddenly resumed. All action in any
direction is best expounded, measured, and made appre-
hensible, by reaction. Now apply this to the case in
Macbeth. Here, as I have said, the retiring of the human
heart, and the entrance of the fiendish heart was to be
expressed and made sensible. Another world has stept
in; and the murderers are taken out of the region of human things, human purposes, human desires. They are
transfigured: Lady Macbeth is 'unsexed;' Macbeth has
forgot that he was born of woman; both are conformed
to the image of devils; and the world of devils is suddenly

revealed. But how shall this be conveyed and made palpable? In order that a new world may step in, this world must for a time disappear. The murderers, and the murder must be insulated—cut off by an immeasurable gulf from the ordinary tide and succession of human affairs—locked up and sequestered in some deep recess; we must be made sensible that the world of ordinary life is suddenly arrested—laid asleep—tranced—racked into a dread armistice; time must be annihilated; relation to things without abolished; and all must pass self-withdrawn into a deep syncope and suspension of earthly passion. Hence it is, that when the deed is done, when the work of darkness is perfect, then the world of darkness passes away like a pageantry in the clouds: the knocking at the gate is heard; and it makes known audibly that the reaction has commenced; the human has made its reflux upon the fiendish; the pulses of life are beginning to beat again; and the re-establishment of the goings-on of the world in which we live, first makes us profoundly sensible of the awful parenthesis that had suspended them.

O mighty poet! Thy works are not as those of other men, simply and merely great works of art; but are also like the phenomena of nature, like the sun and the sea, the stars and the flowers; like frost and snow, rain and dew, hail-storm and thunder, which are to be studied with entire submission of our own faculties, and in the perfect faith that in them there can be no too much or too little, nothing useless or inert—but that, the farther we press in our discoveries, the more we shall see proofs of design and self-supporting arrangement where the careless eye had seen nothing but accident!

A Summary Survey[1]

AFTER this review of Shakspeare's life, it becomes our duty to take a summary survey of his works, of his intellectual powers, and of his station in literature,—a station which is now irrevocably settled, not so much (which happens in other cases) by a vast overbalance of favourable suffrages, as by acclamation; not so much by the *voices* of those who admire him up to the verge of idolatry, as by the *acts* of those who everywhere seek for his works among the primal necessities of life, demand them, and crave them as they do their daily bread; not so much by eulogy openly proclaiming itself, as by the silent homage recorded in the endless multiplication of what he has bequeathed us; not so much by his own compatriots, who, with regard to almost every other author,[2] compose the total amount of his *effective* audience, as by the unanimous 'All hail!' of intellectual Christendom; finally, not by the hasty partisanship of his own generation, nor by the biassed judgment of an age trained in the same modes of feeling and of thinking

---

[1] This is the conclusion of the article on Shakespeare contributed in 1838 to the seventh edition of the *Encyclopædia Britannica*.

[2] An exception ought perhaps to be made for Sir Walter Scott and for Cervantes; but with regard to all other writers, Dante, suppose, or Ariosto amongst Italians, Camoens amongst those of Portugal, Schiller amongst Germans, however ably they may have been naturalised in foreign languages, as all of those here mentioned (excepting only Ariosto) have in one part of their works been most powerfully naturalised in English, it still remains true (and the very sale of the books is proof sufficient) that an alien author never does take root in the general sympathies out of his own country; he takes his station in libraries, he is read by the man of learned leisure, he is known and valued by the refined and the elegant, but he is not (what Shakspeare is for Germany and America) in any proper sense a *popular* favourite.

with himself, but by the solemn award of generation
succeeding to generation, of one age correcting the
obliquities or peculiarities of another; by the verdict of
two hundred and thirty years, which have now elapsed
since the very *latest* of his creations, or of two hundred
and forty-seven years if we date from the earliest;
a verdict which has been continually revived and
re-opened, probed, searched, vexed, by criticism in
every spirit, from the most genial and intelligent, down
to the most malignant and scurrilously hostile which
feeble heads and great ignorance could suggest when
co-operating with impure hearts and narrow sensibilities; a verdict, in short, sustained and countersigned by
a longer series of writers, many of them eminent for
wit or learning, than were ever before congregated upon
any inquest relating to any author, be he who he might,
ancient[1] or modern, Pagan or Christian. It was a most
witty saying with respect to a piratical and knavish pub-
lisher, who made a trade of insulting the memories of
deceased authors by forged writings, that he was 'among
the new terrors of death.' But in the gravest sense it may
be affirmed of Shakspeare that he is among the modern
luxuries of life; that life, in fact, is a new thing, and one
more to be coveted, since Shakspeare has extended the
domains of human consciousness, and pushed its dark
frontiers into regions not so much as dimly descried or
even suspected before his time, far less illuminated (as
now they are) by beauty and tropical luxuriance of life.
For instance,—a single instance, indeed one which in
itself is a world of new revelation,—the possible beauty
of the female character had not been seen as in a dream
before Shakspeare called into perfect life the radiant
shapes of Desdemona, of Imogen, of Hermione, of

---

[1] It will occur to many readers that perhaps Homer may
furnish the sole exception to this sweeping assertion.

Perdita, of Ophelia, of Miranda, and many others. The
Una of Spenser, earlier by ten or fifteen years than most
of these, was an idealised portrait of female innocence
and virgin purity, but too shadowy and unreal for a
dramatic reality. And as to the Grecian classics, let not
the reader imagine for an instant that any prototype in
this field of Shakspearian power can be looked for there.
The *Antigone* and the *Electra* of the tragic poets are the
two leading female characters that classical antiquity
offers to our respect, but assuredly not to our impassioned love, as disciplined and exalted in the school of
Shakspeare. They challenge our admiration, severe,
and even stern, as impersonations of filial duty, cleaving
to the steps of a desolate and afflicted old man; or of
sisterly affection, maintaining the rights of a brother
under circumstances of peril, of desertion, and consequently of perfect self-reliance. Iphigenia, again, though
not dramatically coming before us in her own person,
but according to the beautiful report of a spectator, presents us with a fine statuesque model of heroic fortitude,
and of one whose young heart, even in the very agonies
of her cruel immolation, refused to forget, by a single
indecorous gesture, or so much as a moment's neglect
of her own princely descent, that she herself was 'a lady
in the land.' These are fine marble groups, but they are
not the warm breathing realities of Shakspeare; there is
'no speculation' in their cold marble eyes; the breath of
life is not in their nostrils; the fine pulses of womanly
sensibilities are not throbbing in their bosoms. And
besides this immeasurable difference between the cold
moony reflexes of life, as exhibited by the power of
Grecian art, and the true sunny life of Shakspeare, it
must be observed that the Antigones, &c., of the antique
put forward but one single trait of character, like the
aloe with its single blossom: this solitary feature is

presented to us as an abstraction, and as an insulated quality; whereas in Shakspeare all is presented in the *concrete*;
that is to say, not brought forward in relief, as by some
effort of an anatomical artist; but embodied and imbed-
ded, so to speak, as by the force of a creative nature, in
the complex system of a human life; a life in which all
the elements move and play simultaneously, and with
something more than mere simultaneity or co-existence,
acting and re-acting each upon the other—nay, even
acting by each other and through each other. In Shakspeare's characters is felt for ever a real *organic* life, where
each is for the whole and in the whole, and where the
whole is for each and in each. They only are real in-
carnations.

The Greek poets could not exhibit any approxima-
tions to *female* character, without violating the truth of
Grecian life, and shocking the feelings of the audience.
The drama with the Greeks, as with us, though much
less than with us, was a picture of human life; and that
which could not occur in life could not wisely be exhibited on the stage. Now, in ancient Greece, women
were secluded from the society of men. The conventual
sequestration of the γυναικωνίτις, or female apartment[1]
of the house, and the Mahommedan consecration of its
threshold against the ingress of males, had been transplanted from Asia into Greece thousands of years perhaps before either convents or Mahommed existed.
Thus barred from all open social intercourse, women
could not develop or express any character by word or
action. Even to *have* a character, violated, to a Grecian

[1] *Apartment* is here used, as the reader will observe, in its true
and continental acceptation, as a division or *compartment* of a house
including many rooms; a suite of chambers, but a suite which is
partitioned off (as in palaces), not a single chamber; a sense so
commonly and so erroneously given to this word in England.

mind, the ideal portrait of feminine excellence; whence,
perhaps, partly the too generic, too little individualized,
style of Grecian beauty. But prominently to *express* a
character was impossible under the common tenor of
Grecian life, unless when high tragical catastrophes
transcended the decorums, of that tenor, or for a brief
interval raised the curtain which veiled it. Hence the
subordinate part which women play upon the Greek stage
in all but some half dozen cases. In the paramount
tragedy on that stage, the model tragedy, the *Œdipus
Tyrannus* of Sophocles, there is virtually no woman at
all; for Jocasta is a party to the story merely as the dead
Laius or the self-murdered Sphinx was a party,—viz. by
her contributions to the fatalities of the event, not by
anything she does or says spontaneously. In fact, the
Greek poet, if a wise poet, could not address himself
genially to a task in which he must begin by shocking
the sensibilities of his countrymen. And hence followed,
not only the dearth of female characters in the Grecian
drama, but also a second result still more favourable to
the sense of a new power evolved by Shakspeare. Whenever the common law of Grecian life did give way, it
was, as we have observed, to the suspending force of
some great convulsion or tragical catastrophe. This for
a moment (like an earthquake in a nunnery) would set
at liberty even the timid, fluttering Grecian women,
those doves of the dove-cot, and would call some of
them into action. But which? Precisely those of energetic and masculine minds; the timid and feminine
would but shrink the more from public gaze and from
tumult. Thus it happened, that such female characters
as *were* exhibited in Greece, could not but be the harsh
and the severe. If a gentle Ismene appeared for a moment in contest with some energetic sister Antigone
(and chiefly, perhaps, by way of drawing out the fiercer

character of that sister), she was soon dismissed as unfit
for scenical effect. So that not only were female characters few, but, moreover, of these few the majority
were but repetitions of masculine qualities in female
persons. Female agency being seldom summoned on
the stage except when it had received a sort of special
dispensation from its sexual character, by some terrific
convulsions of the house or the city, naturally it assumed
the style of action suited to these circumstances. And
hence it arose, that not woman as she differed from man,
but woman as she resembled man—woman, in short,
seen under circumstances so dreadful as to abolish the
effect of sexual distinction, was the woman of the Greek
tragedy.[1] And hence generally arose for Shakspeare the
wider field, and the more astonishing by its perfect
novelty, when he first introduced female characters, not
as mere varieties or echoes of masculine characters, a
Medea or Clytemnestra, or a vindictive Hecuba, the
mere tigress of the tragic tiger, but female characters
that had the appropriate beauty of female nature; woman no longer grand, terrific, and repulsive, but woman
'after her kind'—the other hemisphere of the dramatic
world; woman running through the vast gamut of
womanly loveliness; woman as emancipated, exalted,
ennobled, under a new law of Christian morality; woman
the sister and co-equal of man, no longer his slave, his
prisoner, and sometimes his rebel. 'It is a far cry to Loch
Awe;' and from the Athenian stage to the stage of Shakspeare, it may be said, is a prodigious interval. True;
but prodigious as it is, there is really nothing between

---

[1] And hence, by parity of reason, under the opposite circumstances, under the circumstances which, instead of abolish-
ing, most emphatically drew forth the sexual distinctions, viz.
in the *comic* aspects of social intercourse, the reason that we see
no women on the Greek stage; the Greek comedy, unless when
it affects the extravagant fun of farce, rejects women.

them. The Roman stage, at least the tragic stage, as is
well known, was put out, as by an extinguisher, by the
cruel amphitheatre, just as a candle is made pale and
ridiculous by daylight. Those who were fresh from the
real murders of the bloody amphitheatre regarded with
contempt the mimic murders of the stage. Stimulation
too coarse and too intense had its usual effect in making
the sensibilities callous. Christian emperors arose at
length, who abolished the amphitheatre in its bloodier
features. But by that time the genius of the tragic muse
had long slept the sleep of death. And that muse had
no resurrection until the age of Shakspeare. So that,
notwithstanding a gulf of nineteen centuries and up-
wards separates Shakspeare from Euripides, the last of
the surviving Greek tragedians, the one is still the nearest
successor of the other, just as Connaught and the islands
in Clew Bay are next neighbours to America, although
three thousand watery columns, each of a cubic mile in
dimensions, divide them from each other.

A second reason, which lends an emphasis of novelty
and effective power to Shakspeare's female world, is a
peculiar fact of contrast which exists between that and
his corresponding world of men. Let us explain. The
purpose and the intention of the Grecian stage was not
primarily to develop human *character*, whether in men
or in women; human *fates* were its object; great tragic
situations under the mighty control of a vast cloudy
destiny, dimly descried at intervals, and brooding over
human life by mysterious agencies, and for mysterious
ends. Man, no longer the representative of an august
will,—man, the passion-puppet of fate, could not with
any effect display what we call a character, which is a
distinction between man and man, emanating originally
from the will, and expressing its determinations, moving
under the large variety of human impulses. The will is

the central pivot of character; and this was obliterated, thwarted, cancelled, by the dark fatalism which brooded over the Grecian stage. That explanation will sufficiently clear up the reason why marked or complex variety of character was slighted by the great principles of the Greek tragedy. And every scholar who has studied that grand drama of Greece with feeling,—that drama, so magnificent, so regal, so stately,—and who has thought-fully investigated its principles, and its differences from the English drama, will acknowledge that powerful and elaborate character,—character, for instance, that could employ the fiftieth part of that profound analysis which has been applied to Hamlet, to Falstaff, to Lear, to Othello, and applied by Mrs. Jameson so admirably to the full development of the Shakspearian heroines, would have been as much wasted, nay, would have been defeated, and interrupted the blind agencies of fate, just in the same way as it would injure the shadowy grandeur of a ghost to individualize it too much. Milton's angels are slightly touched, superficially touched, with differences of character; but they are such differences, so simple and general, as are just sufficient to rescue them from the reproach applied to Virgil's '*fortemque Gyan, fortemque Cloanthem;*' just sufficient to make them know-able apart. Pliny speaks of painters who painted in one or two colours; and, as respects the angelic characters, Milton does so; he is *monochromatic*. So, and for reasons resting upon the same ultimate philosophy, were the mighty architects of the Greek tragedy. They also were monochromatic; they also, as to the characters of their persons, painted in one colour. And so far there might have been the same novelty in Shakspeare's men as in his women. There *might* have been; but the reason why there is *not*, must be sought in the fact, that History, the muse of History, had there even been no such muse as

Melpomene, would have forced us into an acquaintance with human character. History, as the representative of actual life, of real man, gives us powerful delineations of character in its chief agents, that is, in men; and therefore it is that Shakspeare, the absolute creator of female character, was but the mightiest of all painters with regard to male character. Take a single instance. The Antony of Shakspeare, immortal for its execution, is found, after all, as regards the primary conception, in history: Shakspeare's delineation is but the expansion of the germ already pre-existing, by way of scattered fragments, in Cicero's Philippics, in Cicero's Letters, in Appian, &c. But Cleopatra, equally fine, is a pure creation of art: the situation and the scenic circumstances belong to history, but the character belongs to Shakspeare.

In the great world therefore of woman, as the interpreter of the shifting phases and the lunar varieties of that mighty changeable planet, that lovely satellite of man, Shakspeare stands not the first only, not the original only, but is yet the sole authentic oracle of truth. Woman, therefore, the beauty of the female mind, *this* is one great field of his power. The supernatural world, the world of apparitions, *that* is another: for reasons which it would be easy to give, reasons emanating from the gross mythology of the ancients, no Grecian,[1] no

[1] It may be thought, however, by some readers, that Æschylus, in his fine phantom of Darius, has approached the English ghost. As a foreign ghost, we would wish (and we are sure that our excellent readers would wish) to show every courtesy and attention to this apparition of Darius. It has the advantage of being royal, an advantage which it shares with the ghost of the royal Dane. Yet how different, how removed by a total world, from that or any of Shakspeare's ghosts! Take that of Banquo, for instance: how shadowy, how unreal, yet how real! Darius is a mere state ghost—a diplomatic ghost. But Banquo—he exists only for Macbeth: the guests do not see him, yet how solemn, how real, how heart-searching he is!

Roman, could have conceived a ghost. That shadowy
conception, the protesting apparition, the awful projection of the human conscience, belongs to the Christian
mind: and in all Christendom, who, let us ask, who, but
Shakspeare, has found the power for effectually working
this mysterious mode of being? In summoning back to
earth 'the majesty of buried Denmark,' how like an
awful necromancer does Shakspeare appear! All the
pomps and grandeurs which religion, which the grave,
which the popular superstition had gathered about the
subject of apparitions, are here converted to his purpose,
and bend to one awful effect. The wormy grave brought
into antagonism with the scenting of the early dawn;
the trumpet of resurrection suggested, and again as an
antagonist idea to the crowing of the cock (a bird ennobled in the Christian mythus by the part he is made
to play at the Crucifixion); its starting 'as a guilty thing'
placed in opposition to its majestic expression of offended
dignity when struck at by the partisans of the sentinels;
its awful allusions to the secrets of its prison-house; its
ubiquity, contrasted with its local presence; its aerial
substance, yet clothed in palpable armour; the heart-
shaking solemnity of its language, and the appropriate
scenery of its haunt, viz. the ramparts of a capital fortress,
with no witnesses but a few gentlemen mounting guard
at the dead of night,—what a mist, what a *mirage* of
vapour, is here accumulated, through which the dreadful being in the centre looms upon us in far larger proportions than could have happened had it been insulated and
left naked of this circumstantial pomp! In the *Tempest*,
again, what new modes of life, preternatural, yet far as
the poles from the spiritualities of religion. Ariel in
antithesis to Caliban![1] What is most ethereal to what is

[1] Caliban has not yet been thoroughly fathomed. For all
Shakspeare's great creations are like works of nature, subjects

most animal! A phantom of air, an abstraction of the dawn and of vesper sun-lights, a bodiless sylph on the one hand; on the other a gross carnal monster, like the Miltonic Asmodai, 'the fleshliest incubus' among the fiends, and yet so far ennobled into interest by his intellectual power, and by the grandeur of misanthropy! In the *Midsummer-Night's Dream*, again, we have the old traditional fairy, a lovely mode of preternatural life, remodified by Shakspeare's eternal talisman. Oberon and Titania remind us at first glance of Ariel; they approach, but how far they recede: they are like—'like, but oh, how different!' And in no other exhibition of this dreamy population of the moonlight forests and forest-lawns are the circumstantial proprieties of fairy life so exquisitely imagined, sustained, or expressed. The dialogue between Oberon and Titania is, of itself, and taken separately from its connection, one of the most delightful poetic scenes that literature affords. The witches in Macbeth are another variety of supernatural

of unexhaustible study. It was this character of whom Charles I and some of his ministers expressed such fervent admiration; and, among other circumstances, most justly they admired the new language almost with which he is endowed, for the purpose of expressing his fiendish and yet carnal thoughts of hatred to his master. Caliban is evidently not meant for scorn, but for abomination mixed with fear and partial respect. He is purposely brought into contrast with the drunken Trinculo and Stephano, with an advantageous result. He is much more intellectual than either, uses a more elevated language, not disfigured by vulgarisms, and is not liable to the low passion for plunder as they are. He is mortal, doubtless, as his 'dam' (for Shakspeare will not call her mother) Sycorax. But he inherits from her such qualities of power as a witch could be supposed to bequeath. He trembles indeed before Prospero; but that is, as we are to understand, through the moral superiority of Prospero in Christian wisdom; for when he finds himself in the presence of dissolute and unprincipled men, he rises at once into the dignity of intellectual power.

life, in which Shakspeare's power to enchant and to disenchant are alike portentous. The circumstances of the
blasted heath, the army at a distance, the withered attire
of the mysterious hags, and the choral litanies of their
fiendish Sabbath, are as finely imagined in their kind as
those which herald and which surround the ghost in
Hamlet. There we see the *positive* of Shakspeare's
superior power. But now turn and look to the *negative*.
At a time when the trials of witches, the royal book on
demonology, and popular superstition (all so far useful,
as they prepared a basis of undoubting faith for the
poet's serious use of such agencies) had degraded and
polluted the ideas of these mysterious beings by many
mean associations, Shakspeare does not fear to employ
them in high tragedy (a tragedy moreover which,
though not the very greatest of his efforts as an intellectual whole, nor as a struggle of passion, is *among* the
greatest in any view, and positively *the* greatest for scenical grandeur, and in that respect makes the nearest
approach of all English tragedies to the Grecian model);
he does not fear to introduce, for the same appalling
effect as that for which Æschylus introduced the Eumenides, a triad of old women, concerning whom an
English wit has remarked this grotesque peculiarity in
the popular creed of that day,—that although potent
over winds and storms, in league with powers of darkness, they yet stood in awe of the constable,—yet relying on his own supreme power to disenchant as well as
to enchant, to create and to uncreate, he mixes these
women and their dark machineries with the power of
armies, with the agencies of kings, and the fortunes of
martial kingdoms. Such was the sovereignty of this
poet, so mighty its compass!

A third fund of Shakspeare's peculiar power lies in
his teeming fertility of fine thoughts and sentiments.

From his works alone might be gathered a golden bead-roll of thoughts the deepest, subtlest, most pathetic, and yet most catholic and universally intelligible; the most characteristic, also, and appropriate to the particular person, the situation, and the case, yet, at the same time, applicable to the circumstances of every human being, under all the accidents of life, and all vicissitudes of fortune. But this subject offers so vast a field of observation, it being so eminently the prerogative of Shakspeare to have thought more finely and more extensively than all other poets combined, that we cannot wrong the dignity of such a theme by doing more, in our narrow limits, than simply noticing it as one of the emblazonries upon Shakspeare's shield.

Fourthly, we shall indicate (and, as in the last case, *barely* indicate, without attempting in so vast a field to offer any inadequate illustrations) one mode of Shakspeare's dramatic excellence which hitherto has not attracted any special or separate notice. We allude to the forms of life, and natural human passion, as apparent in the structure of his dialogue. Among the many defects and infirmities of the French and of the Italian drama, indeed we may say of the Greek, the dialogue proceeds always by independent speeches, replying indeed to each other, but never modified in its several openings by the momentary effect of its several terminal forms immediately preceding. Now, in Shakspeare, who first set an example of that most important innovation, in all his impassioned dialogues, each reply or rejoinder seems the mere rebound of the previous speech. Every form of natural interruption, breaking through the restraints of ceremony under the impulses of tempestuous passion; every form of hasty interrogative, ardent reiteration when a question has been evaded; every form of scornful repetition of the hostile words;

every impatient continuation of the hostile statement; in short, all modes and formulæ by which anger, hurry, fretfulness, scorn, impatience, or excitement under any movement whatever, can disturb or modify or dislocate the formal bookish style of commencement,—these are as rife in Shakspeare's dialogue as in life itself; and how much vivacity, how profound a verisimilitude, they add to the scenic effect as an imitation of human passion and real life, we need not say. A volume might be written illustrating the vast varieties of Shakspeare's art and power in this one field of improvement; another volume might be dedicated to the exposure of the lifeless and unnatural result from the opposite practice in the foreign stages of France and Italy. And we may truly say, that were Shakspeare distinguished from them by this single feature of nature and propriety, he would on that account alone have merited a great immortality.

WALTER SAVAGE LANDOR

IMAGINARY CONVERSATIONS

Southey and Porson

Southey. . . . In so wide and untrodden a creation as that of Shakspeare, can we wonder or complain that sometimes we are bewildered and entangled in the exuberance of fertility? Dry-brained men upon the Continent, the trifling wits of the theatre, accurate however and expert calculators, tell us that his beauties are balanced by his faults. The poetical opposition, puffing for popularity, cry cheerily against them, *his faults are balanced by his beauties*; when, in reality, all the faults that ever were committed in poetry would be but as air to earth, if we could weigh them against one single thought or image, such as almost every scene exhibits in every drama of this unrivalled genius. Do you hear me with patience?

Porson. With more; although at Cambridge we rather discourse on Bacon, for we know him better. He was immeasurably a less wise man than Shakspeare, and not a wiser writer: for he knew his fellow-man only as he saw him in the street and in the court, which indeed is but a dirtier street and a narrower: Shakspeare, who also knew him there, knew him everywhere else, both as he was, and as he might be.

Southey. There is as great a difference between Shakspeare and Bacon as between an American forest and a London timber-yard. In the timber-yard the materials are sawed and squared and set across: in the forest we have the natural form of the tree, all its growth, all its branches, all its leaves, all the mosses that grow about it, all the birds and insects that inhabit it: now deep shadows

absorbing the whole wilderness; now bright bursting
glades, with exuberant grass and flowers and fruitage;
now untroubled skies; now terrific thunderstorms;
everywhere multiformity, everywhere immensity.

Works, ed. 1846, vol. i. pp. 14, 15.

The Abbé Delille and Landor

Delille. Even your immortal Shakspeare borrowed from
others.

Landor. Yet he was more original than the originals.
He breathed upon dead bodies and brought them into
life.

Delille. I think however I can trace Caliban, that
wonderful creature, when I survey attentively the Cyclops of Euripides.

Landor. He knew nothing of Euripides or his Cyclops. . . . No good writer was ever long neglected; no great man overlooked by men equally great.
Impatience is a proof of inferior strength, and a des-
troyer of what little there may be. Whether, think you,
would Shakspeare be amused or mortified, if he were
sitting in the pit during the performance of his best
tragedy, and heard no other exclamation from one beside him, than, 'How beautifully those scenes are painted!
what palaces, waterfalls, and rocks!'

Delille. I wish he were more dramatic.

Landor. You would say, more observant of certain
rules established for one species of the drama. Never
was poet so dramatic, so intelligent of stage-effect. I do
not defend his anachronisms, nor his confusion of modern customs with ancient; nor do I willingly join him
when I find him with Hector and Aristoteles, arm-in-
arm, among knights, esquires, and fiddlers. But our
audiences and our princes in those days were resolved

that all countries and all ages should be subservient at
once, and perceived no incongruity in bringing them
together.

Delille. Yet what argument can remove the objection
made against your poet, of introducing those who in
the first act are children, and grown-up men in the last?

Landor. Such a drama I would not call by the name of
tragedy: nevertheless it is a drama; and a very beautiful
species of it. Delightful in the first degree are those pieces
of history in verse and action, as managed by Shakspeare.

Delille. We must contend against them: we must
resist all barbarous inroads on classic ground, all innovations and abuses.

Landor. You fight against your own positions. Such
a work is to Tragedy what a forest is to a garden. Those
alone are wrong who persist in calling it a garden rather
than a forest; who find oaks instead of tulips; who look
about the hills and dales, the rocks and precipices, the
groves and waterfalls, for flues and balusters and vases,
and smooth marble steps, and shepherdesses in hoops
and satin. There are some who think these things as unnatural as that children should grow into men, and that
we should live to see it.

Delille. Live to see it! but in one day or night!

Landor. The same events pass before us within the
same space of time whenever we look into history.

Delille. Ay, but here they act.

Landor. So they do there, unless the history is an
English one. And indeed the histories of our country
read by Shakspeare held human life within them. When
we are interested in the boy, we spring forward to the
man, with more than a poet's velocity. We would
interrogate the oracles; we would measure the thread
around the distaff of the Fates; yet we quarrel with him
who knows and tells us all.

Glory to thee in the highest, thou confidant of our Creator! who alone hast taught us in every particle of the mind how wonderfully and fearfully we are made.

Delille. Voltaire was indeed too severe upon him.

Landor. Severe? Is it severity to throw a crab or a pincushion at the Farnese Hercules or the Belvedere Apollo? It is folly, perverseness, and impudence, in poets and critics like Voltaire, whose best composition in verse is a hard mosaic, sparkling and superficial, of squares and parallelograms, one speck each. He, whose poems are worth all that have been composed from the Creation to the present hour, was so negligent or so secure of fame as to preserve no copy of them. Homer and he confided to the hearts of men the treasures of their genius, which were, like conscience, unengraved words.   .   .   .

Landor. We have wandered (and conversation would be tedious unless we did occasionally) far from the subject: but I have not forgotten our Cyclops and Caliban. The character of the Cyclops is somewhat broad and general, but worthy of Euripides, and such as the greatest of Roman poets was incapable of conceiving; that of Caliban is peculiar and stands single; it is admirably imagined and equally well sustained. Another poet would have shown him spiteful: Shakspeare has made the infringement of his idleness the origin of his malice. He has also made him grateful; but then his gratitude is the return for an indulgence granted to his evil appetites. Those who by nature are grateful are often by nature vindictive: one of these properties is the sense of kindness, the other of unkindness. Religion and comfort require that the one should be cherished and that the other should be suppressed. The mere conception of the monster without these qualities, without the sudden impressions which bring them vividly out, and the circumstances in which they are displayed, would not be to considerate minds so stupendous as it appeared to Warton, who little knew that there is a *nil admirari* as requisite to wisdom as to happiness.

Delille. And yet how enthusiastic is your admiration of Shakespeare.

Landor.

> He lighted with his golden lamp on high
> The unknown regions of the human heart,
> Show'd its bright fountains, show'd its rueful wastes,
> Its shoals and headlands; and a tower he rais'd
> Refulgent, where eternal breakers roll,
> For all to see, but no man to approach.

The creation of Caliban, wonderful as it is, would excite in me less admiration than a single sentence, or a single sentiment, such as I find in fifty of his pages.

Id. pp. 102–5.

Milton and Andrew Marvel

Milton. The historical dramas of Shakspeare should be designated by that name only, and not be called trage-dies, lest persons who reflect little (and how few reflect much?) should try them by the rules of Aristoteles; which would be as absurd as to try a gem upon a touch-stone. Shakespeare, in these particularly, but also in the rest, can only be relished by a people which retains its feelings and character in perfection. The French, more than any other, are transmuted by the stream that runs over them, like the baser metals. Beautiful poems, in dialogue too, may be composed on the greater part of a life, if that life be eventful, and if there be a proper choice of topics. *Votivâ veluti depicta tabellâ.*

No other than Shakspeare hath ever yet been able to give unceasing interest to similar pieces: but he has given

it amply to such as understand him. Sometimes his
levity (we hear) is misplaced. Human life is exhibited
not only in its calamities and its cares, but in the gay
unguarded hours of ebullient and confident prosperity;
and we are the more deeply interested in the reverses of
those whose familiarity we long enjoyed, and whose
festivity we have recently partaken.

Id. p. 123.

Southey and Landor

Landor. A rib of Shakspeare would have made a Milton:
the same portion of Milton, all poets born ever since.

Id. vol. ii. p. 74.

Southey and Landor
(Second Conversation.)

Southey. Shakspeare, whom you not only prefer to
every other poet, but think he contains more poetry
and more wisdom than all the rest united, is surely less
grand in his designs than several.

Landor. To the eye. But *Othello* was loftier than the
citadel of *Troy*; and what a *Paradise* fell before him! Let
us descend; for from *Othello* we *must* descend, whatever
road we take; let us look at *Julius Caesar.* No man ever
overcame such difficulties, or produced by his life and
death such a change in the world we inhabit. But that
also is a grand design which displays the interior workings of the world within us, and where we see the imperishable and unalterable passions depicted *al fresco* on
a lofty dome. Our other dramatists painted only on
the shambles, and represented what they found there;
blood and garbage. We leave them a few paces behind
us, and step over the gutter into the green-market. . . .

Landor. I wish Milton had abstained from calling

'Aeschylus, Sophocles, and Euripides, the three tragic poets unequalled *yet* by any;' because it may leave a suspicion that he fancied he, essentially undramatic, could equal them, and had now done it; and because it exhibits him as a detractor from Shakspeare. I am as sorry to find him in this condition as I should have been to find him in a fit of the gout, or treading on a nail with naked foot in his blindness.

Southey. Unfortunately it is impossible to exculpate him; for you must have remarked where, a few sentences above, are these expressions. 'This is mentioned to vindicate from the *small esteem, or rather infamy*, which in the account of many, it undergoes at this day, with other common interludes; happening through the poet's error of intermixing *comick stuff with tragick sadness and gravity*, or intermixing trivial and vulgar persons, which, by all judicious, hath been counted absurd, and brought in without discretion, corruptly to gratify the people.'

Landor. It may be questioned whether the people in the reign of Elizabeth, or indeed the queen herself, would have been contented with a drama without a smack of the indecent or the ludicrous. They had alike been accustomed to scenes of ribaldry and of bloodshed; and the palace opened on one wing to the brothel, on the other to the shambles. The clowns of Shakspeare are still admired by not the vulgar only.

Southey. The more the pity. Let them appear in their proper places. But a picture by Morland or Frank Hals ought never to break a series of frescoes by the hand of Raphael, or of senatorial portraits animated by the sun of Titian. There is much to be regretted in, and (since we are alone I will say it) a little which might without loss or injury be rejected from, the treasury of Shakspeare.

Landor. It is difficult to sweep away anything and not

to sweep away gold-dust with it! but viler dust lies thick in some places. The grave Milton too has cobwebs hanging on his workshop, which a high broom, in a steady hand, may reach without doing mischief. But let children and short men, and unwary ones, stand out of the way.

Id. pp. 157–61.

THOMAS CARLYLE

The Hero as Poet

OF this Shakspeare of ours, perhaps the opinion one sometimes hears a little idolatrously expressed is, in fact, the right one; I think the best judgement not of this country only, but of Europe at large, is slowly pointing to the conclusion, That Shakspeare is the chief of all Poets hitherto; the greatest intellect who, in our recorded world, has left record of himself in the way of Literature. On the whole, I know not such a power of vision, such a faculty of thought, if we take all the characters of it, in any other man. Such a calmness of depth; placid joyous strength; all things imaged in that great soul of his so true and clear, as in a tranquil unfathomable sea! It has been said, that in the constructing of Shakspeare's Dramas there is, apart from all other 'faculties' as they are called, an understanding manifested, equal to that in Bacon's *Novum Organum*. That is true; and it is not a truth that strikes every one. It would become more apparent if we tried, any of us for himself, how, out of Shakspeare's dramatic materials, *we* could fashion such a result! The built house seems all so fit,—everyway as it should be, as if it came there by its own law and the nature of things,—we forget the rude disorderly quarry it was shaped from. The very perfection of the house, as if Nature herself had made it, hides the builder's merit. Perfect, more perfect than any other man, we may call Shakspeare in this: he discerns, knows as by instinct, what condition he works under, what his materials are, what his own force and its relation to them is. It is not a transitory glance of insight that will suffice; it is deliberate illumination of the whole matter; it is a calmly *seeing* eye; a great intellect, in short. How a man, of some wide thing that he has witnessed, will construct a narrative, what kind of picture and delineation he will give of it,—is the best measure you could get of what intellect is in the man. Which circumstance is vital and shall stand prominent; which unessential, fit to be suppressed; where is the true *beginning*, the true sequence and ending? To find out this, you task the whole force of insight that is in the man. He must *understand* the thing; according to the depth of his understanding, will the fitness of his answer be. You will try him so. Does like join itself to like; does the spirit of method stir in that confusion, so that its embroilment becomes order? Can the man say, *Fiat lux*, Let there be light; and out of chaos make a world? Precisely as there is *light* in himself, will he accomplish this.

Or indeed we may say again, it is in what I called Portrait-painting, delineating of men and things, especially of men, that Shakspeare is great. All the greatness of the man comes out decisively here. It is unexampled, I think, that calm creative perspicacity of Shakspeare. The thing he looks at reveals not this or that face of it, but its inmost heart and generic secret: it dissolves itself as in light before him, so that he discerns the perfect structure of it. Creative, we said: poetic creation, what is this too but *seeing* the thing sufficiently? The *word* that will describe the thing, follows of itself from such clear intense sight of the thing. And is not Shakspeare's *morality*, his valour, candour, tolerance, truthfulness; his whole victorious strength and greatness, which can triumph over such obstructions, visible there too? Great as the world! No *twisted*, poor convex-concave mirror, reflecting all objects with its own convexities and concavities; a perfectly *level* mirror;—that is to say withal, if we will understand it, a man justly related to all things and men, a good man. It is truly a lordly spectacle how this great soul takes in all kinds of men and objects, a Falstaff, an Othello, a Juliet, a Coriolanus; sets them all forth to us in their round completeness; loving, just, the equal brother of all. *Novum Organum*, and all the intellect you will find in Bacon, is of a quite secondary order; earthy, material, poor in comparison with this. Among modern men, one finds, in strictness, almost nothing of the same rank. Goethe alone, since the days of Shakspeare, reminds me of it. Of him too you say that he *saw* the object; you may say what he himself says of Shakspeare: 'His characters are like watches with dial-plates of transparent crystal; they show you the hour like others, and the inward mechanism also is all visible.'

The seeing eye! It is this that discloses the inner harmony of things; what Nature meant, what musical idea Nature has wrapped up in these often rough embodiments. Something she did mean. To the seeing eye that something were discernible. Are they base, miserable things? You can laugh over them, you can weep over them; you can in some way or other genially relate yourself to them;—you can, at lowest, hold your peace about them, turn away your own and others' face from them, till the hour come for practically exterminating and extinguishing them! At bottom, it is the Poet's first gift, as it is all men's, that he have intellect enough. He will be a Poet if he have: a Poet in word; or failing that, perhaps still better, a Poet in act. Whether he write at all; and if so, whether in prose or in verse, will depend on accidents: who knows on what extremely trivial accidents,—perhaps on his having had a singing-master, on his being taught to sing in his boyhood! But the faculty which enables him to discern the inner heart of things, and the harmony that dwells there (for whatsoever exists has a harmony in the heart of it, or it would not hold together and exist), is not the result of habits or accidents, but the gift of Nature herself; the primary outfit for a Heroic Man in what sort soever. To the Poet, as to every other, we say first of all, *See*. If you cannot do that, it is of no use to keep stringing rhymes together, jingling sensibilities against each other, and *name* yourself a Poet; there is no hope for you. If you can, there is, in prose or verse, in action or speculation, all manner of hope. The crabbed old Schoolmaster used to ask, when they brought him a new pupil, 'But are ye sure he's *not a dunce*?' Why, really one might ask the same thing, in regard to every man proposed for whatsoever function; and consider it as the one inquiry needful: Are ye sure he's not a dunce? There is, in this world, no other entirely fatal person.

For, in fact, I say the degree of vision that dwells in a man is a correct measure of the man. If called to define Shakspeare's faculty, I should say superiority of Intellect, and think I had included all under that. What indeed are faculties? We talk of faculties as if they were distinct, things separable; as if a man had intellect, imagination, fancy, &c., as he has hands, feet and arms. That is a capital error. Then again, we hear of a man's 'intellectual nature', and of his 'moral nature', as if these again were divisible, and existed apart. Necessities of language do perhaps prescribe such forms of utterance; we must speak, I am aware, in that way, if we are to speak at all. But words ought not to harden into things for us. It seems to me, our apprehension of this matter is, for most part, radically falsified thereby. We ought to know withal, and to keep forever in mind, that these divisions are at bottom but *names*; that man's spiritual nature, the vital Force which dwells in him, is essentially one and indivisible; that what we call imagination, fancy, understanding, and so forth, are but different figures of the same Power of Insight, all indissolubly connected with each other, physiognomically related; that if we knew one of them, we might know all of them. Morality itself, what we call the moral quality of a man, what is this but another *side* of the one vital Force whereby he is and works? All that a man does is physiognomical of him. You may see how a man would fight, by the way in which he sings; his courage, or want of courage, is visible in the word he utters, in the opinion he has formed, no less than in the stroke he strikes. He is *one*; and preaches the same Self abroad in all these ways.

Without hands a man might have feet, and could still walk: but, consider it,—without morality, intellect were impossible for him; a thoroughly immoral *man* could not know anything at all! To know a thing, what we can call knowing, a man must first *love* the thing, sympathize with it: that is, be *virtuously* related to it. If he have not the justice to put down his own selfishness at every turn, the courage to stand by the dangerous-true at every turn, how shall he know? His virtues, all of them, will lie recorded in his knowledge. Nature, with her truth, remains to the bad, to the selfish and the pusillanimous forever a sealed book: what such can know of Nature is mean, superficial, small; for the uses of the day merely.—But does not the very Fox know something of Nature? Exactly so: it knows where the geese lodge! The human Reynard, very frequent everywhere in the world, what more does he know but this and the like of this? Nay, it should be considered too, that if the Fox had not a certain vulpine *morality*, he could not even know where the geese were, or get at the geese! If he spent his time in splenetic atrabiliar reflections on his own misery, his ill usage by Nature, Fortune and other Foxes, and so forth; and had not courage, promptitude, practicality, and other suitable vulpine gifts and graces, he would catch no geese. We may say of the Fox too, that his morality and insight are of the same dimensions; different faces of the same internal unity of vulpine life!—These things are worth stating; for the contrary of them acts with manifold very baleful perversion, in this time: what limitations, modifications they require, your own candour will supply.

If I say, therefore, that Shakspeare is the greatest of Intellects, I have said all concerning him. But there is more in Shakspeare's intellect than we have yet seen. It is what I call an unconscious intellect; there is more virtue in it than he himself is aware of. Novalis beautifully remarks of him, that those Dramas of his are Products of Nature too, deep as Nature herself. I find a great truth in this saying. Shakspeare's Art is not Artifice; the noblest worth of it is not there by plan or precontrivance. It grows up from the deeps of Nature, through this noble sincere soul, who is a voice of Nature. The latest generations of men will find new meanings in Shakspeare, new elucidations of their own human being; 'new harmonies with the infinite structure of the Universe; concurrences with later ideas, affinities with the higher powers and senses of man.' This well deserves meditating. It is Nature's highest reward to a true simple great soul, that he get thus to be *a part of herself*. Such a man's works, whatsoever he with utmost conscious exertion and forethought shall accomplish, grow up withal *un*consciously, from the unknown deeps in him; —as the oak-tree grows from the Earth's bosom, as the mountains and waters shape themselves; with a symmetry grounded on Nature's own laws, conformable to all Truth whatsoever. How much in Shakspeare lies hid; his sorrows, his silent struggles known to himself;

much that was not known at all, not speakable at all:
like *roots*, like sap and forces working underground!
Speech is great; but Silence is greater.

Withal the joyful tranquillity of this man is notable.
I will not blame Dante for his misery: it is as battle without victory; but true battle,—the first, indispensable
thing. Yet I call Shakspeare greater than Dante, in that
he fought truly, and did conquer. Doubt it not, he had
his own sorrows: those *Sonnets* of his will even testify
expressly in what deep waters he had waded, and swum
struggling for his life;—as what man like him ever failed
to have to do? It seems to me a heedless notion, our
common one, that he sat like a bird on the bough; and
sang forth, free and offhand, never knowing the troubles
of other men. Not so; with no man is it so. How could
a man travel forward from rustic deer-poaching to such
tragedy-writing, and not fall in with sorrows by the
way? Or, still better, how could a man delineate a Hamlet, a Coriolanus, a Macbeth, so many suffering heroic
hearts, if his own heroic heart had never suffered?—
And now, in contrast with all this, observe his mirth-
fulness, his genuine overflowing love of laughter! You
would say, in no point does he *exaggerate* but only in
laughter. Fiery objurgations, words that pierce and
burn, are to be found in Shakspeare; yet he is always in
measure here; never what Johnson would remark as a
specially 'good hater'. But his laughter seems to pour
from him in floods; he heaps all manner of ridiculous
nicknames on the butt he is bantering, tumbles and
tosses him in all sorts of horse-play; you would say,
roars and laughs. And then, if not always the finest, it
is always a genial laughter. Not at mere weakness, at
misery or poverty; never. No man who *can* laugh, what
we call laughing, will laugh at these things. It is some
poor character only *desiring* to laugh, and have the credit

of wit, that does so. Laughter means sympathy; good laughter is not 'the crackling of thorns under the pot'. Even at stupidity and pretension this Shakspeare does not laugh otherwise than genially. Dogberry and Verges tickle our very hearts; and we dismiss them covered with explosions of laughter: but we like the poor fellows only the better for our laughing; and hope they will get on well there, and continue Presidents of the City-watch.—Such laughter, like sunshine on the deep sea, is very beautiful to me.

We have no room to speak of Shakspeare's individual works; though perhaps there is much still waiting to be said on that head. Had we, for instance, all his plays reviewed as *Hamlet*, in *Wilhelm Meister*, is! A thing which might, one day, be done. August Wilhelm Schlegel has a remark on his Historical Plays, *Henry Fifth* and the others, which is worth remembering. He calls them a kind of National Epic. Marlborough, you recollect, said, he knew no English History but what he had learned from Shakspeare. There are really, if we look to it, few as memorable Histories. The great salient points are admirably seized; all rounds itself off, into a kind of rhythmic coherence; it is, as Schlegel says, *epic*; —as indeed all delineation by a great thinker will be. There are right beautiful things in those Pieces, which indeed together form one beautiful thing. That battle of Agincourt strikes me as one of the most perfect things, in its sort, we anywhere have of Shakspeare's. The description of the two hosts: the worn-out, jaded English; the dread hour, big with destiny, when the battle shall begin; and then that deathless valour: 'Ye good yeomen, whose limbs were made in England!' There is a noble Patriotism in it,—far other than the 'indifference' you sometimes hear ascribed to Shakspeare. A true English heart breathes, calm and strong, through the whole business; not boisterous, protrusive; all the better for that. There is a sound in it like the ring of steel. This man too had a right stroke in him, had it come to that!

But I will say, of Shakspeare's works generally, that we have no full impress of him there; even as full as we have of many men. His works are so many windows, through which we see a glimpse of the world that was in him. All his works seem, comparatively speaking, cursory, imperfect, written under cramping circumstances; giving only here and there a note of the full utterance of the man. Passages there are that come upon you like splendour out of Heaven; bursts of radiance, illuminating the very heart of the thing: you say, 'That is *true*, spoken once and forever; wheresoever and whensoever there is an open human soul, that will be recognized as true!' Such bursts, however, make us feel that the surrounding matter is not radiant; that it is, in part, temporary, conventional. Alas, Shakspeare had to write for the Globe Playhouse: his great soul had to crush itself, as it could, into that and no other mould. It was with him, then, as it is with us all. No man works save under conditions. The sculptor cannot set his own free Thought before us; but his Thought as he could translate it into the stone that was given, with the tools that were given. *Disjecta membra* are all that we find of any Poet, or of any man.

Whoever looks intelligently at this Shakspeare may recognize that he too was a *Prophet*, in his way; of an insight analogous to the Prophetic, though he took it up in another strain. Nature seemed to this man also divine; *un*speakable, deep as Tophet, high as Heaven: 'We are such stuff as Dreams are made of!' That scroll in Westminster Abbey, which few read with understanding, is of the depth of any Seer. But the man sang; did not preach, except musically. We called Dante the melodious Priest of Middle-Age Catholicism. May we not call Shakspeare the still more melodious Priest of a *true* Catholicism, the 'Universal Church' of the Future and of all times? No narrow superstition, harsh asceticism, intolerance, fanatical fierceness or perversion: a Revelation, so far as it goes, that such a thousandfold hidden beauty and divineness dwells in all Nature; which let all men worship as they can! We may say without offence, that there rises a kind of universal Psalm out of this Shakspeare too; not unfit to make itself heard among the still more sacred Psalms. Not in disharmony with these, if we understood them, but in harmony!—I cannot call this Shakspeare a 'Sceptic,' as some do; his indifference to the creeds and theological quarrels of his time misleading them. No: neither unpatriotic, though he says little about his Patriotism; nor sceptic, though he says little about his Faith. Such 'indifference' was the fruit of his greatness withal: his whole heart was in his own grand sphere of worship (we may call it such); these other controversies, vitally important to other men, were not vital to him.

But call it worship, call it what you will, is it not a right glorious thing, and set of things, this that Shakspeare has brought us? For myself, I feel that there is actually a kind of sacredness in the fact of such a man being sent into this Earth. Is he not an eye to us all; a blessed heaven-sent Bringer of Light?—And, at bottom, was it not perhaps far better that this Shakspeare, everyway an unconscious man, was *conscious* of no Heavenly message? . . .

Well: this is our poor Warwickshire Peasant, who rose to be Manager of a Playhouse, so that he could live

without begging; whom the Earl of Southampton cast
some kind glances on; whom Sir Thomas Lucy, many
thanks to him, was for sending to the Treadmill! We
did not account him a god, like Odin, while he dwelt
with us;—on which point there were much to be said.
But I will say rather, or repeat: In spite of the sad state
Hero-worship now lies in, consider what this Shakspeare has actually become among us. Which Englishman we ever made, in this land of ours, which million
of Englishmen, would we not give up rather than the
Stratford Peasant? There is no regiment of highest
Dignitaries that we would sell him for. He is the grand-
est thing we have yet done. For our honour among
foreign nations, as an ornament to our English Household, what item is there that we would not surrender
rather than him? Consider now, if they asked us, Will
you give up your Indian Empire or your Shakspeare,
you English; never have had any Indian Empire, or
never have had any Shakspeare? Really it were a grave
question. Official persons would answer doubtless in
official language; but we, for our part too, should not
we be forced to answer: Indian Empire, or no Indian
Empire; we cannot do without Shakspeare! Indian
Empire will go, at any rate, some day; but this Shakspeare does not go, he lasts forever with us; we cannot
give up our Shakspeare!

Nay, apart from spiritualities; and considering him
merely as a real, marketable, tangibly useful possession.
England, before long, this Island of ours, will hold but
a small fraction of the English: in America, in New Hol-
land, east and west to the very Antipodes, there will be
a Saxondom covering great spaces of the Globe. And
now, what is it that can keep all these together into virtually one Nation, so that they do not fall out and fight,
but live at peace, in brotherlike intercourse, helping one

another? This is justly regarded as the greatest practical problem, the thing all manner of sovereignties and governments are here to accomplish: what is it that will accomplish this? Acts of Parliament, administrative prime-ministers cannot. America is parted from us, so far as Parliament could part it. Call it not fantastic, for there is much reality in it: Here, I say, is an English King, whom no time or chance, Parliament or combination of Parliaments, can dethrone! This King Shakspeare, does not he shine, in crowned sovereignty, over us all, as the noblest, gentlest, yet strongest of rallying-signs; *in*-destructible; really more valuable in that point of view, than any other means or appliance whatsoever? We can fancy him as radiant aloft over all the Nations of Englishmen, a thousand years hence. From Paramatta, from New York, wheresoever, under what sort of Parish-Constable soever, English men and women are, they will say to one another: 'Yes, this Shakspeare is ours: we produced him, we speak and think by him; we are of one blood and kind with him.' The most common-sense politician, too, if he pleases, may think of that.

Yes, truly, it is a great thing for a Nation that it get an articulate voice; that it produce a man who will speak forth melodiously what the heart of it means! Italy, for example, poor Italy lies dismembered, scattered asunder, not appearing in any protocol or treaty as a unity at all; yet the noble Italy is actually *one*: Italy produced its Dante; Italy can speak! The Czar of all the Russias, he is strong, with so many bayonets, Cossacks and cannons; and does a great feat in keeping such a tract of Earth politically together; but he cannot yet speak. Something great in him, but it is a dumb greatness. He has had no voice of genius, to be heard of all men and times. He must learn to speak. He is a great dumb monster

hitherto. His cannons and Cossacks will all have rusted
into nonentity, while that Dante's voice is still audible.
The Nation that has a Dante is bound together as no
dumb Russia can be.—We must here end what we
had to say of the *Hero-Poet*.

From On Heroes, Hero-Worship, and the Heroic
in History, *Lecture III, 'The Hero as Poet,' delivered*
12th May, 1840.

SET IN
GREAT BRITAIN
AT THE
UNIVERSITY PRESS
OXFORD
AND
PRINTED BY
HAZELL WATSON AND VINEY LTD
AYLESBURY AND SLOUGH